INTERNATIONAL SERIES IN PHYSICS

G. P. HARNWELL, Consulting Editor

KINETIC THEORY OF GASES

INTERNATIONAL SERIES IN PURE AND APPLIED PHYSICS

LEONARD I. SCHIFF, *Consulting Editor*

Becker Introduction to Theoretical Mechanics
Clark Applied X-rays
Edwards Analytic and Vector Mechanics
Evans The Atomic Nucleus
Finkelnburg Atomic Physics
Green Nuclear Physics
Gurney Introduction to Statistical Mechanics
Hall Introduction to Electron Microscopy
Hardy and Perrin The Principles of Optics
Harnwell Electricity and Electromagnetism
Harnwell and Livingood Experimental Atomic Physics
Harnwell and Stephens Atomic Physics
Houston Principles of Mathematical Physics
Houston Principles of Quantum Mechanics
Hughes and DuBridge Photoelectric Phenomena
Hund High-frequency Measurements
Kemble The Fundamental Principles of Quantum Mechanics
Kennard Kinetic Theory of Gases
Marshak Meson Physics
Morse Vibration and Sound
Morse and Feshbach Methods of Theoretical Physics
Muskat Physical Principles of Oil Production
Read Dislocations in Crystals
Richtmyer, Kennard, and Lauritsen Introduction to Modern Physics
Schiff Quantum Mechanics
Seitz The Modern Theory of Solids
Slater Introduction to Chemical Physics
Slater Microwave Transmission
Slater Quantum Theory of Matter
Slater and Frank Electromagnetism
Slater and Frank Introduction to Theoretical Physics
Slater and Frank Mechanics
Smythe Static and Dynamic Electricity
Squire Low Temperature Physics
Stratton Electromagnetic Theory
Thorndike Mesons: A Summary of Experimental Facts
Townes and Schawlow Microwave Spectroscopy
White Introduction to Atomic Spectra

The late F. K. Richtmyer was Consulting Editor of the series from its inception in 1929 to his death in 1939. Lee A. DuBridge was Consulting Editor from 1939 to 1946; and G. P. Harnwell from 1947 to 1954.

KINETIC THEORY
OF GASES

With an Introduction to
Statistical Mechanics

BY

EARLE H. KENNARD
Professor of Physics, Cornell University

McGRAW-HILL BOOK COMPANY, Inc.

NEW YORK AND LONDON

1938

COPYRIGHT, 1938, BY THE
McGraw-Hill Book Company, Inc.

PRINTED IN THE UNITED STATES OF AMERICA

*All rights reserved. This book, or
parts thereof, may not be reproduced
in any form without permission of
the publishers.*

IX

QC
175
K45
c.2

4136.2

PREFACE

The kinetic theory of gases is a small branch of physics which has passed from the stage of excitement and novelty into staid maturity. It retains a certain importance, however, and an adequate treatment of it in books will always be needed. Formerly it was hoped that the subject of gases would ultimately merge into a general kinetic theory of matter; but the theory of condensed phases, insofar as it exists at all today, involves an elaborate and technical use of wave mechanics, and for this reason it is best treated as a subject by itself.

The scope of the present book is, therefore, the traditional kinetic theory of gases. A strictly modern standpoint has been maintained, however; an account has been included of the wave-mechanical theory, and especially of the degenerate Fermi-Dirac case, which has not been written up systematically in English. There is also a concise chapter on general statistical mechanics, which it is hoped may be of use as an introduction to that subject. On the other hand, the discussion of electrical phenomena has been abbreviated in the belief that the latter voluminous subject is best treated separately.

The book is designed to serve both as a textbook for students and as a reference book for the experimental physicist; but it is not intended to be exhaustive. The more fundamental parts have been explained in such detail that they are believed to be within the reach of college juniors and seniors. The two chapters on wave mechanics and statistical mechanics, however, are of graduate grade. Few exercises for practice have been included, but a number of carefully worded theorems have been inserted in the guise of problems, without proof, partly to save space and partly to give the earnest student a chance to apply for himself the lines of attack that are exemplified in the text.

To facilitate use as a reference book, definitions have been repeated freely, I hope not *ad nauseam*. The chief requisite for convenience of reference, I think, is a careful statement of all important results, with definitions and restrictions not too far away.

Ideas have been drawn freely from existing books such as those of Jeans and Loeb, and from the literature; many references to the latter are given, but they are not intended to constitute a complete list. I am indebted also to Mr. R. D. Myers for valuable criticisms, and to my wife for suggestions in regard to style.

ITHACA, NEW YORK,   EARLE H. KENNARD.
January, 1938.

CONTENTS

PREFACE V

PAGE

CHAPTER I

ELEMENTS OF THE KINETIC THEORY OF GASES. 1

1. The Kinetic Theory of Matter. 1
2. Atoms and Molecules. 3
3. Statistical Nature of the Theory. 5
4. Gaseous Pressure 6
5. Calculation of the Pressure 7
6. Dalton's Law 9
7. Mass Motion 9
8. Reversible Expansion and Compression. 11
9. Free Expansion 14
10. Isothermal Properties of the Ideal Gas 16
11. Avogadro's Law. 18
12. The Temperature 19
13. The Thermodynamic Temperature Scale 20
14. The Perfect-gas Law. 22
15. Molecular Magnitudes 24
16. Rapidity of the Molecular Motion. 26

CHAPTER II

DISTRIBUTION LAW FOR MOLECULAR VELOCITIES 28

17. The Distribution Function for Molecular Velocity 28
18. Distribution Function in Other Variables. 30
19. Remarks on the Distribution Function. 31
20. Proofs of the Distribution Law 32
21. Molecular Chaos. 33
22. The Effect of Collisions upon f 34
23. Velocities after a Collision 36
24. The Inverse Collisions 37
25. The Rate of Change of the Distribution Function 39
26. The Equilibrium State 40
27. Rigorous Treatment of the Equilibrium State. 42
28. Maxwell's Law 45
29. Use of a Distribution-function in Calculating Averages. 48
30. Most Probable and Average Speeds 48
31. Mixed Gases. Equipartition 51
32. Uniqueness of the Maxwellian Distribution. The H-theorem. . . . 52
33. Reversibility and the H-theorem. 55
34. Principle of Detailed Balancing 55
35. Doppler Line Breadth 58

PAGE

CHAPTER III

GENERAL MOTION AND SPATIAL DISTRIBUTION OF THE MOLECULES. . . .   60

Unilateral Flow of the Molecules:
   36. Effusive Molecular Flow   60
   37. Formulas for Effusive Flow.   61
   38. Molecular Effusion.   64
   39. Thermal Transpiration.   66
   40. Knudsen's Absolute Manometer.   67
   41. Evaporation.   68
   42. Observations on the Rate of Evaporation.   70
   43. Test of the Velocity Distribution in Effusive Flow.   71

The General Distribution-function:
   44. A Gas in a Force-field   74
   45. Density in a Force-field.   74
   46. Maxwell's Law in a Force-field   76
   47. The Temperature of Saturated Vapor   79
   48. The Terrestrial Atmosphere.   79
   49. Cosmic Equilibrium of Planetary Atmospheres   81
   50. The General Distribution-function.   85
   51. Differential Equation for the Distribution-function.   85
   52. Applications of the Differential Equation.   89

The Boltzmann Distribution Formula:
   53. The Classical Boltzmann Distribution Formula   90
   54. The Boltzmann Formula in Quantum Theory.   93
   55. Special Cases of the Boltzmann Formula   95

Free Paths and Collisions:
   56. Molecules of Finite Size   97
   57. The Mean Free Path and Collision Rate   98
   58. Dependence of L and Θ upon Density and Temperature 100
   59. Distribution of Free Paths. Absorption of a Beam 101
   60. The Mutual Collision Cross Section 103
   61. The Mean Free Path in a Constant-speed Gas. 105
   62. A Molecular Beam in a Maxwellian Gas 107
   63. Mean Free Path and Collision Rate at Constant Speed. 109
   64. Mean Free Path and Collision Rate in a Maxwellian Gas. 110
   65. Magnitude of the Correction for Maxwell's Law. 113
   66. Mode of Determining L and S or σ. 113
   67. Collisions in a Real Gas 113

Molecular Scattering:
   68. The Scattering Coefficient. 115
   69. Classical Scattering Coefficient for Symmetrical Molecules with Fixed
       Scatterer 116
   70. Examples of the Scattering Coefficient 118
   71. Relative Scattering. 120
   72. Classical Scattering Coefficient for Free Symmetrical Molecules. . . 122
   73. The Experimental Determination of the Collision Cross Section. . . 124
   74. Knauer's Observations on Scattering. 125
   75. The Wave Mechanics of a Particle. 127
   76. The Indetermination Principle. 130
   77. Wave Mechanics and Molecular Collisions 131
   78. Wave-mechanical Scattering Coefficients 132

CHAPTER IV

Viscosity, Thermal Conduction, Diffusion 135

A. Viscosity:
79. Viscosity 136
80. Fluid Stresses in General 137
81. Simple Theory of Viscosity 138
82. The Mean Free Path across a Fixed Plane 141
83. Correction for the Velocity Spread 142
84. Further Correction of the Viscosity Formula 145
85. New View of the Molecular Process 146
86. Final Viscosity Formula. Magnitudes of L and σ 147
87. Variation of Viscosity with Density 148
88. Variation of Viscosity with Temperature 150
89. Viscosity and Temperature with an Inverse-power Force 152
90. Viscosity and Temperature on Sutherland's Hypothesis. 154
91. Viscosity and Temperature: Other Hypotheses. 157
92. Viscosity of Mixed Gases. 160

B. Conduction of Heat:
93. The Kinetic Theory of Heat Conduction 162
94. Simple Theory of the Conductivity. 163
95. Thermal Conductivity of Symmetrical Small-field Molecules. First
Step 165
96. Thermal Conductivity on Meyer's Assumption 168
97. Thermal Conductivity: Second Step 169
98. Effect of One Collision upon $\Sigma v_x v^2$ 172
99. Average of the Effect on $\Sigma v_x v^2$. 173
100. Total Effect of Collisions on $\Sigma v_x v^2$ 175
101. Thermal Conductivity: Final Approximate Formula 177
102. Final Correction of the Conductivity Formula. 179
103. Comparison with Observed Conductivities 180
104. Conduction of Heat by Complex Molecules. 181
105. Properties of the Conductivity. 182

C. Diffusion:
106. Diffusion. 184
107. The Coefficient of Diffusion. 185
108. Simple Theory of Diffusion 188
109. Approximate Coefficient of Diffusion for Spherically Symmetrical
Molecules. 190
110. Self-diffusion 194
111. The Corrected Diffusion Coefficient 195
112. Experiments on the Variation with Composition. 196
113. Diffusion at Various Pressures and Temperatures 197
114. Numerical Values of the Diffusion Coefficient 199
115. Forced Diffusion. 201
116. Thermal Diffusion. 204

CHAPTER V

The Equation of State. 206

117. The Equation of State 206
118. The Equation of van der Waals 206
119. The van der Waals Isothermals 208

PAGE

120. Quantitative Tests of van der Waals' Equation 210
121. More Exact Theory of the Pressure in a Dense Gas 211
122. Hard Attracting Spheres: The Repulsive Pressure 214
123. Equation of State for Hard Attracting Spheres 217
124. The Value of b. 218
125. Other Equations of State. 218
126. Series for pV; Virial Coefficients. 221
127. The Second Virial Coefficient 222
128. The Second Virial Coefficient and van der Waals' Equation. . . . 223
129. Theory of the Second Virial Coefficient, B 225
130. Nature of Molecular Forces. 228
131. B with an Inverse-power Force 229
132. Classical Calculations of B 230
133. Calculations of B by Wave Mechanics 232
134. B for Mixed Gases. 234
135. The Virial Theorem 235

CHAPTER VI

ENERGY, ENTROPY, AND SPECIFIC HEATS 238
Information Obtainable from Thermodynamics:
136. Some Definitions and Basic Principles 239
137. Differential Equations for the Energy U 240
138. Experimental Measurement of Energy and Entropy; the Specific Heats 242
139. Specific-heat Relations. 244
140. Variation of the Specific Heats 245
141. Thermodynamics of Perfect and van der Waals Gases 246
Specific Heat of the Perfect Gas:
142. Molecular Energy 248
143. The Classical Theory of Specific Heat 249
144. Comparison with Actual Specific Heats. 251
145. The Specific-heat Difference. 254
146. The Problem of the Internal Energy. 254
147. Quantum Theory of the Specific Heat 255
148. Variation of Specific Heat with Temperature 257
149. The Case of Harmonic Oscillators 258
150. Hydrogen. 260
151. Para-, Ortho-, and Equilibrium Hydrogen. 262
152. Specific Heat of Hydrogen 264
153. Specific Heats of Mixed Gases. 265

CHAPTER VII

FLUCTUATIONS 267
Phenomena of Dispersion:
154. The Simple Random Walk 268
155. The Varied Random Walk 271
156. Dispersion of a Group of Molecules 272
157. Molecular Scattering of Light. 273
Fluctuations about an Average:
158. Theory of Fluctuations about an Average. 275
159. Examples of Molecular Fluctuations 279

Diffusion and the Brownian Motion:

160. The Brownian Motion 280
161. Theory of the Brownian Motion 281
162. Observations of Brownian Motion 284
163. Diffusion as a Random Walk 286
164. Brownian Motion under External Force 287

CHAPTER VIII

PROPERTIES OF GASES AT LOW DENSITIES 291

Motion in Rarefied Gases:

165. Viscous Slip 292
166. Steady Flow with Slip 293
167. Maxwell's Theory of Slip 295
168. Discussion of the Slip Formula 296
169. Observations of Slip 298
170. Free-molecule Viscosity 300
171. Free-molecule Flow through Long Tubes 302
172. The Long-tube Formula 304
173. Flow through Short Tubes 306
174. Observations of Free-molecule Flow 308
175. Stokes' Law for Spheres 309

Thermal Conduction in Rarefied Gases:

176. Temperature Jump and the Accommodation Coefficient 311
177. Theory of the Temperature Jump 312
178. Free-molecule Heat Conduction between Plates 315
179. Free-molecule Conduction between Coaxial Cylinders 318
180. Observed Variation of the Accommodation Coefficient 320
181. Magnitude of the Accommodation Coefficient 322
182. Spectral Emission by an Unequally Heated Gas 324
183. Theoretical Calculations of the Accommodation Coefficient 325

Thermal Creep and the Radiometer:

184. Thermal Creep 327
185. The Creep Velocity 328
186. Thermal Pressure Gradients and Transpiration 330
187. Thermal Gradients at Moderate Pressures 331
188. The Radiometer and Photophoresis 333
189. The Quantitative Theory of Radiometer Action 335

CHAPTER IX

STATISTICAL MECHANICS 338

190. Nature of Statistical Mechanics 338

A. Classical Statistical Mechanics:

191. System Phase Space 339
192. Representative Ensembles 340
193. The Ergodic Surmise 341
194. Liouville's Theorem 343
195. The Ergodic Layer and the Microcanonical Ensemble 344
196. The Point-mass Perfect Gas 346
197. The Molecular Distribution. Molecular Chaos 348
198. The Loose Many-molecule System 350

PAGE

199. The Most Probable Distribution. 352
200. The Most Probable as a Normal Distribution. 354
201. Some Generalizations of the Loose Many-molecule System 355
202. Introduction of the Temperature. 357
203. Entropy 360
204. Entropy of the Monatomic Gas 361
205. The General Boltzmann Distribution Law. 362
206. The Equipartition of Energy 364
207. The Canonical Distribution and Ensemble 366
208. Entropy under a Canonical Distribution 367
209. The Second Law of Thermodynamics. 367
210. Entropy and Probability 368
211. Relations with Boltzmann's H. 371
212. Entropy as a Measure of Range in Phase. 371
213. Relativity and Statistical Theory 372
B. Statistical Wave Mechanics:
214. The Wave-mechanical Description. 373
215. The Exclusion Principle 375
216. The State of Equilibrium. 375
217. A Priori Probabilities. 377
218. The Many-molecule System without Interaction. 379
219. Fermi-Dirac and Bose-Einstein Sets of Similar Molecules 380
220. The Loosely Coupled Many-molecule System 382
221. Statistics of the Loose Many-molecule System. 382
222. Introduction of the Temperature. 385
223. Case of Large Energies: Classical Theory as a Limit Form. 387
224. Entropy of a Loose Many-molecule System. 388
225. Statistics of Mixed Systems. 389
226. The Canonical Distribution in Wave Mechanics. 390
227. The Entropy 391

CHAPTER X

WAVE MECHANICS OF GASES 393
228. The Perfect Gas in Wave Mechanics. 393
229. The Point-mass Perfect Gas. 395
230. The Two Types of Point-mass Gas 397
231. The Homogeneous Point-mass Gas in Equilibrium. 397
232. The Approach to Classical Behavior 401
233. The Number of States 402
234. The Zero-point Entropy 405
235. Chemical Constant and Vapor Pressure. 407
236. The Fermi-Dirac Gas of Point Masses 409
237. The Degenerate Fermi-Dirac Gas 412
238. The Bose-Einstein Gas of Point Masses. 416
239. Complex Gases 417
240. Free Electrons in Metals 419
241. Degeneracy in Actual Gases. 421
242. Dissociation. 422
243. Dissociation in the Classical Limit. 425
244. A Gas Not in Equilibrium 427

CHAPTER XI

ELECTRIC AND MAGNETIC PROPERTIES OF GASES 432

The Dielectric Constant:

245. Polarization and the Dielectric Constant 432
246. The Local Electric Field 433
247. The Mean Molecular Moment $\bar{g}$. 435
248. The Molecular Polarizability α 436
249. The Clausius-Mossotti Law. 437
250. Polarization Due to a Permanent Moment 438
251. Behavior in Intense Fields 441
252. The Variation with Temperature. 441
253. Quantum Theory of Polarization. 442
254. Initial Polarizability by Perturbation Theory 444
255. Wave Mechanics of the Dumbbell Molecule. 448
256. Polarizability of a Dumbbell Molecule with a Structural Moment. . 450

Magnetic Susceptibility:

257. Magnetism and Molecular Magnetizability 454
258. Langevin's Theory of Paramagnetism. 455
259. Quantum Theory and Magnetizability 456
260. Sources of Molecular Magnetism. 457
261. Wave Mechanics in a Magnetic Field. 458
262. Magnetizability by Perturbation Theory 460
263. Diamagnetism. 462
264. Paramagnetism 463

Motion of Electricity in Gases:

265. The Motion of Ions in Gases 464
266. The Mobility 466
267. Mobility of Heavy Ions. 467
268. The Mobility of Free Electrons 469
269. Elementary Theory of Electronic Mobility 470
270. Actual Electron Mobilities 473

SOME INTEGRALS. 477

IMPORTANT CONSTANTS. 478

INDEX. 479

KINETIC THEORY OF GASES

CHAPTER I

ELEMENTS OF THE KINETIC THEORY OF GASES

Of all states of matter the simplest is the gaseous state. The laws of this state were discovered long ago; and during the middle part of the last century the essentials of an adequate theoretical interpretation of these laws were worked out. This theory, of course, constitutes only a part of a general kinetic theory of matter, which is the ultimate goal. It has become clear, however, that the theory of liquids and solids must necessarily involve an extensive use of quantum mechanics, and such a theory is as yet only in its beginning stage. Since the methods and conceptions required to handle these condensed phases of matter are thus widely different from those that are appropriate to the treatment of the gaseous phase, it is still convenient to treat the theory of gases by itself as a distinct subdivision of physics.

The purpose of the present volume is to give a concise account of the kinetic theory of gases as this theory exists today, and of its principal applications to the results of experiment.

1. The Kinetic Theory of Matter. The structure of matter is a very old problem, and for the beginnings of modern theory we must go back to the early Greek philosophers. Driven by their basic urge to see in all phenomena the operation of a few fundamental principles, these philosophers sought to reduce to simpler terms the immense variety of natural phenomena by which they were surrounded. Heraclitus, about 500 B.C., played a large part in initiating one of the principal lines of Greek thought by advancing the view that everything is composed in varying proportions of the four elements, earth, water, air, and fire; the elements and all mixtures of them he assumed to be capable of unlimited subdivision into finer and ever finer particles without losing their essential properties. On the other hand, Leucippus and especially Democritus (about 400 B.C.), holding that motion would be impossible unless there existed empty space into which a moving body could move, preferred the hypothesis that all matter consists of very small particles separated by void. These particles were supposed to be of many different sizes and shapes and to be

1

engaged in continual rapid motion, the various properties of material objects arising from differences in the kinds of atoms or from differences in their motion. This view was rejected by Aristotle, but in spite of his great authority it remained current to some extent, and we find it developed at great length in the poem "De rerum natura" by the Roman writer Lucretius (A.D. 55).

The kinetic theory of matter thus arose in fairly definite form among the ancients; but they discovered no proofs of its truth which were of the convincing quantitative sort so characteristic of modern science. In ancient times and during the Middle Ages the theory remained merely one among several alternative speculations, accepted by some thinkers on the basis of its general attractiveness, but emphatically rejected by others.

After the Revival of Learning the theory underwent a slow growth as physical conceptions took on more precise forms. The phenomena of heat were frequently attributed to the assumed motion of the atoms, and Gassendi (1658) recognized the relatively wide spacing of the particles in a gas such as air. On this basis Hooke (1678) attempted, although in a confused way, to give an explanation of Boyle's law. The first clear explanation of this law, however, including the assumption that at constant temperature the mean velocity of the particles remains constant, seems to have been given by D. Bernoulli in 1738. The contributions of Bernoulli to the theory might be regarded as the beginning of the truly *quantitative* kinetic theory of gases.

Soon after 1800, a very important development of the atomic theory occurred, in the use that Davy and others made of it to explain the law that chemical combination always occurs in simple proportions. Then, between 1840 and 1850, the work of Mayer and Joule on the mechanical equivalent of heat, reinforcing the qualitative but very convincing experiments of Rumford and Davy thirty years before, finally brought general conviction that heat is not a substance but a form of energy, consisting, at least in large part, of the kinetic energy of motion of the molecules.

The time was now ripe for the development of a thoroughgoing quantitative kinetic theory of gases, and we find the principal framework laid within the next twenty-five years (1857–1880) by Clausius, Maxwell, Boltzmann, and others. The remaining years of the nineteenth century were then a period of quiet during which only a few further refinements were added.

The twentieth century has seen not only a still further slow growth of the theory along the lines initiated by Clausius and Maxwell, but also successful applications to new experiments which served finally to convince the last doubters of its truth. There came first the experiments of Perrin (1908) and others on the Brownian movement, which showed pretty definitely that here we are actually witnessing the eternal dance of the molecules that is postulated by kinetic theory, the suspended particles playing the role of giant molecules. Then followed a number of phenomena in which detectable effects are produced by one atom or molecule at a time, such as the scintillations made by alpha particles upon a fluorescent screen, or the click in a Geiger counter recording the passage of a single electron; and finally, during the last twenty years, there has come the overwhelmingly successful quantum theory of the internal structure of the atom itself.

At the present time the atomic theory of matter and, as a special case, the kinetic theory of gases, is perhaps second only to the Copernican theory of the solar system in the completeness of its experimental verification. Today we know the mass and size—in so far as it possesses a size!—of an atom of any chemical element with the same certainty, although not yet the same degree of precision, as the astronomer knows the mass and size of the sun.

2. Atoms and Molecules. One of the most important advances in atomic theory was the distinction introduced a hundred years ago between atoms on the one hand and molecules on the other. This distinction has lost a little of its sharpness of late, but we can still say with substantial truth that an atom is the smallest portion of matter which has the property of remaining essentially intact in every chemical reaction, whereas a molecule is the smallest portion which possesses the chemical properties of a definite chemical substance.

Until some thirty years ago, atoms were commonly described as indivisible, and the fact that nowadays we are breaking them up rather freely is sometimes held up as an example of the mutability and hence unreliability of the results of science. Such a view rests, however, upon a misinterpretation of scientific statements, for which the blame must sometimes be laid at the door of scientific men themselves, especially the writers of textbooks. Those old statements about indivisibility really meant only that the division could not be accomplished by any means known at that time, and this statement remains (so far as we know!) as true today as it was then; the modern methods of breaking up an atom require experimental methods that have been discovered only recently.

Of the internal structure of atoms* we possess today a fairly complete theory. All known facts agree excellently with the assumption

* A good summary of the theory can be found in "Introduction to Modern Physics." by F. K. Richtmyer, 2d ed., 1934.

that each atom consists of a positively charged nucleus surrounded (in general) by a cloud of negatively charged electrons. Under ordinary conditions the number of electrons present is just sufficient to make the whole atom electrically neutral. Chemical combination then consists in a union of two or more atoms into a close group or molecule, one or more of the outer electrons of each atom changing position, in many cases, so as to belong rather to the molecule as a whole than to any particular atom in it. In the gaseous state of matter the molecules are separated most of the time by distances that are rather large in comparison with their diameters (about nine times, in air of normal density). In liquids and solids, on the other hand, the spaces between them tend to be even smaller than the molecules themselves, and in many crystal lattices (e.g., potassium chloride) the arrangement is such that the identity of the molecule seems to become entirely lost— such a crystal is really itself "one big molecule" (Bragg).

In a gas we should expect, accordingly, that the molecules would move about freely during most of the time; they should move almost in straight lines until two of them happen to come so close together that they act strongly upon each other and something like a "collision" occurs, after which they separate and move off in new directions and probably with different speeds. Just what happens in a collision must depend on the laws of molecular force-action. As the gas is made rarer, however, the collisions must become less frequent, and the intervening free paths longer; then the details of the process of collision will be less important and only the resulting changes of molecular velocity will be significant. Thus we are led to idealize the gas for the purpose of making the first steps toward a theory, as was done almost unconsciously by the earliest theorizers. For our first deductions we shall assume an *ideal* or *perfect* gas in which the molecules are negligibly small, i.e., exert appreciable forces upon each other only when their centers of mass approach within a distance that is very small compared with their average separation in the gas. In later chapters we shall then endeavor to soften, and if possible to remove, this restriction.

We assume, of course, that the molecules obey the laws of mechanics. For phenomena on the molecular scale these depart so far from the Newtonian laws as to raise real doubt whether the conceptions of classical kinetic theory are applicable to actual gases at all. We shall return to this subject later (Chap. III, end, and Chap. X); it appears that a theory based upon classical mechanics is nevertheless practically correct for the ideal, indefinitely rare gas at high temperature. Such a theory still possesses, therefore, great usefulness as a first approximation to the true quantum-mechanical theory, which is decidedly complicated.

Heat energy we shall, of course, interpret as mechanical energy of the molecules.   At least part of it will be kinetic energy of translation of the molecules as wholes, but there may also be kinetic energy of rotation; if the atoms constituting the molecule are capable of vibratory motion relative to each other, there will furthermore be internal energy of vibration; and finally there may be energy of motion of the electrons in the atom, or rather its quantum-mechanical equivalent.   Finally, corresponding to the forces that act between the molecules when they approach closely, there will be in greater or less degree a store of inter-molecular potential energy; in liquids and solids, in so far as we can employ the classical picture at all, this part of the energy must be large. In our thinking we must not forget that all of these various forms are included in the "heat energy" of the substance and contribute more or less to its specific heat.

Friction we assume, of course, to be entirely absent in the interac-tion of the molecules themselves; these constitute conservative mechan-ical systems.   The ordinary conversion of mechanical work into heat by friction we interpret merely as a conversion of mechanical energy into molecular forms whose exact nature can no longer be recognized by the ordinary methods of experimental physics; in the case of gaseous friction the mechanism by which this conversion is effected is easily followed and will be discussed later.   The motion of a visible body represents an organized component in the motion of the molecules; after the body has been brought to rest by friction, there may be, especially in a rare gas, just as much motion as there was before it was stopped, only now the motion formerly visible has become part of the completely disorganized heat motion and so is no longer perceptible as motion at all.

3. Statistical Nature of the Theory.   Since we cannot possibly follow every molecule and calculate its exact path, we must in kinetic theory be content almost entirely with statistical results, and these are in all cases sufficient for practical purposes.   By the *density* of a gas, for instance, what we really mean is the ratio of mass to volume for a *macroscopically small* volume, i.e., a volume just small enough so that for the experimental purpose in hand it can be treated as indefinitely small.   If the gas is dense enough so that such a volume contains many molecules, the density as thus defined will vary only to a negligible extent as individual molecules enter and leave the volume. If the density becomes too low for this condition to hold, we may still be able to secure a sufficiently steady macroscopic density by averaging the number of molecules in the volume over a macroscopically small interval of time, during which individual molecules pass into and out of the volume many times; or we may turn our attention to the *fluctuations* of the density caused by the irregular molecular motion. When all such devices fail, the common methods of kinetic theory simply become inapplicable and we are compelled to treat the molecules as individuals.

A similar discussion applies to all other magnitudes associated with a gas (or with any other physical body, for that matter), such as pressure or temperature.   These conceptions are all statistical in nature, and the relations between them that are expressed by our formulas, while they may be mathematically exact, represent the real situation only with a certain degree of approximation.

4. Gaseous Pressure.   The most characteristic property of a gas, as contrasted with a liquid or solid, is its tendency to expand indefinitely or, if confined, to exert a positive pressure upon the walls of the containing vessel.   This property is interpreted in the kinetic theory as arising from the continual motion of the molecules, and on this basis a quantitative expression for the pressure is easily obtained.

In practice, however, it is also convenient to think of any portion of the gas as exerting pressure upon contiguous portions of the gas itself. To cover this case, a definition of the pressure is convenient in which the latter is represented as stream density of momentum.   If an imaginary plane surface is drawn through a mass of matter, momentum is continually being transmitted across this surface in both directions, either by means of forces or by being carried across it by molecules which themselves actually cross the surface.   Let us choose a certain direction normal to the surface as the positive one and take only the component of the momentum in this direction.   Then the *pressure* acting across the surface can be defined as the net rate at which momentum normal to it is being transmitted across it per unit area in the positive direction, momentum transmitted in the opposite direction being counted as negative.

We shall show first that in a gas in equilibrium the pressure so defined is the same in the midst of the gas as the pressure on the walls of the vessel.   The pressure upon a rigid wall arises from forces exerted upon it by those molecules which happen at any instant to be undergoing collision with it.   If δF_n denotes the sum of the components normal to the wall of all such forces acting upon a macroscopically small element of area δS, then the pressure is $\delta F_n/\delta S$ (or the time average of this expression over a macroscopically short time).   These forces can be supposed to be imparting normal momentum to the wall at a rate equal to the pressure; if the wall nevertheless stands still, that is only because other forces acting simultaneously from without impart to it momentum in the opposite direction at an equal rate. Corresponding to δF_n there are also, by the law of action and reaction, equal and opposite forces exerted by the wall upon the gas molecules, and these impart equal and opposite momentum to the gas.

Suppose now we draw an imaginary plane surface S through the gas parallel to the wall. Then, gas and wall being assumed at rest, the amount of momentum possessed at each instant by those molecules that lie between the surface S and the wall remains constant. The continual inflow into this region of momentum directed away from the wall, due to the action of the wall upon the gas, must therefore be balanced by an equal inflow across S of momentum directed toward the wall. Thus the pressure of the gas lying beyond S upon the layer of gas inside of S, defined as stated above, must be equal to the pressure of the gas upon the wall. The pressure can, therefore, be calculated as a transfer of momentum between contiguous portions of the gas.

5. Calculation of the Pressure. Consider a macroscopically small plane of area δS drawn anywhere in the midst of a stationary mass of an ideal gas as defined above (cf. Fig. 1). In such a gas the only appreciable mechanism for the transfer of momentum is that of molecular convection, the momentum being carried across by molecules which themselves cross the plane; for we can neglect the very rare cases in which two molecules lie close enough together, one on one side of S and one on the opposite, to exert forces upon each other. Now a molecule moving with speed v in a certain direction will cross δS during a given

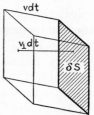

FIG. 1.

interval of time dt, provided at the beginning of dt it lies within a certain cylinder of slant height vdt drawn on δS as a base (cf. Fig. 1); and if it does cross, it will carry over a normal component of momentum $mv_\perp$ where m is its mass and $v_\perp$ denotes the component of its velocity in a direction perpendicular to δS. The volume of this cylinder being $v_\perp\,dt\,\delta S$, the number of such molecules lying within it at the beginning of dt will be $n_v v_\perp\,\delta S\,dt$, n_v being the number of molecules per unit volume that are moving in the manner assumed. The total normal component of momentum thus transferred will therefore be

$$(n_v v_\perp\,\delta S\,dt)mv_\perp. \tag{1}$$

All of the molecules can be divided into such groups. Let us take $v_\perp$ to be positive when it has that direction along the normal to δS which we choose as the positive one. Then molecules with a positive value of $v_\perp$ can cross and transfer positive normal momentum $mv_\perp$ in the positive direction across δS; those with negative $v_\perp$ will carry negative momentum, but they also cross in the negative direction, hence their effect upon the momentum in the gas lying on the positive side of δS is the same as if they had crossed positively carrying an equal amount of positive momentum, and accordingly the same expression (1) can be used for their contribution to the net momentum transfer. Hence we get the total transfer of momentum by summing (1) over all groups of molecules in the gas. Dividing the result thus obtained by $\delta S\, dt$, we find for the amount of momentum normal to δS transferred across it by convection in the positive direction per unit area per second or, by definition, the pressure, $p = \Sigma n_v m v_\perp{}^2$. We can also write for this simply

$$p = \Sigma m v_\perp{}^2, \tag{2a}$$

the sum extending over all molecules in unit volume (more exactly, since only molecules near δS can contribute to the pressure, the sum is to be extended over all molecules in a macroscopically small volume and the result is then to be divided by the volume).

The same result is obtained, of course, from the conventional calculation of the pressure on the wall. The momentum delivered to the wall by molecules falling on it at a certain angle is twice as large as expression (1) because each molecule has its normal component of velocity reversed; but then the final sum extends only over those molecules that are moving toward the wall, which is half of them, and the pressure thus comes out as given in (2a).

Equation (2a) holds for any ideal gas at rest. In the special case in which all molecules have the *same mass*, we can take out m as a constant factor in all terms of the sum and write

$$p = m\Sigma v_\perp{}^2 = n m \overline{v_\perp{}^2} = \rho \overline{v_\perp{}^2} \tag{2b}$$

where n = total number of molecules per unit volume, $\rho = nm$ = ordinary density of the gas, and the bar over a symbol denotes the average of that quantity taken for all molecules in unit volume. Let us assume, as we should expect to be the case in a gas in complete equilibrium and shall verify later, that all directions of motion are equally probable (cf. the principle of molecular chaos in Chap. II). Then, taking the x-axis of a set of cartesian coordinates in the direction of the positive normal to δS and denoting the components of the velocity by v_x, v_y, v_z, we have from symmetry $\overline{v_x^2} = \overline{v_y^2} = \overline{v_z^2}$, and, since $v^2 = v_x^2 + v_y^2 + v_z^2$, $\overline{v^2} = \overline{v_x^2} + \overline{v_y^2} + \overline{v_z^2} = 3\overline{v_x^2} = 3\overline{v_\perp{}^2}$. Hence (2b) can be written in either of the forms:

$$p = \tfrac{1}{3} n m \overline{v^2} = \tfrac{1}{3} \rho \overline{v^2}, \qquad pV = \tfrac{1}{3} \overline{v^2}, \tag{3a, b}$$

$V = 1/\rho$ standing for the volume of a gram.

If the molecules are of *several different kinds* with respective masses m_i and densities n_i in terms of molecules and ρ_i in terms of grams, we can treat in the preceding way the part of the sum in (2a) that corresponds to each kind and obtain thereby for the total pressure, as an extension of (3a),

$$p = \frac{1}{3}\sum_i n_i m_i \overline{v_i^2} = \frac{1}{3}\sum_i \rho_i \overline{v_i^2}, \tag{4}$$

summed over the different kinds of molecules. As an alternative expression, since the kinetic energy of translation of a group of molecules of mass m is $\Sigma \frac{1}{2} mv^2 = \frac{1}{2} nm\overline{v^2}$, by (3a) or (4) we can write for either a simple or a mixed gas

$$p = \tfrac{2}{3} K, \tag{5}$$

where K stands for the total translatory kinetic energy of the molecules per unit volume.

Problem. Show that in a two-dimensional gas $p = \frac{1}{2} \rho\overline{v^2} = K$, ρ being here the number of molecules in unit area and K, as before, their mean translatory kinetic energy.

6. Dalton's Law. From (4) we have at once the important result that, according to our theory, the pressure of a mixture of two or more perfect gases is simply the sum of the pressures which they would exert if each occupied the same volume by itself. This is Dalton's law and is known experimentally to be true at sufficiently low densities; the departures from it are at most of the same order as the departures from the perfect-gas law for each of the component gases, becoming noticeable in ordinary gases only when under considerable pressure. For example, mixtures of equal parts of argon and ethylene, of oxygen and ethylene, and of argon and oxygen, when actually exerting a total pressure of 100 atmospheres, according to Dalton's law should be exerting a pressure respectively 8 per cent, 7.2 per cent, and 1.45 per cent higher; at 30 atmospheres, however, the argon-ethylene mixture shows a deficit of only 0.85 per cent. In some other cases the departure from the law of additivity of pressure is in the opposite direction.*

7. Mass Motion. We often speak of a gas as being "at rest" or as "moving" with a certain velocity. From the molecular standpoint these statements are obviously to be understood as referring to the *mean* velocity of the molecules. It will be useful to consider at this point the relation between this mean velocity and the true rapid and irregular molecular motion.

* *Cf.* Masson and Dolley, *Roy. Soc. Proc.* **103**, 524 (1923).

The symbol v will be used consistently to stand for the actual speed of a molecule relative to whatever basic frame of reference is being employed at the time; to denote its velocity both in direction and in magnitude, i.e., regarded as a vector, we shall use **v** printed in heavy type, and the three components of the velocity referred to a set of cartesian axes we shall denote by v_x, v_y, v_z. Thus at all times

$$v^2 = v_x^2 + v_y^2 + v_z^2. \tag{6}$$

For the *mean* or *mass velocity* we shall similarly write v_0 or **v₀**; it is defined by the equations

$$\mathbf{v_0} = \overline{\mathbf{v}}, \qquad \text{i.e.,} \qquad v_{0x} = \bar{v}_x, \qquad v_{0y} = \bar{v}_y, \qquad v_{0z} = \bar{v}_z, \tag{7}$$

the averages being taken over all molecules in a macroscopically small volume surrounding the point in question. A gas at rest is then one in which

$$\overline{\mathbf{v}}_0 = 0, \qquad \text{i.e.,} \qquad \bar{v}_{0x} = \bar{v}_{0y} = \bar{v}_{0z} = 0. \tag{8}$$

For the *total* velocity we can then write

$$\mathbf{v} = \mathbf{v_0} + \mathbf{v'} \tag{9a}$$

or

$$v_x = v_{0x} + v_x', \qquad v_y = v_{0y} + v_y', \qquad v_z = v_{0z} + v_z', \tag{9b}$$

the sum in (9a) being a vector sum; the new velocity **v'** thus defined is called the velocity of *thermal agitation* and obviously has the property that always

$$\overline{\mathbf{v}'} = 0, \qquad \text{i.e.,} \qquad \overline{v_x'} = \overline{v_y'} = \overline{v_z'} = 0. \tag{10}$$

It is then **v'** and not **v** for which all directions are equally probable when the gas is in equilibrium, so that

$$\overline{v_x'^2} = \overline{v_y'^2} = \overline{v_z'^2} = \tfrac{1}{3}\overline{v'^2}.*$$

Corresponding to this division of the molecular motion into mass motion and motion of thermal agitation, there exists an important theorem concerning the kinetic energy. The translatory kinetic energy of the molecules in any macroscopically small element of volume $\delta\tau$ can be written

$$\Sigma'\tfrac{1}{2} mv^2 = \Sigma'\tfrac{1}{2} m(v_x^2 + v_y^2 + v_z^2) = \Sigma'\tfrac{1}{2} m(v_{0x}^2 + v_{0y}^2 + v_{0z}^2)$$
$$+ \Sigma'm(v_{0x}v_x' + v_{0y}v_y' + v_{0z}v_z') + \Sigma'\tfrac{1}{2} m(v_x'^2 + v_y'^2 + v_z'^2)$$

---

* In a mixed gas whose composition varies from point to point, so that inter-diffusion of its constituents is going on, the mass motion is different for different kinds of molecules and the theory requires modification to make it entirely satisfactory, but such refinements seem to be of no practical importance at present.

by (6) and (9b).   Now suppose that the molecules are all alike, or, if different kinds are present, let the mass velocity v_0 be the same for all kinds.   Then in any sum like $\Sigma' m v_{0x} v_x'$ we can take out v_{0x} as a common factor and write

$$\Sigma' m v_{0x} v_x' = v_{0x} \Sigma' m v_x' = v_{0x} \Sigma' m_j \Sigma' v_{xj}',$$

$\Sigma' v_{xj}'$ representing a sum over all molecules in $\delta\tau$ of kind no. j and the sum Σ' extending over all the different kinds.   But by (10), $\Sigma' v_{xj}' = 0$, since the mean value $\bar{v}_x'$ for molecules of kind no. j is simply $\Sigma' v_{xj}'$ divided by their number in $\delta\tau$.   Hence, after reasoning in the same way about the y- and z-components, we have

$$\Sigma' m v_{0x} v_x' = \Sigma' m v_{0y} v_y' = \Sigma' m v_{0z} v_z' = 0.$$

Furthermore, by (6),

$$\Sigma' \tfrac{1}{2} m(v_{0x}^2 + v_{0y}^2 + v_{0z}^2) = \Sigma' \tfrac{1}{2} m v_0^2 = \tfrac{1}{2}(\Sigma' m) v_0^2.$$

Thus the expression given above for the kinetic energy reduces to

$$\Sigma' \tfrac{1}{2} m v^2 = \tfrac{1}{2}(\Sigma' m) v_0^2 + \Sigma' \tfrac{1}{2} m v'^2,$$

in which each sum extends over all molecules in $\delta\tau$.   If we now divide this equation through by $\delta\tau$ and note that $\Sigma' m / \delta\tau = \rho$, the density, we finally obtain for the translatory kinetic energy of the molecules per unit volume

$$\Sigma \tfrac{1}{2} m v^2 = \tfrac{1}{2}\rho v_0^2 + \Sigma \tfrac{1}{2} m v'^2, \tag{11}$$

the sums now extending over unit volume in the sense explained just under eq. (2).

Thus the *total kinetic energy of translation* of the molecules is simply the *sum* of the kinetic energy due to the observable macroscopic *mass motion* and the kinetic energy of *thermal agitation*.

Another quantity that requires reconsideration in the presence of mass motion is the *pressure*.   The pressure in a moving gas is best defined as the rate of transfer of normal momentum across a surface that is moving "with the gas," i.e., with a velocity equal to the mass velocity $\mathbf{v}_0$.   Its value is obviously given by (2a), (3a, b) or (4), with $\mathbf{v}$ replaced by $\mathbf{v}'$.

8. Reversible Expansion and Compression.   The conceptions and the theorem of the last section find an interesting application in the molecular interpretation of those reversible expansions and compressions which are so important in thermodynamics. It may help in forming clear conceptions of the molecular processes in a gas if we analyze to some extent a case of this sort.

Consider, for example, a mass of gas that is being compressed very slowly by a moving piston in a cylinder whose walls do not conduct heat. The motion being slow, the gas will be everywhere close to equilibrium and moving with a mass velocity v_0 that grades downward, from a maximum value at the piston equal to its speed, to zero at the other end of the cylinder (cf. Fig. 2).

Under these circumstances the piston does work upon the gas; the amount of this work as the volume V of the gas decreases by

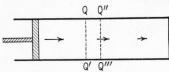

$-dV$ is, as shown in elementary physics, $-p\,dV$, p being the pressure, and at the same time the gas does negative work $p\,dV$ on the piston. Since no energy is allowed to leave in the form of heat, the work done upon the gas

FIG. 2.—Adiabatic compression.

must remain stored in it in the form of an increase in its "internal" or "intrinsic" energy, which we shall call simply the energy of the gas.

Let us now view this process from the molecular standpoint. According to the laws of mechanics the molecules that strike the moving piston rebound from it with an increase in their kinetic energy representing the work done on them by the piston. This does not imply an increase of equal magnitude in the energy of *thermal agitation* of these particular molecules, however. Suppose, for example, a molecule moving at velocity **v** strikes the piston. Then just before the impact its thermal velocity, according to (9a), is $\mathbf{v}' = \mathbf{v} - \mathbf{v}_0$ where $\mathbf{v}_0$, the mass velocity of the gas at the piston, is the same as the velocity of the piston itself. Thus $\mathbf{v}'$ is also the velocity of the molecule relative to the piston; and since, according to the laws of elastic impact, relative velocity undergoes an alteration only in direction but not in magnitude, we see that the molecules that strike the piston do not themselves experience any gain in energy of thermal agitation at all!

Of course, it is an observed fact that the heating produced by the compression under these circumstances is distributed equally throughout the gas. To see how this becomes about, let us consider first the flow of translatory kinetic energy of the molecules across any cross section QQ' that is moving with the gas in its mass motion. According to the analysis of the last section, the motion of molecules across QQ' will be determined by their thermal component of velocity alone, and the number crossing unit area per second with a thermal component of velocity $v_\perp'$ perpendicular to QQ' will be $\Sigma v_\perp'$ summed over unit volume, as in the deduction of the pressure. Each molecule that crosses carries with it total kinetic energy $\frac{1}{2}mv^2$; hence an amount of kinetic energy is carried across unit area of QQ' per second equal to $\frac{1}{2}\Sigma mv_\perp'v^2$.

Now we can obviously write $v^2 = v_\perp{}^2 + v_\parallel{}^2$, $v_\parallel$ being the component of $\mathbf{v}$ parallel to QQ'; and by (9a) $v_\perp = v_0 + v_\perp'$, $v_\parallel = v_\parallel'$, v_0 denoting the mass velocity and $v_{0\parallel}$ being zero and $v_{0\perp} = v_0$ in our case. Hence, for the rate of transfer of energy we have

$$\tfrac{1}{2}\,\Sigma mv_\perp'v^2 = \tfrac{1}{2}\Sigma mv_\perp'(v_\perp{}^2 + v_\parallel{}^2) = \tfrac{1}{2}\,[v_0^2\Sigma mv_\perp' + 2v_0\Sigma mv_\perp'^2 +$$
$$\Sigma mv_\perp'(v_\perp'^2 + v_\parallel'^2)].$$

Here $\Sigma mv_\perp' = 0$ by (10), or by the argument used in order to dispose of $\Sigma mv_{0x}v_x'$ in arriving at eq. (11). We should also expect the last sum in the equation to vanish by symmetry, positive and negative values of $v_\perp'$ occurring equally often for the same value of the quantity $(v_\perp'^2 + v_\parallel'^2)$; and we shall find later that this is correct so long as there is no temperature gradient. In the middle term, finally, $\Sigma mv_\perp'^2 = p$, the pressure [cf. (2a) and the end of the last section].

The expression for the translatory kinetic energy carried across unit area of QQ' per second thus reduces to pv_0 or to the rate at which, according to ordinary mechanical analysis, the gas behind QQ' is doing work on that ahead. Now if we consider the mass of gas that lies between two such moving cross sections, as between QQ' and $Q''Q'''$, the flow of energy will be greater across the first than across the second because of the difference in the values of v_0. Kinetic energy, therefore, is accumulating between these two cross sections. Since, however, the total energy is the sum of the thermal energy and the energy of the mass motion, as shown in the last section, and the mass motion is constant, the increase must occur in the thermal kinetic energy alone, except in so far as this may subsequently pass over into energy of vibration or the like inside the molecules. To see in detail just how v', the thermal part of the velocity, comes to increase, is a bit tedious, but we can understand it qualitatively if we note that those molecules which mingle at a given moment in a given region of the contracting gas have come from neighboring regions whose relative mass motion was one of mutual approach, and the molecules thus mingle with higher relative velocities than they otherwise would.

Because of simple relations such as these it suffices to develop a large part of the kinetic theory for a gas at rest. Accordingly, hereafter mass motion will be understood to be absent unless the contrary is specified. The extension of the results to moving gases can then be made easily when required.

Problem. Show that the total momentum of an element of the gas is that due to the mass motion, or, as a vector, it is ρv_0 per unit volume.

9. Free Expansion. Quite a different case from the preceding is presented by free expansion, in which a gas is allowed neither to exchange heat with its surroundings nor to do external work. The ideal way to perform such an expansion would be to put the gas into one compartment A of a vessel with a vacuum in an adjoining compartment B, and then suddenly to open in the partition holes so tiny that the molecules of gas could go through only one by one (cf. Fig. 3). It is very difficult, however, to perform an expansion in this ideal manner, and in practice rougher equivalents must be substituted.

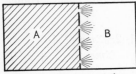

Fig. 3.—Free expansion.

Such an equivalent was tried by Joule in 1845; improving upon an arrangement used by Gay-Lussac in 1807, he simply connected a vessel of air suddenly to an evacuated vessel. With this arrangement, when the stopcock in the connecting tube is opened and some of the air rushes into the vacuum, the air left behind is cooled greatly by an approximately reversible expansion under pressure. If, however, the gas could then be left to itself for a time without exchanging heat with its surroundings, it would soon come to rest, and eventually, by conduction of heat through the gas itself, it would come to the same uniform temperature as would have resulted from an ideal free expansion. Joule evaded the difficulty of so thoroughly insulating the gas by surrounding both vessels with a water bath and looking for a change in the temperature of the water, which would certainly have occurred if there had been a final net change in the temperature of the air. Being unable to detect any change, he concluded that the heat of free expansion of air, i.e., the heat that must be added to a gram of it to keep its temperature constant when it is allowed to expand freely, is either zero or at least very small.

In later experiments by Kelvin and others* the gas was caused to expand slowly and continuously through a porous plug, such as a wad of glass wool closing a tube through which the gas was forced to flow, and the difference of temperature between the gas entering and the gas leaving the plug was noted [the Joule-Thomson effect, cf. Fig. (4)]. With this arrangement, however, the true effect of free

* Cf. T. Preston, "Heat," pp. 269, 771; Edser, "Heat," rev. ed., p. 376.

expansion is overlaid by another. As a volume V of the gas enters the plug under pressure p, the gas behind does work pV upon it; as it leaves the plug under a lower pressure p', it in turn does work $p'V'$ upon the gas ahead; but usually $p'V'$ is slightly different from pV, and the energy of the gas is thus altered by an amount equal to the negative difference of the two works or by $-\Delta(pV) = -(p'V' - pV)$.

Fig. 4.—The porous-plug arrangement.

The latter effect can be calculated from known values of pV as a function of the pressure, and so allowance can be made for it.

If we may judge from the few cases that have been tried, the heat of free expansion is always positive, but it is extremely small in the case of the almost perfect gases, as is also the more complicated Joule-Thomson effect itself. In air at 0°C, for example, the Joule-Thomson cooling at moderate pressures amounts only to 0.26° per atmosphere drop in pressure; in carbon dioxide under the same conditions it is 1.5°, but in hydrogen there is a heating of 0.03°.

It may be of interest to see how from such data we can calculate the heat of free expansion, and also the temperature drop in an adiabatic free expansion. Suppose a gram of gas enters the porous plug at 0°C and under a pressure of 2 atmospheres, and emerges at a temperature $(\delta T)_{JT}$ and a pressure of 1 atmosphere; $(\delta T)_{JT}$ thus represents the Joule-Thomson temperature change per atmosphere. Now imagine this gas restored to 0°C, but still at a pressure of 1 atmosphere; to do this we must give it heat $-c_p(\delta T)_{JT}$, c_p being its specific heat at constant pressure measured in ergs. During each of these two processes the gas does external work equal to its change in pV; hence the net external work that it has done since entering the plug is the change in pV as p changes from 2 atmospheres to 1 atmosphere at 0°C, which will be denoted by $\delta(pV)$. Accordingly, by conservation of energy the gas has on the whole gained an amount of energy (measured algebraically) equal to the heat absorbed less the work done or $\delta U = -c_p(\delta T)_{JT} - \delta(pV)$.

Now the gain in energy depends only on the initial and final states of the gas. Hence the same gain would have occurred if we had allowed the gas to expand *freely*, without doing work, into the same final volume as it occupied in the first case after being brought back to 0°C. If at the same time we supply enough heat to keep its temperature at 0°C, this heat will be, by definition, the heat of free expansion, L_p; and it will also equal the gain in energy. Hence, equating the two values thus found for δU, we have for the heat of free expansion

$$L_p = -c_p(\delta T)_{JT} - \delta(pV) \tag{12}$$

ergs per gram and per atmosphere drop. This equation connects the Joule-Thomson effect with the heat of free expansion.

On the other hand, in the alternative process just described we might have allowed the gas to expand without supplying any heat, the gas then changing in temperature by a certain amount δT; and then we could have brought it back to 0°C by supplying heat $-c_V \, \delta T$, c_V being the specific heat at constant volume. In this case the gas, just after expanding, occupies the volume that it occupies at 0°C and 1 atmosphere, but at a temperature δT. Its pressure at that moment can differ only slightly from 1 atmosphere, however; hence, we can replace δT approximately by the drop that occurs in a free expansion from 2 atmospheres to exactly 1 atmosphere, which we shall denote by $(\delta T)_f$. Then, the change in energy being the same as before, we have $-c_V(\delta T)_f = L_p$ or $(\delta T)_f = -L_p/c_V$, and from (12)

$$(\delta T)_f = \gamma \left[(\delta T)_{JT} + \frac{1}{c_p} \delta(pV) \right], \qquad (\delta T)_{JT} = \frac{1}{\gamma} (\delta T)_f - \frac{1}{c_p} \delta(pV), \tag{13a, b}$$

where $\gamma = c_p/c_V$.

Now for air $(\delta T)_{JT} = -0.26$ as stated above, $\gamma = 1.41$,
$$c_p = 0.24 \times 4.186 \times 10^7,$$

and $\delta(pV)/p_0 V_0 = 0.00060$ where p_0, V_0 refer to standard conditions, so that $\delta(pV) = 0.00060 \times 1.031 \times 10^6/0.001293$; hence

$$(\delta T)_f = 1.41(-0.26 + 0.047) = -0.30°.$$

For hydrogen, $(\delta T)_{JT} = +0.03°$, $\gamma = 1.41$, $c_p = 3.4 \times 4.186 \times 10^7$, $\delta(pV)/p_0 V_0 = -0.00060$, and $V_0 = 1/0.0000899$; hence

$$(\delta T)_f = 1.41(0.03 - 0.047) = -0.024°.$$

Thus a free expansion cools hydrogen just as it does air, only much less; the positive Joule-Thomson effect for hydrogen is due to the decrease in pV upon expansion.

The heat of free expansion in calories per gram per atmosphere drop, or $\dfrac{L_p}{4.186 \times 10^7}$, comes out at 0.051 cal for air and about 0.06 cal for hydrogen.

10. Isothermal Properties of the Ideal Gas. To make further progress we need now an understanding of the relation between molecular energy and the thing that we call the *temperature*. The common method of measuring the temperature of a gas is to place a thermometer in it and read the thermometer. Let us see what this implies in regard to the molecular motion.

A molecule of the gas impinging upon the wall of the thermometer must sometimes lose energy to it and sometimes gain energy from it, for the result of an impact depends, according to classical conceptions, both upon the motion of the molecule and upon the motion at that instant of the particular wall molecule that is struck. In consequence of these impacts, a state of statistical equilibrium soon comes into being in which on the whole the gains and the losses of energy balance each other, and when this state has been established, the mean trans-latory energy of the gas molecules and also their $\overline{v^2}$ will have definite values which may be associated with the temperature shown by the thermometer. Now the reactions of the separate molecules with the wall must be independent processes, provided the density of the gas is very low, the effect of an individual impact being in practically all cases unaffected by the positions or velocities of the other molecules. We should expect, therefore, that in the state of equilibrium the value of $\overline{v^2}$ for each type of molecule would be independent of the density and, therefore, a function of the temperature only. This surmise we shall find to be confirmed later by the elaborate method of analysis known as statistical mechanics (cf. the treatment of equipartition of energy and of temperature in Chap. IX).

Accordingly, it will be assumed that in a rarefied gas in thermal equilibrium $\overline{v^2}$ for a given kind of molecule is a function of the temperature alone.

It follows then at once by (3) or (4) that in our ideal gas, when the temperature remains constant, p is proportional to ρ, or pV is constant, V being the volume of a given mass of the gas. This is Boyle's law, obtained here as a deduction from kinetic theory. The law is found by experiment to hold very nearly for all real gases when the density is only a small fraction of the critical density.

The fact that $\overline{v^2}$ depends only on the temperature and not on the density suggests, as a further conclusion, that the energy, also, ought to be independent of the density at a given temperature. To be sure, the molecules will usually possess not only translational but also internal energy of various sorts, such as energy of rotation or of vibra-tion of the atoms. The distribution of the energy between these forms, on the one hand, and the translatory kinetic energy on the other, comes about, however, through the agency of collisions, and there should be, therefore, a definite average ratio for each kind of molecule between the amounts of the different forms; increasing the density must increase the frequency of collisions and so increase the *rapidity* with which the equilibrium state is set up, but it ought not to alter the distributional characteristics of the equilibrium state itself. This conclusion, again, we shall find to be confirmed by statistical mechanics. We conclude, therefore, that the energy of our ideal gas will be, like $\overline{v^2}$, a function of its temperature only and not of its density. It follows then also that its heat of free expansion will be zero.

From the experimental standpoint it has been found convenient to define a "perfect" gas as one which both obeys Boyle's law and has a zero heat of free expansion. The Joule-Thomson effect for such a gas must then likewise be zero. The ideal gas of kinetic theory has thus the essential properties of the perfect gas of experimental physics. It appears from experiment that all gases become perfect in this sense in the limit of zero density.

11. Avogadro's Law. According to a famous theorem of statistical mechanics the mean kinetic energy associated with each degree of freedom of a mechanical system in statistical equilibrium has the same value (cf. Sec. 206 in Chap. IX). In the case before us, this means that in gases in equilibrium at a given temperature the average translatory kinetic energy of all molecules has the same value; for two kinds of molecules with masses m_1, m_2 and velocities $\mathbf{v}_1$, $\mathbf{v}_2$, we have thus

$$\tfrac{1}{2} m_1 \overline{v_1^2} = \tfrac{1}{2} m_2 \overline{v_2^2}. \tag{14}$$

According to the theorem of equipartition this holds whether the molecules are in different vessels or are mixed together. Hence at a given temperature the *root-mean-square speed*,

$$v_s = (\overline{v^2})^{\frac{1}{2}}$$

for different kinds of molecules is inversely proportional to the square root of the molecular weight.

On the other hand, if we also make the pressure the same for separate masses of gas composed each of one kind of molecule, we have by $(3a)$

$$\tfrac{1}{3} n_1 m_1 \overline{v_1^2} = \tfrac{1}{3} n_2 m_2 \overline{v_2^2}. \tag{15}$$

Hence, dividing (14) into (15), we find that

$$n_1 = n_2. \tag{16}$$

We reach thus the very important conclusion that all perfect gases at the same pressure and temperature contain the *same number of molecules per unit volume*. This statement, which is of considerable utility in chemistry,* was proposed as a hypothesis by Avogadro in 1811 to help in explaining the chemical fact that gases unite in simple proportions both by weight and by volume, and it is very often referred to as Avogadro's hypothesis; we shall prefer to call it Avogadro's law.   It appears here not as a separate hypothesis but as a deduction from kinetic theory.

From Avogadro's law it follows that the *densities* of different perfect gases at the same temperature and pressure are proportional to their *molecular weights*.   The values of the product pV are thus inversely proportional to the molecular weights if V stands for the volume of a *gram;* but if V stands for the volume of a *gram molecule* or mole (i.e., a number of grams equal to the molecular weight), then at any given temperature and pressure V itself is the same for all gases.   The volume occupied by a gram molecule of a perfect gas under standard conditions is thus a universal constant, and it has been made the object of very careful experiment.   The usual method is to observe at a given temperature the values of pV for a series of decreasing pressures and then to extrapolate to $p = 0$; from the limiting value of pV as thus found, V can be calculated subsequently for any pressure.   The accepted experimental value of V for a gram molecule at $0°$ and a pressure of 1 atmosphere is

$$V_0 = 22{,}414 \text{ cc.} \tag{17}$$

The volume V_1 of a *gram* of a gas whose molecules have molecular weight M (in the chemical sense), and the density ρ of such a gas, under standard conditions are then:

$$V_1 = \frac{22{,}414}{M} \text{ cc}, \qquad \rho = \frac{M}{V_0} = 4.461 \times 10^{-5}M \text{ g/cc.} \tag{17a}$$

12. The Temperature.   In our references to temperature we have hitherto said nothing at all about any temperature scale.   This was justified by the fact that we have been employing only the equilibrium property of temperature, viz., the fact that several bodies placed in contact come ultimately into a state of mutual equilibrium, whereupon we say that they possess the same temperature.   We must now introduce a scale for the quantitative comparison of different temperatures.

The first temperature scale to be widely adopted was that determined by the expansion of mercury in a glass tube.   This scale has important advantages but is limited to the range between the freezing

* See W. Nernst, "Theoretical Chemistry," or H. S. Taylor, "Treatise on Physical Chemistry."

and boiling points of mercury; furthermore the selection of a particular substance such as mercury for the thermometric substance is a very arbitrary procedure. Hence, when it was found more than a century ago that at least the common gases expand nearly equally with rise of temperature and also almost uniformly as judged by the mercury thermometer (Charles's law), the proposal was made to adopt the perfect gas as the basic thermometric substance; and during the last century · the constant-volume hydrogen thermometer was actually adopted for the ultimate standard as constituting the best practical approximation to a perfect-gas thermometer. All perfect gases would necessarily lead to the same scale, since according to eq. (14) their mean kinetic energies, and hence also, according to eq. (3a), their pressures, vary at the same rate with temperature. We might, therefore, define the absolute temperature T as a quantity proportional to the pressure p of a perfect gas at constant volume. The ratio T/p must then be proportional to the volume V, since by Boyle's law $p \propto 1/V$ when T is constant; thus we should have $T \propto pV$ or $pV = RT$, where R is a constant for a given mass of gas.

On the other hand, with the development of thermodynamics during the last century there arose the possibility of setting up a temperature scale that would not be dependent upon the special properties of any body whatever; and this scale has now come to be regarded as the ultimate one. Fortunately it agrees exactly with the perfect-gas scale, as we shall proceed to show. The argument is a somewhat abstract one, however, and any student who prefers to be satisfied with the perfect-gas definition of T can omit the proof and pass at once to Sec. 14.

13. The Thermodynamic Temperature Scale. The thermodynamic absolute temperature T is most concretely defined as a quantity which, like the temperature on any scale, has the same value for any two bodies that are in thermal equilibrium with each other, but which at two different temperatures is proportional to the heats absorbed and rejected in a Carnot cycle working between those temperatures. The theory of the Carnot cycle for a gas is not especially simple, however, unless one adds the customary further assumption that the specific heat is independent of temperature, which is by no means necessary for the validity of the result that we here wish to establish. On the other hand, thermodynamic reasoning leads also to the equivalent but more abstract idea that, when a little heat dQ is imparted to a body in a reversible manner, we can write for it $dQ = T\,dS$ where dS is the differential of another quantity, called the entropy, which has a single definite value corresponding to each possible state of the body.

This principle serves to define T equally well with a Carnot cycle and it is very easy to apply it to the perfect gas in the following way:

Let U denote the energy of a mass of gas whose pressure and volume are p and V, and let a small amount of heat dQ be given to it in a reversible manner. Then, by the conservation of energy,

$$dQ = dU + p \, dV,$$

$p \, dV$ representing, as is shown in elementary physics, the loss of energy from the gas due to the work it does on its surroundings. Now dU is the differential of a single-valued function of the state of the gas, or of any two independent variables such as temperature and volume that may be employed to define its state; for the energy U has always the same value when those variables take on given values. The reversible heat dQ, on the other hand, is *not* the differential of any such function. If, for example, we consider two different paths on the pV diagram by which the gas can be carried from a state A to a state B, whereas the change $\int_A^B dU$ in U is the same along both paths, $\int dQ$ or the total heat absorbed must be greater along that path along which the pressure is larger in order to provide for the larger amount of external work that is done (the excess being represented, of course, by the area enclosed between the two paths on the diagram). For the same reason $p \, dV$ is obviously not the differential of any single-valued function.

But suppose now we divide the above equation through by pV, thus:

$$\frac{1}{pV} \, dQ = \frac{dU}{pV} + \frac{dV}{V}.$$

According to Boyle's law, pV is a definite function of the temperature alone (as measured on any scale); and we saw in Sec. 10 that for a perfect gas, U is likewise a function of the temperature alone. Hence dU/pV must be the differential of some function of the temperature, which could be found by evaluating $\int dU/pV$. Also,

$$\frac{dV}{V} = d(\log V).$$

Hence the right-hand member of the equation is now the differential of a definite function of the temperature and volume as independent variables. The same must, therefore, be true of dQ/pV.

Accordingly, we can write $dQ/pV = d\psi$, where ψ is some function of the temperature and volume. Suppose, now, we define the temperature T by the equation $T = apV$, where a is a constant. Then $dQ = Td(\psi/a)$; and this agrees with the thermodynamic equation, $dQ = T \, dS$, if we define S as $S = \psi/a$. The constant a can then be chosen for each body separately so as to give the temperature the property of being always the same for two bodies in thermal equilibrium; for, if this is done at one temperature, it will remain true at all temperatures because by (3b) $pV = \frac{1}{3}\overline{v^2}$ and hence, in consequence of equipartition as expressed in eq. (14), pV must vary with change of temperature in the same ratio for all gases. Since this requirement fixes only the *ratios* of the values of a for different bodies, T still remains arbitrary to the extent of a constant factor.

There are, to be sure, other quantities that might be employed in order to throw dQ into the general form $T \, dS$; from the mathematical standpcint what we have shown is merely that $1/pV$, and hence also $1/apV$ for any value of a, is an "integrating factor" for dQ. It can be shown mathematically, however, that all integrating factors are closely connected with each other, and that all whose reciprocals can be given the necessary comparative property for different bodies are simply proportional to each other and so must be included in the general form, $1/apV$.

14. The Perfect-gas Law. Whether we adopt the thermodynamic or the perfect-gas definition of the absolute temperature T, we arrive at the usual equation for a perfect gas,

$$pV = RT. \tag{18}$$

If we then add the requirement that the temperature interval between melting ice and saturated steam under 1 atmosphere shall be 100, the absolute temperature of the ice point is easily found to be given by the formula, $p_1V_1 - p_0V_0 = 100 \, p_0V_0/T_0$ or

$$T_0 = \frac{100 \, p_0V_0}{p_1V_1 - p_0V_0},$$

p_0V_0 and p_1V_1 being observed values at the ice point T_0 and at the saturated-steam point, $T_0 + 100°$, respectively. This formula corresponds to the actual method employed nowadays in the experimental measurement of T_0; the most recent determination by this method gave,[*] in excellent agreement with others,

$$T_0 = 273.14°. \tag{19}$$

[*] Keesom, van der Horst, and Jaconis, *Physica*, **1**, 324 (1934).

The perfect-gas law, eq. (18), can be applied to any desired quantity of gas, the proper value of R being calculated as pV/T. In physics the mass is usually understood to be a gram; in that case it is often more convenient to write the equation in terms of the density,

$$\rho = \frac{1}{V}:$$

$$p = \rho R T. \tag{18a}$$

In physical chemistry, on the other hand, a gram molecule or mole is almost always chosen; then, in consequence of Avogadro's law, the gas constant R has a universal value for all gases, which we shall denote by R_M and whose value, found by dividing T_0 from (19) into V_0 as given in (17), is

$$R_M = 82.06 \text{ cc atm/deg} = 83.15 \times 10^6 \text{ cm dynes/deg.} \tag{20a}$$

For a gas whose molecules are all alike

$$R_M = MR \tag{20b}$$

in terms of the molecular weight M. In the case of a mixture of molecules of different masses, if 1 g contains γ_j g of each kind no. j in a volume V, the partial pressure due to each kind will be

$$p_j = \gamma_j \frac{R_j T}{V},$$

R_j being the constant for a whole gram of kind no. j, and by Dalton's law the total pressure will then be $p = \sum_j p_j = RT/V$ where

$$R = \sum_j \gamma_j R_j \tag{20c}$$

and represents the gas constant for a gram of the mixture.

The perfect gas could be defined as one which obeys the perfect-gas equation, (18), instead of defining it, as above, by the two conditions that it obeys Boyle's law and also has a zero heat of free expansion. For it is obvious that any gas which obeys this equation also obeys Boyle's law, and it can be shown from the laws of thermodynamics that any gas obeying the perfect-gas equation must also have a zero heat of free expansion (Sec. 137, problem).

Problem. Show that for a perfect gas the coefficient of expansion α (at constant pressure) and the coefficient of pressure increase (at constant volume) are given, in terms of values V_1 or p_1 which hold at any base temperature T_1, by

$$\alpha = \frac{1}{V_1} \frac{V - V_1}{T - T_1} = \frac{1}{V_1} \left(\frac{\partial V}{\partial T}\right)_p = \frac{1}{T_1},$$

$$\epsilon = \frac{1}{p_1} \frac{p - p_1}{T - T_1} = \frac{1}{p_1} \left(\frac{\partial p}{\partial T}\right)_V = \frac{1}{T_1}.$$

The coefficient at 0°C, $\alpha_0 = \epsilon_0 = 1/T_0 = 0.003661$, is of particular interest.

15. Molecular Magnitudes. Since the product nm of the mass m of a molecule and the number n of molecules in unit volume equals the density ρ, this product can be calculated at once, but our equations do not enable us to calculate n and m separately. As a matter of fact, kinetic theory by itself does not furnish any very exact method of estimating these two molecular magnitudes. The best values that we possess today are derived from the following indirect evidence.

The electrical charge carried by a gram atom of a monovalent element such as silver is easily measured and has been found to be 96,494 international or 96,489 absolute coulombs (the Faraday)*; and each atom carries the same numerical charge as the electron. For the latter it now appears that Millikan's value (4.774×10^{-10}) was too low because of an error in the viscosity of air. If Kellström's recent value for the viscosity† is combined with Millikan's oil-drop results, the value $4.816 \pm 0.013 \times 10^{-10}$ is obtained for the electronic charge; this agrees within the probable error with the value calculated from x-ray wave lengths as measured by means of a grating, which is 4.8036 ± 0.0005.‡ Since accurate repetitions of some of these experiments are under way and indicate that the grating wave length is at least not too low, we shall adopt the value

$$e = 4.805 \times 10^{-10}$$

electrostatic unit. Dividing this number by 2.9979×10^9* to convert it into coulombs and then dividing the result into 96,489, we have then as the number of atoms in a gram atom, or of molecules in a gram molecule or mole, often called Avogadro's (or Loschmidt's) number,

$$N_0 = 6.021 \times 10^{23}, \tag{21}$$

and for the number of molecules in a cubic centimeter of perfect gas at 0° and 1 atmosphere pressure, $n_0 = N_0/V_0$ or, by (17),

$$n_0 = 2.686 \times 10^{19}, \text{ or } 2.69 \times 10^{19} \tag{22}$$

---

* Cf. BIRGE, *Rev. Mod. Physics*, **1**, 1 (1929).
† *Nature*, **136**, 682 (1935).
‡ BIRGE, *Phys. Rev.* **48**, 918 (1935).

to three places.   The mass of an imaginary atom of molecular weight 1 is then the reciprocal of N_0 or

$$m_0 = 1.661 \times 10^{-24} g; \tag{23}$$

and the mass of any atom or molecule is the product of this number into the atomic or molecular weight.

A related number of great importance to theory is the *Boltzmann constant,* or gas constant for one molecule,

$$k = \frac{R_M}{N_0} = mR = 1.381 \times 10^{-16} \text{ cm dyne/deg}, \tag{24a}$$

m being the actual mass of a molecule and R the gas constant for 1 g. In terms of k we can write for the pressure, in place of $pV = RT$,

$$p = nkT; \tag{24b}$$

for $V = 1/\rho = 1/nm$.

On the other hand, from (3b), (18), (20b), and (24a),

$$\overline{v^2} = 3RT = \frac{3R_M T}{M} = \frac{3kT}{m}, \tag{25a}$$

M being the molecular weight.   It follows that the root-mean-square speed of the molecules, $v_s = (\overline{v^2})^{1/2}$, varies directly as the square root of the absolute temperature, and for different gases inversely as the square root of the molecular weight.   The same thing is true of the mean speed, which we shall find in the next chapter to be $\bar{v} = 0.921 v_s$.

The mean translatory kinetic energy of a molecule is also of interest:

$$\tfrac{1}{2} m\overline{v^2} = \tfrac{3}{2} kT. \tag{25b}$$

This last equation has sometimes in kinetic theory been made the basis of the temperature scale.

Equation (25a) is difficult to test experimentally, but it can be employed the other way round as a means of calculating v_s and $\bar{v}$. Values obtained in this way for a number of gases at 15°C* are given in the table on p. 26, along with values of R (for 1 g) in absolute units, as well as the molecular weight M and the actual mass of a molecule m calculated in the manner described above.

With three exceptions the values of M were taken or calculated from the table of International Atomic Weights for 1931†; R in atmos-

---

* 15°C was chosen instead of 0°C because in most applications the actual temperature is room temperature.

† See *Jour. Amer. Chem. Soc.,* **53,** 1627 (1931).

pheres was then calculated as R_M/M, and these values were multiplied by 1.01325×10^6 to get R in absolute units. The three exceptions are as follows. The atomic weight of H^2, the atom of deuterium or heavy hydrogen, was taken from a note by Bainbridge.* For air, R in atmospheres was found by dividing 1000 by the accepted mass of a normal liter of air, 1.2929 g, and by $T_0 = 273.14$, and then multiplying by 1.0006† to extrapolate to zero density. For the electron, M was calculated as $\dfrac{F}{e/m}$, F standing for the Faraday in electromagnetic units, and e/m having the value $= 1.7576 \times 10^7$;‡ m was calculated directly from e/m and e.

	M	m (unit, 10^{-24} g)	R (unit, 10^6 erg/deg)	$v_s(15°C)$ (unit, 10^3 cm/sec)	$\bar{v}(15°C)$ (unit, 10^3 cm/sec)
H$_2$......	2.016	3.349	41.25	188.8	174.0
H$_2^2$......	4.027	6.689	20.65	133.6	123.1
Helium...	4.002	6.648	20.78	134.0	123.5
H$_2$O......	18.016	29.93	4.615	63.16	58.19
Neon.....	20.18	33.52	4.120	59.68	54.98
N$_2$......	28.02	46.54	2.968	50.65	46.67
O$_2$........	32.00	53.16	2.598	47.39	43.66
HCl......	36.46	60.56	2.280	44.40	40.90
Argon....	39.94	66.34	2.082	42.42	39.08
CO$_2$......	44.00	73.09	1.890	40.42	37.24
Krypton..	82.9	137.7	1.0030	29.45	27.13
Xenon....	130.2	216.3	.6386	23.50	21.65
Hg......	200.6	333.2	.4145	18.93	17.44
Air......	(28.96)	(48.11)	2.871	49.82	45.90
Electrons.	5.49×10^{-4}	$m = 9.119$ $\times 10^{-28}$ g	$R = 1.514$ $\times 10^8$ erg/deg	$v_s = 11.44$ $\times 10^6$ cm/sec	$\bar{v} = 10.54$ $\times 10^6$ cm/sec

16. Rapidity of the Molecular Motion. The first calculation of molecular speeds by this method was made by Joule in 1848. The values found are high as compared with most speeds produced by human agency. The slowness of gaseous diffusion in spite of these high speeds, which was at one time advanced as an objection against the theory, arises, of course, from the continual interference of the molecules with each other's motions. For example, if chlorine gas is

* Bainbridge, *Phys. Rev.*, **44**, 57 (1933).

† Cf. Holborn and Otto, *Zeits. Physik*, **33**, 1 (1925), where the unit of pressure, however, is 1 M of Hg.

‡ Birge, *Phys. Rev.*, **49**, 204 (1936).

released in one corner of a room, it may be minutes before the odor is perceptible in the opposite corner; a molecule of chlorine goes nearly a quarter of a mile in every second, but this long path is converted into a complicated zigzag by collisions with other molecules and is thereby tangled up into a space less than an inch across.

A comparison with the velocity of sound is also interesting.   The familiar formula for the velocity of sound in a gas is

$$\left(\frac{\gamma p}{\rho}\right)^{1/2} = (\gamma p V)^{1/2} = (\gamma R T)^{1/2}$$

where $\gamma \leqq \frac{5}{3}$.   Comparing this quantity with v_s or the square root of $\overline{v^2}$ as given by (25a), we see that the velocity of sound is less than v_s in the ratio $(\gamma/3)^{1/2}$ or something under $\frac{3}{4}$.   It could hardly exceed v_s, since the sound waves are actually propagated by the motion of the molecules, so this result really constitutes a confirmation of the theory; but it may seem surprising at first sight that the two velocities should be so nearly equal.

The high values of the molecular velocities and the enormous magnitude of N_0 or n_0 serve to explain why matter behaves in so many ways as if it were continuously distributed.

Problems

1. Calculate values of v_s from eq. (3a) for hydrogen, air and carbon dioxide at 0°C, using actual values of ρ under standard conditions, and compare results with the values given in the table.   (The slight discrepancy is due, of course, to departures from the perfect-gas law.)

2. Compute the temperature at which the root-mean-square speed is just equal to the "speed of escape" from the surface of the earth (i.e., the minimum speed necessary to carry a molecule to infinity) for (a) hydrogen and (b) oxygen.

Repeat for the moon, assuming gravity on its surface to be 0.164 as strong as on the earth.

CHAPTER II

DISTRIBUTION LAW FOR MOLECULAR VELOCITIES

In the last chapter we found that the pressure and temperature of perfect gases depend only upon the mean square of the molecular speeds and are independent of the manner in which the molecular velocities vary among themselves. There are other properties of gases, however, which do depend to some extent upon the actual distribution of the velocities, and a knowledge of these is, therefore, needed. Accordingly, we shall take up next, in this chapter, the law according to which the molecular velocities are distributed in a gas in equilibrium.

17. The Distribution Function for Molecular Velocity. If we could follow an individual molecule in its motion, we should observe it to undergo many and large changes in velocity as it moves about and collides with others. For example, one can easily invent collisions which, according to the laws of mechanics, would leave one of the colliding molecules after the collision momentarily at rest, and others which would give to one molecule, in consequence of a string of collisions in which it is struck repeatedly from the side, as large a speed as might be desired. We should expect at any given moment, therefore, to find the individual molecules moving in all directions and with speeds varying all the way from zero up to values many times as great as the average.

All that we can hope to do as physicists under such circumstances is to describe the situation in statistical terms. To obtain a description in mathematical form, let us as usual denote the vector velocity of a molecule by $\mathbf{v}$ and its cartesian components by v_x, v_y, v_z; and let us fix our attention upon those molecules whose components at a given moment lie respectively between a certain value v_x and a slightly greater value $v_x + dv_x$, between v_y and $v_y + dv_y$, and between v_z and $v_z + dv_z$. We shall say for short that the velocity of such a molecule lies in the range dv_x, dv_y, dv_z. When the number of molecules is very great, we should expect that even for small ranges the number of included molecules will be proportional to the product $dv_x\, dv_y\, dv_z$; hence we can write for this number $Nf(v_x, v_y, v_z)\, dv_x\, dv_y\, dv_z$, where N stands for the total number of molecules and f for some function of v_x, v_y, v_z. For brevity it will be convenient, however, to indicate the variables in f by writing just $f(\mathbf{v})$ and to think of f as a function of the vector velocity $\mathbf{v}$.

The function f is called the *distribution function* or *probability function* for molecular velocity and obviously has the fundamental significance that $f\,dv_x\,dv_y\,dv_z$ is the fraction of all the molecules that have velocities in the range dv_x, dv_y, dv_z. Because of this significance, it obviously satisfies the equation

$$\int\int\int f\,dv_x\,dv_y\,dv_z = 1, \tag{26}$$

the integrals extending over all values of v_x, v_y, v_z from $-\infty$ to $+\infty$; the total number of molecules thus comes out correctly as

$$\int\int\int Nf\,dv_x\,dv_y\,dv_z = N\int\int\int f\,dv_x\,dv_y\,dv_z = N. \tag{27}$$

The situation can be visualized if desired by imagining the velocities plotted in a *velocity space* in which v_x, v_y, v_z serve as cartesian coordinates (cf. Fig. 5). A particular velocity $\mathbf{v}$ is then represented either by the vector drawn from the origin to that point in this space whose coordinates are v_x, v_y, v_z, or, if preferred, just by this point itself; and the small velocity range dv_x, dv_y, dv_z is obviously represented by a small parallelepiped with edges having lengths dv_x, dv_y, dv_z, respectively. Frequently, however, we shall write more briefly for an element of volume

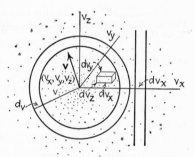

Fig. 5.—Molecular points in velocity space.

in velocity space simply $d\kappa$ in place of $dv_x\,dv_y\,dv_z$, and the element then need not be a parallelepiped but may have any shape.

In general f will vary with the time. When it does not, the gas is said to be in a *steady state*. The latter term is often restricted to refer to gases in *complete equilibrium*, in which not only is the distribution of molecular velocities a steady one, but also the mass acceleration of the gas vanishes everywhere, and neither energy nor matter is flowing into or out of it at any point. These further restrictions serve to eliminate, among other things, steady states of heat conduction or of viscous flow, whose treatment requires special methods of attack. This chapter and the next will be concerned with gases in such a state of complete equilibrium.

The *number* of the molecules which are under consideration has so far been left indefinite. If desired, it can be taken to be the total number in a certain mass of gas. More frequently, however, f refers to the molecules in a macroscopically small element of spatial volume; in this case f may vary with the position of the element, so that in general it is a function of the seven variables $v_x, v_y, v_z, x, y, z, t$. In the state of complete equilibrium, however, even f defined for the molecules in an element of volume turns out to be independent of x, y, z, and t and is accordingly a function only of v_x, v_y, v_z.

18. Distribution Function in Other Variables. Often it is more convenient to employ polar coordinates in velocity space. When we do this, v plays the role of r, the distance from the origin; then the element of volume in velocity space is $v^2 \sin \theta \, d\theta \, d\varphi \, dv$ and

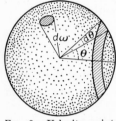

$$v^2 f(\mathbf{v}) \sin \theta \, d\theta \, d\varphi \, dv \qquad (28)$$

represents the fraction of the molecules that are moving with speeds between v and $v + dv$ and in a direction which makes an angle between θ and $\theta + d\theta$ with the polar axis and lies in a plane through the axis making an angle between φ and $\varphi + d\varphi$ with the reference plane for φ.

Fig. 6.—Velocity points on the unit sphere.

For future reference several other ways of grouping the velocities may also be noted at this point. When we are interested for the moment primarily only in the directions of motion of the molecules, but not in their speeds, it is often useful to imagine long lines drawn from an origin in the directions of the various velocities and to take as representing the velocities themselves the points in which these lines cut a sphere of unit radius drawn about the origin as center (cf. Fig. 6, in which all the points are supposed to be on the surface of the sphere).

Consider, now, the important case in which the velocities are distributed equally as regards their directions. The points will then be distributed uniformly over the sphere. Now a small solid angle $d\omega$ drawn at the center intercepts an area $d\omega$ on the unit sphere, whose total area is 4π. Hence we have the useful result that, when the molecules are moving equally in all directions, those that are moving in a direction lying within an element $d\omega$ of solid angle constitute a fraction

$$\frac{d\omega}{4\pi} \qquad (29)$$

of the whole number. If polar coordinates are being used we usually write $d\omega = \sin\theta\, d\theta\, d\varphi$. But in the case under discussion we can also give to $d\omega$ the form of a ring including all velocities whose directions make an angle between θ and $\theta + d\theta$ with a given line, regardless of φ; the area of this ring, which is a narrow strip on the unit sphere $d\theta$ wide and $2\pi \sin\theta$ in circumference, is $2\pi \sin\theta\, d\theta$, hence these velocities will constitute a fraction

$$2\pi \sin\theta \frac{d\theta}{4\pi} = \frac{1}{2}\sin\theta\, d\theta \tag{30}$$

of the total. This holds when all directions are equally probable. As a check, we note that $\int_0^\pi \frac{1}{2}\sin\theta\, d\theta = 1.$*

In other connections, however, the distribution function for a separate component of the velocity is needed. This is easily found from f by integration. Denoting this function for v_x by $f_x(v_x)$, we note that all velocity points for which v_x has a value in a given range dv_x, constituting the fraction $f_x\, dv_x$ of the whole, lie between two parallel planes drawn perpendicular to the v_x axis and a distance dv_x apart (cf. Fig. 5); the fraction of the whole number of points included is thus equal to $\iint\!\!\int f\, dv_x\, dv_y\, dv_z = dv_x \!\int\!\!\int f\, dv_y\, dv_z$, to the first order in dv_x. Hence, equating this expression to $f_x\, dv_x$ and canceling dv_x, we have

$$f_x = \int\!\!\int f\, dv_y\, dv_z, \tag{31}$$

integrated over all values of v_y and v_z while the value of v_x in $f(v_x, v_y, v_z)$ remains fixed.

19. Remarks on the Distribution Function. In our mathematical work we shall treat the ranges dv_x, dv_y, dv_z as infinitesimals, as we have already done in writing such integrals as those in eqs. (26) and (27). This might seem objectionable in view of the fact that when these ranges are made very small the number of included molecules must be small, perhaps even mostly zero, and the number must in any case jump discontinuously by unity every time the shrinking element of volume in velocity space happens to pass over a molecule.

This objection can be met in several different ways. We can say that dv_x, dv_y, dv_z are to be made only macroscopically but not mathematically small, i.e., they are to be small as compared with the scale of physical observation but large relatively to the spacing of the

---

* The upper limit is π and not 2π, since all azimuths around the given line are included within each $d\theta$ (cf. Fig. 6).

molecular velocities; a process of mathematical integration as in (31) is then employed merely for reasons of convenience and yields results differing slightly but not appreciably from the truth.   A second and better way would be to regard $Nf\,d\kappa$ as representing merely the *average* number of molecules in the element of velocity space $d\kappa$ during a time that is macroscopically short but still long enough to allow many molecules to enter and leave the element; the element itself can then be made as small as we please, perhaps so small that it never contains more than one molecule and during most of the time none at all.   The quantity $f\,d\kappa$ then represents the fraction of the time during which the element does contain a molecule.

The best view, however—but also the most abstract one—is probably to treat f as being of the nature of a probability.   In this view, $Nf\,d\kappa$ represents the *expectation*, or $f\,d\kappa$ itself represents the *fractional expectation*, of molecules in $d\kappa$.   If P_0 is the chance that there is no molecule in $d\kappa$, P_1 the chance that there is one, P_2 that there are 2, and so on, then $Nf\,d\kappa = P_1 + 2P_2 + \cdots + jP_j + \cdots$. If we were to make a great many observations with conditions remaining the same, the average of all the different numbers of molecules that we should find in $d\kappa$ would be $Nf\,d\kappa$.   The meaning here is the same as in the common term, "expectation of life."

We shall commonly speak of f in this book in terms of the probability interpretation and shall work freely with f rather than with Nf.   The logical argument is thereby made a little more concise. Readers who dislike to attach meaning to the probability of a single event and prefer to interpret all probabilities as representing averages of some sort should find no difficulty in modifying our treatment to fit their preferences; it is only necessary to multiply our equations through by N so as to be dealing always with Nf, and to substitute for our language a description in terms of one of the alternative views.

20. Proofs of the Distribution Law.   The velocity distribution law for a gas in equilibrium, known as Maxwell's law, was first guessed and partially established by J. C. Maxwell (1859)*; the proof of it by direct methods was first carried to completion (in so far as this is possible) by L. Boltzmann.   Proofs of this type have been given, however, only for certain simple cases.   The much more general methods of statistical mechanics, on the other hand, furnish a proof resting on a firmer foundation and applicable to all cases (in so far as classical theory itself applies).

---

* J. C. Maxwell, *Phil. Mag.*, **19**, 31 (1860); *Sci. Papers*, I, p. 377.

From the standpoint of strict logic it might seem more natural simply to rely upon this proof by statistical mechanics, which is given in Chap. IX. The analysis involved in Boltzmann's proof gives, however, such a lively idea of the processes at work in a gas that it seems worth while to take it up at this point, for the simplest case only. The discussion will be so conducted that the thread of the argument can be followed if desired without reading the rather voluminous mathematical details; any reader who prefers to do so can, as an alternative, pass over the proof entirely and proceed at once to the discussion of Maxwell's law in Sec. 28 without encountering any difficulties with the notation.

21. Molecular Chaos. The Maxwell-Boltzmann proof proceeds by calculating the effect of collisions between the molecules upon the distribution of their velocities.* This effect depends, of course, upon the distribution already existing at the moment. Accordingly the procedure is to seek such a distribution that the effect of collisions upon it vanishes, and this distribution is then taken as that proper to a state of complete equilibrium.

Now the frequency of collisions of any particular type depends upon the positions as well as the velocities of the molecules. At this point Boltzmann simplifies the analysis by making a famous basic assumption called that of "molecular chaos." This assumption states that in a gas whose molecules interact only during collisions all possible states of motion occur with equal frequency. Thus each molecule is as likely to be found in one position as in another; furthermore, except for the simple fact that the molecules cannot get inside each other, there is on the average no correlation whatever between the positions and velocities of different molecules. If, for instance, we know that a certain molecule is at a certain point and moving with a certain velocity, then at that moment another molecule is just as likely to be at any given point in the neighborhood of the first and to be moving with any given velocity as it would be if the first molecule were in any other position or moving with any other velocity.

Perhaps the assumption of molecular chaos may seem plausible enough, in view of the highly varied and tangled motion of the molecules. There have been some who refused to accept it, however, and it certainly needs further support in order to be quite satisfactory as a basis for the theory. If the molecules were to be simply scattered around at random, the assumption would certainly be true. In reality, however, the distribution comes about as the result of mechanical motion, and it is quite thinkable that for this reason regularities

---

* Cf. L. BOLTZMANN, "Vorlesungen über Gastheorie," vol. I, 1896.

would occur in it; for example, molecules in a given neighborhood might tend, for all we can see, to have similar velocities. Furthermore, special states that are not chaotic can, of course, easily be described; for example, at a given moment half of the molecules might be moving east while the other half were moving west, and the latter half might be just on the point of striking the first half in head-on collisions. Such a state of the gas Boltzmann calls "molecularly ordered." He assumes that such states can be ignored, the gas being almost all of the time molecularly unordered ("molekular ungeordnet").

Fortunately it can be shown from statistical mechanics that in the state of complete equilibrium the condition of molecular chaos does, in fact, exist during practically the whole of the time (cf. Sec. 197). Part of Boltzmann's proof requires the existence of molecular chaos even when the gas is not in equilibrium. This, too, can be justified to the following extent: It follows from statistical mechanics that states in which there is an appreciable departure from molecular chaos constitute only a small part of all possible states and so can be expected to occur only very rarely. This is about all that one could hope to prove.

22. The Effect of Collisions upon f. We shall assume further, with Boltzmann, that the distribution function is the same at all points in the gas. The effect of dropping this assumption will be considered in Sec. 50. Its importance lies in the fact that when f is uniform, diffusion of the molecules from one point to another does not tend to alter it, since as many molecules with given velocities arrive at any point as leave it, and vice versa; changes in f thus arise only as a result of collisions.

Finally, to avoid unnecessary repetition of details, let us assume for generality that two different kinds of molecules are present, with masses m_1 and m_2 and distribution functions $f_1(\mathbf{v}_1)$ and $f_2(\mathbf{v}_2)$, respectively. Both kinds will be assumed to be hard spheres free from mutual force-action, except in the collisions which are assumed to be instantaneous. An extension of the argument to other cases may be found in Boltzmann's "Gastheorie" and elsewhere.

We are now ready to analyze the effect of the collisions upon the distribution function f. The method will be to select first a group of molecules having the same mass and almost the same velocity, and to study their collisions with another similarly selected group, calculating with the laws of mechanics the effect that these collisions have upon the distribution function f of the first group. This effect depends upon the velocities of the colliding molecules, and also upon the position of their line of centers, which is a line joining the centers of two colliding molecules at the instant of collision. We then integrate over all possible velocities that the second group can have and also over all possible positions of the line of centers, and thereby arrive finally at expressions giving the rate of change of f with time. These expressions are stated in eqs. (42a), (42b), and (43) below.

As the two groups of molecules to be considered first, let us select a group of the first kind having mass m_1 and velocity $\mathbf{v}_1$ lying within a certain range $d\kappa_1$ and a group of the second kind having mass m_2 and velocity $\mathbf{v}_2$ lying in a range $d\kappa_2$. During a short time dt some of the molecules of the first group will collide with molecules of the second group. Among these collisions let us select first those in which the line of centers drawn from the first molecule to the second lies within a certain solid angle $d\omega$ of possible directions (Fig. 7). The number of these collisions can be written down in sufficient detail for our purpose in the following way. Their number will obviously be proportional to dt, to $d\omega$, to the number of molecules in each group, and to the relative velocity between the two groups, whose magnitude we shall denote by $v_r = |\mathbf{v}_1 - \mathbf{v}_2|$. Now there are $n_1 f_1(\mathbf{v}_1)\, d\kappa_1$ molecules of the first group and $n_2 f_2(\mathbf{v}_2)\, d\kappa_2$ of the second in unit volume,

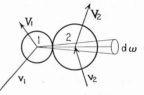

Fig. 7.—A molecular collision.

n_1 and n_2 being the molecular densities for the two kinds of molecules.
Hence we can write for the number of these collisions in unit volume

$$n_1 n_2 \varphi v_r f_1(\mathbf{v}_1) f_2(\mathbf{v}_2)\, d\kappa_1\, d\kappa_2\, d\omega\, dt. \qquad (32)$$

The factor of proportionality φ in this expression will probably depend upon the angle between the chosen line of centers and the direction of the relative velocity $\mathbf{v}_r$ (for example, glancing collisions may not have the same probability as central ones); but it cannot depend upon the velocities themselves, for, with $\mathbf{v}_r$ fixed, the velocities can vary only by the vector addition of a common velocity to each group, and such an addition obviously cannot directly affect the number of collisions, nor can it affect their number indirectly by altering the likelihood of the various possible positions of the molecules, since these positions, by the principle of molecular chaos, show no correlation whatever with the molecular velocities. Nor can φ depend upon the position of the line of centers, for a rotation like a rigid body of the whole situation, velocities and all, while it may affect f_1 and f_2, cannot affect φ because v_r and all angles would be unchanged and, by the principle of molecular chaos, the new positions of the molecules would be just as likely as the old. It follows that φ can depend only upon the angle between $\mathbf{v}_r$ and the line of centers.

The total number of collisions made by molecules of the first group can now be found by integrating (32) over all values of v_{2x}, v_{2y}, v_{2z} and over all possible positions of the line of centers. With an eye to future developments, it will be convenient also to extend the first group somewhat by integrating v_{1x}, v_{1y}, v_{1z} as well over a small but finite range Δ_1. We thus find for the number of all collisions made in dt by molecules in the range Δ_1 colliding with any molecules whatever of the second kind, per unit volume,

$$n_1 n_2 \, dt \int d\omega \int \int_{\Delta_1} \varphi v_r f_1 f_2 \, d\kappa_1 \, d\kappa_2. \tag{33}$$

23. Velocities after a Collision. To ascertain completely the effect of the collisions upon the distribution, we must now find out what velocities the molecules take on after colliding. At each collision the laws of classical mechanics require the conservation of linear momentum and also, since no effect on any possible rotation of the molecules can occur, because of their assumed symmetry, conservation of translatory kinetic energy. Wave mechanics leads to the same conservation laws whenever an experiment is arranged in such a way as to yield observations of momentum and kinetic energy. Accordingly, if $\mathbf{V}_1$, $\mathbf{V}_2$ be the respective velocities of the molecules of the first and second groups *after* collision, just as $\mathbf{v}_1$, $\mathbf{v}_2$ are their velocities before, we have

$$m_1 v_{1x} + m_2 v_{2x} = m_1 V_{1x} + m_2 V_{2x}, \tag{34a}$$
$$m_1 v_{1y} + m_2 v_{2y} = m_1 V_{1y} + m_2 V_{2y}, \tag{34b}$$
$$m_1 v_{1z} + m_2 v_{2z} = m_1 V_{1z} + m_2 V_{2z}, \tag{34c}$$
$$\tfrac{1}{2} m_1 v_1^2 + \tfrac{1}{2} m_2 v_2^2 = \tfrac{1}{2} m_1 V_1^2 + \tfrac{1}{2} m_2 V_2^2, \tag{35}$$

the first three equations expressing the conservation of the three components of momentum.

In addition to these four equations, however, two more are needed in order to fix all of the six components after collision, $V_{1x} \cdots V_{2z}$, in terms of those before collision, $v_{1x} \cdots v_{2z}$. These additional equations are furnished by the position of the line of centers and can be obtained as follows. The increment of vector momentum imparted to each molecule by the impact is in a direction parallel to the line of centers, the momentum given one molecule being just opposite to that given to the other; hence the components of this increment will be proportional to the direction cosines λ, μ, ν of this line and, these components being $m_1(V_{1x} - v_{1x})$, $m_1(V_{1y} - v_{1y})$, etc., we can write $\dfrac{m_1(V_{1x} - v_{1x})}{m_1(V_{1y} - v_{1y})} = \dfrac{\lambda}{\mu}$, etc., or

$$\lambda(V_{1y} - v_{1y}) = \mu(V_{1x} - v_{1x}), \qquad \mu(V_{1z} - v_{1z}) = \nu(V_{1y} - v_{1y}),$$
$$\nu(V_{1x} - v_{1x}) = \lambda(V_{1z} - v_{1z}). \qquad (36a, b, c)$$

Only two of these equations are independent, of course, for it is easily seen that one can always be deduced from the other two, in correspondence with the fact that the line of centers has only two degrees of freedom of position; nor do the corresponding equations in terms of $\mathbf{v}_2$ and $\mathbf{V}_2$ add anything, because of (34a, b, c).

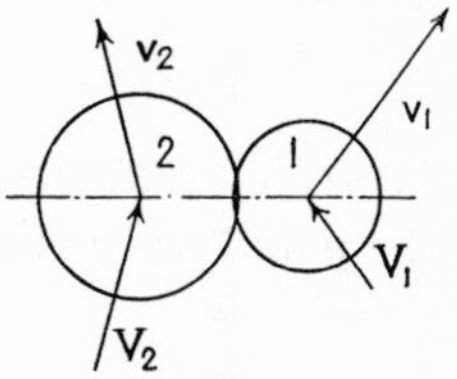

24. The Inverse Collisions. It is evident from these equations, and also from elementary ideas, that the molecular velocities are usually altered profoundly by a collision and that molecules of the first kind which were in the velocity range Δ_1 to begin with, will very often be thrown entirely outside of it. For every type of collision which removes a molecule of the first kind from Δ_1, however, another type is possible that restores one to it. We can, in fact, take any two molecules that have just collided in the manner described above and, by shifting their positions without changing their velocities, cause them to collide again with the line of centers exactly reversed in direction and with the roles of initial and final velocities interchanged (cf. Figs. 7 and 8). This appears algebraically from our equations in the fact that they still remain true if the values of v_1 and v_2 are interchanged with those of V_1 and V_2; the necessity of reversing the line of centers, however, i.e., of replacing λ, μ, ν by $-\lambda$, $-\mu$, $-\nu$, becomes apparent only when we reflect that the molecules must be approaching each other just before they collide.

Furthermore, the whole class of collisions formed by inverting the original ones in this manner actually includes *all* that can restore molecules of the first kind to the range Δ_1; for the result of inverting in its turn any inverted collision is to recover the original collision, and accordingly, given any collision which restores a molecule to Δ_1, we find an original collision of which it is an inverse merely by inverting the given restoring collision.

The number of such inverse collisions corresponding to the original ones will be given, obviously, by an expression similar to (33), viz.,

$$n_1 n_2 \, dt \int d\Omega \int\int\int\int\int \Phi V_r F_1 F_2 \, dV_{1x} \, dV_{1y} \, dV_{1z} \, dV_{2x} \, dV_{2y} \, dV_{2z}, \quad (37)$$

Fig. 8.—The inverse collision.

in which $V_r = |\mathbf{V}_1 - \mathbf{V}_2|$, $F_1 = f_1(\mathbf{V}_1)$, $F_2 = f_2(\mathbf{V}_2)$, $d\Omega$ is an element of direction for the inverted line of centers, and the range of integration for $dV_{1x} \cdots dV_{2z}$ covers all values corresponding to values of v_{1x}, v_{1y}, v_{1z} in Δ_1.

Before making use of this expression, however, we shall make a change in the variables of integration in it. To simplify the procedure, let us, for any given position of the line of centers, imagine the axes of coordinates to be rotated so that the x-axis is parallel to this line, such a rotation having no effect, of course, upon the value of the definite integral containing $dV_{1x} \cdots dV_{2z}$. Then in (36a, b, c) $\lambda = 1$, $\mu = \nu = 0$, whence, using (34b, c) as well,

$$V_{1y} = v_{1y}, \qquad V_{1z} = v_{1z}, \qquad V_{2y} = v_{2y}, \qquad V_{2z} = v_{2z}. \qquad (38)$$

(34a) and (35) then become, since $v_1^2 = v_{1x}^2 + v_{1y}^2 + v_{1z}^2$, etc., and since the y and z-terms all cancel out,

$$m_1(v_{1x} - V_{1x}) = m_2(V_{2x} - v_{2x}),$$
$$m_1(v_{1x}^2 - V_{1x}^2) = m_2(V_{2x}^2 - v_{2x}^2);$$

and, dividing the first of these two equations into the second and then solving, we find

$$V_{1x} = \frac{(m_1 - m_2)v_{1x} + 2m_2 v_{2x}}{m_1 + m_2}, \qquad V_{2x} = \frac{(m_2 - m_1)v_{2x} + 2m_1 v_{1x}}{m_1 + m_2}. \qquad (39)$$

Accordingly, in (37) we can replace* $dV_{1x} \, dV_{2x}$ by $|J| \, dv_{1x} \, dv_{2x}$ where

$$J\left(\frac{V_{1x}, V_{2x}}{v_{1x}, v_{2x}}\right) = \begin{vmatrix} \dfrac{\partial V_{1x}}{\partial v_{1x}} & \dfrac{\partial V_{1x}}{\partial v_{2x}} \\[2mm] \dfrac{\partial V_{2x}}{\partial v_{1x}} & \dfrac{\partial V_{2x}}{\partial v_{2x}} \end{vmatrix} = \frac{1}{(m_1 + m_2)^2}\begin{vmatrix} m_1 - m_2, & 2m_2 \\ 2m_1, & m_2 - m_1 \end{vmatrix} = -1,$$

so that $|J| = 1$; and, of course, by (38)

$$dV_{1y} \, dV_{1z} \, dV_{2y} \, dV_{2z} = dv_{1y} \, dv_{1z} \, dv_{2y} \, dv_{2z}.$$

The fact that in (37) we can thus replace $dV_{1x} \cdots dV_{2z}$ by

$$dv_{1x} \cdots dv_{2z}$$

is an example of the famous Liouville theorem that plays so important a role in statistical mechanics.

Furthermore, by (39) $V_{rx} \equiv V_{2x} - V_{1x} = -(v_{2x} - v_{1x}) = -v_{rx}$, whereas by (38) $V_{ry} \equiv V_{2y} - V_{1y} = v_{2y} - v_{1y} = v_{ry}$ and similarly

---

* This can be done, of course, only under the integral sign, as a rule, since $dv_{1x} \, dv_{2x}$ represents a rectangular area but the corresponding element on the V_{1x}, V_{2x} plane, although of area $|J| \, dv_{1x} \, dv_{2x}$, will not usually be a rectangle.

$V_{rz} = v_{rz}$; that is, we have the familiar result that the component of the relative velocity in the direction of the line of centers is reversed by the collision, whereas its components perpendicular to that line remain unchanged. As a consequence, not only is $V_r = v_r$ in magnitude, but also the angle between the relative velocity and the line of centers is the same after the collision as before, and the latter fact, according to what was said above about φ, means that $\Phi = \varphi$. Finally, $d\Omega = d\omega$, being just the vertically opposite element of solid angle. Hence (37) can be written

$$n_1 n_2 \, dt \int d\omega \int \int_{\Delta_1} \varphi v_r F_1 F_2 \, d\kappa_1 \, d\kappa_2. \tag{40}$$

25. The Rate of Change of the Distribution Function. If we now subtract from this expression that given in (33), we have the gain less the loss, or the net gain, of molecules of the first kind in the range Δ_1 caused by all collisions with molecules of the second kind; the result can be written

$$n_1 n_2 \, dt \int_{\Delta_1} d\kappa_1 \int \int \varphi v_r (F_1 F_2 - f_1 f_2) \, d\kappa_2 \, d\omega, \tag{41}$$

the order of integration having been changed in preparation for the next step. There are, to be sure, some molecules which are merely transferred by collisions of the type considered to another point in Δ_1 and so are not actually either lost from the group or restored to it; we could show that no error results from this circumstance, but we may as well dodge the issue by proceeding at once to make Δ_1 infinitesimal, whereupon the collisions in question become negligible in number and can be ignored.

A similar expression with the subscript 2 changed to 1 throughout will then give the net gain in Δ_1 due to all collisions between the first group and all molecules of the *first* kind; and the sum of this expression and (41) finally gives us the total net gain in unit volume during time dt of molecules of the first kind in Δ_1. On the other hand, this net gain can also be written

$$dt \frac{d}{dt} \int_{\Delta_1} n_1 f_1 \, d\kappa_1 = n_1 \, dt \int_{\Delta_1} \frac{\partial f_1}{\partial t} \, d\kappa_1.$$

Equating the two expressions thus found for the net gain we have:

$$n_1 \, dt \int_{\Delta_1} \frac{\partial f_1}{\partial t} \, d\kappa_1 = n_1 n_2 \, dt \int_{\Delta_1} d\kappa_1 \int \int \varphi v_r (F_1 F_2 - f_1 f_2) \, d\kappa_2 \, d\omega$$

$$+ n_1^2 \, dt \int_{\Delta_1} d\kappa_1 \int \int \varphi v_r (F_1 F_1' - f_1 f_1') \, d\kappa_1' \, d\omega,$$

in which we have primed $\mathbf{v}_1$ or $\mathbf{V}_1$ and functions of them when they refer to a molecule of the first kind functioning as the second molecule in a collision.

Let us now suppose, as we have already done, that Δ_1 is made indefinitely small; then in the limit we can replace each integral over Δ_1 by the integrand multiplied by Δ_1 (provided the integrand is assumed to be continuous). We thus find finally, after canceling $n_1\Delta_1\,dt$:

$$\frac{\partial f_1}{\partial t} = n_1 \int\int \varphi v_r (F_1 F_1' - f_1 f_1')\, d\kappa_1'\, d\omega + n_2 \int\int \varphi v_r (F_1 F_2 - f_1 f_2)\, d\kappa_2\, d\omega.$$

(42a)

In a similar manner can be found for molecules of the second kind

$$\frac{\partial f_2}{\partial t} = n_2 \int\int \varphi v_r (F_2 F_2' - f_2 f_2')\, d\kappa_2'\, d\omega + n_1 \int\int \varphi v_r (F_2 F_1 - f_2 f_1)\, d\kappa_1\, d\omega.$$

(42b)

These results are easily extended to cases in which more than two kinds of molecules are present. On the other hand, if only one kind is present, we can drop the subscripts and write simply

$$\frac{\partial f}{\partial t} = n \int \varphi v_r (FF' - ff')\, d\kappa'\, d\omega.$$

(43)

In this last equation, to repeat for convenience in reference scattered statements already made or implied, $d\omega$ is an element of solid angle within which the line of centers may lie at the instant of collision and φ is a geometrical factor expressing the likelihood of a collision between molecules approaching with velocities $\mathbf{v}$ and $\mathbf{v}'$ and relative velocity v_r; $f = f(\mathbf{v})$ and represents the distribution function for molecular velocity, $f' = f(\mathbf{v}')$, and F, F' stand for similar functions of the new velocities $\mathbf{V}$ and $\mathbf{V}'$ after collision; $d\kappa'$ is an element of volume in the velocity space for $\mathbf{v}'$. The negative term represents the effect of collisions in removing molecules from a given region in velocity space, while the positive term represents the effect of other collisions in throwing molecules into that region. Analogous statements hold for eqs. (42a) and (42b). n is the number of molecules in unit volume and n_1, n_2 the numbers of the two kinds taken separately.

26. The Equilibrium State. The values of the time derivatives as given by (42a, b) or (43) tell us how the velocity distribution changes with time in terms of its form at any given moment, whatever this form may be. The most important case, however, is that of a gas in equilibrium, and we shall now confine our attention to this case. Equilibrium requires that the distribution of velocities shall be steady or independent of the time; and this means, when two kinds of molecules are present, that

$$\frac{\partial f_1}{\partial t} = \frac{\partial f_2}{\partial t} = 0 \tag{44}$$

for all values of $\mathbf{v}_1$ and $\mathbf{v}_2$.

If we insert in this double equation the values of the derivatives as given by (42a) and (42b), we obtain two integral equations for the determination of f_1 and f_2. Now, no simple general method of solving such equations exists, but in the present instance a solution is easily guessed; $\partial f_1/\partial t$ and $\partial f_2/\partial t$ will certainly vanish, provided

$$F_1 F'_1 = f_1 f'_1, \qquad F_2 F'_2 = f_2 f'_2, \qquad F_1 F_2 = f_1 f_2 \tag{45a, b, c}$$

for all values of the independent variables. We shall first work out this solution in detail, and then later we shall take up Boltzmann's proof that it is the only one.

In (45a, b, c), in turn, we have *functional* equations to solve for f_1, f_2. They happen to become easier to handle if we introduce $g = \log f$, so that (45c), for instance, becomes (after an interchange of the members)

$$g_1(v_{1x}, v_{1y}, v_{1z}) + g_2(v_{2x}, v_{2y}, v_{2z})$$
$$= g_1(V_{1x}, V_{1y}, V_{1z}) + g_2(V_{2x}, V_{2y}, V_{2z}). \tag{46}$$

From this equation we see at once that g must be such a function of the molecular velocity that the sum of its values for two molecules is unaltered by a collision. Now we are already acquainted with several quantities that have this property; the kinetic energy is one and the three components of the momentum are three others. Obviously, also, any linear combination of these four quantities with arbitrary constant coefficients would enjoy the same property. This observation suggests that g itself might be such a linear combination; certainly such a function does constitute one possible solution of eq. (46). A little reflection will serve, indeed, to develop a healthy doubt whether there can be any other form of solution; but really to complete our proof we must actually show that there cannot be another, and this we shall now do. It frequently happens in theoretical work that the correct solution of a problem can be guessed with ease, whereas the proof that it really is the only solution requires considerable labor; in such a case the proof ought eventually to be sought, but even before this has been done, considerable importance should be attached to the result of the guess, since it is almost always right.

The reader who is satisfied with the argument just given can turn at once to the results for f_1 and f_2 or for f, as expressed in eqs. (53a) and (53b) below together with the restrictions expressed in (54a, b), or in eq. (53c) for a homogeneous gas, and proceed from that point without reading the rigorous treatment that is now to be given.

27. Rigorous Treatment of the Equilibrium State. The usual method of solving rigorously a functional equation such as (46) is to differentiate and then try to eliminate the unknown functions one by one until a differential equation is obtained for one of them. Equation (46) must hold for all values of $v_{1x} \cdots v_{2z}$, and also for all values of λ, μ, ν, that make $\lambda^2 + \mu^2 + \nu^2 = 1$, the quantities $V_{1x} \cdots V_{2z}$ being determined by (34a, b, c), (35), and (36a, b, c). It turns out, however, that to reach our goal we need only consider such changes of the variables as leave $V_{1x} \cdots V_{2z}$ unaltered, and the work is simplified by such a restriction because the latter variables can then be left out of consideration altogether. With this further restriction the variables $v_{1x} \cdots v_{2z}$ can vary only in such a way as to satisfy the following equations of condition, obtained by differentiating (34a, b, c) and (35) with $V_{1x} \cdots V_{2z}$ kept constant:

$$m_1 \, dv_{1x} + m_2 \, dv_{2x} = 0, \qquad m_1 \, dv_{1y} + m_2 \, dv_{2y} = 0,$$
$$m_1 \, dv_{1z} + m_2 \, dv_{2z} = 0, \quad (47)$$
$$m_1(v_{1x} \, dv_{1x} + v_{1y} \, dv_{1y} + v_{1z} \, dv_{1z})$$
$$+ m_2(v_{2x} \, dv_{2x} + v_{2y} \, dv_{2y} + v_{2z} \, dv_{2z}) = 0. \quad (48)$$

Equation (46) will then also remain satisfied, provided

$$\frac{\partial g_1}{\partial v_{1x}} \, dv_{1x} + \frac{\partial g_1}{\partial v_{1y}} \, dv_{1y} + \frac{\partial g_1}{\partial v_{1z}} \, dv_{1z} + \frac{\partial g_2}{\partial v_{2x}} \, dv_{2x}$$
$$+ \frac{\partial g_2}{\partial v_{2y}} \, dv_{2y} + \frac{\partial g_2}{\partial v_{2z}} \, dv_{2z} = 0. \quad (49)$$

Now we can eliminate some of these differentials by solving (47) for $dv_{2x}, dv_{2y}, dv_{2z}$ and substituting the values so found in (48), obtaining thus in place of (47) and (48)

$$m_1(v_{1x} - v_{2x}) \, dv_{1x} + m_1(v_{1y} - v_{2y}) \, dv_{1y} + m_1(v_{1z} - v_{2z}) \, dv_{1z} = 0. \quad (48a)$$

Any values can be assigned to $dv_{1x}, dv_{1y}, dv_{1z}$ that satisfy this equation; the corresponding values of $dv_{2x}, dv_{2y}, dv_{2z}$ are then given by (47). Equations (36a, b, c) can always be preserved, with no change in $V_{1x} \cdots V_{2z}$, by varying two of the quantities λ, μ, ν, the third being then chosen so as to keep $\lambda^2 + \mu^2 + \nu^2 = 1$. The argument could be completed now by further elimination of differentials, but it is neater to make use at this point of Lagrange's method of "undetermined multipliers." To do this, we first eliminate dv_{2x}, dv_{2y}, dv_{2z} in a similar way from (49) as well; then we add to the equation thus obtained eq. (48a) multiplied by a quantity Q, "undetermined" as yet, obtaining

$$\left[\frac{\partial g_1}{\partial v_{1x}} - \frac{m_1}{m_2} \frac{\partial g_2}{\partial v_{2x}} + Qm_1(v_{1x} - v_{2x}) \right] dv_{1x}$$

$$+ \left[\frac{\partial g_1}{\partial v_{1y}} - \frac{m_1}{m_2} \frac{\partial g_2}{\partial v_{2y}} + Qm_1(v_{1y} - v_{2y}) \right] dv_{1y}$$

$$+ \left[\frac{\partial g_1}{\partial v_{1z}} - \frac{m_1}{m_2} \frac{\partial g_2}{\partial v_{2z}} + Qm_1(v_{1z} - v_{2z}) \right] dv_{1z} = 0. \quad (50)$$

The coefficients of the three differentials in (50) must now vanish just as if the differentials were completely arbitrary. For, suppose the coefficient of some one differential in (48a) is different from zero. Let us choose both of the other differentials in (48a) arbitrarily, and then give to the first one such a value as will make (48a) true; let us cause the coefficient of the latter differential in (50) to vanish by means of a suitable choice of Q. Then the two remaining coefficients in (50) must also vanish because the other two differentials are arbitrary.

From the three equations obtained by equating to zero each bracket in (50), we can then in turn eliminate Q. For example, the first two yield

$$(v_{1y} - v_{2y})\left(\frac{\partial g_1}{\partial v_{1x}} - \frac{m_1}{m_2} \frac{\partial g_2}{\partial v_{2x}} \right) = (v_{1x} - v_{2x})\left(\frac{\partial g_1}{\partial v_{1y}} - \frac{m_1}{m_2} \frac{\partial g_2}{\partial v_{2y}} \right). \quad (51)$$

This equation, like (46), must hold for all values of $v_{1x} \cdots v_{2z}$ as independent variables; hence we can differentiate both members partially with respect to any one of these variables without destroying the equation. Differentiating first by v_{1z}, then by v_{2y}, we thus find in succession, many terms dropping out:

$$(v_{1y} - v_{2y}) \frac{\partial^2 g_1}{\partial v_{1z} \partial v_{1x}} = (v_{1x} - v_{2x}) \frac{\partial^2 g_1}{\partial v_{1z} \partial v_{1y}}, \qquad \frac{\partial}{\partial v_{1z}} \frac{\partial g_1}{\partial v_{1x}} = 0.$$

Choosing two other equations and proceeding similarly, we find that $\frac{\partial(\partial g_1/\partial v_{1x})}{\partial v_{1y}} = 0$. Hence $\frac{\partial g_1}{\partial v_{1x}}$ is independent of v_{1z} and v_{1y} and so is a function of v_{1x} alone.

In a similar way one finds that every first derivative of g_1 or g_2 is a function solely of the variable named in the derivative. Using this result and differentiating (51) by v_{1x} and v_{1y} in succession and then again by v_{1x}, we find successively:

$$(v_{1y} - v_{2y}) \frac{\partial^2 g_1}{\partial v_{1x}^2} = \frac{\partial g_1}{\partial v_{1y}} - \frac{m_1}{m_2} \frac{\partial g_2}{\partial v_{2y}}, \tag{52a}$$

$$\frac{\partial^2 g_1}{\partial v_{1x}^2} = \frac{\partial^2 g_1}{\partial v_{1y}^2}, \qquad \frac{\partial^3 g_1}{\partial v_{1x}^3} = 0. \tag{52b, c}$$

In (52c) we have finally before us a differential equation from which we can find g_1. Integrating this equation three times we find

$$g_1 = C_1 v_{1x}^2 + C_2 v_{1x} + G_1(v_{1y}, v_{1z}),$$

where C_1, C_2, G_1 are constants of integration; G_1 may, as indicated, be a function of v_{1y} and v_{1z}, but C_1 and C_2 cannot be because we found $\partial g_1/\partial v_{1x}$ to be a function of v_{1x} only. Working similarly with v_{1y} and then with v_{1z}, one finds also that $g_1 = C_3 v_{1y}^2 + C_4 v_{1y} + G_2(v_{1x}, v_{1z})$ and $g_1 = C_5 v_{1z}^2 + C_6 v_{1z} + G_3(v_{1x}, v_{1y})$. Substituting these various values of g_1 in (52b), and in its analogue containing v_{1z} in place of v_{1y}, we find, however, that $C_1 = C_3 = C_5$. Comparison of the three forms then shows that g_1 can be written finally in the form,

$$\log f_1 \equiv g_1 = -\beta_1^2(v_{1x}^2 + v_{1y}^2 + v_{1z}^2) + \alpha_1' v_{1x} \\ + \alpha_1'' v_{1y} + \alpha_1''' v_{1z} + B_1, \tag{53a}$$

$-\beta_1^2$ being written in place of C_1 for future convenience and α_1', α_1'', α_1''', B_1 being four other constants.

In a similar way one finds

$$\log f_2 \equiv g_2 = -\beta_2^2(v_{2x}^2 + v_{2y}^2 + v_{2z}^2) + \alpha_2' v_{2x} + \alpha_2'' v_{2y} + \alpha_2''' v_{2z} + B_2 \tag{53b}$$

in terms of five additional constants.

If we then substitute these values of g_1 and g_2 in the three equations obtained by equating to zero the three brackets in (50) and then set all of the variables $v_{1x} \cdots v_{2z}$ equal to zero, we obtain such results as $\alpha_1' - \frac{m_1 \alpha_2'}{m_2} = 0$, and then, using this and making only v_{1x} or v_{2x} not zero in the same equations, $-2\beta_1^2 + Qm_1 = 0$ and $2m_1\beta_2^2/m_2 - Qm_1 = 0$, etc.; from these results we find that we must make

$$m_2\beta_1^2 = m_1\beta_2^2, \tag{54a}$$

$$m_2\alpha_1' = m_1\alpha_2', \qquad m_2\alpha_1'' = m_1\alpha_2'', \qquad m_2\alpha_1''' = m_1\alpha_2''' \tag{54b}$$

(and incidentally $Q = -2\beta_2^2/m_2$).

Aside from these restrictions the constants α, β, and B are arbitrary. This assertion requires verification because of the way in which we restricted the variations of $v_{1x} \cdots v_{2z}$, but its truth becomes apparent when we reflect that we have carefully preserved the validity of (34a, b, c) and (35), and note that substitution of g_1 and g_2 in (46), with any choice of the constants that satisfies (54a, b), yields an equation that can also be deduced by adding (34a, b, c) and (35) multiplied respectively by α_1', α_1'', α_1''', and $-\beta_1^2$ and canceling out m_1.

Finally, we may note that our work has in no way depended upon the existence of a difference in the values of m_1 and m_2 and, accordingly, it will hold good also if only one kind of molecule is present; the result in that case can be written

$$\log f \equiv g = -\beta^2(v_x^2 + v_y^2 + v_z^2) + \alpha' v_x + \alpha'' v_y + \alpha''' v_z + B, \quad (53c)$$

where α', α'', α''', β, and B are all arbitrary.

28. Maxwell's Law.   The usual form of the velocity distribution law for a gas in equilibrium is now obtained if in (53c) we put

$$\alpha' = \alpha'' = \alpha''' = 0,$$

viz.,

$$f(\mathbf{v}) = f(v_x, v_y, v_z) = A e^{-\beta^2 v^2} \quad (55)$$

in terms of β and a new constant $A = e^B$. We shall see in Sec. 30 below that

$$\beta^2 = \frac{m}{2kT} = \frac{1}{2RT} = \frac{M}{2R_M T}, \quad (56)$$

m being the mass or M the molecular weight of a molecule and k, R and R_M the gas constant for one molecule, 1 g and 1 gram molecule, respectively; hence we can also write

$$f(v_x, v_y, v_z) = A e^{-mv^2/2kT} = A e^{-v^2/2RT}. \quad (57)$$

When f has this form, it is obvious from its symmetry that $\bar{\mathbf{v}} = 0$, or the mass velocity vanishes. Accordingly, (55) or (57) has reference to a gas at rest. If we then change to a frame of reference relative to which the gas has a mass velocity $\mathbf{v}_0$, these equations will still hold for the velocity relative to the new frame or the velocity of thermal agitation $\mathbf{v}'$, so that the fraction of the molecules with thermal velocities in the range dv_x', dv_y', dv_z' is $f'(\mathbf{v}')\, dv_x'\, dv_y'\, dv_z'$, where

$$f'(\mathbf{v}') = A e^{-\beta^2 v'^2}; \quad (57a)$$

but now for the distribution of the new total velocities or values of $\mathbf{v} = \mathbf{v}_0 + \mathbf{v}'$ we shall have

$$f(\mathbf{v}) = f'(\mathbf{v}') = A e^{-\beta^2[(v_x - v_{0x})^2 + (v_y - v_{0y})^2 + (v_z - v_{0z})^2]}, \quad (57b)$$

since for the same group of molecules by definition of f' and f we have

$$f(\mathbf{v}') \, dv'_x \, dv'_y \, dv'_z = f(\mathbf{v}) \, dv_x \, dv_y \, dv_z$$

and obviously $dv'_x = dv_x$, $dv'_y = dv_y$, $dv'_z = dv_z$, whence $f(\mathbf{v}) = f(\mathbf{v}')$. This last expression for $f(\mathbf{v})$ can be obtained from the general form (53c) by choosing v_0 and A so that $v_{0x} = \alpha'/2\beta^2$, $v_{0y} = \alpha''/2\beta^2$, $v_{0z} = \alpha'''/2\beta^2$ and $Ae^{-\beta^2 v_0^2} = e^B$. Thus we see that the more general result that was obtained in the last section had reference to a gas possessing uniform mass motion with an arbitrary velocity $\mathbf{v}_0$.

Equation (55) or (57) represents Maxwell's famous law of velocity distribution in a gas at rest.   In view of what has been said it is obvious that a detailed discussion of this equation will suffice to cover the case of a moving gas as well.

The constant A is fixed by the condition that

$$\int\!\!\int f \, d\kappa = A \int e^{-\beta^2 v^2} \, d\kappa = 1,$$

the integral extending over all values of the velocity.   Now

$$\int e^{-\beta^2 v^2} \, d\kappa = \int_{-\infty}^{\infty} e^{-\beta^2 v_x^2} \, dv_x \int_{-\infty}^{\infty} e^{-\beta^2 v_y^2} \, dv_y \int_{-\infty}^{\infty} e^{-\beta^2 v_z^2} \, dv_z = \frac{\pi^{3/2}}{\beta^3} \quad (58)$$

since

$$\int_0^{\infty} e^{-x^2} \, dx = \tfrac{1}{2} \sqrt{\pi}, \qquad \int_{-\infty}^{\infty} e^{-x^2} \, dx = \sqrt{\pi}, \qquad (59a, b)$$

as is shown in books on calculus.   Hence, by (56)

$$A = \frac{\beta^3}{\pi^{3/2}} = \left(\frac{m}{2\pi kT}\right)^{3/2} = \left(\frac{1}{2\pi RT}\right)^{3/2}. \qquad (60)$$

Unfortunately a three-dimensional function like f cannot be adequately exhibited by a graph; we have tried, however, to suggest it by the distribution of the dots in Fig. 5.   Although only the speed v occurs as a variable in f, it must not be forgotten that f has reference to a definite direction of the velocity as well, for the meaning is that out of, say, N molecules, $Nf(v_x, v_y, v_z) \, dv_x \, dv_y \, dv_z$ is the number having components respectively between v_x and $v_x + dv_x$, v_y and $v_y + dv_y$, v_z and $v_z + dv_z$, and these limits effectively fix the direction of $\mathbf{v}$ itself within narrow limits.

Because of the symmetry, however, the distribution function for the molecular speeds irrespective of the direction of motion is also very useful; and this is easily found.   The velocity points for molecules having speeds between v and $v + dv$ lie in a spherical shell in velocity space of inner radius v and of thickness dv (cf. Fig. 5); since dv is an infinitesimal, we can write for the volume of this shell the product of its thickness into the area of its inner boundary or $dv \times 4\pi v^2$. The value of f is the same at all points of this shell, hence the fraction of the molecules included in it is $f \times 4\pi v^2 \, dv$, and if we also write for this $f_v \, dv$, where $f_v(v)$ is the distribution function for the speed v, we find

$$f_v = 4\pi v^2 f = 4\pi A v^2 e^{-\beta^2 v^2}. \qquad (61a)$$

A graph of $\frac{3}{2} f_v$ is shown in Fig. 9, drawn on the assumption that $\beta = 1$. This graph really serves to give practically a complete conception of the distribution of velocities, for the only feature not exhibited is the fact that all directions of motion occur with equal frequency.

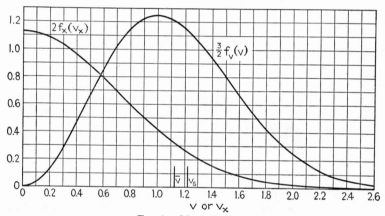

FIG. 9.—Maxwell's law.

Problems.   1. Show that if $f_\zeta \, d\zeta$ is the fraction of the molecules whose kinetic energy, $\zeta = \frac{1}{2} m v^2$, lies in a range $d\zeta$, then

$$f_\zeta = 4\pi A \sqrt{\frac{2}{m^3}} \sqrt{\zeta} \, e^{-\frac{\zeta}{kT}} = \frac{2\sqrt{\zeta}}{\sqrt{\pi}(kT)^{3/2}} \, e^{-\frac{\zeta}{kT}}. \qquad (61b)$$

2. Show that the distribution function for one component, say $f_x(v_x)$, $f_x \, dv_x$ being the fraction of the molecules with v_x in dv_x, is

$$f_x = \frac{\beta}{\sqrt{\pi}} e^{-\beta^2 v_x^2} = \left(\frac{m}{2\pi kT}\right)^{1/2} e^{-\frac{m v_x^2}{2kT}} \qquad (62)$$

[cf. eq. (31)]. The curve for f_x has thus the shape of an error curve. It also is shown, on a reduced scale and with $\beta = 1$, in Fig. 9.

3. Show that the distribution of the y- and the z-components of velocity among molecules selected with x-component between v_x and $v_x + dv_x$ is independent of v_x.

4. Show that f is the function that would result if each component of velocity were distributed *independently of the others* according to the law expressed by (62). (The assumption that the three components are independent constituted the basis of Maxwell's first attempt at a deduction of his law.)

29. Use of a Distribution Function in Calculating Averages. Knowing f, we can easily calculate mean values of various functions of the velocity. It may be useful to describe first the general method of calculating averages on the basis of a distribution function.

Suppose $f(x)$ is the distribution function for some variable x, so that $f(x)\,dx$ is the fraction of all cases in which x has a value lying between x and $x + dx$, and also $\int f(x)\,dx = 1$, the integral extending over all possible values of x. Then, if there are N cases in all, the average value of any function $Q(x)$ is $\Sigma\, Q(x)/N$, $\Sigma\, Q(x)$ denoting the sum of the values of Q for all cases. In those cases in which x lies in any given range dx, however, which are $Nf\,dx$ in number, Q has practically a constant value; hence the contribution of these cases to ΣQ will be $QNf\,dx$. Thus we can write $\Sigma Q = \Sigma QNf\,dx = N\Sigma Qf\,dx$ or $N\int Qf\,dx$. The average of Q is then $\bar{Q} = N\int Qf\,dx/N$ or

$$\bar{Q} = \int Q(x)\,f(x)\,dx, \tag{63a}$$

the integral extending over all possible values of x.

Frequently, however, the "normalizing factor" in f that makes $\int f\,dx = 1$ is not yet known, i.e., we have not f itself but a function of x proportional to it, say $f_1(x) = Cf(x)$. Then

$$f = f_1/C, \qquad \int f\,dx = \int f_1\,dx/C = 1 \qquad \text{and} \qquad C = \int f_1(x)\,dx.$$

In terms of the unnormalized distribution function $f_1(x)$, expression (63a) for the average value of Q can therefore be written

$$\bar{Q} = \frac{\int Q(x)\,f_1(x)\,dx}{\int f_1(x)\,dx}. \tag{63b}$$

30. Most Probable and Average Speeds. According to (55), the most probable single value of the *velocity* is zero, since f is a maximum for $\mathbf{v} = 0$. On the other hand, the most probable value of the *speed*, or the value of v that gives a maximum value to f_v in eq. (61a), is found by equating df_v/dv to zero and solving for v and is

$$v_m = \frac{1}{\beta}.\tag{64}$$

To find the mean speed $\bar{v}$, and the root-mean-square speed v_s, we substitute f_v from (61a) in (63a) and set first $Q = v$ and then $Q = v^2$; this gives us the two equations,

$$\bar{v} = 4\pi A \int_0^\infty v^3 e^{-\beta^2 v^2}\, dv, \qquad \overline{v^2} = 4\pi A \int_0^\infty v^4 e^{-\beta^2 v^2}\, dv.$$

Such integrals are readily reduced with the help of an integration by parts, those containing an even power of v reducing finally to (59a, b); a table of the ones most used in kinetic theory is given at the end of the book. We shall work out only one example in detail:

$$\int_0^\infty v^2 e^{-\beta^2 v^2}\, dv = \left(-\frac{v}{2\beta^2}\, e^{-\beta^2 v^2}\right)_{v=0}^{v=\infty} + \frac{1}{2\beta^2}\int_0^\infty e^{-\beta^2 v^2}\, dv$$

$$= \frac{1}{2\beta^3}\int_0^\infty e^{-x^2}\, dx = \frac{\sqrt{\pi}}{4\beta^3},$$

by (59a), the change to x being made by writing $\beta v = x$, and the integrated part vanishing at the upper limit because, if $v \to \infty$, $v^n e^{-av^s} \to 0$ for $a > 0$, $s > 0$ and any value of n. The equations previously obtained reduce in this way, after inserting A from (60), to

$$\bar{v} = \frac{2}{\sqrt{\pi}}\frac{1}{\beta} = \frac{2}{\sqrt{\pi}}\, v_m = 1.1284\, v_m = 0.9213\, v_s,\tag{65a}$$

$$v_c^2 = \overline{v^2} = \frac{3}{2}\frac{1}{\beta^2},\tag{65b}$$

$$v_s = (\tfrac{3}{2})^{1/2} v_m = 1.2248\, v_m = 1.0854\, \bar{v}.\tag{65c}$$

We note that the mean speed $\bar{v}$ exceeds v_m slightly, obviously because the curve for f_v bulges a little toward larger values of v; the root-mean-square speed v_s then exceeds $\bar{v}$ in turn because the squares of large values of v contribute especially heavily to $\overline{v^2}$. The relations between v_m, $\bar{v}$, and v_s are indicated in Fig. 9. Some physical phenomena, such as the pressure, depend in a simple way upon v_s, but we shall encounter others presently that are more simply described in terms of $\bar{v}$. Hardly any phenomena involve v_m directly. For many purposes of rough calculation, however, it does not matter much which average is employed.

Equations (65b) and (25a) in Sec. 15 taken together yield the values of β given in (56) above. Using these values of β, we obtain also the alternative expressions:

$$\bar{v} = 2\left(\frac{2RT}{\pi}\right)^{\frac{1}{2}} = 2\left(\frac{2R_M T}{\pi M}\right)^{\frac{1}{2}} = 2\left(\frac{2kT}{\pi m}\right)^{\frac{1}{2}}, \qquad (66a)$$

$$v_s = (3RT)^{\frac{1}{2}} = \left(\frac{3R_M T}{M}\right)^{\frac{1}{2}} = \left(\frac{3kT}{m}\right)^{\frac{1}{2}}, \qquad (66b)$$

M being the molecular weight or m the actual mass of a molecule.

Another quantity derivable from f that is sometimes of use is the total fraction of the molecules that have speeds or velocity components within some given *finite range*. Such fractions are easily written down in terms of integrals.

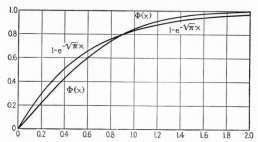

Fig. 10.—The probability integral, $\Phi(x) = \dfrac{2}{\sqrt{\pi}} \displaystyle\int_0^x e^{-x^2} dx$.

For example, the fraction of the molecules that have speeds above a certain value v is simply

$$\int_v^\infty f_v \, dv = 4\pi A \int_v^\infty v^2 e^{-\beta^2 v^2} \, dv = \frac{2}{\sqrt{\pi}} \beta\left(v e^{-\beta^2 v^2} + \int_v^\infty e^{-\beta^2 v^2} \, dv\right),$$

after integrating by parts and inserting $A = \beta^3/\pi^{\frac{3}{2}}$. The last integral here cannot be expressed in terms of ordinary functions but must be regarded as defining a new transcendental function. The latter, known as the probability integral, is commonly defined thus:

$$\Phi(x) = \frac{2}{\sqrt{\pi}} \int_0^x e^{-x^2} \, dx, \qquad (67)$$

so that $\Phi(0) = 0$ and $\Phi(\infty) = 1$ by (59a). Tables of Φ are given in many reference books (e.g., in Peirce's "Table of Integrals" or in Jahnke-Emde's "Table of Functions"); a graph of it, along with $1 - e^{-\sqrt{\pi}x}$, which has the same area under it, is shown in Fig. 10. In terms of Φ we can write, since

$$\beta\int_v^\infty e^{-\beta^2 v^2} \, dv = \beta\int_0^\infty e^{-\beta^2 v^2} \, dv - \beta\int_0^v e^{-\beta^2 v^2} \, dv = \int_0^\infty e^{-x^2} \, dx - \int_0^{\beta v} e^{-x^2} \, dx,$$

$$\int_v^\infty f_v \, dv = 1 + \frac{2}{\sqrt{\pi}} \beta v e^{-\beta^2 v^2} - \Phi(\beta v). \qquad (68)$$

Substituting values from the tables in this formula, in which we put $x = \beta v = (2/\sqrt{\pi})(v/\bar{v})$ by (65a), we find for the percentage of the molecules that exceed various values of $v/\bar{v}$ the following:

$v/\bar{v}$	0.5	1.0	1.5	2.0	2.5	3.0
%	88.80	46.70	12.55	1.70	0.12	0.01

Problem. Show that, if v_1 is any cartesian component of **v**, $(\overline{v_1^2})^{1/2} = (p/\rho)^{1/2}$ or Newton's value for the speed of sound in a gas.

31. Mixed Gases. Equipartition. When two different kinds of molecules are present, their separate distribution functions for the state of complete equilibrium are given by (53a, b) above. Let us simplify these expressions by subtracting the common mass velocity **v**$_0$ given by $v_{0x} = \alpha_1'/2\beta_1^2 = \alpha_2'/2\beta_2^2$, $v_{0y} = \alpha_1''/2\beta_1^2 = \alpha_2''/2\beta_2^2$,

$$v_{0z} = \frac{\alpha_1'''}{2\beta_1^2} = \frac{\alpha_2'''}{2\beta_2^2} \qquad [\text{cf. (54a, b)}];$$

that is, we substitute $\mathbf{v}_1 = \mathbf{v}_0 + \mathbf{v}_1'$, $\mathbf{v}_2 = \mathbf{v}_0 + \mathbf{v}_2'$ with the stated values of $\mathbf{v}_0$ in (53a, b). We thus obtain:

$$\log f_1 = -\beta_1^2(v_{1x}'^2 + v_{1y}'^2 + v_{1z}'^2) + B_1 + \beta_1^2 v_0^2,$$
$$\log f_2 = -\beta_2^2(v_{2x}'^2 + v_{2y}'^2 + v_{2z}'^2) + B_2 + \beta_2^2 v_0^2,$$

where, of course, v_0^2 stands for $v_{0x}^2 + v_{0y}^2 + v_{0z}^2$. The fact that this simplification succeeds with the same value of **v**$_0$ for both kinds of molecules shows that the mass velocity is the same for both. We shall drop the primes, however, since it suffices, as before, to discuss the motion of thermal agitation only, and write as the result:

$$f_1(\mathbf{v}_1) = A_1 e^{-\beta_1^2 v_1^2}, \qquad f_2(\mathbf{v}_2) = A_2 e^{-\beta_2^2 v_2^2}.$$

These equations represent a maxwellian distribution for each component gas. As an extension of (65b) we shall accordingly have $\overline{v_1^2} = \frac{3}{2} 1/\beta_1^2$, $\overline{v_2^2} = \frac{3}{2} 1/\beta_2^2$, and taken in conjunction with (54a), which can be written $m_2\beta_1^2 = m_1\beta_2^2$, this means that

$$\tfrac{1}{2} m_1 \overline{v_1^2} = \tfrac{1}{2} m_2 \overline{v_2^2}. \tag{69}$$

Thus our analysis of the effects of collisions leads to equality of the mean translatory kinetic energy of gas molecules when mixed together and confirms eq. (14) in Sec. 11 of Chap. I. This is a special case of the general theorem of the *equipartition of energy* which is proved in statistical mechanics (Sec. 206). That collisions in a gas tend to set up translatory equipartition of energy was shown in a less satisfactory but more direct way by Maxwell.*

All of the results that we have obtained for a homogeneous gas, which rested in part upon eq. (14), will accordingly hold with suitable modification of the constants for each component of a mixed gas. This conclusion is easily extended to mixtures of three or more components. Accordingly, we can summarize by saying that in a gaseous mixture of molecules of different sorts in complete equilibrium each kind of molecule has the same maxwellian distribution in velocity that it would have if the other kinds were not present.

32. Uniqueness of the Maxwellian Distribution. The H-theorem. In Secs. 26 to 27 we showed that the maxwellian distribution was a possible equilibrium distribution for the molecular velocities. We have not yet shown, however, that it is the only one. Any such distribution must make the right-hand members vanish in (42a, b) or (43), but our solution accomplished this in a drastic fashion, for the integrand is made to vanish in each integral for all values of the variables of integration; it is conceivable that other forms of the function f might exist such that the integrals would vanish by mere mutual cancellation of positive and negative contributions from different parts of the region of integration. To this question we may also add the further one whether there would be any tendency for an equilibrium distribution to be set up if it did not already exist; the possibility that the distribution of velocity might under some circumstances never tend to become steady at all, while perhaps not plausible physically, is left open by the mathematics.

Both questions were answered by Boltzmann.† He was able to show from his analysis of the effects of collisions that the maxwellian distribution actually is the only steady one, and furthermore that any other distribution would almost certainly be altered by the collisions in such a way as to approach the maxwellian form. Since the argument by which he did this, called the "H-theorem," possesses interest for thermodynamics as well as for kinetic theory, we shall give it here, but only for the case of a homogeneous gas; the extension to mixed gases is easy to make.

Boltzmann studies the quantity

$$H = \int f \log f \, d\kappa \qquad (70a)$$

---

* Maxwell, *Phil. Mag.*, **20**, 21 (1860).

† L. Boltzmann, Weitere Studien über das Wärmegleichgewicht unter Gasmolekulen; *K. Akad. Wiss. (Wien) Sitzb.*, II Abt. 66, p. 275 (1872).

in which as usual $d\kappa$ stands for $dv_x\, dv_y\, dv_z$, $f = f(v_x,\, v_y,\, v_z,\, t)$ or the velocity distribution function, and the integral extends over all values of $\mathbf{v}$; we have written t as one of the variables in f to indicate explicitly the fact that f may be changing with the time.   If f does not change, we have a steady distribution, and then H is constant.   Otherwise H will be a function of the time with a derivative

$$\frac{dH}{dt} = \int \frac{\partial}{\partial t}\,(f \log f)\, d\kappa = \int (\log f + 1)\,\frac{\partial f}{\partial t}\, d\kappa,$$

since the limits of the integral in the expression for H do not involve t. The 1 added to $\log f$ here, however, adds nothing to the integral, for $\int \left(\dfrac{\partial f}{\partial t}\right) d\kappa = \dfrac{d}{dt} \int f\, d\kappa = 0$ because $\int f\, d\kappa$ must always remain equal to unity.   Hence, if we insert the value of $\partial f/\partial t$ from (43) in Sec. 25, we have

$$\frac{dH}{dt} = n \int \int \int \varphi v_r (FF' - ff') \log f\, d\kappa\, d\kappa'\, d\omega.$$

Now this definite integral is distinctly asymmetric in the variables of integration.   Such a circumstance should always arouse a suspicion that something interesting may turn up if the variables are interchanged.   We can, for instance, interchange the variables $\mathbf{v}$ and $\mathbf{v}'$ (i.e., $v_x,\, v_y,\, v_z$ with $v_x',\, v_y',\, v_z'$) without altering the value of the integral and obtain as another form of the equation the following:

$$\frac{dH}{dt} = n \int \int \int \varphi v_r (FF' - ff') \log f'\, d\kappa\, d\kappa'\, d\omega.$$

But we can also change to the velocities after collision as variables of integration, i.e., to $\mathbf{V}$ and $\mathbf{V}'$ as determined by (34a, b, c), (35), and (36a, b, c) in Sec. 23 in terms of $\mathbf{v}$ and $\mathbf{v}'$; the method of making this change is just the reverse of that explained above in arriving at (40) of that section.   The result is [cf. the form of (37)]

$$\frac{dH}{dt} = n \int \int \int \Phi V_r (FF' - ff') \log f'\, dK\, dK'\, d\Omega.$$

It is immaterial, however, what symbol is written for a variable of integration in a definite integral, so nothing prevents us from simply replacing the variables $\mathbf{V}$, $\mathbf{V}'$ by $\mathbf{v}$ and $\mathbf{v}'$, respectively, whereupon f and F change places and likewise f' and F', and we can also write $d\omega$ for $d\Omega$; then Φ and V_r become those functions of the variables which we previously denoted by φ and v_r. This gives us another possible form of the equation expressed in terms of $\mathbf{v}$ and $\mathbf{v}'$; and then interchanging $\mathbf{v}$ and $\mathbf{v}'$ again gives us a fourth. We thus obtain

$$\frac{dH}{dt} = n \int \int \int \varphi v_r (ff' - FF') \log F \, d\kappa \, d\kappa' \, d\omega,$$

$$\frac{dH}{dt} = n \int \int \int \varphi v_r (ff' - FF') \log F' \, d\kappa \, d\kappa' \, d\omega.$$

Now let us add these two values of dH/dt to the first two and divide by 4. This gives finally a form that is symmetric in the variables $\mathbf{v}$ and $\mathbf{v}'$:

$$\frac{dH}{dt} = -\frac{n}{4} \int \int \int \varphi v_r (ff' - FF')(\log ff' - \log FF') \, d\kappa \, d\kappa' \, d\omega. \quad (70b)$$

Here the integrand can never be negative, since $\log ff' \gtreqless \log FF'$ according as $ff' \gtreqless FF'$. Hence we have the important result that in all cases

$$\frac{dH}{dt} \leqq 0.$$

Now for a steady distribution dH/dt must vanish. But in (70b) we now have an integral which can vanish only if the integrand vanishes for all values of the variables of integration. If this happens, we are led at once to eqs. (45a, b, c) of Sec. 26 and, from those equations, as we have seen, to Maxwell's law. This shows that the maxwellian distribution is the only steady one.

Any other form of f must undergo such changes by collisions that H continually decreases. It is easy to show,* however, that H has a minimum value for the maxwellian distribution as compared with any other that gives the same value to $\overline{v^2}$, a quantity that does not change with the time in an isolated ideal gas. Hence we reach the further conclusion that the effect of collisions upon f is such as to make H approach the value corresponding to a maxwellian distribution; and

* In general, let f_0, f be any two functions of $\mathbf{v}$ such that $\int f \log f_0 \, d\kappa = \int f_0$ $\log f_0 \, d\kappa$ and $\int f \, d\kappa = \int f_0 \, d\kappa = 1$. Then $D \equiv \int f \log f \, d\kappa - \int f_0 \log f_0 \, d\kappa = \int f$ $\log (f/f_0) \, d\kappa = \int [f \log (f/f_0) - f + f_0] \, d\kappa$ (the terms added here canceling each other), and $[f \log (f/f_0) - f + f_0]$ has an absolute minimum value of 0 for $f = f_0$. Hence $D \geqq 0$. As a special case, the first condition imposed on f is equivalent, in view of the second, to the conservation of $\overline{v^2}$ if $f_0 = A e^{-\beta^2 v^2}$.

we can take this as an indication that the distribution must itself tend to take on maxwellian character with the passage of time.

Light could be thrown upon the rapidity of the approach in any given case by calculating the value of dH/dt from (70b). In Sec. 100, however, we shall meet with a more convenient means of estimating the rapidity; it is shown there that equilibrium is approached exceedingly rapidly as judged by physical standards.

33. Reversibility and the H-theorem. Although the proof just given of the H-theorem is mathematically rigorous, an illuminating objection was formerly raised against it. Suppose we were to let the gas move, with H decreasing, for a short time and then instantaneously reverse all of the molecular velocities. Since every dynamical motion is reversible, the molecules would then retrace their paths, and H would increase, in spite of our proof that it never can do this!

The explanation of this paradox is connected, of course, with the fact that the formula for $\partial f/\partial t$ which we obtained above rests upon the assumption of *molecular chaos*. Now, after a few collisions have occurred, there is no reason to suppose the molecular motion to be ordered toward the future, so that chaos should still exist so far as subsequent collisions are concerned; but the past motion may not have been chaotic. Accordingly, when we reverse the velocities and thereby interchange future and past, it may happen that we have converted the motion from a chaotic one to an ordered one (as regards the new future), and the H-theorem will then no longer be applicable. Only in the case of equilibrium can it be assumed that the reverse of every molecularly chaotic motion is again a chaotic one.

Some further remarks upon the H-theorem and in particular upon an interesting connection between the quantity H and the entropy will be found in the chapter on statistical mechanics.

34. Principle of Detailed Balancing. As we have seen, the equilibrium of the velocity distribution is maintained by the molecules in an exceedingly simple fashion, for in each of eqs. (42a, b) or (43) of Sec. 25 the two terms of the integrand cancel each other for each individual type of collision. This means, as is evident from the origin of those terms, that for every type of collision the inverse type occurs with equal frequency and exactly undoes the effect of the first.

Many cases can be cited in which a physical equilibrium is maintained in a similar simple fashion. The characteristic feature is that for every process which alters the distribution there exists an inverse process, and in the state of equilibrium each process and its inverse occur with equal frequency and just offset each other's effects tending to disturb the equilibrium. This has been called the phenomenon or principle of *detailed balancing** and it has sometimes been set up as a universal law of nature. The principle seems, however, to be rather difficult to state in terms that are broad enough to cover all cases of interest and yet so as to admit of no exceptions, nor can it readily be deduced in general terms from the laws either of mechanics or of thermodynamics. It seems rather to constitute a generalization which is subject to a few exceptions but nevertheless possesses great utility when we are endeavoring to form conceptions of the processes that occur in nature or to make a first-trial analysis of an unfamiliar phenomenon.

In some instances the motion involved in the inverse process is just the reverse of that in the direct process, but in many other cases this is not so, and there does not seem to exist any fundamental connection between detailed balancing and the fact that mechanical motions can always be "reversed" or made to occur in the reverse direction (in classical theory at least). In the particular case of molecular collisions which we have been studying, for example, the inverse of a direct collision which offsets the effect of the latter is not the same as the reverse collision that results if we simply reverse the velocities of the two molecules after the first collision and allow them to retrace their paths, nor is it even (in general) this reverse collision rotated through some angle.

On the other hand, in phenomena such as the following it is convenient to apply detailed balancing in such a way that the inverse process *is* the direct one reversed. When liquid in a tube is in equilibrium with its saturated vapor, just as many molecules condense in every second at any point of the surface as evaporate there, so that no mass streaming is set up, such as might conceivably occur in the liquid from the meniscus at the edge back toward the center, or in the opposite direction, owing to possible differences in the rate of evaporation over a flat and over a curved surface. Examples of detailed balancing of this sort are common in physical chemistry. As a rather similar example in another branch of physics, we may cite the fact that the emitting and absorbing powers of a body for radiation are always equal, not only on the whole but also in every individual direction and for every separate wave length.

Another case that is of particular interest in connection with the question of mechanical reversibility is furnished by the motion of ions

---

* Detailed balancing appears to be a better term than Tolman's "microscopic reversibility" (*Nat. Acad. Proc.*, **11**, 436 (1925)) because the latter suggests that the motions in the balancing process are just those in the direct process reversed, which is often not the case.

or electrons in a fixed magnetic field.   This motion is completely non-reversible; if an ion moves along a right-handed spiral in following a line of force in one direction it will follow a left-handed spiral on the return trip.   To reverse the motion, we should have to reverse the field as well.   Nevertheless, even in the fixed field, under conditions of equilibrium, there exists the usual maxwellian distribution of velocity, so that at every point there are equal numbers of ions moving equally in all directions, and hence, for example, as many cross any area in one direction as in the other, as is required by detailed balancing.

Perhaps the simplest example of a *failure* of detailed balancing is furnished by the effect of the walls of the containing vessel upon the velocity distribution in a gas.   Suppose, for simplicity, that the density is so low that intermolecular collisions are rare and suppose that the walls reflect specularly (in other words, like the reflection of light by a mirror).   Impacts upon the walls will now serve to set up and maintain an equal distribution of molecular velocities in direction, although, of course, without affecting their magnitudes, provided only that the vessel has not some special shape such as that of a rectangular parallelepiped.   The equilibrium as to directions of motion is maintained in a complicated circular fashion.   For concreteness, let the vessel be hemispherical in form.   Then each shower of molecules moving in some definite direction downward toward the plane base is continually being transformed by impact on it into a shower moving in a definite direction upward.   Very few of the molecules of this second shower, however, are restored to the original downward-moving one upon striking the curved surface; they are scattered equally in all directions throughout a certain solid angle, which rises to a maximum of 2π in the case of the particular shower that is moving vertically upward.   The process inverse to reflection from the base is thus almost entirely absent.   The first shower is continually being recruited somehow by reflection from the curved wall; but the molecules that are thrown into it are drawn from a wide range of different upward-moving showers.

Perhaps we should say that detailed balancing fails in this case because the equilibrium is not a true one, and we have, therefore, not really employed the fundamental form of the principle; a mass of gas enclosed in a vessel of any sort represents, in fact, a *metastable* state of the system.   To have true equilibrium, there must exist some path by which molecules can pass from one side of the wall of the vessel to the other, since they are capable of existing on both sides; and if the wall itself is composed of molecules, then these must occasionally rearrange themselves so as to take on, in the course of time, all possible arrangements.   If such changes were possible, it is probably true that in the long run detailed balancing would hold.   In other words, detailed balancing probably holds for all interactions between particles that are statistically free to get eventually into all positions that are mechanically possible, and also for the emission and absorption of radiation by such particles.

35. Doppler Line Breadth.   Aside from many phenomena in which the distribution of molecular velocities plays a role, in the sense that an average must be taken over all velocities, there are a few which exhibit details corresponding to the distribution itself.   The most straightforward one of these phenomena involves an additional bit of kinetic theory and is described in the next chapter as a deliberate test of Maxwell's law.   On the other hand, the effect of molecular motion on the shape of spectral lines, while it involves an additional process optical in nature, depends so directly upon the velocity distribution itself that it will be described briefly here.

The spectrum emitted by gaseous atoms and molecules consists under most conditions principally of lines which have a natural width that is too small to be observed with ease.   As seen by the spectroscopist, however, these lines are usually widened into narrow bands in consequence of molecular motion.   When a source emitting light of wave length λ_0 is moving in vacuo away from the observer with a component of velocity u, the wave length as measured by the observer is, by the usual theory of the Doppler effect, $\lambda = \lambda_0\left(1 + \dfrac{u}{c}\right)$, c being the speed of light.   Accordingly, if there are $nf_u\, du$ molecules in unit volume, which are emitting radiation of natural wave length λ_0 and are moving away from the observing apparatus with a component of velocity lying in the range du, the light from these will be received in a spectral range $d\lambda = \lambda_0 \dfrac{du}{c}.$ If we write $J\, d\lambda$ for this radiation, J representing, therefore, the intensity of the line at wave length λ, we have the equation, $J\, d\lambda = J\lambda_0 \dfrac{du}{c} = \gamma n f_u\, du$, where γ represents the amount of radiation received from one molecule.   If we then cancel out du and insert the value of f_u for a maxwellian distribution from (62), changing v_x in that formula to $u = \dfrac{c(\lambda - \lambda_0)}{\lambda_0}$, we obtain

$$J = J_0 e^{-\frac{mc^2(\lambda - \lambda_0)^2}{2\lambda_0^2 kT}}$$

J_0 standing for a new constant.

A plot of J against λ thus has the form of an error curve with its maximum at $J = J_0$; and if $\log J$ is plotted against $(\lambda - \lambda_0)^2$ for either half of the spectral line, a straight line is obtained from whose slope the temperature of the gas can be calculated (cf. Fig. 11).

An experiment that confirms this form of the curve was performed, although for another purpose, by Ornstein and van Wyk in 1932.* In this experiment they studied one of the lines emitted from an electric discharge passing through helium at very low pressure. The

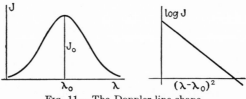

FIG. 11.—The Doppler line-shape.

observed shape of the line corresponded closely to that due to a maxwellian distribution but at a temperature some 50° above the tube containing the helium; this difference was ascribed to heating of the gas by the discharge. Some classical experiments made much earlier by Fabry and Buisson† had shown only that the widths of certain lines emitted by the gases helium, neon, and krypton varied with temperature very nearly in the right way to correspond with the Doppler explanation, being directly proportional to the square root of the absolute temperature.

* ORNSTEIN and VAN WYK, *Zeits. Physik*, **78**, 734 (1932).
† FABRY and BUISSON, *Acad. Sci., Compt. Rend.*, **154**, 1224 (1912).

CHAPTER III

GENERAL MOTION AND SPATIAL DISTRIBUTION OF THE MOLECULES

Up to this point we have discussed effects of the velocities of the molecules without paying much attention to their positions, and we have found that certain properties of gases can be adequately handled in this way. There are other phenomena, however, which depend also in large part upon the distribution of the molecules in space. It will be convenient to prepare for the treatment of such phenomena by taking up at this point certain aspects of the molecular motion which involve their distribution in space. The tedium of the abstract argument will be relieved at intervals by the discussion of concrete applications.

UNILATERAL FLOW OF THE MOLECULES

36. Effusive Molecular Flow. As our first topic, we may take up for consideration the general flow of the molecules from place to place in a gas. A concrete example suggesting such a study is presented by the *effusion* of a gas through a hole into a region of lower pressure.

The character of this latter phenomenon varies greatly according as the hole is large or small. If the hole is sufficiently large, the motion can be handled theoretically by the methods of ordinary hydrodynamics; the treatment of this case accordingly lies outside of our field, but its general conclusions may be cited for purposes of comparison. It turns out that, as the pressure difference between the gas in the vessel and that in the region outside is increased, the outflow of gas varies at first in proportion to this difference. If, however, the outer pressure is lowered so as to lie below a certain critical value, which is a little more than half of the inner pressure, then the magnitude of the outer pressure no longer makes any difference at all in the outflow. The maximum velocity of the gas in the issuing jet is then equal to the speed of sound through it at the temperature and density existing in the jet, which is cooled by expansion. The fact that under these circumstances the outside pressure has no influence upon the rate of outflow can be explained by saying that it is no longer possible for a signal to work back through the jet into the vessel and, as it were, notify the gas inside of the very low pressure existing outside. Under such conditions, and even before such speeds are reached, the issuing jet has a contracted form, narrowing to a certain minimum cross section at a short distance from the hole, beyond which it expands again, but often with oscillating cross section; and at speeds of outflow above a certain low minimum the jet is also surrounded by eddies and the whole motion is more or less turbulent.

Suppose, however, for contrast, we now go to the other extreme and make the hole small even as compared with the molecular "mean free path" or average distance traversed by the molecules between collisions. Then, according to classical theory, the molecules must issue independently of each other in the form of a molecular stream, each one moving with the velocity it had as it came up to the hole. The loss of a single molecule now and then through the hole should disturb only slightly their general distribution inside of it; a trace of mass motion toward the hole must develop because of the absence of those collisions that the lost molecule would have made with others on its return from the wall, but this effect will be wiped out promptly by the molecular interplay, which is always tending to set up and preserve the equilibrium state.   If there is gas in equilibrium on *both sides* of the hole, a process of effusion of this sort will occur in each direction just as if the gas on the other side were absent.

If the hole is now widened until its diameter is comparable to the mean free path, an intermediate type of flow occurs. As the hole is widened, mass motion toward it develops more and more in the vessel as a result of intermolecular collisions (or their absence), and this mass motion, carried along in the issuing gas, tends to result in the formation of a jet of forward-moving gas outside.   In this way a continuous transition occurs from molecular to what might be called hydrodynamical streaming.

In the case of the *very small* hole the outflow of molecules through it should be the same as their flow across any small plane area of equal size drawn in the body of the gas.   Accordingly, we shall now consider the latter more general case in detail.

37. Formulas for Effusive Flow.   Consider a small plane of area S drawn anywhere in a mass of gas that is in complete equilibrium. Molecules will be crossing S continually in both directions; let us fix our attention upon those that cross toward one side only.   These molecules might be said to constitute a *maxwellian effusive stream*.

Out of n molecules per unit volume, $4\pi n A v^2 e^{-\beta^2 v^2}\, dv$ are moving with speeds in a given range dv, by (61a), and, since they are moving equally in all directions, the fraction $d\omega/4\pi$ of them are moving in directions lying in a given solid angle $d\omega$ whose axis makes an angle θ with the normal to S [cf. (29) in Sec. 18]. Of these molecules, as many will cross S during a given interval dt as lie at the beginning of dt within a cylinder standing on S as base and having slant height $v\,dt$ and hence a volume $Sv\,dt\cos\theta$ (cf. Fig. 12). Hence the number so crossing

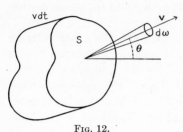

is the number in the cylinder at the beginning of dt or

FIG. 12.

$$4\pi n A v^2 e^{-\beta^2 v^2}\,dv\left(\frac{d\omega}{4\pi}\right)Sv\,dt\cos\theta.$$

Dividing this expression by S and by dt, we have, accordingly, as the number of molecules crossing S per unit area per second, with velocities lying in the range dv in magnitude and in the solid angle $d\omega$ of directions,

$$nA v^3 e^{-\beta^2 v^2}\cos\theta\,dv\,d\omega \tag{71a}$$

where $A = \beta^3/\pi^{3/2}$ by eq. (60) and β is given by (56) in Sec. 28.

Thus the molecules that cross a plane in a given time are distributed in direction according to the law that is familiar in optics as Lambert's or the cosine law.

As in the analogous optical case, it is often useful to sum further *over all azimuths* about the normal. Taking the normal to S as the axis for polar coordinates θ, φ, we can write $d\omega = \sin\theta\,d\theta\,d\varphi$ and then integrate (71a) over all values of φ (cf. Fig. 13). Since the integrand is independent of φ and $\int_0^{2\pi} d\varphi = 2\pi$, the result is

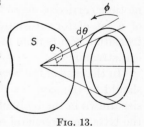

$$2\pi n A v^3 e^{-\beta^2 v^2}\sin\theta\cos\theta\,dv\,d\theta, \tag{71b}$$

representing the total number of molecules that cross S per unit area per second with speed in the range dv and with a direction of motion that makes an angle lying in the range $d\theta$ with the normal to S; the values of A and β are as stated above, just below eq. (71a).

FIG. 13.

Of course, we could also have obtained this result directly by writing $\frac{1}{2}\sin\theta\,d\theta$ from (30) in the place of $d\omega/4\pi$.

The presence of v^3 in (71a) and (71b), as contrasted with v^2 in the distribution formula, means that high speeds are relatively commoner among the molecules that cross a plane than they are in the gas in general, obviously because the faster molecules stand a larger chance of crossing the plane in a given time.

These formulas characterize adequately the distribution of velocities in a maxwellian effusive stream at temperature T. In some connections, however, much less detail suffices; we may need to know only the *total number* of molecules that cross, regardless of their speed or direction.

This number can be obtained by integrating (71b) over all values of θ from 0 to $\pi/2$ and of v from 0 to ∞. Since $\int_0^{\frac{\pi}{2}} \sin\theta \cos\theta \, d\theta = \frac{1}{2}$, and an integration by parts gives $\int_0^\infty v^3 e^{-\beta^2 v^2} \, dv = 1/(2\beta^4)$, we thus obtain $\frac{1}{2}\pi n A/\beta^4$, or, after substituting $A = \beta^3/\pi^{3/2}$ from (60) in Sec. 28 and $1/\beta = \sqrt{\pi}\bar{v}/2$ from (65a),

$$\Gamma_n = \tfrac{1}{4} n\bar{v} \tag{72a}$$

as the total number of molecules crossing unit area of S per second toward one side. Here $\bar{v}$ stands as usual for the mean molecular speed. For practical applications, however, it is more convenient to replace $n\bar{v}$ by immediately observable quantities. Writing Γ_m for the mass and Γ_V for the volume of the gas that crosses unit area per second toward one side, or Γ_{pV} for the pV value of this gas, we have $\Gamma_m = m\Gamma_n$ with $nm = \rho = p/RT$, $\Gamma_V = \Gamma_n/n$ and $\Gamma_{pV} = p\Gamma_V$, and hence, after inserting $\bar{v} = 2(2RT/\pi)^{1/2}$ from (66a) in Sec. 30,

$$\Gamma_m = \frac{1}{4}\rho\bar{v} = \rho\left(\frac{RT}{2\pi}\right)^{1/2} = \frac{p}{(2\pi RT)^{1/2}}, \tag{72b}$$

$$\Gamma_V = \frac{1}{4}\bar{v} = \left(\frac{RT}{2\pi}\right)^{1/2}, \qquad \Gamma_{pV} = p\left(\frac{RT}{2\pi}\right)^{1/2}. \tag{72c, d}$$

Here ρ is the density and p the pressure of the gas, T is its absolute temperature, and R refers to a gram, or $R = R_M/M$, where R_M is the gas constant for a mole and M is the molecular weight. Equation (72b) shows that the rate of molecular flow (in either direction) across S is the same as if the gas were moving bodily across it with a speed equal to one quarter of the mean speed of the molecules.

According to what has been said above, these formulas should apply not only in the interior of the gas but also to effusion through a hole in the wall of the containing vessel, provided its diameter is small as compared with the molecular mean free path. The symbol p in (72b, d) then stands for the pressure on the side from which the gas comes. If there is gas on both sides of the hole, effusion will obviously occur in both directions independently, for under these conditions a molecule runs very little risk of being stopped by a collision as it passes through; the net flow through the hole is then the difference of the two opposing unilateral flows.

For convenience of future reference a number of other useful formulas are appended below, the proofs being left as exercises for the student.

Problems 1. Show that the total number of molecules crossing unit area of S per second in a direction lying within an element $d\omega$ of solid angle is

$$\frac{1}{4\pi} n\bar{v} \cos\theta \, d\omega = \frac{n}{\pi} \left(\frac{kT}{2\pi m}\right)^{1/2} \cos\theta \, d\omega. \tag{73a}$$

[E.g., integrate (71a) and use (65a), (56).]

2. Show [e.g., from (62)] that the number of molecules crossing unit area of S per second toward one side with a component of velocity normal to S lying between $v_\perp$ and $v_\perp + dv_\perp$ is

$$\frac{2n}{\pi\bar{v}} v_\perp e^{-\beta^2 v_\perp^2} \, dv_\perp = n\left(\frac{m}{2\pi kT}\right)^{1/2} v_\perp e^{-\beta^2 v_\perp^2} \, dv_\perp. \tag{73b}$$

3. Show that, if the x-axis is taken perpendicular to S, of those molecules that cross S toward one side in a given time the fraction

$$\frac{2\beta^4}{\pi} v_x e^{-\beta^2 v^2} \, dv_x \, dv_y \, dv_z \tag{74}$$

has velocity components in the ranges dv_x, dv_y, dv_z, where as usual $v^2 = v_x^2 + v_y^2 + v_z^2$ (cf. Sec. 28, Prob. 3).

4. Show that the mean translational energy of the molecules that cross S in a given time exceeds that of those present in a given volume by the factor $4/3$ and so amounts to $2kT$ ergs per molecule or $2RT$ per gram.

38. Molecular Effusion. The effusion of gases through small holes is sometimes applied in technical operations as a convenient rough means of determining gaseous densities.* In such applications, however, the holes employed are usually so large that mass motion occurs and the phenomena are consequently of little interest for kinetic theory.

The first case of true molecular streaming to be subjected to experimental study was the motion of gases through plates made of some porous material, such as gypsum or meerschaum, the phenomenon being usually called *transpiration*. If the canals through such a plate are small enough, or in any case when the gaseous density is low

---

* Cf. Buckingham and Edwards, *Bull. Bur. Stand.*, **15**, 573 (1920).

enough, the molecules should wander through them as individuals, little affected by collisions with other gas molecules. We cannot expect our formulas to apply quantitatively to such motion, but it seems clear at least that the mean rate of passage of the gas through the plate should be proportional to the mean molecular velocity, as in eqs. (72a, b, c, d), and so, according to (66a) in Sec. 30, to $\sqrt{T/M}$, where T = absolute temperature and M = the molecular weight. The presence of another gas on the opposite side of the plate should make little difference, since collisions with a molecule of the other gas are much rarer than collisions with the walls of the canal; the two bodies of gas should transpire through the plate independently of each other or nearly so.

The predicted variation with molecular weight was tested by Graham in the course of a series of experiments (1829 to 1863) and was found to hold reasonably well. Rates of transpiration have, accordingly, sometimes been employed in the determination of molecular weights, but it is difficult to make this method very exact. In his pioneer separation of helium from nitrogen Ramsey employed differential transpiration through unglazed clay pipe stems, the helium passing through the clay at a rate $(28/4)^{1/2}$ or 2.6 times as fast as the nitrogen so that by repeated fractionation in this manner it could be got out fairly pure.

True *molecular effusion* through a visible hole has, however, been observed and studied by Knudsen.* He employed in one series of observations a hole roughly 0.025 mm in diameter in a platinum strip 0.0025 mm thick and worked with hydrogen, oxygen, and carbon dioxide at pressures ranging from 10 cm down to 0.001 cm of Hg, and at a temperature of either 22°C or 100°C. The gas was passed steadily through the hole under a pressure p' on one side and p'' on the other, and the quantity of gas that passed through in a given time was noted. Effusion being bilateral in this case, eq. (72d) gives us for the net rate of flow measured in terms of pV (Knudsen's Q)

$$\Gamma_{pV} = \left(\frac{RT}{2\pi}\right)^{1/2}(p' - p'').$$

The general result of Knudsen's work was to obtain a good check of the theory when the pressure was low enough so that the mean free path in the gas was at least ten times the diameter of the hole. At higher pressures the rate of flow was found to be somewhat greater than the theoretical value as given above; and at a pressure sufficiently

* KNUDSEN, *Ann. Physik*, **28**, 75 (1909).

great to make the mean free path less than a tenth of the diameter of the hole he found agreement with the formula furnished by hydrodynamics for the case of slow isothermal flow through an opening. Knudsen's results thus check the kinetic theory very satisfactorily.

39. Thermal Transpiration. A peculiar case of considerable theoretical interest is that called thermal transpiration. Suppose two vessels containing the same kind of gas are connected through a porous plug of the sort described above, and let them be maintained at different temperatures. Then, according to (72b), the rates at which molecules enter the pores of the plug per unit area on the two sides are proportional to $p/\sqrt{T}$. If the pores were merely small holes in an indefinitely thin sheet, we should, accordingly, expect a differential flow to continue until the gaseous densities became so adjusted that the quantity $p/\sqrt{T}$ had the same value on the two sides, i.e., until

$$\frac{p_1}{p_2} = \left(\frac{T_1}{T_2}\right)^{\frac{1}{2}}$$ (75)

It is commonly assumed that the same condition of equilibrium ought to occur in the case of an actual plug; and we shall support this theoretical conclusion in a later chapter by analyzing the effect of a temperature gradient along a very narrow tube (cf. Sec. 186).

Experiments of this type were performed long ago by Osborne Reynolds.* A plate of earthenware, stucco, or more usually meerschaum, $\frac{1}{16}$ to $\frac{5}{16}$ in. thick, was mounted between hard-rubber rings so as to leave exposed on each side a circular area $1\frac{1}{2}$ in. in diameter (Fig. 14); the rings were then closed by sheets of tin so as to form disk-shaped spaces containing the transpiring gas, and outside of these still other spaces were formed in a similar way through which steam could be circulated on one side and cooling water of known temperature on the other. Conduction through the tin plates was relied upon to give the gas between the tin sheets and the porous plate approximately the temperature of the steam or water, respectively.

Reynolds found that when the pressure of the gas was sufficiently low, the law expressed by eq. (75) held as closely as he could judge

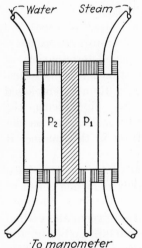

FIG. 14.—Reynolds' experiment on transpiration.

* REYNOLDS, *Phil. Trans.*, **170**, II, 727 (1879).

with his rather crude way of observing the temperature, but at higher pressures departures occurred; since the mean free path is, as we shall see presently, inversely proportional to the pressure, this is just what we should expect. He was not able, however, to observe the actual size of the passages through the porous plate and so to make sure by comparison of these sizes with known values of the mean free path that the transition to eq. (75) occurred at a pressure of the right order.

In an arrangement of this sort it is interesting to imagine the two vessels to be connected, not only through the plug, but also through a tube *large* in diameter relative to the mean free path. Then any tendency for a difference of pressure to be set up by transpiration through the plug will give rise to mass flow through the tube in the opposite direction. Thus there will occur a steady circulation of the gas as long as the temperature difference lasts.

It might, perhaps, be thought that this steady circulation, or even the pressure difference in the original arrangement, involves a violation of the second law of thermodynamics. One might, for instance, connect an engine so as to take gas from the high-pressure vessel and discharge it into the one at low pressure and thereby obtain an indefinitely large amount of work out of the system. Thermodynamic compensation for this process is furnished, however, by the conduction of heat through the gas which is in the act of transpiring through the plug; it can easily be shown* that the degradation of energy resulting from this conduction is ample to protect the second law from violation.

40. Knudsen's Absolute Manometer. Knudsen proposed to utilize the phenomenon of transpiration in the construction of a gauge for the measurement of very low pressures.† He suspended a copper disk on a torsion fiber (shown from above at α in Fig. 15); this disk hung with half of its surface very close and parallel to the plane face of a copper block β which was heated electrically and surrounded by another unheated block γ, designed to serve as a guard ring.

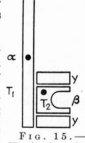

F i g . 15.— Knudsen's absolute manometer.

Temperatures of disk and block were read on mercury thermometers inserted into them. The narrow space between the disk α and the block β should then act more or less like a vessel in which the gas has a temperature halfway between the temperatures T_2 of the block and T_1 of the disk, and if the pressure is so low that the mean free

* Kennard, *Nat. Acad.*, **18**, 237 (1932).
† Knudsen, *Ann. Physik*, **32**, 809 (1910).

path in the gas is long relative to the distance between disk and block, the formula for thermal transpiration should apply.

Knudsen assumes that the disk has sensibly the same temperature as the surrounding gas, whose pressure p is what we desire to measure, and this assumption seemed to be justified by his observations. The pressure in the layer of gas between disk and block will accordingly be, by (75),

$$p' = p\left[\frac{\frac{1}{2}(T_1 + T_2)}{T_1}\right]^{\frac{1}{2}},$$

so that if $T_2 - T_1$ is small, there is a net outward force per unit area on the disk equal to

$$p' - p = p\left[\left(\frac{T_1 + T_2}{2T_1}\right)^{\frac{1}{2}} - 1\right] = \frac{1}{4}\frac{T_2 - T_1}{T_1}\,p,$$

since

$$\left[\frac{T_1 + T_2}{T_1}\right]^{\frac{1}{2}} = \left[2 + \frac{T_2 - T_1}{T_1}\right]^{\frac{1}{2}}.$$

This force can be determined by observing the resulting small displacement of the disk with the help of a mirror mounted on it, and since T_1 and T_2 are known, p can then be calculated. Knudsen showed by observations that the formula held when the pressure was low enough and $T_2 - T_1$ small enough; for larger $T_2 - T_1$ he verified a more accurate formula that he obtained by making a detailed analysis of the molecular motion between disk and block and so introducing a small correction on the mean temperature of the gas there, his result being that $p' = p[(T_2/T_1)^{\frac{1}{2}} - 1]$.

Because of the absence of doubtful constants in these formulas Knudsen called his instrument an "absolute" manometer. In the more convenient direct-reading form devised later by Riegger, however, this feature is sacrificed and calibration at one pressure with a ·MacLeod gauge is necessary.*

41. Evaporation. The formula for effusive molecular flow obtained in Sec. 37 finds an interesting application to the rate of evaporation of a substance from the solid or liquid state. The equilibrium between a condensed phase and its saturated vapor is a kinetic one; molecules are rapidly evaporating all the time and passing off into the vapor, but at the same time a stream of other molecules is condensing out of the vapor, and when equilibrium exists, these two processes just balance each other. If we upset the equilibrium by lowering the density of the

---

* RIEGGER, *Zeits. tech. Physik*, p. 16, 1920.

vapor a little, the rate of condensation is lowered in proportion; then evaporation exceeds condensation and there is a net passage of molecules from the solid or liquid into the vapor. What is commonly called evaporation is this net flow of molecules. Similarly, if the density of the vapor is raised a little above the saturation value, the continual precipitation of molecules is augmented and net condensation occurs. In the case of volatile substances the unilateral evaporation and condensation go on at such enormous rates that only an imperceptible change in the density of the vapor is required to produce the relatively slow net evaporation or condensation that ordinarily occurs under the limitation imposed by the necessity of supplying or removing the heat of vaporization. It follows that in such cases the density of the vapor in contact with the liquid can be assumed not to depart appreciably from its saturation value.

The *maximum possible* rate of net evaporation would occur if arrangements could be made to remove the vapor as fast as formed, so as to eliminate condensation entirely; observations of this maximum rate would then give us also an experimental measure of the *unilateral* rate of evaporation or condensation, which is not itself observable.

On the theoretical side, a direct calculation of this maximum rate of evaporation is hard to make, but we can get at it indirectly by utilizing the fact that when the vapor is saturated, unilateral evaporation and condensation are going on at equal rates, and the rate of condensation can be calculated from kinetic theory. The mass of vapor molecules striking the surface of the solid or liquid per second is easily found from eq. (72b). A difficulty arises, however, from the fact that some of these molecules upon striking the surface of the solid or liquid rebound from it without condensing. The best that we can do, therefore, is to introduce an unknown factor α to represent the fraction of the impinging molecules that do condense; α has been called the *coefficient of evaporation*. The amount of a substance continually being evaporated from a liquid or solid phase, and also being returned to it from the vapor when this is saturated, measured in grams per unit area per second, is then $G = \alpha\Gamma_m$ or, by (72b),

$$G = \alpha\rho\left(\frac{RT}{2\pi}\right)^{\frac{1}{2}} = \frac{\alpha p}{(2\pi RT)^{\frac{1}{2}}}. \tag{76}$$

Here R is the gas constant for a gram, T the absolute temperature, and ρ the density or p the pressure of the saturated vapor, so that $p = \rho RT$. G then represents likewise the "maximum rate of evaporation," which is observed when the vapor is removed as fast as formed.

Unless α can be determined somehow independently, there is no hope of testing this result experimentally, beyond the fact that, since α cannot exceed unity, the equation obviously sets a theoretical upper limit which the rate of evaporation cannot exceed. We can, however, turn the argument around and use observed evaporation rates in combination with eq. (76) to determine α. This will be done in the next section.

It should be remarked that throughout the discussion up to this point we have been assuming foreign gases to be absent. In a case such as the evaporation of water into the atmosphere, departure of the vapor from the neighborhood of the water surface is impeded by the presence of the air, so that if there is no wind to keep sweeping the saturated air away from the water, the vapor is compelled to diffuse away through the air. In such cases evaporation may be a very slow process indeed.

42. Observations on the Rate of Evaporation. Interesting observations of the maximum evaporation rate G for mercury have

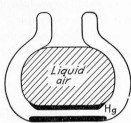

been made by Knudsen, by Brönsted and Hevesy, and by Volmer and Estermann.* The principle of the methods employed was to introduce the mercury into a high vacuum between the walls of a vessel shaped somewhat like a Dewar flask, and then to control its temperature by means of a surrounding bath while cooling the inner wall of the vessel with liquid air or other refrigerant so as to

FIG. 16.—Arrangement for measuring the evaporation rate of mercury.

condense and hold upon it the mercury that evaporated. The arrangement is shown in principle in Fig. 16. The pressure was kept low enough so that the evaporating molecules on their way to the cold surface would stand little chance of colliding with another molecule, and there is good reason to believe that reflection of mercury molecules from a mercury surface at liquid-air temperatures is negligible; the rate of deposition on the upper surface should therefore equal the rate of unilateral evaporation from the mercury below. In the experiments of Brönsted and Hevesy the deposit on the cold surface was measured by melting it and then running it out and weighing it.

* KNUDSEN, *Ann. Physik*, **47**, 697 (1915), also a book, "The Kinetic Theory of Gases—Some Modern Aspects" (Methuen). BRÖNSTED and HEVESY, *Nature*, **107**, 619 (1921), and *Zeits. Phys. Chem.*, **99**, 189 (1921). VOLMER and ESTERMANN, *Zeits. Phys.*, **7**, 1 (1921).

The accuracy obtained in such experiments does not go beyond possible errors of several per cent, but the results obtained by all workers point consistently to the conclusion that α is at least very close to 1 for liquid mercury, and also for solid mercury below $-140°C$, while for solid mercury above $-100°C$ it is certainly less than 1, perhaps by 8 or 10 per cent. The fact that no definite evidence was found for a value of α *exceeding unity* constitutes a confirmation of kinetic theory.

The rate of evaporation of mercury is diminished very greatly by any contamination of the surface, as was shown by Knudsen; for the surface of a certain brownish-looking drop he found α to be only $\frac{1}{2000}$. This is presumed to be the reason that even very small drops of mercury may lie around in the laboratory for days before they finally disappear.

On the other hand, if we assume the truth of eq. (76) and somehow know (or assume) α, we can employ the formula the other way round for the calculation of vapor pressures from observations on the maximum rate of evaporation. This was actually done for mercury itself by Knudsen;[*] and later a similar use of the formula was made by Langmuir.[†] The latter investigator had made an extensive study of the rate of evaporation of tungsten to serve as a guide in the practical handling of tungsten filaments in lamp bulbs and vacuum tubes, and as a by-product he calculated from his results the vapor pressure of tungsten at various temperatures, which would be very difficult to measure directly in the case of such a nonvolatile substance. The rate of evaporation was found by keeping a tungsten filament at a known temperature for a given length of time and then weighing it to find the loss of material from its surface. Several not too definite considerations convinced him that α was probably unity, so that the equivalent of eq. (76) with α omitted would give correct values of p in terms of the observed values of G. Some of the results thus found were: at 2000°K, $G = 1.14 \times 10^{-13}$ g/cm²/sec, and $p = 6.45 \times 10^{-12}$ mm Hg; at 2400°K, which is not much above the operating temperature of a common tungsten lamp, $G = 8 \times 10^{-10}$ and $p = 4.9 \times 10^{-8}$; at the melting point of tungsten, 3540°K, $G = 0.00107$ and $p = 0.08$ mm.

43. Test of the Velocity Distribution in Effusive Flow. Several experiments have been performed which permit a more or less direct test of the distribution of velocities in an effusing gas, and these are of considerable theoretical interest because they constitute a fairly

---

* Knudsen, *Ann. Physik*, **29**, 179 (1909).

† Langmuir, *Phys. Rev.*, **11**, 329 (1913).

direct test of Maxwell's law. In these experiments use is made of the method of producing molecular rays that was worked out by Stern and his coworkers at Hamburg.* From an oven heated uniformly so as to become filled with vapor of some substance in thermal equilibrium, vapor is allowed to stream out through a very narrow slit in one side, and a narrow beam of molecules is selected out of this stream of vapor by means of a second slit placed opposite the first and at some distance from it. Beyond the second slit the beam thus formed is split up or otherwise experimented upon and is then measured in some sort of receiving device. The entire path of the beam outside of the oven lies in a high vacuum, all issuing molecules being condensed as they strike various parts of the apparatus, which are cooled if necessary by liquid air.

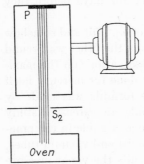

FIG. 17.—Hall's velocity-spectrum arrangement.

Special interest for kinetic theory attaches to the arrangement invented by E. E. Hall, constructed by Zartman† and improved by Ko.‡ In this apparatus there is mounted above the second collimating slit (S_2 in Fig. 17) a rapidly revolving drum having a narrow slit in one side and carrying on its inner surface, opposite this slit, a glass plate P. The molecular beam is thus received for the most part on the exterior of the drum, but once in each revolution, when the slit in the drum comes opposite the exit slit S_2 of the beam, a short spurt of molecules enters the drum, crosses its interior, and is deposited upon the glass plate. Since, however, the drum has time to turn through a certain angle while the molecules are crossing its interior, the point of deposition on the glass plate varies with the molecular speed, and in this way a velocity spectrum is formed.

According to eq. (71a), the number of molecules issuing through the slits with speeds between v and $v + dv$ can be written $Cv^3e^{-\beta^2v^2}\,dv$, C being a proportionality factor. The point at which molecules with speed v strike the glass plate is displaced a distance s from the point at which they are directly aimed as they enter the drum, given by $s = (D/v)(\pi Dn) = \pi nD^2/v$, D being the diameter of the drum and n its frequency of revolution. The molecules in the range dv will thus be spread over a distance $ds = -\dfrac{\pi nD^2}{v^2}\,dv$, and, if I is the number depos-

* STERN, *Zeits. f. Physik*, **39**, 751 (1926).

† ZARTMAN, *Phys. Rev.*, **37**, 383 (1931).

‡ KO, *Jour. Franklin Inst.*, **217**, 173 (1934).

ited per unit length, we have $I\,ds = -Cv^3e^{-\beta^2v^2}\,dv$ and

$$I = \frac{C}{\pi nD^2}\,v^5e^{-\beta^2v^2} = \frac{C'}{s^5}e^{-\frac{\pi^2n^2D^4\beta^2}{s^2}}$$

in terms of a new proportionality factor C'.

The substance studied by both Zartman and Ko was bismuth, which deposits readily at room temperature, provided the surface is coated with a preliminary layer of bismuth. Unfortunately for the point we are interested in, however, bismuth evaporates partly as Bi and partly as Bi_2, and probably even slightly as Bi_8, so that several kinds of molecules are present in the beam; the determination of the molecular composition of bismuth vapor was, in fact, Ko's main object, rather than a check of Maxwell's law. He found that the observed deposits as measured photo-metrically after a run with the oven at 827°C were in fair agreement with the assumption that in the beam 44 per cent of the molecules were Bi, 54 per cent Bi_2, and 2 per cent Bi_8. In Fig. 18 is reproduced Ko's Fig. 10, showing the observed points for the mass deposited, in comparison with the theoretical curve; in calculating the latter the relative magnitude of the three component curves was adjusted to secure the best fit with the observations, but the form of each was determined theoretically in terms of the observed oven temperature.

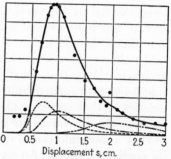

FIG. 18.—Ko's velocity spectrum of a bismuth beam. Abscissa, distance along plate s; ordinate, density of molecular deposit.

From his data Ko deduced in the following way a value of the heat of dissociation of the bismuth molecule; and this he regarded as his most significant result. According to the last member in (72*b*), for the separate components of a beam $p \propto \Gamma_m\sqrt{R} \propto \Gamma_m/\sqrt{M}$, since the molecular weight $M \propto 1/R$; but the number of atoms passing is proportional to Γ_m/M; hence the pressure is proportional to the number of atoms multiplied by $\sqrt{M}$. Now the ratio of M for Bi_2 to M for Bi is 2. Hence in the example cited above the atomic ratio 54/44 or 1.23 in the beam means a partial-pressure ratio

$$\frac{54}{44} \times \sqrt{2} = 1.74$$

for Bi_2 as compared with Bi. In addition, a second relation involving the partial pressures was obtained experimentally by observing the total rate of loss of bismuth through the slit, the bismuth in the oven being weighed before and after a run; the area of the slit being known, these observations give the sum of the values for Bi and Bi_2 of the quantity denoted by Γ_m in (72b), and from this sum another expression containing the partial pressures in the saturated vapor could be found. The two relations thus obtained were solved for the actual partial pressures, and from values of these corresponding to two different temperatures the heat of dissociation was calculated with the help of the theory of dissociation.

THE GENERAL DISTRIBUTION FUNCTION

44. A Gas in a Force-field. Up to this point we have dealt only with gases that are free from the action of external forces other than those exerted by the containing vessel. There are many cases, however, in which forces such as gravity are present, and it is important to investigate the effect of such forces upon the molecular motion.

In almost all cases of this sort the external forces may be regarded as due to a *force-field*, by which is meant that the force on each molecule depends in some definite way upon the position and other characteristics of that molecule alone. In by far the most important case, furthermore, the forces are derivable from a scalar potential function, so that a molecule possesses a potential energy depending only upon its spatial position. An example of a force-field of a more general type is presented by ions in a magnetic field.

When a potential function exists, the force that acts on the molecule is the *negative gradient* of the potential-energy function; its direction is that in which this function decreases most rapidly and its magnitude is equal to this maximum rate of decrease of the function. In vector or in cartesian notation the force, denoted by **F** or F_x, F_y, F_z, can be written thus in terms of the potential-energy function ω:

$$\mathbf{F} = -\nabla\omega$$

or

$$F_x = -\frac{\partial\omega}{\partial x}, \qquad F_y = -\frac{\partial\omega}{\partial y}, \qquad F_z = -\frac{\partial\omega}{\partial z}. \tag{77}$$

45. Density in a Force-field. The effect of a simple potential-energy force-field upon the spatial distribution of the molecules can be obtained very simply without any use of kinetic theory. Consider the gas inside an element of space having the form of a short right cylinder of cross-sectional area δS and height δh (Fig. 19). Its mass will be $\rho\,\delta S\,\delta h$, where ρ is the density of the gas. Let Ω denote the potential energy of unit mass of the gas due to the field; then the component of the force on unit mass in a direction normal to the faces of the cylinder can be written $-\partial\Omega/\partial h$, where h as a variable denotes distance in the specified direction. (We must choose one of the two directions along the normal as positive and then represent all displacements dh and components of force by positive numbers when they have this direction and by negative numbers when they have the opposite one.) The field thus exerts on the gas inside the cylinder a component of force normal to its faces whose magnitude can be written

$$-\rho\ \delta h\ \delta S\frac{\partial\Omega}{\partial h} = -\rho\ \delta S\ d\Omega$$

after replacing $\delta h\ \partial\Omega/\partial h$ by $d\Omega$, the difference in Ω at perpendicularly opposite points on the two faces. This is allowable at least in the limit when the cylinder is made indefinitely small, the difference between the values of $d\Omega$ for different pairs of opposite points becoming then negligible in comparison with $d\Omega$ itself.

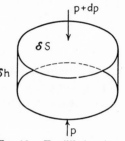

Fig. 19.—Equilibrium in a force-field.

To preserve equilibrium, this force must now be balanced by an equal and opposite force arising from the pressure of the surrounding gas on the surfaces of the cylinder. Pressure on the curved sides, however, causes no force in the direction normal to the faces. Let p denote the pressure at any point on the lower face and $p + dp$ the pressure at the perpendicularly opposite point on the upper face ("upper" meaning, situated toward larger values of h); then the difference of the pressure forces on the two faces can be written

$$p\ \delta S - (p + dp)\ \delta S = -dp\ \delta S,$$

this expression again being accurate in the limit.

The sum of this force and the force due to the field must now be zero. Hence $-\rho\ \delta S\ d\Omega - dp\ \delta S = 0$ and

$$dp = -\rho\ d\Omega. \tag{78}$$

By properly locating the cylinder, whose axis need not be vertical but may have any direction, dp and $d\Omega$ can obviously be made to represent differences between values of p and Ω at any two neighboring points. Hence eq. (78) holds throughout the force-field.

If a general relation between p and ρ is known, the integral of (78) can be written down at once. Suppose, for example, the temperature

T is uniform throughout. Then, the gas being assumed perfect, $p = \rho RT$, R being the gas constant for a gram, and by (78)

$$\frac{RT\, dp}{p} = -d\Omega.$$

Integrating this equation, we find $RT \log p = -\Omega + \text{const.}$, which can be written

$$p = p_0 e^{-\frac{\Omega}{RT}}, \qquad \rho = \rho_0 e^{-\frac{\Omega}{RT}}, \qquad (79a)$$

where p_0 or $\rho_0 = p_0/RT$ replaces the constant of integration and has the significance of the pressure or density at points (if there are any) where $\Omega = 0$. Equation (79a) expresses the law of *isothermal distribution* of a gas in a force-field. Sometimes, however, it is more convenient to write $\Omega = \omega/m$, m being the mass of a molecule and ω, as before, its potential energy in the field; if at the same time we introduce $k = mR$, (79a) becomes

$$p = p_0 e^{-\frac{\omega}{kT}}, \qquad \rho = \rho_0 e^{-\frac{\omega}{kT}}. \qquad (79b)$$

In a *uniform gravitational* field we can also write $\Omega = gh$, $\omega = mgh$, in terms of g, the gravitational acceleration and h, the elevation above some chosen datum level; then (79b) takes the special form

$$p = p_0 e^{-\frac{mgh}{kT}}, \qquad \rho = \rho_0 e^{-\frac{mgh}{kT}}. \qquad (79c)$$

In Fig. 20 the isothermal distribution is compared with the adiabatic distribution described below, for air, which has $\gamma = 1.4$. It is assumed in both cases that $T = T_0$ where $\Omega = 0$.

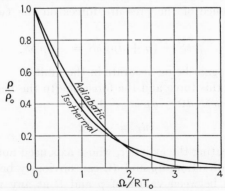

FIG. 20.—Density ρ in a field of potential Ω.

Problem. Show that if the distribution is *adiabatic*, so that pV^γ is constant from point to point, (79a) is replaced by

$$p = p_0\left(1 - \frac{\gamma - 1}{\gamma}\frac{\Omega}{RT_0}\right)^{\frac{\gamma}{\gamma-1}}, \qquad \rho = \rho_0\left(1 - \frac{\gamma - 1}{\gamma}\frac{\Omega}{RT_0}\right)^{\frac{1}{\gamma-1}}, \quad (80)$$

where γ = ratio of specific heats and p_0, ρ_0 and T_0 stand for values at any point where $\Omega = 0$ (or may be regarded as merely representing integration constants). According to these formulas $\rho = 0$ (and also $p = 0$, $T = 0$) at any point where $\Omega = \gamma RT_0/(\gamma - 1)$, and there can be no gas at all in regions of larger Ω.

46. Maxwell's Law in a Force-field. The next question that naturally presents itself is whether Maxwell's law can hold for the molecular velocities in a force-field or whether, perhaps, it requires modification. As molecules move into regions of higher potential they must lose kinetic energy, and vice versa; it might be thought, therefore, that there would be a tendency for a difference of temperature to be set up through the agency of thermal agitation, conceivably like the temperature gradient that is actually observed in the atmosphere. The equilibrium distribution would then be one in which the temperature is a function of Ω.

To throw light on this question, let us consider first the concrete case of a homogeneous gas in the earth's gravitational field. Take two horizontal planes P_1 and P_2 so close together that a molecule can cross from one to the other without appreciable chance of a collision, and take the z-axis vertically upward (cf. Fig. 21). Then if Maxwell's law holds in the neighborhood of the lower plane, the mean density of the gas being n_1 and its temperature T, according to (73b) with $\beta^2 = m/2kT$ inserted from (56) in Sec. 28, there will be

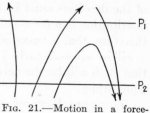

Fig. 21.—Motion in a force-field.

$$n_1\left(\frac{m}{2\pi kT}\right)^{\frac{1}{2}} v_z e^{-mv_z^2/2kT}\, dv_z \qquad (81)$$

molecules that leave unit area of the lower plane per second moving in an upward direction with z-components of velocity in the range dv_z. Each of these molecules upon reaching the upper plane will have lost kinetic energy equal to its increase $\Delta\omega$ in potential energy. Only the z-component of the velocity is affected, however; hence, if we let $\mathbf{v}'$ denote the velocity at the upper plane of a molecule that left the lower with a z-component v_z, we have

$$\tfrac{1}{2}mv_z'^2 = \tfrac{1}{2}mv_z^2 - \Delta\omega, \qquad \tfrac{1}{2}mv_z^2 = \tfrac{1}{2}mv_z'^2 + \Delta\omega. \qquad (82)$$

From this equation we have $v_z \, dv_z = v_z' \, dv_z'$. Hence, remembering that $v^2 = v_x^2 + v_y^2 + v_z^2$, $v'^2 = v_x'^2 + v_y'^2 + v_z'^2$ and noting that

$$v_x' = v_x, \qquad v_y' = v_y,$$

we can write in place of (81) for the number of the molecules under consideration

$$n_1 e^{-\Delta\omega/kT} \left(\frac{m}{2\pi kT}\right)^{1/2} v_z' e^{-mv_z'^2/2kT} \, dv_z'.$$

Upon arriving at the upper plane P_1, these molecules form part of whatever distribution exists there; then they pass on upward as an actual part of the stream of molecules that is continually leaving in an upward direction from P_1. The last expression found for their number is, however, the same function of v_z' and dv_z' that (81) is of v_z and dv_z, except for the added factor $e^{-\frac{\Delta\omega}{kT}}$. Thus the expression is just what it would be if the gas at the upper plane had likewise a maxwellian distribution at the same temperature T but a density decreased in the ratio $e^{-\frac{\Delta\omega}{kT}}$; and this latter is just what the ratio of the densities must be in order to agree with the law of isothermal distribution in a force-field, as expressed by (79b). We may conclude, therefore, that a maxwellian distribution at the uniform temperature T will be left undisturbed by the flow of the molecules and, accordingly, that such will be the actual distribution when the gas is in a state of equilibrium.

There are, however, two points that require further examination. In the first place, those molecules that start upward from the lower plane with v_z so small that $\frac{1}{2} mv_z^2 < \Delta\omega$ never reach the upper plane at all. However, they are not missed there, for those molecules that have exactly $\frac{1}{2} mv_z^2 = \Delta\omega$ just barely arrive with $v_z' = 0$, and obviously all greater values of v_z' are adequately represented in the stream that crosses P_1. On the other hand, we can obviously deal in the same way with downward motion, locating the second plane below the first; then molecules leaving with $v_z < 0$ will arrive with

$$v_z' < -(-2m\Delta\omega)^{1/2}$$

($\Delta\omega$ being now negative), and very slow molecules might thus seem here to be missing at the second plane. But now the molecules that should cross the second plane with a negative v_z' of smaller numerical magnitude than $(-2m\Delta\omega)^{1/2}$ will be supplied by exactly those molecules noted above which leave the lower plane in an upward direction and, after failing entirely to reach the upper plane, fall back and recross the lower one in a downward direction with v_z just reversed (cf. Fig. 21); the maxwellian flow downward is thereby made complete.

The second point concerns the effect of collisions, which we have completely ignored in our discussion. If, however, a maxwellian distribution exists at each point, collisions will throw as many molecules into a group moving in any particular direction as are removed from it, so that their net effect will be nil and we are justified in ignoring them.

Since all of this reasoning is obviously applicable to a gas in any force-field that has a scalar potential, we may conclude that when a gas is in complete equilibrium in any such field its density varies in accord with the eq. (79a) or (79b) that we obtained above, and also that the temperature is uniform throughout and a corresponding maxwellian distribution of velocities holds at every point.

47. The Temperature of Saturated Vapor. The conclusion that Maxwell's law holds in a force-field with no inequalities of temperature can be drawn also from the general differential equation for the molecular distribution which we shall obtain presently [eq. (87) in Sec. 51], or, still more satisfactorily, from the Boltzmann distribution law [cf. (92) in Sec. 55]. On this latter basis the conclusion holds universally for systems in equilibrium. It throws an interesting light upon the question as to the temperature of freshly formed vapor.

One might suppose that the vapor would be cooler than the liquid or solid from which it comes because the evaporating molecules do a large amount of work in escaping from the attraction of others that stay behind, this work forming in fact almost the whole of the ordinary heat of vaporization. Our results on the motion of molecules in a force-field indicate, however, that it should be only the fastest moving molecules which escape at all and that, by the time they have escaped from the attractive field of the liquid or solid, they will have become slowed down exactly into a maxwellian distribution corresponding to the temperature of the region from which they came.

Freshly formed vapor, therefore, ought to have the temperature of the surface of the evaporating liquid or solid. The experimental facts bearing on this point seem to be somewhat uncertain but at least it may be said that they do not definitely contradict the theoretical prediction.

48. The Terrestrial Atmosphere. The most famous case of a gas in a force-field is, of course, the earth's atmosphere. Modern work, however, has shown that many different influences are at work here and, in consequence, the state of the atmosphere does not exemplify

any one simple theory.*   We have space here only to discuss briefly a
few aspects of the subject that are of particular interest from the
standpoint of kinetic theory.

Observations made from balloons show that with increasing height
the temperature of the atmosphere, as a rule, drops at first approximately at the adiabatic rate, i.e., it varies with the pressure in the
same way as it would in an adiabatic expansion $\left(T \propto p^{\frac{\gamma-1}{\gamma}}\right)$. The
decrease ceases, however, when a certain minimum temperature is
reached, this temperature varying from about $-54°$ at a height of
12 km (7½ miles) in latitude 45° to $-84°C$ at a height of 17 km
(10½ miles) over the equator.   The atmosphere below this height is
called the troposphere.   In the region above, called the stratosphere,
the temperature either is constant or actually rises with increasing
height.

The accepted explanation of these observed features ascribes them
to the circumstance that the troposphere receives heat primarily by
conduction at its base from the earth and loses it through infra-red
radiation to the stratosphere, the absorption of the sun's rays by the
troposphere being only a minor factor.   The continual warming of
the troposphere at its base then sets up the familiar processes of
convection by which the air is continually carried up and down in
storm movements and in the general terrestrial circulation, and is
thereby subjected to repeated adiabatic expansions and compressions,
as a result of which the approximately adiabatic distribution of temperature is brought about.   The continual mixing also causes the
composition of the air to be closely the same everywhere, except, of
course, for the variable content of water vapor.

Thus it is only in the stratosphere that considerations based upon
kinetic theory are likely to be of importance.   Here clouds are rare
and there is probably little rapid vertical movement.   Observations
of auroral heights indicate that the stratosphere extends at least to
300 km (or 200 miles) and even slightly to 1000 km (or 600 miles).
The density is extremely slight at such great heights, of course, and
it seems to vary greatly from day to night, and from winter to summer.
For example, at a height of 100 km (62 miles) the density, relative
to that under standard conditions, has been estimated to be something like 6×10^{-6} on a summer day, 6×10^{-7} on a summer night,
10^{-6} on a winter day, and 3×10^{-7} on a winter night.   At 300 km
(nearly 200 miles) the estimated figures are nearly 10 million times

* Cf. W. J. Humphreys, "Physics of the Air," 2d ed., 1929.

smaller, but even at the latter height there are still around a million molecules in each cubic centimeter.

The most interesting feature for kinetic theory is to be found in the very long free paths of the molecules at such altitudes. At 100 km the free paths are only a few cm long, but at 300 km the mean free path ranges from 200 km (125 miles) on a summer day up to a maximum of perhaps 15,000 km (over 9000 miles). At still greater heights the molecules can be thought of as moving like tiny satellites in elliptical orbits with the earth at the focus. At such heights as these the atmosphere must be very far from a state of thermal equilibrium. Many ions must be formed through ionization by the sun's ultraviolet rays, and these ions will then spiral for long distances about the magnetic lines of the earth's field; a spray of such ions produced in equatorial regions and spiraling off to descend into lower altitudes in the region of the earth's magnetic poles has been suggested recently as a possible cause of the aurora.

Interest attaches also to the question of the distribution of the various constituents of the atmosphere. If the latter were in isothermal equilibrium, we could apply eq. (79c) to each of the constituent gases separately, each one being distributed according to this law just as if the others were not present. The coefficient of h in the exponent in (79c) increases with the molecular mass m; hence it would follow that the heavier gases are much more concentrated near the surface of the earth than the lighter ones. On the basis of this result from kinetic theory, the view has frequently been expressed that at great heights helium must form a much larger fraction of the atmosphere than it does lower down; at the earth's surface helium forms only 0.04 per cent of the total, but from 100 km, or 60 miles, up it should predominate over nitrogen and oxygen. At still greater heights the atmosphere should be nearly all hydrogen.

Unfortunately, satisfactory observations to test these conclusions do not yet exist. Furthermore, it is by no means certain that there must be any appreciable amount of hydrogen at great heights, even if there is a trace of it at the earth's surface, which is in itself not certain; for any hydrogen that wanders up into the upper atmosphere may be promptly oxidized to water vapor by the ozone which is known to occur there in considerable quantities.

49. Cosmic Equilibrium of Planetary Atmospheres. The problem of the upper boundary of a planetary atmosphere presents features of interest not only for the astrophysicist but also for the student of kinetic theory. If such an atmosphere were *isothermal*, it would extend to indefinite distances from the planet, for in (79a) the potential

Ω would be finite even at infinity. An *adiabatic* atmosphere, on the other hand, distributed in accord with eq. (80), would have a sharp upper boundary at the level at which $\Omega = \gamma R T_0/(\gamma - 1)$. In view of other properties of gases it is obvious, however, that such a boundary could not persist for any length of time, for the rapidity with which inequalities of temperature are ironed out in a gas in consequence of the conduction of heat becomes infinite at vanishing density, and consequently the gas immediately beneath a bounding surface of zero density would be brought quickly to a condition approximating uniformity of temperature and would thereupon proceed to spread out toward infinity.

Only two possibilities are open, therefore, in regard to the uppermost part of a planetary atmosphere. Either it passes continuously into a general distribution of matter in thermal equilibrium filling the surrounding space, or it is not in equilibrium and is continually streaming off into space, or being built up, although perhaps at a very slow rate.

Now, it is a fact that certain absorption lines in stellar spectra point toward the existence of diffuse matter scattered throughout space, consisting largely of atoms of sodium and calcium, to the extent of something like 10^{-24} g or 20,000 molecules per cubic meter. The density of an atmosphere that would be in equilibrium with such an interstellar gas can be estimated and turns out to be consistent with the observed densities. On the other hand, a serious difficulty is presented for such a hypothesis by the enormous variation in the observed *composition* of planetary atmospheres, for on the outer planets prominent atmospheric constituents are ammonia and methane,* which are not found in measurable amounts on the earth.

In view of this latter fact it seems most likely that the atmospheres of the planets are only in pseudo-equilibrium; it is usually supposed that they are continually leaking away into space but that the rate of this leakage is so slow that the loss even during cosmological ages is not large. An exact calculation of the rate of escape from an atmosphere into empty space would require a knowledge of conditions in its uppermost layers, and these conditions are hard to determine theoretically because of the extremely long paths that occur there.

We can probably obtain a sufficiently accurate estimate to reveal the various possibilities, however, if we imagine simply that (1) the upper part of the atmosphere extends in isothermal equilibrium at least up to a certain great height h_0, and (2) above that height the density is so low that collisions may be neglected altogether. The

* Cf. *Science*, **81**, 1 (1935).

reasonableness of assumption (1) is supported by the fact that, as we saw in Sec. 46, a maxwellian distribution of velocities in a force-field is preserved automatically without any help from collisions as the molecules move about in the field. As a matter of fact, a slight extension of the analysis of that section leads to the conclusion that the stream of molecules leaving any level in an upward direction is the same in number as if the upward stream entering the bottom of the isothermal layer simply rose unhindered to higher levels, collisions merely substituting other molecules for the initial ones without producing any other change.

Accordingly, to find the rate of loss to infinity we need only find at what rate molecules start upward from the bottom with speeds exceeding the "speed of escape" from the planet. This speed, which we shall denote by v_c, is so defined that a molecule leaving with speed v_c has barely enough energy to carry it to infinity and leave it at rest there, provided it makes no collision on the way out; its initial kinetic energy $\frac{1}{2}mv_c^2$, therefore, equals the total work that it must do against gravity. Now the gravitational force on a molecule of mass m can be written mgr_0^2/r^2, where r denotes distance from the center of the planet, r_0 the radius of the planet, and g the acceleration due to gravity at its surface, the force thus reducing at the surface to mg. The work done in escaping is, accordingly, $\int_{r_0}^{\infty} (mgr_0^2/r^2)dr = mgr_0$; hence $\frac{1}{2}mv_c^2 = mgr_0$ and

$$v_c^2 = 2gr_0.$$

On the other hand, by (71b) the number of molecules leaving unit area with an upward component of velocity and with speeds above v_c is

$$\frac{2n}{\sqrt{\pi}} \beta^3 \int_{v_c}^{\infty} v^3 e^{-\beta^2 v^2} \, dv \int_0^{\pi/2} \sin \theta \cos \theta \, d\theta = \frac{n}{2\beta\sqrt{\pi}} (\beta^2 v_c^2 + 1)e^{-\beta^2 v_c^2}.$$

It is convenient to divide this number by n and thereby obtain the rate of loss expressed in terms of centimeters of thickness of the gas, a form of statement that is independent of the density. Introducing $v_c^2 = 2gr_0$ as just found, $\beta^2 = M/2R_M T$ from (56) in Sec. 28 in terms of the molecular weight M, $R_M = 83.15 \times 10^6$ and the absolute temperature T, we find finally for the rate of loss, in centimeters of the gas at the bottom of the isothermal layer lost per second,

$$\frac{1}{\sqrt{2\pi}}\left(\frac{R_M T}{M}\right)^{1/2}\left(1 + \frac{gr_0 M}{R_M T}\right)e^{-\frac{gr_0 M}{R_M T}}.$$

In a mixed atmosphere this formula will obviously apply to each kind of molecule separately. As a final result it is perhaps most illuminating to calculate the temperature at which a given depth of gas would be lost from various bodies of the solar system or from the sun itself during a period of time that is cosmically long. The following table shows a few absolute temperatures, calculated in this way, at which a kilometer of various kinds of gas would be lost in 10 billion (10^{10}) years, which is several times the age of the oldest known rocks on the earth's surface. The rate of loss is naturally very sensitive to the temperature; a change of only 10 to 20 per cent in the latter would suffice to change the time of loss either to 10^7 or to 10^{12} years, or to make the removed layer, say, 10 km in thickness. For different gases the temperatures are proportional to the molecular weight.

	H_2	He	H_2O	N_2	Electrons
Earth......................	350°	694°	3130°	4860°	
Moon......................	16°	32°	145°	225°	
Mars......................	70°	140°	630°	980°	
Sun........................	....	....	.....	.....	978,000°

In using this table it must be remembered that the temperatures refer to the stratosphere or to an equivalent isothermal layer in the upper part of the atmosphere. So understood, it is clear from the table that according to our estimate the earth ought now to be holding all gases; in the past when it was molten it should probably have lost hydrogen and helium. Perhaps the free helium now in the atmosphere has been produced subsequently as a consequence of radioactivity.

The case of the moon is less clear, however. Since its illuminated side is observed to reach a temperature of well over 300°K, it can probably hold nothing, and this conclusion agrees well with the entire absence of any detectable atmosphere on the moon; but whether it might be able to hold a layer of nitrogen or heavier gases of sufficient thickness to develop a stratosphere at a temperature considerably below that of the surface is a question not capable of offhand decision. Perhaps such gases were all lost long ago when the moon was hot.

Mars should now be retaining water vapor, in agreement with the fact that, according to its temperature as calculated from thermopile observations of its radiation, the polar caps can scarcely consist of anything other than ordinary snow. Perhaps nitrogen and heavier gases were lost when the planet was molten, but in that case the water vapor must have been evolved from the interior during the later stages of cooling.   Finally, not even the sun at 5500°C or higher can retain electrons by means of gravitational attraction; they may, of course, be retained by the attraction of a positive charge, but there is some reason to think that electrons are actually being emitted freely from the sun.

All of the other known facts concerning planetary atmospheres are in similarly good agreement with the view here described.

50. The General Distribution Function.   In discussing above the distribution of a gas in a force-field we considered only the state of equilibrium.   More general cases were dealt with in the last chapter, but the distribution function was assumed to be the same throughout the gas.   At this point it will be convenient to take up Boltzmann's treatment of the still more general case of a gas that may not be in equilibrium, and in which both the density and the distribution of velocities may vary from point to point.

We shall assume, however, that this variation is slow enough so that in any macroscopically small element of volume the molecular distribution can be treated as practically uniform and as possessing the property called molecular chaos.   Usually the number of molecules in any such element is assumed to be large, but this condition can be dropped provided we interpret the distribution as referring to averages taken over a molecularly long but macroscopically short interval of time, an interpretation which will not invalidate any of the conclusions that we shall reach.

Such a distribution can be expressed by writing for the number of molecules per unit volume $n(x, y, z, t)$ and for the (fractional) distribution function $f(x, y, z, v_x, v_y, v_z, t)$; the product nf has then the significance that

$$nf \, dx \, dy \, dz \, dv_x \, dv_y \, dv_z$$

is the number of molecules lying in the spatial element $dx \, dy \, dz$ and also having velocities in the range $dv_x \, dv_y \, dv_z$, so that nf can be regarded as a distribution function for position and velocity taken together.

51. Differential Equation for the Distribution Function.   As a general foundation for statistical calculations, let us now seek an expression for the variation of nf with time, as represented by $\dfrac{\partial(nf)}{\partial t}$, to replace the expression obtained in the last chapter for the variation of f alone.   We shall do this only for a homogeneous gas, but the resulting equation will then hold also in a gas composed of different kinds of molecules for each constituent separately.   For generality we shall also allow external forces to be acting; the external force **F**

on each molecule will be allowed to be a function of both its position and its velocity, but we shall assume that this function is the same for all molecules of a given kind. In actual cases the force upon a molecule moving with given velocity usually is also sensibly constant over any region that is macroscopically small, as when electric or magnetic fields are applied to a gas, and such regions can usually be taken large enough to include many molecules; but even if the density is too low for this condition to be satisfied, the theory developed below can be shown to apply provided we interpret nf as representing an average over a macroscopically small interval of time.

To find the rate of variation of nf with time, we select for study those molecules that simultaneously have their centers in an element

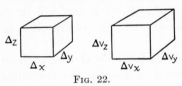

Fig. 22.

$\Delta x \, \Delta y \, \Delta z$ drawn about any point (x, y, z) in space and their velocities in an element $\Delta v_x \, \Delta v_y \, \Delta v_z$ drawn about any point (v_x, v_y, v_z) in velocity space. There will obviously be, to the first order of small quantities, $nf \, \Delta x \, \Delta y \, \Delta z$ $\Delta v_x \, \Delta v_y \, \Delta v_z$ of these molecules, and their number will change at the rate of

$$\frac{\partial}{\partial t} \, (nf) \, \Delta x \, \Delta y \, \Delta z \, \Delta v_x \, \Delta v_y \, \Delta v_z \tag{83}$$

molecules per second, both nf and its derivatives having here their values at the six-dimensional point (x, y, z, v_x, v_y, v_z) and at time t.

Such a change in the number can occur, however, only through passage of molecules across the boundary of one of the elements. Let us calculate the change produced in this way; and let us first consider the effect of molecules that cross those two faces of the element $\Delta x \, \Delta y \, \Delta z$ which are perpendicular to the x-axis (cf. Fig. 22). The space density of molecules with velocities in the range $\Delta v_x \, \Delta v_y \, \Delta v_z$ is $nf \, \Delta v_x \, \Delta v_y \, \Delta v_z$. Hence, by an argument such as we have used several times before, the number of molecules with these velocities that enter the space element per second by crossing the left-hand face in the direction toward $+x$ is $\Delta v_x \, \Delta v_y \, \Delta v_z \iint nf \, v_x \, dy \, dz$ integrated over the face; and a similar expression for the right-hand face gives the rate at which molecules leave the element by crossing that face. The difference between these two expressions then gives the net gain of molecules in the element due to passage over these two faces; it can be written in the following way as a single integral, v_x having the same nearly constant value over both faces:

$$\Delta v_x \, \Delta v_y \, \Delta v_z \, v_x \!\! \int \!\! \int [(nf)_l - (nf)_r] \, dy \, dz, \qquad (84a)$$

the integral extending over Δy and Δz. Here $[(nf)_l - (nf)_r]$ stands for the difference between values of nf at two points having the same values of y and z and located on the left and right faces, respectively; by the "mean-value theorem" we can replace it by $-\Delta x \left[\dfrac{\partial (nf)}{\partial x} \right]_1$ where $\left[\dfrac{\partial (nf)}{\partial x} \right]_1$ is the value of $\dfrac{\partial (nf)}{\partial x}$ at some intermediate point on the line joining the two points on the faces. This value of the derivative, however, becomes indistinguishable from its value at the fixed point (x, y, z, v_x, v_y, v_z) in the limit as we make both of our elements indefinitely small; so we may as well insert the latter value in place of it at once. The integrand is then independent of y and z, and if we put all constant factors in front of the integral sign we have as an integral simply $\int \int dy \, dz$, which equals $\Delta y \, \Delta z$. Expression (84a) for the net gain of molecules thus becomes

$$- v_x \frac{\partial (nf)}{\partial x} \, \Delta x \, \Delta y \, \Delta z \, \Delta v_x \, \Delta v_y \, \Delta v_z. \qquad (84b)$$

The other two pairs of faces yield similarly

$$-\left[v_y \frac{\partial (nf)}{\partial y} + v_z \frac{\partial (nf)}{\partial z} \right] \Delta x \, \Delta y \, \Delta z \, \Delta v_x \, \Delta v_y \, \Delta v_z. \qquad (84c)$$

Now the crossing of a face of the element $\Delta x \, \Delta y \, \Delta z$ by a molecule involves no change in its position in *velocity space*. Accordingly, the molecules just considered remain in that element in velocity space in which they lay to begin with. The expressions just obtained represent, therefore, contributions to the net gain in the number of those molecules that lie simultaneously in both elements.

On the other hand, molecules lying in the space element $\Delta x \, \Delta y \, \Delta z$ may, without leaving this element, cross the faces of the velocity element $\Delta v_x \, \Delta v_y \, \Delta v_z$ through experiencing a change in their velocities. The force $\mathbf{F}$ causes the vector velocity of each molecule to change continually at a rate equal to the acceleration $\mathbf{F}/m$ and so causes the representative point to move through velocity space at a velocity equal to $\mathbf{F}/m$. The resulting net inflow of molecules lying in $\Delta x \, \Delta y \, \Delta z$, into the element $\Delta v_x \, \Delta v_y \, \Delta v_z$, across those two of its faces which are perpendicular to v_x can, therefore, be written, in close analogy with (84a) and (84b),

$$\Delta x \, \Delta y \, \Delta z \int \int \frac{1}{m} \left[(F_x \, nf)_l - (F_x \, nf)_r \right] dv_y \, dv_z,$$

the integral extending over Δv_y and Δv_z, or

$$-\frac{1}{m} \frac{\partial (F_x \, nf)}{\partial v_x} \Delta x \, \Delta y \, \Delta z \, \Delta v_x \, \Delta v_y \, \Delta v_z; \tag{85a}$$

F_x must follow the sign of differentiation here unless we know that it is independent of v_x. The other two pairs of faces of the element $\Delta v_x \, \Delta v_y \, \Delta v_z$ yield similarly

$$-\frac{1}{m} \left[\frac{\partial (F_y \, nf)}{\partial v_y} + \frac{\partial (F_z \, nf)}{\partial v_z} \right] \Delta x \, \Delta y \, \Delta z \, \Delta v_x \, \Delta v_y \, \Delta v_z. \tag{85b}$$

In addition to the effect of the external force **F,** there remains then finally the effect of collisions. As molecules in $\Delta x \, \Delta y \, \Delta z$ and $\Delta v_x \, \Delta v_y \, \Delta v_z$ collide with others, they are thrown entirely out of the velocity element $\Delta v_x \, \Delta v_y \, \Delta v_z$, and at the same time other molecules in $\Delta x \, \Delta y \, \Delta z$ undergo collisions of the inverse type and are thereby thrown *into* the given velocity element. This is the same effect of collisions that was studied in detail for a particular type of molecule in the last chapter. Instead of attempting a similar analysis here, we shall simply write down a symbolic expression to denote the contribution of collisions to the rate of change of the number of those molecules that lie in both elements, writing for it

$$\Delta x \, \Delta y \, \Delta z \, \Delta v_x \, \Delta v_y \, \Delta v_z \left[\frac{\partial (nf)}{\partial t} \right]_{\text{coll}}. \tag{86}$$

If no association or dissociation of the molecules occurs, so that n is unaffected by collisions, we can also write this in the form

$$n \, \Delta x \, \Delta y \, \Delta z \, \Delta v_x \, \Delta v_y \, \Delta v_z \left(\frac{\partial f}{\partial t} \right)_{\text{coll}};$$

and if the molecules are hard spheres $(\partial f / \partial t)_{\text{coll}}$ has then the value given for $\partial f / \partial t$ in eq. (43) or by an expression similar to (42a) and (42b) in the case of a mixed gas. We shall employ here the more general form in order that our final equation may hold also in the case of a dissociating gas.

We may now add up all of the expressions (84b), (84c), (85a), (85b), and (86), thereby obtaining the total change in the number of molecules due to all causes, and then equate their sum to (83) above. After canceling out $\Delta x \, \Delta y \, \Delta z \, \Delta v_x \, \Delta v_y \, \Delta v_z$ on both sides of the resulting equation and moving all terms but one into the left member, we thus obtain

$$\frac{\partial}{\partial t}(nf) + v_x \frac{\partial(nf)}{\partial x} + v_y \frac{\partial(nf)}{\partial y} + v_z \frac{\partial(nf)}{\partial z}$$

$$+ \frac{1}{m}\left[\frac{\partial}{\partial v_x}(F_x nf) + \frac{\partial}{\partial v_y}(F_y nf) + \frac{\partial}{\partial v_z}(F_z nf) \right] = \left[\frac{\partial(nf)}{\partial t} \right]_{\text{coll}}. \quad (87)$$

52. Applications of the Differential Equation. In eq. (87) we have a differential equation for the general distribution function nf in a homogeneous gas or for the distribution function of each constituent of a mixed one; as remarked above, it holds even for each constituent of a dissociated gas. The equation has a number of uses.

In all practical cases, however, it can be simplified somewhat because F_x is independent of v_x, F_y of v_y, and F_z of v_z; for this reason the force term is usually written

$$\frac{1}{m}\left[F_x \frac{\partial}{\partial v_x}(nf) + F_y \frac{\partial}{\partial v_y}(nf) + F_z \frac{\partial}{\partial v_z}(nf) \right].$$

Furthermore, the external force is usually either derivable from a potential or gyroscopic in character, or a combination of these two types; as a general expression for such forces we can write

$$F_x = -\frac{\partial \omega}{\partial x} + \gamma_z v_y - \gamma_y v_z$$

$$F_y = -\frac{\partial \omega}{\partial y} + \gamma_x v_z - \gamma_z v_x$$

$$F_z = -\frac{\partial \omega}{\partial z} + \gamma_y v_x - \gamma_x v_y$$

where $\omega(x, y, z, t)$ is the potential energy of a molecule in the external field, which may perhaps vary with the time, and γ_x, γ_y, γ_z are components of a vector $\boldsymbol{\gamma}$ which may likewise be a function of position in the field, and perhaps also of the time.

Examples of the potential type of force have already been encountered in considering a stationary gas in a gravitational field. An example of forces of gyroscopic character is furnished by a group of ions in a magnetic field; if e is the charge on each ion in electrostatic units and $\mathbf{H}$ the vector magnetic intensity, then $\boldsymbol{\gamma} = e\mathbf{H}/c$.[*] Another example is encountered if we employ a rotating frame of reference, such as a frame rotating with the earth; the effect of such a

---

[*] Cf. L. Page and Adams, "Principles of Electricity," p. 244.

rotation with uniform vector angular velocity **w**, when without it
$\gamma = 0$, can be allowed for simply by adding a term $-\frac{1}{2} mw^2s^2$ in ω
and setting $\gamma = 2m\mathbf{w}$, m being the mass of the molecule and s its
perpendicular distance from the axis of rotation.* In the case of
the earth the term $-\frac{1}{2}mw^2s^2$ simulates a slight change in the potential
energy due to gravity, and its effect is automatically included in the
ordinary "acceleration due to gravity" g.

Problems. 1. Show that when the forces are derivable from
a potential or else are partly or wholly gyroscopic in character (i.e.,
of the form written for F_x, F_y, F_z just above) the steady distribution
function

$$nf = Be^{-\frac{\omega}{kT} - \frac{mv^2}{2kT}} \tag{88}$$

is a solution of (87), the collision term vanishing by the argument
given in the last chapter and the terms that contain derivatives with
respect to x, y, z, v_x, v_y, v_z canceling out; B is a constant such that
$\iiint\!\!\iiint nf\, dx\, dy\, dz\, dv_x\, dv_y\, dv_z = N$, the total number of molecules, and kT is just another arbitrary constant so far as the differential
equation is concerned but can be shown to have its usual physical
significance, k being the Boltzmann constant and T the absolute
temperature.

Equation (88) contains as a special case eq. (79b) and leads also
at once to the conclusion reached in Sec. 46 that Maxwell's law holds
even in a force-field along with uniformity of the temperature [cf. eq.
(55) in Sec. 28]; here we have established the result for the more
general type of force-field described above. As a particular example,
we may draw the important conclusion that the presence of a magnetic
field does not affect the equilibrium in space of ions or electrons, nor
their maxwellian distribution of velocity, in spite of the resulting
curvature of their paths.

2. Show that a gas can rotate as a rigid body with Maxwell's
law holding at every point (velocities being defined in terms of stationary axes), provided the density is proportional to $e^{mw^2s^2/2kT}$,
where w = angular velocity and s = distance from the axis of rotation.

THE BOLTZMANN DISTRIBUTION FORMULA

53. The Classical Boltzmann Distribution Formula. Our treatment
of the distribution function in the last section was restricted in scope
in two ways. For one thing, we treated the molecules as if they were

* Cf. H. LAMB, "Dynamics," p. 88. or other books on analytical mechanics.

mass points, ignoring their internal motions. Then in the second place we also restricted the forces to be of the nature of a force-field. The mutual interaction between molecules, however, cannot be regarded as a force-field, for the force exerted by one molecule on another varies not only with the position and internal condition of the molecule acted on but also with the position of the other molecule. Accordingly, we have been able hitherto to introduce such interaction only in the special form of occasional collisions between extremely small molecules, a restriction which does not correspond to the true situation in gases of appreciable density.

A treatment in which both of these restrictions are removed can be profitably developed only by means of the methods of statistical mechanics, and the fundamental basis for such a treatment will duly appear in Chap. IX below. The principal results there obtained are so simple and so useful, however, that it is convenient to cite them here and to proceed hereafter to make free use of them. The reader who prefers a strictly logical order can readily secure it by reading alternately in Chap. IX and in the present chapter. The rest of the book can be understood, however, without reading Chaps. IX and X at all.

In order to state conveniently the statistical results just mentioned we need to have in mind the language used in general dynamical theory, which is explained in books on analytical mechanics. Each molecule can be described by means of a certain number of variables called coordinates, which we shall denote by q_1, q_2, $q_3 \cdot \cdot \cdot q_s$; their number is often called the number of degrees of freedom of the molecule. Corresponding to these coordinates there are then s other variables called generalized momenta, which we shall denote by p_1, p_2, $\cdot \cdot \cdot p_s$. The three coordinates of the center of mass can be taken as three of the q's, the corresponding p's being the components of the ordinary momentum; then, in general, the three Eulerian angles representing the orientation of the molecule constitute three more; and there may be any number of others representing different possible modes of internal vibration. It is often useful to think of the q's and p's as cartesian coordinates in a space of $2s$ dimensions.

Now consider, first, the case of a *homogeneous* rarefied gas in which, as hitherto assumed, molecular interaction occurs for each molecule only during a very small part of the time. In such a gas, when it is in thermal equilibrium at an absolute temperature T, statistical mechanics tells us that at any given moment the fraction of the molecules that have the coordinate q_1 lying between a given value q_1 and $q_1 + dq_1$, q_2 similarly in a range dq_2, and so on through the p's, is $P\, dq_1\, dq_2\, \cdots\, dq_s\, dp_1\, dp_2\, \cdots\, dp_s$, where

$$P = C_1 e^{-\frac{\epsilon}{kT}}, \qquad C_1 = \left[\int e^{-\frac{\epsilon}{kT}}\, dq_1\, \cdots\, dq_s\, dp_1\, \cdots\, dp_s \right]^{-1}. \quad (89a)$$

Here ϵ is the energy of the molecule when its variables have the values stated, k is the Boltzmann constant, and the integral in the expression given for the constant C_1 is to be extended over all possible values of all of the variables so as to make

$$\int P\, dq_1\, dq_2\, \cdots\, dq_s\, dp_1\, dp_2\, \cdots\, dp_s = 1.$$

[Cf. eq. (249c, e) in Sec. 199 below]. Or, fixing our attention upon a particular molecule, we can interpret $P\, dq_1\, \cdots\, dp_s$ as the probability that any given molecule is, at a given moment, in the condition specified, or the fraction of the time during which it is. The energy ϵ may include a term ω representing potential energy of the molecule as a whole in an external fixed force-field; and this field may include gyroscopic terms of the sort described in the last section, these being without influence on the probability.

When the gas is *not homogeneous*, a formula like (89a) exists for each kind of molecule separately, containing a common T but, in general, different values of C_1.

When, on the other hand, *interaction* between the molecules extends beyond the occurrence of almost instantaneous collisions, this formula no longer holds, at least not accurately. Then, however, we can fall back on a still more general conclusion from statistical mechanics. Let us number off in a single series all of the Ns coordinates of all the N molecules in the gas, denoting them by $q_1, \cdots q_{Ns}$, and the momenta similarly: $p_1, \cdots p_{Ns}$. Then we can suppose that, while it is in thermal equilibrium at absolute temperature T, the whole gas spends a fraction $P\, dq_1\, dq_2\, \cdots\, dq_{Ns}\, dp_1\, dp_2\, \cdots\, dp_{Ns}$ of its time, or has a probability of that magnitude of being found with its variables lying in the ranges specified, where

$$P = C_2 e^{-\frac{E}{kT}}, \qquad C_2 = \left[\int e^{-\frac{E}{kT}}\, dq_1\, \cdots\, dq_{Ns}\, dp_1\, \cdots\, dp_{Ns} \right]^{-1}, \quad (89b)$$

E being now the energy of the whole gas. [Cf. eq. (254) in Sec. 207.] If the gas is in contact with other much larger bodies so that its energy can fluctuate a little, it actually does what we here suppose it to do; if, on the other hand, the gas is isolated and its energy is therefore constant, it does not really behave in this manner, but calculations based upon the assumption that it does will nevertheless lead to correct physical results; for the physical behavior of a gas in equilibrium does not depend, either in theory or in observation, upon the nature of its surroundings.

Equation (89a) is coming to be known as the *Boltzmann (distribution) formula* and is of extremely wide usefulness. Equation (89b) expresses what Gibbs called a *canonical distribution in phase*, but it can obviously be regarded simply as an extension of the Boltzmann formula to the whole gas (the physical reason for the validity of the formula is of the same sort in either case). The canonical distribution can be shown to lead to the ordinary Boltzmann formula as a corollary in any case to which the latter formula is applicable.

54. The Boltzmann Formula in Quantum Theory. We must next note the modifications that are required in these principles when quantum theory is substituted for classical mechanics. According to quantum mechanics the description of a system in terms of q's and p's is only an approximate method whose usefulness is limited to cases of sufficiently high energy; the fundamental mode of description is quite different. The general quantum theory of gases will be taken up in Chap. X, but only a few simple details are needed here; they can easily be understood without ever reading that chapter.

In dealing with a system in thermal equilibrium we can speak as if it were always in some one of a definite series of possible quantum states (disregarding the fine question whether it really is in a single state); to each quantum state there corresponds a certain value of the energy. Each of these quantum states then takes the place, for statistical purposes, of a certain region in the classical q, p space of the system. By a "quantum state" without further qualification we shall always mean, as here, one of the complete fundamental series of stationary states for the molecule. When several of these states have the same energy, however, they are often grouped into a single *multiple* "state"; the number of fundamental states composing the multiple one is then called its *multiplicity* or *statistical weight*.

The Canonical Distribution. The principle of the canonical distribution now takes the following form. The probability that the whole system is in quantum state i with energy E_i can be assumed to be

$$P_i = Ce^{-\frac{E_i}{kT}}, \qquad C = \left[\sum_i e^{-\frac{E_i}{kT}} \right]^{-1},$$

the summation in the expression for C extending over all quantum states that are possible for the system. [Cf. eq. (272) in Sec. 226.]

The resolution of a gas into molecules, on the other hand, is a more ticklish matter in quantum than in classical theory. It turns out, however, that in nearly all practical cases the use of quantum theory is essential only as regards the internal condition of the molecules, including their motions of rotation, and that a hybrid theory in which classical methods are employed for the translatory motion is quite accurate enough (cf. Sec. 241). Using this form of theory, we suppose each molecule to be in a certain internal quantum state while moving as a whole with a certain momentum; and, under the conditions under which this theory is approximately valid, it appears that the Boltzmann distribution holds in the limiting case of a perfect gas in the following form.

General Distribution Formula. The fraction of the molecules that at a given moment are in molecular quantum state j and also have the cartesian coordinates and momenta of their centers of mass in certain ranges dx, dy, dz, dp_x, dp_y, dp_z (or lie in the element $dx\,dy\,dz\,dp_x\,dp_y\,dp_z$ of molecular phase space) is $P_{jm}\,dx\,dy\,dz\,dp_x\,dp_y\,dp_z$ where

$$P_{jm} = C e^{-\frac{\epsilon}{kT}}; \tag{90}$$

here ϵ is the total energy of the molecule and the constant C has the value

$$C = \left[\sum_j \int e^{-\frac{\epsilon}{kT}}\, dx\,dy\,dz\,dp_x\,dp_y\,dp_z \right]^{-1}$$

integrated over the volume of the vessel and over all possible values of p_x, p_y, p_z and summed over all of the internal quantum states. We can also write for the energy

$$\epsilon = \zeta + \omega + \eta_j, \tag{91}$$

where ζ represents the kinetic energy of the center of mass, so that

$$\zeta = \frac{1}{2}\,mv^2 = \frac{p_x^2 + p_y^2 + p_z^2}{2m},$$

whereas ω is the potential energy of the molecule as a whole in whatever fixed force-field may be present and η_j is the internal energy corresponding to the jth quantum state. The force-field may include gyroscopic terms of the type described in Sec. 52. This principle has been shown to hold well whenever the scale of variation of ω is large relative to the molecular wave length $\lambda = h/p$.

In a mixed gas there will be a separate formula like (90) for each kind of molecule, T being the same in all but usually not C. These formulas are valid for actual gases only at low density, of course; even the division of the energy into parts as in (91) tends to fail at higher densities.

55. Special Cases of the Boltzmann Formula. All of the distribution functions obtained previously and many others are included in the Boltzmann formula as special cases, and this fact gives them a basis independent of the special analyses of molecular processes by which we originally obtained them. It will be convenient to collect here some formulas for the principal cases that can arise.

Distribution of Centers of Mass. Suppose that we are interested only in the translatory motion of the molecules. Then, disregarding all internal features and summing P_{jm} as given by (90) over all of the internal quantum states with the energy split up as in (91), we obtain as the fraction of the molecules with their centers of mass in the range $dx\,dy\,dz\,dp_x\,dp_y\,dp_z$ the value $P_m\,dx\,dy\,dz\,dp_x\,dp_y\,dp_z$, where

$$P_m = \sum_j P_{jm} = C_m e^{-\frac{\zeta+\omega}{kT}} \tag{92}$$

C_m being a new constant of magnitude $C\sum_j e^{-\frac{\eta_j}{kT}}$. Since $p_x = mv_x$, $p_y = mv_y$, $p_z = mv_z$, we see that $dx\,dy\,dz\,dp_x\,dp_y\,dp_z = m^3\,dx\,dy\,dz\,dv_x\,dv_y\,dv_z$ in the notation of Sec. 50, so that $f = m^3 P_m$. Accordingly, ζ being also equal to $mv^2/2$, the value of P_m just found leads at once to eq. (88) and so also, among other things, to Maxwell's law.

Distribution in Position Alone. If we are interested, not in the velocities or momenta, but only in the positions of the molecules, we can also integrate P_m over momentum space and so obtain as the total number of molecules in the element $dx\,dy\,dz$ of space the number $P_{mq}\,dx\,dy\,dz$ where P_{mq}, the total distribution function for spatial position, is

$$P_{mq} = C_q e^{-\frac{\omega}{kT}}, \tag{92a}$$

C_q being a new constant standing for $C_m \iiint e^{-\frac{\zeta}{kT}}\,dp_x\,dp_y\,dp_z$.

Molecules in a Particular Internal State. Sometimes, viewing the situation in greater detail, we wish to select for consideration only those molecules that happen to be in a particular internal quantum state. According to (90) and (91), of all the molecules in state j, the fraction $P_m^{(j)} \, dx \, dy \, dz \, dp_x \, dp_y \, dp_z$ will have their centers of mass in the range here specified where

$$P_m^{(j)} = \frac{Ce^{-\frac{\zeta + \omega + \eta_j}{kT}}}{\int Ce^{-\frac{\zeta + \omega + \eta_j}{kT}} \, dx \, dy \, dz \, dp_x \, dp_y \, dp_z},$$

the denominator representing the total fraction which molecules in state j form of the whole number and serving to make $\int P_m^{(j)} \, dx \cdots dp_z = 1$, or, after canceling the η_j factor,

$$P_m^{(j)} = C'e^{-\frac{\zeta + \omega}{kT}}, \qquad C' = \left[\int e^{-\frac{\zeta + \omega}{kT}} \, dx \, dy \, dz \, dp_x \, dp_y \, dp_z \right]^{-1}.$$

Molecules with Definite Position and Velocity. Reversing our choice we might select those molecules in a given range $dx \, dy \, dz \, dp_x \, dp_y \, dp_z$ of translational phase space and ask for their internal distribution. The fraction of them that are in state j is

$$P_j^{(m)} = \frac{Ce^{-(\zeta + \omega + \eta_j)/kT} \, dx \cdots dp_z}{\sum_j Ce^{-(\zeta + \omega + \eta_j)/kT} \, dx \cdots dp_z} = \frac{e^{-\eta_j/kT}}{\sum_j e^{-\eta_j/kT}}. \qquad (93a)$$

Since $P_m^{(j)}$ is independent of the quantum state and $P_j^{(m)}$ of the spatial motion, we see that the distributions of the molecules in space, in velocity, and in internal condition are quite *independent* of each other.

General Internal Distribution. It follows also that the fraction of all the molecules in the gas that are in state j is the same as $P_j^{(m)}$ and so can be written, for future reference,

$$P_j = \frac{e^{-\eta_j/kT}}{\sum_j e^{-\eta_j/kT}}. \qquad (93b)$$

If multiple quantum states are employed, with multiplicities w_n and energies η_κ, we have from (93a) or (93b) for their probability

$$P_\kappa = P_\kappa^{(m)} = \frac{w_\kappa e^{-\eta_\kappa/kT}}{\sum_\kappa w_\kappa e^{-\eta_\kappa/kT}}, \qquad (93c)$$

the multiple states being numbered here in order and the indicated summation extending over all of them.

Molecules with Interaction. For further use we may mention a special result that can readily be obtained in the classical case from the canonical distribution and constitutes a sort of extension of the Boltzmann distribution law to the relative positions of the molecules. Suppose each molecule is surrounded by a force-field so that when another comes near it the two possess a mutual potential energy ω_{12}, depending upon the relative positions of their centers of mass. Then if we fix our attention on two particular molecules and assume the first to be in some definite position, the chance that the second is at the same time in a given element of volume $dx\,dy\,dz$ or $d\tau_2$ near the first is proportional to

$$e^{-\frac{\omega_{12}}{kT}}\,d\tau_2; \tag{94a}$$

or, under the same conditions, the chance that of *two* other molecules one is in an element $d\tau_2$ and the other in a second element $d\tau_3$ is proportional to

$$e^{-\frac{\omega_{12}+\omega_{13}+\omega_{23}}{kT}}\,d\tau_2\,d\tau_3, \tag{94b}$$

and so on. Here ω_{ij} stands in general for the mutual potential energy of molecules i and j. In all such cases the distribution in velocity is independent of the distribution in position.

These latter results are obtained readily from (89b) by fixing the variables of all the other molecules than those under consideration, and also the velocities of the latter, and noting that then ω_{12} or $\omega_{12} + \omega_{13} + \omega_{23}$ is the only variable part of the total energy E and $d\tau$ or $d\tau_2\,d\tau_3$ are the only variable differential ranges.

Problem. The ordinary states of the *sodium atom* are multiple; for the normal or lowest (a $^2S_{\frac{1}{2}}$ state) $w = 2$, whereas for the next higher or first excited state, jumps out of which into the normal state result in emission of the familiar D lines, $w = 6$ ($^2P_{\frac{1}{2}}$ plus $^2P_{\frac{3}{2}}$). The two states lie $h\nu_D = 3.37 \times 10^{-12}$ erg apart. If a little sodium is introduced into a Bunsen flame at 1800°C and if thermal equilibrium may be assumed to occur, what fraction of the sodium atoms are excited? (All higher excited states may be neglected. *Ans.:* One atom in 4.3×10^4.)

FREE PATHS AND COLLISIONS

56. Molecules of Finite Size. Up to this point in the present chapter we have been considering aspects of the molecular motion in which the finite size of the molecules is merely a disturbing feature, one which has to be made negligible by assuming their size to be extremely small; these phenomena would not, therefore, be altered if we imagined the molecular diameters to decrease further toward zero.   There are other features of the motion, however, which depend directly upon molecular size, and it will be useful to turn now to some of these, particularly in preparation for the treatment presently to be given of transport phenomena.

The molecules will still be assumed small in comparison with their average distance apart, but no longer vanishingly small.   The results that we shall obtain will thus be accurate only in the limit of vanishing density, but, of course, they will apply approximately also to cases of sufficiently low but finite density, and consequently a theory strictly valid for zero density constitutes a valuable first approximation to the correct theory for an actual gas.

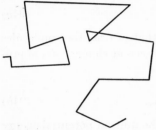

FIG. 23.—Path of a molecule.

Except as otherwise specified, we shall in the rest of this chapter make the further simplifying assumption that the molecules are entirely free from mutual force-action, except when they are very close together.   We shall call molecules of this sort *small-field* molecules.   The existence of a finite limited region in which the molecular field is effective is more or less equivalent to the molecule's having a certain size or diameter; and, of course, the requirement would be met if the molecules were in reality small elastic solid bodies free from force except when in contact.

57. The Mean Free Path and Collision Rate.   The path of the center of mass of a small-field molecule must be an irregular zigzag having at each corner a collision with another molecule and consisting of straight free paths between these (Fig. 23).   The individual lengths of these free paths will vary widely; if, however, we follow the molecule until it has traversed a great many free paths, the average of their lengths will have a definite value, which is called the *mean free path* and will be denoted by L.   The collisions will likewise be distributed in time in a very irregular manner, but over a period long enough to include a great many there will be on the average in each second a definite number of them; this number is called the *collision rate* and we shall denote it by Θ.   The mean free path and the collision rate necessarily stand in a simple and important relation to each other.   For in a longish time t the molecule moves a total distance $\bar{v}t$, $\bar{v}$ being its average speed, and this distance is broken up by Θt collisions into free paths of average length L; hence $\bar{v}t = \Theta t L$ and

$$\bar{v} = \Theta L. \tag{95}$$

Both L and Θ may also be regarded as having reference to a group of molecules instead of to a single one, and this other viewpoint is often useful. For it is obvious that if we take the mean value of all the free paths that are executed in a given time by all the molecules in a given volume, we again obtain L, provided the time and the volume are not too small. Similarly, if we select at random a group of molecules containing a huge number N, this group will make collisions to the number of $N\Theta$ per second; for, when N is very large, this rate is sensibly steady, and the total number of collisions made by the group in any time t must obviously be N times the number made by one molecule or $N\Theta t$. The total number of molecular impacts made by n molecules in unit volume is, therefore, $n\Theta$; but the corresponding number of complete collisions, each involving two impacts, is, of course, only $n\Theta/2$.

Up to this point we have ignored the variation in molecular speed. For a given molecule, however, the chance of a collision must vary with its speed, being certainly greater when the molecule is itself moving rapidly than when it is merely standing still and waiting to be struck. In some connections it is necessary to make allowance for this variation, and for this purpose we need to consider separately those molecules that are moving at each particular speed.

Suppose we select just those free paths that are executed by a molecule while it is moving with a speed between v and $v + dv$; let the average of these paths be L_v. Then if t_v denotes the total integrated time during which the molecule so moves, not counting time during which it moves at other speeds, the total distance covered during this time will be vt_v. This distance being assumed to be broken up into paths of average length L_v, the number of collisions that terminate these paths is vt_v/L_v; and if we write $\Theta_v t_v$ for this number, we have

$$v = \Theta_v L_v \qquad (96)$$

in exact analogy to (95).

The quantity Θ_v, the collision rate for a molecule while moving at speed v, can also be thought of in terms of *probability*, and this view of it is perhaps the simplest and most useful one. As a particular molecule moves along, during each short interval of time dt there is a certain chance that it collides with another one. This chance will be proportional to the length of the interval dt; but if molecular chaos exists (cf. Sec. 21 above), the chance cannot vary otherwise so long as v remains the same, since in molecular chaos the position of one molecule has no correlation with the positions or velocities of others. Accordingly, if $P_v \, dt$ denotes the chance of a collision during dt, out of a large number N of molecules moving similarly with speed v the number $NP_v \, dt$ will collide during dt. Let us suppose that, as each molecule of our chosen group collides, we select another moving with the same speed to take its place, thereby keeping the total number constant. Then we can integrate with respect to t, regarding N and P_v as constants, and obtain $\int NP_v \, dt = NP_v t$ for the number that collide in a finite time t. But this is also represented by $N\Theta_v t$, according to the definition of Θ_v. Hence $\Theta_v = P_v$. Thus the collision rate Θ_v at speed v represents the chance per second that a particular molecule collides; it might appropriately be called the *collision probability per unit time*.

Even in a maxwellian gas we shall find that Θ_v and L_v vary somewhat with v and are therefore equal, respectively, to Θ and to L only at one definite speed.

58. Dependence of L and θ upon Density and Temperature. The actual values of the mean free path L and the collision rate Θ for small-field molecules will obviously depend in part upon their shape and size, i.e., upon the character of their force-fields. Without knowing anything more about these fields, however, than is implied in our assumption that they are confined within small limited regions, we can discover the mode of dependence of L and Θ upon density and temperature.

For, in the first place, increasing the *temperature* is equivalent merely to multiplying the velocity of each molecule by a certain uniform factor, the relative distribution of velocities being the same at all temperatures. The collision probability per unit time Θ_v of each molecule thereby becomes multiplied by the same factor as the velocities, and so does the general collision rate Θ. Thus $\Theta \propto \bar{v} \propto \sqrt{T}$. But then, according to (95), the mean free path L is independent of the temperature.

The situation is quite different, however, when we keep the temperature constant and increase the *density*. Then, as a molecule moves along, its chance of meeting another one is increased; if the other molecules were distributed at random, this chance would be exactly proportional to the mean density of the other molecules and the collision rate would accordingly be directly, and the mean free path indirectly, proportional to the density. Now, according to the principle of molecular chaos, the molecules actually are distributed at random, with the single restriction that when they come too close together their fields tend to keep them apart. The effect of this limitation must be to produce a shortening of the mean free path and a corresponding increase in the collision rate; this effect must be large when the molecules are jammed tightly together, as in a liquid or solid, but it must become small as the distances between the molecules are made large as compared with their effective diameters, and it must vanish in the limit of zero density.

Thus we may conclude that in a gas composed of small-field molecules, as this term was defined in the last section, the mean free path varies only with the density and is inversely proportional to it, being, therefore, at a given temperature inversely proportional to the pressure. The collision rate, on the other hand, is directly proportional to the density and also to the square root of the absolute temperature. These conclusions are of fundamental importance.

59. Distribution of Free Paths. Absorption of a Beam. In addition to the mean free path the distribution of the lengths of the individual paths is a matter of interest. The method of finding this distribution is the same as that for dealing with the important problem of the absorption of a beam of molecules or ions in its passage through a gas, hence we shall develop first a general formula applicable to both problems.

For this purpose let us consider a group of similar molecules of any sort that are moving with velocity $\mathbf{v}$ through a region where there is gas. They may have been shot into it from the outside, or, as a special case, they may be a group of molecules of the gas itself which we select for contemplation. As time goes on, these chosen molecules will collide one after the other with molecules of the gas; as each one does this, we shall drop it out of the group under consideration. Let the number originally in the group at time $t = 0$ be N_0, and at time t let N of them still be going without having had a collision. Then during the next interval dt the number $N\Theta_v\, dt$ will collide and drop out of the group, Θ_v denoting the collision rate for a molecule of the group when moving at speed v among molecules composing the gas. N is thereby changed by the amount

$$dN = -N\Theta_v\, dt.$$

If we divide this equation through by N, we can integrate it, Θ_v being a constant as explained above, thus: $dN/N = -\Theta_v\, dt$, hence log $N = -\Theta_v t + \text{const.}$; choosing the constant of integration so as to make $N = N_0$ at $t = 0$, we thus find

$$N = N_0 e^{-\Theta_v t} = N_0 e^{-\Theta_v l/v}, \tag{97a}$$

if we write l for the length vt of free path that has been covered at time t by each molecule from the start. The number of molecules that collide between t and $t + dt$ and so terminate a path whose length lies between l and $l + dl$ is thus

$$|dN| = -dN = N_0 \Theta_v e^{-\Theta_v t}\, dt = N_0 \frac{\Theta_v}{v} e^{-\Theta_v l/v}\, dl. \qquad (97b)$$

These results can be expressed also in the following useful form. Let us write $\varphi(l)$ for the fraction of the original N_0 molecules that are still going after traversing a distance l without collision and $\psi(l)\, dl$ for the fraction of all the free paths that have a length between l and $l + dl$. Then $\varphi = N/N_0$ and $\psi(l)\, dl = |dN|/N_0$, whence from (97a, b), in which we may introduce L_v from (96) in place of Θ_v,

$$\varphi(l) = e^{-\frac{\Theta_v l}{v}} = e^{-\frac{l}{L_v}}, \qquad \psi(l) = \frac{1}{L_v} e^{-\frac{l}{L_v}}. \qquad (98a, b)$$

Both $\varphi(l)$ and $\psi(l)$ are thus exponential in form (cf. Fig. 24).

If we are dealing with a *molecular beam*, φ represents the ratio by which its intensity is diminished after going a distance l, Θ_v and L_v

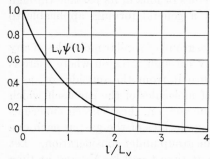

having values appropriate to the motion of a beam molecule through the gas.

On the other hand, to apply these results to *free paths in a gas* we consider a group of molecules that have just collided and are now moving with speed v. Then φ is the fraction of these that go at least a distance l without collision,

Fig. 24.—Distribution of free paths; l = length, L_v = mean length.

and ψ is the distribution function for free paths at speed v, $\psi(l)\, dl$ being the fraction of all of the free paths executed in the gas at speed v whose lengths lie in the range dl. It is obvious from the formulas that very long free paths, while not absent, are comparatively rare, whereas unusually short ones are comparatively common, the single length of maximum frequency being $l = 0$.

In either case the average of all the free paths comes out equal to L_v, as would be expected, for our formula gives (cf. 63a in Sec. 29)

$$\bar{l} = \int_0^\infty l\, \psi(l)\, dl = \frac{1}{L_v} \int_0^\infty l e^{-\frac{l}{L_v}}\, dl = L_v.$$

Problems. **1.** Show that, of the free paths executed by a molecule at speed v, 37 per cent exceed L_v, but only 14 per cent exceed $2L_v$ in length and 0.7 per cent, $5L_v$.

2. Show that in throwing a die the probability that just n throws (i.e., acts of throwing) occur between two successive occurrences of a six (or any other given face number) is $\frac{1}{6}\,(\frac{5}{6})^{n-1}$. Compare this with $\psi(l)$ as given by (98b) with $L_v = 6$, $l = (n - 1)\dfrac{L_v}{6}$. The average number of throws between sixes is, of course, 6.

60. The Mutual Collision Cross Section. The relation between molecular dimensions and collision probabilities is perhaps best approached by way of the conception of a *mutual collision cross section* for any pair of molecules. To define this quantity, suppose we have a beam of molecules all of the same kind, and suppose they are moving with the same speed along parallel paths but are otherwise distributed at random; in this beam let us hold in a fixed position a single molecule, which may be of a different sort. Let all of the molecules be of the small-field type described in Sec. 56. Then a certain fraction of the beam molecules will collide with the fixed one and will be scattered by it out of the beam; if we draw a plane through the fixed molecule perpendicular to the direction of motion of the beam, the molecules that are scattered will be just those whose directions of

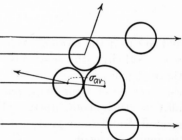

FIG. 25.—Scattering of a molecular beam.

motion pass through a *certain area* on this plane. The magnitude of this area is what is called the mutual collision cross section for a beam molecule and the scattering molecule. We shall denote it by S.

If both of the colliding molecules are hard *elastic spheres*, the area in question is a circle; for, if σ_1, σ_2 are their respective diameters, the distance between centers at the instant of collision will be $\sigma_{av} = \frac{1}{2}\,(\sigma_1 + \sigma_2)$, and obviously the beam molecules that collide will be just those whose paths of approach pass the fixed molecule at a distance less than σ_{av} and so pass through a circle of radius σ_{av} on the plane (cf. Fig. 25). Thus when both molecules are hard spheres

$$S = \pi\sigma_{av}{}^2.$$

If also $\sigma_1 = \sigma_2 = \sigma$,

$$S = \pi\sigma^2$$

or four times the cross-sectional area of one molecule. The sphere of radius σ_{av} is often called the mutual *sphere of influence* for the two molecules.

If the molecules are not elastic spheres but are at least of the *small-field* type, there will still be a definite collision cross section of some magnitude or other.   The chance of a collision may depend now upon the relative orientation of the molecules (being smaller, for instance, for disks when meeting edgewise than when meeting flatwise), but if the beam molecules are oriented according to some definite rule, for example at random, the number scattered will be the same as the number that are incident upon some definite area S, and this area can then be taken as the mean or equivalent cross section.   The final result is thus in any case the same as if the molecules had a certain size, and it is convenient to define a quantity σ_{av} by the equation

$$\sigma_{av} = \left(\frac{S}{\pi}\right)^{\frac{1}{2}}$$

and to call it the *mean diameter* for the pair of colliding molecules, or, more explicitly, the *equivalent elastic-spherical mean diameter;* in case the molecules actually are elastic spheres σ_{av} as so defined is simply the average of their diameters, and in other cases it gives a useful idea of their comparative effectiveness in mutual collisions.   In general, S and σ_{av} may, of course, depend upon the relative speed of the impinging molecule.

The collision cross section obviously has simple and important relationships with *scattering rates* and with *collision frequencies*.   The number of the beam molecules *scattered* per second, if there are n of them in unit volume and they are moving at speed v, will be

$$\Theta_1 = nSv; \tag{99a}$$

for those that collide in a second are those that are contained in a cylinder of cross-sectional area S and length v.

The same collision rate, obviously, would result if we brought the beam molecules to rest and set the scattering molecule itself moving among them at the same speed in the opposite direction, the relative motion being then the same as before.   In doing this we may leave the beam molecules free to recoil when struck and restore the scatterer to its original velocity after each collision, or we may hold the other molecules fixed and let the moving one bounce off each time in some new direction; the collision rate will be the same in either case, since the other molecules are assumed to be distributed at random.   Accordingly Θ_1, as given by (99a), represents also the *collision rate or probability* for a molecule moving with constant speed v among a collection of stationary ones which are all alike and distributed at random, whether these are free to move or are held fixed. The *mean free path* of the moving one among the others is then clearly $L_1 = v/\Theta_1$ or

$$L_1 = \frac{1}{nS}. \qquad (99b)$$

If *several kinds* of stationary molecules are present, we have only to replace (99a, b) by

$$\Theta_1 = v \sum_i n_i S_{1i}, \qquad L_v = \frac{1}{\sum_i n_i S_{1i}}, \qquad (99c)$$

n_i being the density in molecules per cubic centimeter of kind i and S_{1i} the mutual collision cross section for a molecule of this kind colliding with the moving one.

In the special case of hard *elastic spheres* of diameters σ_1 and σ_2 (99a) becomes

$$\Theta_1 = \tfrac{1}{4} n\pi(\sigma_1 + \sigma_2)^2 v. \qquad (99d)$$

If all the molecules involved have also the same diameter σ, Θ_1 and the corresponding mean free path are

$$\Theta_1 = n\pi\sigma^2 v, \qquad L_1 = \frac{1}{n\pi\sigma^2}. \qquad (99e, f)$$

We shall have many uses for these formulas in dealing with molecular collisions.

61. The Mean Free Path in a Constant-speed Gas. The first extensive calculations of the general mean free path in a mass of gas were made by Clausius (about 1857). The law of distribution of velocities being unknown to him, he assumed for definiteness that all the molecules move at the same speed. The analysis required by this case forms a convenient stepping stone toward the treatment of the actual case, and we shall therefore take it up as a preliminary. The molecules will be supposed, as usual, to be of the small-field type as described in Sec. 56.

In order to obtain results of wide applicability, which we can do with almost no increase in labor, let us first calculate the collision rate for a *single molecule* of a certain kind moving among others of a different type which are all moving with the same speed but chaotically as to direction. Let the vector velocity of the first be denoted by $\mathbf{v}_1$ and the constant speed of the others by v_2.

The collision probability per second for the first molecule will be given by eq. (99a) above with v replaced by the average of its speed relative to the other molecules, which we shall denote by $\bar{v}_r$, and can therefore be written

$$\Theta_{12} = nSv_r; \tag{100}$$

here n is the molecular density of the others and S is the mutual collision cross section for the first molecule and one of the others. If this statement is not immediately obvious, it suffices to divide the other molecules into groups according to the value of their speed v_r relative to the first one; then we can add expectations of collision with the various groups and can write for the total expectation of collision during an infinitesimal time dt, in an obvious nota-tion,

FIG. 26.—Relative velocity.

$$\Theta_{12}\, dt = \sum_j n_j Sv_{rj}\, dt = S\sum_j n_j v_{rj}\, dt = Sn\bar{v}_r\, dt.$$

The problem of finding Θ_{12} thus reduces to the calculation of $\bar{v}_r$.

Now, under the conditions assumed, the speed of the first molecule relative to one of the others varies only with the angle between their respective directions of motion; and since the other molecules are moving equally in all directions, a fraction $\frac{1}{2} \sin \theta\, d\theta$ of them [cf. eq. (30) in Sec. 18] will be moving in directions making an angle θ with the direction of $\mathbf{v}_1$. Hence for the average value of the relative speed v_r we have [cf. (63a) in Sec. 29 for the method of averaging]

$$\bar{v}_r = \tfrac{1}{2} \int_0^\pi v_r \sin \theta\, d\theta.$$

But $v_r^2 = v_1^2 + v_2^2 - 2v_1 v_2 \cos \theta$ (cf. Fig. 26).   Hence

$$\begin{aligned}
\bar{v}_r &= \tfrac{1}{2} \int_0^\pi (v_1^2 + v_2^2 - 2v_1 v_2 \cos \theta)^{\frac{1}{2}} \sin \theta\, d\theta \\
&= \frac{1}{6v_1 v_2}(v_1^2 + v_2^2 - 2v_1 v_2 \cos \theta)^{\frac{3}{2}} \Big|_{\theta=0}^{\theta=\pi} \\
&= \frac{1}{6v_1 v_2}[(v_1 + v_2)^3 - |v_1 - v_2|^3].
\end{aligned}$$

Here $|v_1 - v_2|^3$ is written for $(v_1^2 + v_2^2 - 2v_1 v_2)^{\frac{3}{2}} = [(v_1 - v_2)^2]^{\frac{3}{2}}$ instead of $(v_1 - v_2)^3$ because the latter will be negative if $v_2 > v_1$, whereas of the two values of $(v_1^2 + v_2^2 - 2v_1 v_2 \cos \theta)^{\frac{3}{2}}$, one positive and the other negative, we must choose the positive one because this is the one whose derivative contains the positive value of $(v_1^2 + v_2^2 - 2v_1 v_2 \cos \theta)^{\frac{1}{2}}$, which occurs in the integral.   If $v_1 > v_2, |v_1 - v_2| =$

$v_1 - v_2$, whereas if $v_1 < v_2$, $|v_1 - v_2| = v_2 - v_1$; hence we get different results according as v_1 or v_2 is the greater:

$$\bar{v}_r = v_1 + \frac{v_2^2}{3v_1} \qquad \text{if} \qquad v_1 > v_2, \tag{101a}$$

$$\bar{v}_r = v_2 + \frac{v_1^2}{3v_2} \qquad \text{if} \qquad v_1 < v_2. \tag{101b}$$

Insertion of the proper one of these values into (100) gives us the desired collision rate.

To obtain the *special case of the homogeneous gas of Clausius* we then put $v_1 = v_2 = v$, whereupon both values of $\bar{v}_r$ reduce to

$$\bar{v}_r = \tfrac{4}{3} v.$$

Θ_{12} in (100) then also becomes simply the general collision rate Θ for a molecule of the gas.   The mean free path in such a gas is, therefore,

$$L = \frac{v}{\Theta} = \frac{3}{4nS}, \tag{102a}$$

n being now the total number of molecules per unit volume and S their mutual collision cross section.   In case they are all spheres of diameter σ we have $S = \pi\sigma^2$ and

$$L = \frac{3}{4} \frac{1}{n\pi\sigma^2}, \tag{102b}$$

which is Clausius' formula.

Comparing (102a) with (99b), we see that the simultaneous motion of the other molecules has the effect of raising the collision rate, and reducing the mean free path, in the ratio $\tfrac{4}{3}$ or $\tfrac{3}{4}$, respectively, obviously because a given molecule is often struck from the side by others which it would not strike in consequence of its own motion alone.

62. A Molecular Beam in a Maxwellian Gas.   The results just obtained can now be utilized in treating collisions in an actual gas having a maxwellian distribution of velocities.   In order to do this, however, we shall again begin with quite a general case; let us first work out the rate of collision and the mean free path for a molecule that is moving at a definite speed v through a maxwellian gas.   Let the molecules of the gas be all alike but different in kind from the first molecule.   Such generality scarcely increases the labor of arriving at our main goal, and the more general result has an interest of its own.

Out of all the possible collisions of the first or ray molecule with a molecule of the gas, let us select those in which the second molecule is moving before collision with a speed between v' and $v' + dv'$; the number of such molecules in unit volume will be, by (61a) in Sec. 28, $dn = 4\pi n \, Av'^2 e^{-\beta^2 v'^2} \, dv'$. Since these molecules are moving equally in all directions, the chance per second of a collision between one of them and the ray molecule will be Θ_{12} as given by (100) with n replaced by dn or

$$4\pi n \, AS\bar{v}_r v'^2 e^{-\beta^2 v'^2} \, dv'.$$

The integral of this expression over all values of v' then gives the total expectation of collision per second between a ray molecule and the molecules of the gas, which we shall denote by Θ_{vT}. Inserting values of $\bar{v}_r$ from (101a, b) according to the relative values of v and v', which are to be put in place of v_1 and v_2, respectively, we can write the result thus:

$$\Theta_{vT} = 4\pi n AS\left\{\int_0^v \left(v + \frac{v'^2}{3v}\right)v'^2 e^{-\beta^2 v'^2} \, dv' + \int_v^\infty \left(v' + \frac{v^2}{3v'}\right)v'^2 e^{-\beta^2 v'^2} \, dv'\right\}.$$

The integrals occurring here can be simplified and in part evaluated completely by means of several integrations by parts, or with the aid of the table at the end of the book. We can thus obtain:

$$\Theta_{vT} = 4\pi n AS\left\{\left(-\frac{v^2}{2\beta^2} - \frac{1}{4\beta^4} - \frac{v^2}{6\beta^2} + \frac{1}{2\beta^4} + \frac{v^2}{2\beta^2} + \frac{v^2}{6\beta^2}\right)e^{-\beta^2 v^2} \right.$$
$$\left. + \left(\frac{v}{2\beta^2} + \frac{1}{4\beta^4 v}\right)\int_0^v e^{-\beta^2 v'^2} \, dv'\right\},$$

or, if we now insert $A = \beta^3/\pi^{3/2}$ from (60) in Sec. 28 and write $x = \beta v$, $y = \beta v'$,

$$\Theta_{vT} = \frac{nS}{\sqrt{\pi}\,\beta}\left[e^{-x^2} + \left(2x + \frac{1}{x}\right)\int_0^x e^{-y^2} \, dy\right]. \tag{103a}$$

Θ_{vT} as given by this expression represents the expectation of collision per second for a ray molecule moving with speed v through a homogeneous maxwellian gas at absolute temperature T, for which $\beta^2 = 1/(2RT)$ in terms of the gas constant R for a gram; n is the number of molecules per unit volume in the gas and S, assumed constant, is the mutual collision cross section for one of the molecules of the gas and the ray molecule. Unfortunately the expression cannot be reduced further in terms of ordinary functions, but numerical values for it can easily be found if one has tables of the "probability integral,"

$$\Phi(x) = \frac{2}{\sqrt{\pi}} \int_0^x e^{-y^2} \, dy$$

[cf. (67) in Sec. 30 and references there]. As a check, we may note that if $v \to \infty$, $\int_0^x e^{-y^2} \, dy \to \sqrt{\pi}/2$ and so $\Theta_{vT} \to nSv$, which is the same as the collision rate when the other molecules are standing still [cf. Θ_1 as given by (99a)].

The mean free path for the ray molecule in the gas is then

$$L_{vT} = \frac{v}{\Theta_{vT}}.$$

For reference we may note that the generalized result for a *mixed gas* is now easily written down. If the gas contains several kinds of molecules which have mutual cross sections with the ray molecule denoted by $S_{01}, S_{02} \cdots S_{0\nu}$ and have molecular densities $n_1, n_2 \cdots n_\nu$ and values of β denoted by $\beta_1, \beta_2 \cdots \beta_\nu$, (103a) is to be replaced by

$$\Theta_{vT} = \frac{1}{\sqrt{\pi}} \sum_{\tau=1}^{\nu} \frac{n_\tau S_\tau}{\beta_\tau} \left[e^{-x_\tau^2} + \left(2x_\tau + \frac{1}{x_\tau} \right) \int_0^{x_\tau} e^{-y^2} \, dy \right] \quad (103b)$$

where $x_\tau = \beta_\tau v$. It is still true, however, that $L_{vT} = v/\Theta_{vT}$.

One possible application of these results is to a homogeneous beam of molecules moving through a foreign gas. Beams of this sort consisting of neutral molecules are seldom produced, however, at present in the laboratory; homogeneous beams of ions are often worked with, but in such cases the velocities are usually so high that the motion of the molecules of the gas through which the ions pass can be neglected altogether and the simpler approximate value $\Theta_1 = nSv$, as in (99a), can be employed in place of the more complicated form.

63. Mean Free Path and Collision Rate at Constant Speed. Another application of the results just obtained is to those molecules of the gas itself which happen momentarily to be moving at a particular speed. For this application let us replace β by its value $\beta = 2/(\sqrt{\pi}\bar{v})$ in terms of the mean molecular speed $\bar{v}$ in the gas; and for convenience of reference let us also anticipate a little and insert the values presently to be found for the general collision rate Θ and mean free path L in a homogeneous gas. Then, from (106a, b) below,

$$\frac{nS}{\sqrt{\pi}\beta} = \frac{\Theta}{\sqrt{2\pi} \, \bar{v}\beta} = \frac{\Theta}{2\sqrt{2}}$$

and, writing Θ_v now in place of Θ_{vT}, we have from (103a) for the collision expectancy per second of a molecule of a homogeneous maxwellian gas that is moving at speed v

$$\Theta_v = \frac{\Theta}{2\sqrt{2}} \left[e^{-x^2} + \left(2x + \frac{1}{x} \right) \frac{\sqrt{\pi}}{2} \Phi(x) \right] \tag{104a}$$

where $x = (2/\sqrt{\pi})(v/\bar{v})$ and $\Phi(x) = (2/\sqrt{\pi})\int_0^x e^{-y^2}\, dy$ as in Sec. 30.

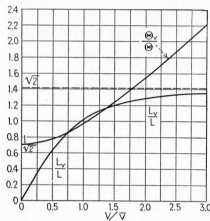

Fig. 27.—Mean free path L_v and collision rate Θ_v at speed v.

The corresponding mean free path is $L_v = v/\Theta_v = x/\beta\Theta_v = \sqrt{\pi}\bar{v}x/2\Theta_v$, or, since $1/\Theta = L/\bar{v}$,

$$L_v = \frac{\sqrt{2\pi}xL}{e^{-x^2} + \left(2x + \frac{1}{x} \right)\dfrac{\sqrt{\pi}}{2}\Phi(x)} \tag{104b}$$

in terms of the general mean free path L.

From (104a) we see that for a molecule standing still ($x = 0$) $\Theta_v = \Theta/\sqrt{2}$. In Fig. 27 are plotted the ratios Θ_v/Θ and L_v/L as functions of $v/\bar{v}$. Both curves rise as v increases, but the one for the mean free path L_v starts, of course, from $L_v/L = 0$ and becomes asymptotic to $L_v = \sqrt{2}L$ as $v \to \infty$, whereas that for the collision rate Θ_v starts from the finite value mentioned above and rises indefinitely.

64. Mean Free Path and Collision Rate in a Maxwellian Gas. The general collision rate for the molecules of a gas in equilibrium can be obtained now simply by averaging Θ_v over all values of v. Little complication is caused if, in order again to kill two birds with a single stone, we allow at once for possible heterogeneity of composition. Accordingly, we shall calculate first the rate at which a maxwellian set of molecules of density n_1 per unit volume for which $\beta = \beta_1$ collide with another maxwellian set of molecular density n_2 for which $\beta = \beta_2$, the differences in β being due, of course, to a difference of molecular weight. At the end we can then obtain the value for a homogeneous gas simply by putting $\beta_1 = \beta_2$.

The total number of collisions made in a second by the n_1 molecules of the first kind with all molecules of the second kind is $n_1\Theta_{12}$ in terms of the collision rate Θ_{12} for one molecule. Now, of the n_1 molecules, $4\pi n_1 A_1 v_1^2 e^{-\beta_1^2 v_1^2}\, dv_1$ are moving in the range dv_1 [cf. (61a) in Sec. 28]. If we multiply this number by Θ_{vT}, as given by (103a), with v changed to v_1, n to n_2, S to S_{12}, β to β_2, x to $\beta_2 v_1$, and y for simplicity to $\beta_2 v_2$, and then integrate over all values of v_1 from 0 to ∞, we obtain another expression for the total number of the collisions in question; hence we can write

$$
n_1\Theta_{12} = (4\sqrt{\pi}\,n_1 n_2 A_1 S_{12}) \int_0^\infty v_1^2 e^{-\beta_1^2 v_1^2}\left[\frac{1}{\beta_2}e^{-\beta_2^2 v_1^2} \right.
$$
$$
\left. + \left(2\beta_2 v_1 + \frac{1}{\beta_2 v_1}\right)\int_0^{v_1} e^{-\beta_2^2 v_2^2}\, dv_2\right] dv_1.
$$

The iterated integral occurring in this expression can be evaluated without trouble, provided we first invert the order of integration, a device that is frequently useful. The original range of integration is shown by the shading in Fig. 28, v_2 running for a given value of v_1 from 0 to v_1 and then v_1 from 0 to ∞. Obviously we can just as well let v_1 run from v_2 to ∞ and then v_2 from 0 to ∞. In this order the integrations can be carried out because odd powers of the variable now occur in that integral which has finite limits. Thus we find, with the help of integrations by parts and formula (59a) in Sec. 28 (or the table of integrals at the end of the book):

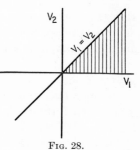

Fig. 28.

$$
\int_0^\infty v_1^2 e^{-\beta_1^2 v_1^2}\left(2\beta_2 v_1 + \frac{1}{\beta_2 v_1}\right)dv_1 \int_0^{v_1} e^{-\beta_2^2 v_2^2}\, dv_2
$$
$$
= \int_0^\infty dv_1 \int_0^{v_1}\left(2\beta_2 v_1^3 + \frac{v_1}{\beta_2}\right)e^{-\beta_1^2 v_1^2 - \beta_2^2 v_2^2}\, dv_2
$$
$$
= \int_0^\infty dv_2 \int_{v_2}^\infty\left(2\beta_2 v_1^3 + \frac{v_1}{\beta_2}\right)e^{-\beta_1^2 v_1^2 - \beta_2^2 v_2^2}\, dv_1
$$
$$
= \int_0^\infty\left[\frac{\beta_2 v_2^2}{\beta_1^2} + \frac{\beta_2}{\beta_1^4} + \frac{1}{2\beta_2\beta_1^2}\right]e^{-(\beta_1^2 + \beta_2^2)v_2^2}\, dv_2
$$
$$
= \frac{\sqrt{\pi}}{\beta_2\beta_1^4}\left(\frac{1}{2}\frac{\beta_2^2 + \frac{1}{2}\beta_1^2}{(\beta_1^2 + \beta_2^2)^{1/2}} + \frac{1}{4}\frac{\beta_1^2\beta_2^2}{(\beta_1^2 + \beta_2^2)^{3/2}}\right).
$$

The first part of the integral in the original expression for $n_1\Theta_{12}$, on the other hand, has the value

$$\int_0^\infty \frac{1}{\beta_2} v_1^2 e^{-(\beta_1^2 + \beta_2^2)v_1^2}\, dv_1 = \frac{1}{4\beta_2} \frac{\sqrt{\pi}}{(\beta_1^2 + \beta_2^2)^{3/2}}.$$

The entire integral is then the sum of these two expressions or

$$\frac{1}{2}\frac{\sqrt{\pi}}{\beta_2\beta_1^4}\left(\frac{\beta_2^2 + \frac{1}{2}\beta_1^2}{(\beta_1^2 + \beta_2^2)^{1/2}} + \frac{1}{2}\frac{\beta_1^2\beta_2^2 + \beta_1^4}{(\beta_1^2 + \beta_2^2)^{3/2}}\right) = \frac{\sqrt{\pi}}{2\beta_1^4\beta_2}(\beta_1^2 + \beta_2^2)^{1/2}.$$

Inserting this value in the expression obtained for $n_1\Theta_{12}$ and also inserting $A_1 = \beta_1^3/\pi^{3/2}$, and then dividing through by n_1, we find:

$$\Theta_{12} = \frac{2}{\sqrt{\pi}}\frac{n_2 S_{12}}{\beta_1\beta_2}(\beta_1^2 + \beta_2^2)^{1/2} = n_2 S_{12}(\bar{v}_1^2 + \bar{v}_2^2)^{1/2} \qquad (105a)$$

in terms of

$$\bar{v}_1 = \frac{2}{\sqrt{\pi}\,\beta_1}, \qquad \bar{v}_2 = \frac{2}{\sqrt{\pi}\,\beta_2}.$$

Here Θ_{12} represents the collision rate per molecule of a group distributed in velocity in a maxwellian manner with mean speed $\bar{v}_1$, moving through another maxwellian group of a different sort whose density is n_2 and mean speed $\bar{v}_2$; S_{12} is the mutual cross section for a molecule of the first kind in collision with one of the second.

If *more than two kinds* of molecules are present the appropriate generalized formula can at once be written down, for the total collision rate Θ_i for the ith kind will simply be the sum of expressions such as (105a) representing the effects of collisions with all of the various kinds of molecules that are present, including its own kind. By (66a) in Sec. 30 $1/\bar{v}^2 \propto M$, the molecular weight; hence Θ_i and the corresponding mean free path, $L_i = \bar{v}_i/\Theta_i$, can conveniently be written thus, with obvious meanings for the symbols:

$$\Theta_i = \sum_j n_j S_{ij}(\bar{v}_i^2 + \bar{v}_j^2)^{1/2} = \bar{v}_i \sum_j n_j S_{ij}\left(1 + \frac{M_i}{M_j}\right)^{1/2}, \qquad (105b)$$

$$L_i = \left[\sum_j n_j S_{ij}\left(1 + \frac{M_i}{M_j}\right)^{1/2}\right]^{-1}. \qquad (105c)$$

Finally, if only *one kind* of molecule is present with density n molecules per unit volume, mean speed $\bar{v}$ and mutual collision cross section S, we need only put $\bar{v}_1 = \bar{v}_2 = \bar{v}$ and $S_{12} = S$ in (105a) in order to obtain the collision rate Θ and the mean free path, $L = \bar{v}/\Theta$, in a *homogeneous maxwellian* gas:

$$\Theta = \sqrt{2}\,nS\bar{v}, \qquad L = \frac{1}{\sqrt{2}\,nS}. \qquad (106a,\ b)$$

For hard elastic spheres of diameter σ these become

$$\Theta = \sqrt{2}\,\pi n\bar{v}\sigma^2, \qquad L = \frac{1}{\sqrt{2}\,\pi n\sigma^2}, \qquad (106c,\ d)$$

which are the formulas most commonly given.

65. Magnitude of the Correction for Maxwell's Law.   It is instructive to compare formulas (106b) and (102a).   The comparison shows that the introduction of Maxwell's law in place of Clausius' assumption of equal speeds, after greatly complicating the calculation, only changes the final result in the ratio $1/\sqrt{2} \div \frac{3}{4} = 0.94$, or by 6 per cent.   The effect of introducing Maxwell's law is very much greater than this in the case of some phenomena, such as heat conduction, which depend essentially upon *differential* motion of the molecules; when, however, the motion affects the phenomenon only indirectly, the maxwellian correction amounts quite commonly, as in the present case, only to a few per cent.   In view of our ignorance as to the true molecular forces the smallness of the correction often justifies the expedient of saving labor by assuming uniform speed instead of Maxwell's law.

66. Mode of Determining L and S or σ.   If we were now to attempt to compare the results just obtained with experimentally determined magnitudes we should encounter the difficulty that eqs. (106a, b) contain two new molecular constants, L and S, concerning which the development of the theory up to this point has given us no other information.   A second relation between them is, therefore, necessary before either one can even be calculated from observed data.   The best source of additional information for this purpose lies in a comparison between the theoretical and observed values of the viscosity; this will be discussed in the next chapter, and a table will be given of values of L and σ for a number of the commoner gases.

67. Collisions in a Real Gas.   Up to this point in our discussions of collision phenomena in a gas we have uniformly made the assumption that the molecules exert forces upon each other only when they come into close proximity.   Various considerations indicate, on the contrary, that in reality the mutual force does not quite vanish at any distance, however great.   If this is true, then strictly speaking every molecule is in collision with every other one all the time and there are actually no free paths at all.   The mutual collision cross section for any pair appears, therefore, to be infinite; a molecule held in a beam as contemplated in Sec. 60 throws a shadow free from beam molecules which flares out to an infinite diameter at infinity.

This circumstance presents a difficulty that has been met in practice in various ways. In connection with some phenomena deflections of very small size are unimportant and in such cases it may be sufficient simply to say that, by definition, a collision occurs only when the resulting deflection exceeds a certain arbitrarily chosen minimum amount. A finite cross section then exists by definition, but, of course, it will vary somewhat with the choice of the critical deflection.

Such a solution of the difficulty is not likely to be widely useful, however, and from the theoretical standpoint it is unsatisfactory. A better procedure, and one often tacitly employed, is to replace the actual gas in thought by a set of elastic spheres moving classically and of such a size that they are equivalent to the actual molecules insofar as the particular phenomenon under discussion is concerned; the cross-sectional area of one of these spheres is then taken as the cross section or, to speak precisely, the *equivalent classical-sphere cross section* of the molecule for the phenomenon in question, the diameter of the sphere representing the equivalent mean diameter for the two molecules. Such a procedure has the disadvantage of yielding, as we shall see in the next chapter, different equivalent cross sections for diffusion and for viscosity and heat conduction; nevertheless, it seems to be the best sort of conception for practical use in thinking about transport phenomena.

When we substitute wave mechanics for classical theory, the difficulty in a sense disappears, for according to wave mechanics the number of molecules thrown out of a beam is always finite. However, this advantage over classical theory does not turn out to be very helpful, for the collision cross section as defined above is in actual cases enormously influenced by a preponderating number of small deflections, and for this reason it is not actually a very useful quantity. As a matter of fact, the most interesting theoretical results obtained from wave mechanics have reference to finer details of the collision phenomenon, especially the angular distribution afterward; this distribution, furthermore, besides its great importance in scattering experiments of various sorts, is what we shall have to employ when we come to develop an accurate theory of transport phenomena. Accordingly, we shall now drop our gross view of the collision process and proceed to consider it as a phenomenon of scattering.

For this purpose we shall return first to the use of classical theory; then later the results will be described that have been obtained by wave mechanics.

MOLECULAR SCATTERING

68. The Scattering Coefficient. The phenomenon of molecular scattering can be analyzed quantitatively as follows. As before, let a homogeneous beam of particles approaching along lines that are parallel, but otherwise distributed at random, pass over a given molecule held in a fixed position; but consider, out of all particles incident on unit area of a plane perpendicular to their direction of approach, only the fraction which undergo a particular deflection by the fixed molecule. Let us consider those molecules that acquire a velocity whose direction lies in a definite element of solid angle $d\omega$. We can write for the fraction that these form of the total, $G\,d\omega$; the quantity G thus defined is called the *scattering coefficient* for collisions of this type.

If N particles arrive in the beam per unit area per second, $NG\,d\omega$ of them will be scattered per second, or $NG\,d\omega\,dt$ is the chance that one is scattered during an infinitesimal time dt, in the direction of $d\omega$. G has therefore the dimensions of $1/Nt$ or the dimensions of area. If there are N' scattering molecules per unit volume, then $NN'G\,d\omega$ of the beam molecules are scattered within $d\omega$ per second upon their first encounter with a scattering molecule. The same definition can be applied also to the more important case in which the second molecule, although momentarily at rest, is free to move, provided we require that after each collision it shall be brought to rest before being struck again.

Clearly the scattering coefficient will vary in general with the direction of scattering; we can conveniently regard it as a function of polar coordinates whose axis is parallel to the incident beam, and if we prefer we can write $G(\theta, \varphi)\,d\omega = G(\theta, \varphi) \sin\theta\,d\theta\,d\varphi$. G will also depend upon the nature of the colliding molecules and upon their velocity of approach, and it will be different according as the scattering molecule is held fixed or is left free to move; furthermore, it may depend upon the orientation of the molecules. Questions involving orientation lie far beyond the reach of present experiment, however; all that we can hope to observe is an effect averaged over all orientations of both of the colliding particles. Such average effects will necessarily be symmetrical about the direction of the incident beam, and they can therefore be described in terms of a mean scattering coefficient which is a function of θ alone. Hereafter we shall understand G to stand for this mean coefficient and shall regard it as a function $G(\theta)$.

The mean *solid-angle scattering coefficient* $G(\theta)$ must not be confused with a differently defined coefficient that may be more useful under some circumstances. We might define a *polar scattering coefficient* $F(\theta)$

by the requirement that $F(\theta)\, d\theta$ shall represent the fraction of the beam molecules incident on unit area which are scattered by one scattering molecule in all directions making an angle between θ and $\theta + d\theta$ with the direction of the incident beam. Then, if we give to $d\omega$ the form of a ring so that $d\omega = 2\pi \sin\theta\, d\theta$, we can write for the molecules scattered into the range $d\theta$ either $G\, d\omega = 2\pi G \sin\theta\, d\theta$ or $F(\theta)\, d\theta$, and it follows that

$$F(\theta) = 2\pi G(\theta) \sin\theta. \tag{107a}$$

In any case the scattering coefficient necessarily bears a simple relation to the *collision cross section*. The mutual collision cross section S represents the *total* fraction scattered out of unit area of the beam at all angles by one molecule. Hence it is

$$S = \int_0^\pi F(\theta)\, d\theta = 2\pi \int_0^\pi G(\theta) \sin\theta\, d\theta = \int_0^{2\pi} \int_0^\pi G(\theta,\, \varphi) \sin\theta\, d\theta\, d\varphi, \tag{107b}$$

the last expression being a more general form in terms of the original nonaveraged G. These two equations must hold whether the scattering molecule is held fixed or is left free.

It will be worth while now to calculate the classical scattering coefficient for a few simple cases.

69. Classical Scattering Coefficient for Symmetrical Molecules with Fixed Scatterer. In the case of field-free hard spheres G is very

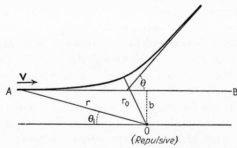

Fig. 29.—Deflection by a scattering center O.

easy to find, but it is also not very difficult to find a more general expression applicable to any spherically symmetrical type of force.

To do the latter, let us suppose that the scattering molecule has its center fixed at a point O (Fig. 29), and that a beam molecule approaches with speed v along a line AB passing at a distance b from O. Let the mutual potential energy of the two molecules be $U(r)$, where r is the distance between their centers. Because of the force the beam molecule will be deflected so as to move along a plane curve having as asymptotes the line of approach AB and another line making the angle of deflection, θ, with AB.

Let θ_1 denote the instantaneous angular position about O of the approaching molecule, measured positively from a line drawn through O parallel to AB but backward toward A, and let the mass of the molecule be m. Then at any moment the molecule has angular momentum about O equal to $mr^2\dot{\theta}_1$, r being its distance from O, and it has kinetic energy $\frac{1}{2}m(\dot{r}^2 + r^2\dot{\theta}_1^2)$; since the initial values of these quantities are clearly mvb and $\frac{1}{2}mv^2$, respectively, we have, according to the laws of the conservation of angular momentum and of energy,

$$mr^2\dot{\theta}_1 = mvb, \qquad \tfrac{1}{2}m(\dot{r}^2 + r^2\dot{\theta}_1^2) + U(r) = \tfrac{1}{2}mv^2.$$

Solving the first of these equations for $\dot{\theta}_1$ and substituting this value in the second, we have, therefore,

$$\dot{\theta}_1 = \frac{d\theta_1}{dt} = \frac{vb}{r^2}, \qquad \dot{r} = \frac{dr}{dt} = \left(v^2 - \frac{2U}{m} - \frac{v^2b^2}{r^2}\right)^{\!\frac12},$$

and finally, dividing these two equations,

$$\frac{d\theta_1}{dr} = \frac{b}{r^2}\left[1 - \frac{2U}{mv^2} - \frac{b^2}{r^2}\right]^{-\frac12}.$$

Now the path is symmetrical about its point of closest approach to O, at which we shall write $r = r_0$. Hence we can write for the total increase in θ_1 during the entire collision $2\displaystyle\int_{r_0}^{\infty} (d\theta_1/dr)\, dr$. This is equal also to $\pi - \theta$ in the case of repulsion, and the same relation can be used in the case of attraction provided we let θ be negative in that case [cf. Fig. (29)]. Hence in either case we have for the angle of deflection

$$\theta(b) = \pi - 2b\int_{r_0}^{\infty} \frac{dr}{r\{[1 - 2U(r)/mv^2]\, r^2 - b^2\}^{\frac12}} \qquad (108a)$$

or, in terms of $x = r_0/r$, since $dr/r = -dx/x$,

$$\theta(b) = \pi - 2\int_{0}^{1} \frac{dx}{\{[1 - 2U(r_0/x)/mv^2][r_0{}^2/b^2] - x^2\}^{\frac12}}. \qquad (108b)$$

Since the original lower limit r_0 is that value of r for which $\dot{r} = 0$, we see from the general expression for $\dot{r}$ given above that it is the value of r that makes the denominator in the integrand vanish in $(108a)$ or the root of the equation

$$\left[1 - \frac{2U(r_0)}{mv^2}\right]r_0^2 = b^2; \qquad (109)$$

the denominator in $(108b)$ vanishes for $x = 1$.

Equation (108a) or (108b) gives θ as a function of b. From this function $\theta(b)$ the scattering coefficient $G(\theta)$ or $F(\theta)$ as defined in Sec. 68 can then be obtained as follows. In the homogeneous beam that is contemplated in the definition of G or F the lines of approach of the beam molecules are (on the average) uniformly distributed over any plane perpendicular to their common direction, and in particular over such a plane drawn through O; and those lines for which b lies in a given range db pass through an annular ring on this plane of radius b and width db and thus of area $2\pi b\ db$, so that they form a fraction $2\pi b\ db$ of the lines crossing unit area. This fraction is also the fraction of the molecules that are scattered into a range $d\theta$ such that $d\theta = |\theta'(b)|\ db$. Hence $2\pi b\ db = F(\theta)\ d\theta = 2\pi G(\theta) \sin \theta\ d\theta = 2\pi G(\theta) \sin \theta\ |\theta'(b)|\ db$ and

$$G(\theta) = \frac{b}{|\theta'(b)| \sin \theta}, \qquad F(\theta) = \frac{2\pi b}{|\theta'(b)|}. \qquad (110a, b)$$

The absolute-value sign is needed on $\theta'(b)$ because in defining G and F the differential $d\theta$ is supposed to be positive whereas $\theta'(b)$ may be negative; $\theta'(b)$ might also be positive for some values of b and negative for others, in which case the formulas would have to be made more complicated but in a rather obvious way.

From these equations G and F can be calculated, provided the potential function $U(r)$ is known or assumed.

70. Examples of the Scattering Coefficient. There are two special cases of considerable interest in which the calculations are easily carried out.

Suppose, first, that both molecules are hard *elastic spheres* free from force except at contact. Then $U = 0$ except during the very short interval of collision, and during the latter the change in θ_1 is negligible, so that the corresponding part of the integral in (108b) can be neglected. Hence in that integral we can without appreciable error put $U(r) = 0$ everywhere. Furthermore, the distance of closest approach is in this case $r_0 = \sigma_{12} = (\sigma_1 + \sigma_2)/2$, the mean of the diameters of a beam molecule and the fixed one. Accordingly, (108b) gives

$$\theta(b) = \pi - 2 \int_0^1 \frac{dx}{(r_0^2/b^2 - x^2)^{1/2}} = \pi - 2 \sin^{-1} \frac{b}{\sigma_{12}};$$

then

$$b = \sigma_{12} \sin \frac{1}{2}(\pi - \theta) = \sigma_{12} \cos \frac{\theta}{2},$$

$$\theta'(b) = -\frac{2}{\sigma_{12}} \left(1 - \frac{b^2}{\sigma_{12}^2} \right)^{-1/2} = -\frac{2}{\sigma_{12}} \left(\sin \frac{\theta}{2} \right)^{-1},$$

$$G(\theta) = \frac{\frac{1}{2}\sigma_{12}^2 \cos\frac{\theta}{2} \sin\frac{\theta}{2}}{\sin\theta} = \frac{1}{4}\sigma_{12}^2. \tag{110c}$$

As a check we may note that this value of G substituted in (107b) gives a cross section

$$S = \frac{1}{2}\pi\sigma_{12}^2 \int_0^{\pi} \sin\theta\, d\theta = \pi\sigma_{12}^2, \tag{110d}$$

which is obviously correct.

The fact that according to (110c) G is independent of θ means that uniformly distributed spheres incident upon a fixed sphere are scattered by it equally in all directions, a result which is, of course, more easily obtained directly.

As a second example, let us consider the general case of *slight deflections*, characterized by the condition that $2U/mv^2$ is small throughout the collision and θ is consequently also small. (With some forms of the function U a small θ might, of course, occur without $2U/mv^2$ being at all times small.) Then, if we expand in powers of U and drop all after the first, we can write, from (108b), after substituting for r_0^2/b^2 from (109),

$$\theta = \pi - 2\int_0^1 \left\{ \left[1 - \frac{2U(r_0/x)}{mv^2}\right]\left[1 + \frac{2U(r_0)}{mv^2} \cdots \right] - x^2 \right\}^{-\frac{1}{2}} dx$$

$$= \pi - 2\int_0^1 \left\{ (1 - x^2)^{-\frac{1}{2}} - \frac{U(r_0) - U(r_0/x)}{mv^2(1 - x^2)^{\frac{3}{2}}} \cdots \right\} dx$$

or approximately

$$\theta = \frac{2}{mv^2}\int_0^1 \frac{U(r_0) - U(r_0/x)}{(1 - x^2)^{\frac{3}{2}}}\, dx.$$

As a special case, suppose $U(r) = C/r^n$, where n is some positive integer and C is a constant, positive or negative. Then, if we substitute $x = \sin\zeta$, we have

$$\theta = \frac{2C}{mv^2 r_0^n}\int_0^{\pi/2} \left(\frac{1}{\cos^2\zeta} - \frac{\sin^n\zeta}{\cos^2\zeta}\right) d\zeta$$

$$= \frac{2C}{mv^2 r_0^n}\left[\left(\tan\zeta - \frac{\sin^{n-1}\zeta}{\cos\zeta}\right)\Big|_0^{\pi/2} + (n - 1)\int_0^{\pi/2} \sin^{n-2}\zeta\, d\zeta\right]$$

after integration by parts. Here the integrated expression equals -1 at $\zeta = 0$ if $n = 1$ but otherwise vanishes at the limits, for we can write it

$$\frac{\sin\zeta - \sin^{n-1}\zeta}{\cos\zeta} = \frac{\sin^2\zeta - \sin^{2(n-1)}\zeta}{\cos\zeta(\sin\zeta + \sin^{n-1}\zeta)} = \frac{(n - 2)\cos\zeta \cdots}{\sin\zeta + \sin^{n-1}\zeta}$$

after substituting $\sin^2 \zeta = 1 - \cos^2 \zeta$, higher powers of $\cos \zeta$ not being written.   Let

$$K_n = \int_0^{\pi/2} \sin^n \zeta \, d\zeta = \frac{2 \cdot 4 \cdot \cdots \cdots (n - 1 + \delta_n^1)}{1 \cdot 3 \cdots n} \text{ for odd } n,$$

$$= \frac{1 \cdot 3 \cdot \cdots \cdots (n - 1)}{2 \cdot 4 \cdots n} \frac{\pi}{2} \text{ for even } n$$

($\delta_n^1 = 1$ if $n = 1$ but otherwise $= 0$).   Then it is easily seen that for any positive integral n, r_0 being replaced by b because we are keeping only the first power of the small number C,

$$\theta = \frac{2nK_nC}{mv^2b^n}.$$

For the scattering coefficient we have then from (110a), letting θ stand now for its absolute value,

$$G = \frac{mv^2b^{n+2}}{2n^2K_nC \sin \theta} = \frac{1}{n} \left(\frac{2nK_n|C|}{mv^2} \right)^{2/n} \frac{1}{\theta^{1+\frac{2}{n}} \sin \theta} \tag{110e}$$

after eliminating b in favor of θ.

Formula (110e) indicates a spinelike concentration of the scattered molecules in directions near that of incidence; the fact that it contributes to $\int_0^\pi G \sin \theta \, d\theta$ the infinite part $\int_0 d\theta/\theta^{1+\frac{2}{n}} = (n/2\theta^{\frac{2}{n}})|_0$ merely illustrates the infinity of the classical cross section that was referred to above.   For $n = 6$, which is suggested by wave mechanics for the attractive or van der Waals molecular field of all molecules, $G \propto 1/(v^{2/3}\theta^{4/3} \sin \theta)$ and, by (107a), $F(\theta) \propto 1/(v^{2/3}\theta^{4/3})$.

Problems.   1. Show directly that elastic spheres falling with equal and parallel velocities but otherwise at random on a fixed sphere are reflected equally in all directions.

2. Show that if $n = 1$, i.e., $U = C/r$ as in a Coulomb field,

$$\theta = 2 \tan^{-1} \frac{C}{mv^2b}, \qquad G = \frac{C^2}{4m^2v^4} \frac{1}{\sin^4 (\theta/2)}, \text{ accurately.}$$

(These formulas are easily obtained directly, or from (108b), by eliminating with the help of (109) first C and then, in the result, r_0.   The case $n = 2$ can likewise be worked out completely.)

71. Relative Scattering.   The preceding calculation had reference to the very simple situation in which the beam molecules all have the same velocity and the scattering molecule is held fixed.   In actual experiments, on the other hand, the beam passes through a cluster of molecules that are not only free to move but are already in motion, perhaps forming a gas in thermal equilibrium; and the beam molecules themselves may be distributed in velocity either in a maxwellian manner or otherwise.   The general treatment of such cases is complicated and will not be given here; it may be worth while, however, to take one or two easy steps toward it by investigating the effect of the motion of the scattering molecule alone.

This effect can be divided into two parts, one arising from the *initial motion* of the scattering molecule, the other caused by its *acceleration* during the collision process.   The first effect reduces to a simple problem in change of axis.   It turns out, furthermore, that the second effect can be handled in a similar way; we have only to make use of the well-known theorem concerning the two-body problem of planetary theory which states that, when just two particles move under the action of mutual central forces, the motion of either one relative to the other is the same as would be its actual motion if the other one were held fixed and if at the same time its own mass were reduced in a certain ratio.

The truth of this theorem is so quickly seen from the differential equations of motion that we shall prove it here.   Let m_1, m_2 be the masses of the two particles and $\mathbf{r}_1$ and $\mathbf{r}_2$ their vector distances from the origin.   Then, if $f(r)$ is the magnitude of the force that each particle exerts upon the other, expressed as a function of r and measured positively as a repulsion, Newton's second law of motion leads to the vectorial equations:

$$m_1 \frac{d^2}{dt^2} \mathbf{r}_1 = f(r)\mathbf{r}_0, \qquad m_2 \frac{d^2}{dt^2} \mathbf{r}_2 = -f(r)\mathbf{r}_0,$$

$\mathbf{r}_0$ being a unit vector drawn from the second particle toward the first. From these two equations we find for $\mathbf{r} = \mathbf{r}_1 - \mathbf{r}_2$, the vector position of the first particle relative to the second,

$$\frac{d^2\mathbf{r}}{dt^2} = \frac{d_2\mathbf{r}_1}{dt^2} - \frac{d^2\mathbf{r}_2}{dt^2} = \frac{m_1 + m_2}{m_1 m_2} f(r)\mathbf{r}_0.$$

This is exactly the same equation that would hold for the first particle if the second one were fixed while the first had a mass, not m_1, but $m' = m_1 m_2/(m_1 + m_2)$.

Accordingly the theory of the scattering by a fixed molecule can be utilized in arriving at formulas appropriate to the more general case in which the scattering molecule is free to move; we have only to apply that theory to the relative motions and to make the proper change in the mass.

Suppose, now, a scattering molecule of mass m_2 moves with velocity $\mathbf{v}_2$ into a uniform beam of molecules of mass m_1 moving with velocity $\mathbf{v}_1$. Then relative to the scattering molecule, the beam molecules approach as a uniform beam moving with vector velocity $\mathbf{v} = \mathbf{v}_1 - \mathbf{v}_2$ (cf. Fig. 30). Let us denote by θ_r the angle of deflection of a beam molecule in this relative motion, or the angle through which the velocity of the

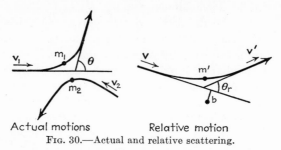

Actual motions   Relative motion
Fig. 30.—Actual and relative scattering.

first molecule relative to the second is turned by a collision. Then the scattering coefficient for θ_r will be, by (110a, b),

$$G_r(\theta_r) = \frac{b}{|\theta_r'(b)|\,\sin\theta_r}, \qquad F_r(\theta_r) = \frac{2\pi b}{|\theta_r'(b)|}, \qquad (111a, b)$$

b denoting the perpendicular distance of the scattering molecule from the initial line of relative approach of the beam molecule; $\theta_r(b)$ is the same function $\theta(b)$ as is given by (108a) or (108b), in terms of r_0 as determined by (109), but with m replaced in all three equations by $m' = m_1 m_2/(m_1 + m_2)$ and with v now representing the magnitude of the relative velocity. The collision does not alter the magnitude of v, as we showed in Sec. 24, using only the same principles of momentum and energy that were employed above in calculating the deflection.

72. Classical Scattering Coefficient for Free Symmetrical Molecules. By means of the coefficient $G_r(\theta_r)$ or $F_r(\theta_r)$ for scattering in the relative motion we can then find the coefficient $G(\theta)$ or $F(\theta)$ for scattering in terms of the total motion of the beam molecules; it is only necessary to find the relation between θ and θ_r. The general formulas thus obtained are rather intricate, however, so we shall treat in detail only the simplest case, that in which the scattering molecule is initially at rest. The resulting formula should give some idea of the average relation between $G(\theta)$ and $G_r(\theta_r)$ for a beam passing through any gas that is free from mass motion.

To have the scattering molecule initially at rest, we put $\mathbf{v}_2 = 0$ in the analysis of the last section. Then the beam velocity $\mathbf{v}_1$ is the same as the initial relative velocity $\mathbf{v}$, while b, which was defined above in terms of the relative motion, represents also the distance of the second molecule from the actual initial line of approach of the first.   Furthermore, the entire motion occurs in this case in a single plane.

Let the velocities of the two molecules after the collision be v_1' and v_2', respectively, and let the subscripts $\parallel$, $\perp$ denote components respectively parallel and perpendicular to the beam velocity v_1 (cf. Fig. 31). Then, the relative velocity v' after collision being still of magnitude v

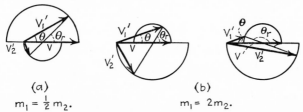

(a)   (b)

$m_1 = \frac{1}{2}m_2.$ $m_1 = 2m_2.$

Fig. 31.—Scattering by a free molecule initially at rest; velocity diagrams

but inclined at the angle θ_r to the beam direction, we can write for its components

$$v_\parallel' = v_{1\parallel}' - v_{2\parallel}' = v \cos \theta_r, \qquad v_\perp' = v_{1\perp}' - v_{2\perp}' = v \sin \theta_r.$$

Conservation of momentum during the collision requires now that

$$m_1 v_{1\parallel}' + m_2 v_{2\parallel}' = m_1 v_1 = m_1 v, \qquad m_1 v_{1\perp}' + m_2 v_{2\perp}' = 0.$$

From these equations and the obvious relation, $\tan \theta = v_{1\perp}'/v_{1\parallel}'$, we readily find that

$$\tan \theta = \frac{\sin \theta_r}{\dfrac{m_1}{m_2} + \cos \theta_r} = \frac{\tan \frac{1}{2}\theta_r}{1 + \dfrac{1}{2}\left(\dfrac{m_1}{m_2} - 1\right)\sec^2 \frac{1}{2}\theta_r}. \qquad (112)$$

It is then easy to find $F(\theta)$, for $F(\theta)|d\theta| = F_r(\theta_r)|d\theta_r|$.   Calculating $d\theta/d\theta_r$ from (112), we thus find

$$F(\theta) = \left[2 + \frac{\dfrac{m_1^2}{m_2^2} - 1}{1 + \dfrac{m_1}{m_2}\cos \theta_r} \right] F_r(\theta_r). \qquad (113)$$

This gives us $F(\theta)$ as a function of b in terms of the value of F_r given by (111b), and then by (107a) $G(\theta) = \dfrac{F(\theta)}{2\pi \sin \theta}.$

As a special case of these formulas, we may note that if $m_1 = m_2$, by (112) $\theta = \frac{1}{2}\theta_r$, and by (113) $F = 2F_r$.   Thus in this case, as θ_r ranges from 0 to π, θ is confined to the first quadrant, so that the beam molecule retains at least a slight forward component except in the one case of a central impact. If, on the other hand, $m_1 < m_2$, $\tan \theta$ passes through ∞ and θ increases continually with increasing θ_r up to a maximum of π for a central impact [case (a) in Fig. 31]. Finally, if $m_1 > m_2$, a calculation using (112) shows that θ attains a maximum value when $\cos \theta_r = -m_2/m_1$, beyond which θ decreases to zero again [case (b) in Fig. 31]; at the turning point $F(\theta)$ and $G(\theta)$ become infinite, while corresponding to any other angle there are two values, say, F_1 and F_2, or G_1 and G_2, and the particles scattered into a given range $d\theta$ consist of two groups moving at different speeds and form a fraction $[F_1(\theta) + F_2(\theta)]\, d\theta$ or $2\pi[G_1(\theta) + G_2(\theta)] \sin \theta\, d\theta$ of the whole. The two groups for the same θ are shown by the two diagrams for case (b) in Fig. 31.

The speed of the scattered beam molecule is easily found to be

$$v_1' = (v_{1\parallel}'^2 + v_{1\perp}'^2)^{1/2} = \frac{v(m_1^2 + m_2^2 + 2m_1m_2 \cos \theta_r)^{1/2}}{(m_1 + m_2)}.$$

The ends of the vectors $\mathbf{v}_1'$ and $\mathbf{v}_2'$ can be shown to lie for varying b on two semicircles as indicated in the figure.

Problem. Show directly that for field-free hard elastic spheres of equal mass, when the scattering one is initially at rest but left free to move

$$\theta = \frac{1}{2}\,\theta_r = \frac{\pi}{2} - \sin^{-1} \frac{b}{\sigma_{12}},$$
$$G(\theta) = \sigma_{12}^2 \cos \theta, \qquad F(\theta) = \pi\sigma_{12}^2 \sin 2\theta,$$

where $\sigma_{12} = \frac{1}{2}(\sigma_1 + \sigma_2)$ and $0 \leqq \theta \leqq \pi/2$.

73. The Experimental Determination of the Collision Cross Section.[*] Very interesting experiments have begun to be reported in recent years which furnish directly values of the collision cross section and of the scattering coefficient. The general arrangement in such experiments consists of a source chamber emitting a stream of molecules, out of which there is selected by means of a pair of collimating slits a narrow beam moving in a fairly definite direction, as shown schematically in Fig. 32. The beam then passes through a region into which various sorts of scattering gas can be introduced, and the number of molecules that pass through it or are scattered in various directions is determined by means of some sort of device for detecting and measuring molecular beams. The density is kept very low throughout by pumping, and often also in part by keeping the walls sufficiently cool to condense all molecules that strike them; if the source

[*] Cf. R. G. Fraser, "Molecular Rays," 1931.

is an oven in which a substance is being evaporated at high temperatures, the outer walls of the tube may be at room temperature, whereas in other cases they may need to be cooled with liquid air. For accuracy it is important that collisions of beam molecules with each other be rare occurrences, and also that those beam molecules which have collided more than once with the scattering gas do not enter the detector in disturbing numbers.

When determinations of the total collision cross section are to be made, the detector is placed in line with the direct beam (at D_1 in the figure) and the intensity of the beam is noted both with and without

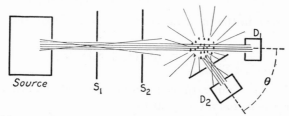

FIG. 32.—Arrangement for measuring collision cross sections.

the presence of the scattering gas. Let I_1, I_2 be the numbers of beam molecules received per second by the detector in these two cases and let x denote the distance traversed by the beam through the scattering gas, which can be made effectively equal to the distance from S_2 to D_1. Then, if the beam molecules are moving with uniform velocity v, we have, by (98a) in Sec. 59,

$$\frac{I_2}{I_1} = e^{-\frac{x}{L_v}},$$

from which the mean free path L_v of the beam molecules moving through the gas can be calculated; the mutual collision cross section is then $S = 1/(nL_v)$, n being the number of scattering molecules per cubic centimeter [cf. (99b)]. Unfortunately, however, it is difficult in practice to select out a beam of uniform speed, and consequently up to the present only a maxwellian distribution in the beam has been worked with, the results being then taken to represent scattering at the mean speed with an accuracy that is sufficient in view of the rather large experimental errors.

74. Knauer's Observations on Scattering. Some extensive observations made in this way have been reported recently by Knauer.* His results on the passage of several gases through mercury vapor illustrate beautifully the variation in the apparent mean free path with

* KNAUER, *Zeits. f. Physik,* **80**, 80 (1933); **90**, 559 (1934).

the criterion adopted for a collision. Since it is always possible in such experiments for a molecule to be deflected very slightly and yet enter the detecting device and be counted as an undeflected molecule, Knauer estimated for each of his detectors the average maximum angle through which a beam molecule could be deflected by collision with a mercury atom and still enter the detector. His values for the mean free path in centimeters of hydrogen and helium in mercury vapor at a pressure of 1 dyne/cm² are shown below for various values of the limiting angle, which was fixed experimentally by the size of the slit placed in front of the detector; for comparison we have added under the heading "by η" the equivalent-sphere value as calculated from the molecular diameters given in the table in Sec. 86 below and the equation

$$L = \frac{v}{\Theta_1} = 4[n\pi(\sigma_1 + \sigma_2)^2]^{-1}.$$

[Cf. (99d).] The temperatures given are those of the beam; the mercury vapor was at room temperature.

	H₂	H₂		He				
Limiting angle........	0.9°	7°	By η	0.9°	5°	7°	10–15°	By η
Absolute temp.								
120°	1.4	2.7		2.5	3.0	5.5	4.7	
295°	1.7	3.5	10.5	3.0	3.4	7.2	5.8	12.4

If these results are really typical of the behavior of uncharged gaseous molecules, the enormous variation of the apparent cross section with the limiting angle seems almost to rule out, in such cases, any application whatever of the conception of a collision cross section, or even of the idea of a progressive absorption of a beam of molecules. A beam passing through a scattering gas must undergo a weakening as judged by any test, but these results indicate that it also straggles more and more during its passage and that the line of distinction between straggling and weakening is decidedly indefinite.

The most probable cause of the large difference between the mean free paths observed by Knauer and the values deduced from viscosity data is presumably to be found in the occurrence of an enormous number of small deflections. This is strikingly borne out, indeed, by Knauer's own principal results, which had to do with the scattering coefficient itself. In Fig. 33 are shown on a log-log scale his values of $f(\theta)$, proportional to our $G(\theta)$, for H₂ and He passing through mercury vapor at 295°K; one curve is also plotted for $f(\theta)$ sin θ, proportional to our $F(\theta)$, in order to give an idea of the total distribution with respect to θ. Because the mercury atom is very heavy and consequently moves very slowly, we might perhaps expect G to be somewhere near constant, as was found above to be the case theoretically for spheres incident at random upon a fixed sphere; but on the contrary the observations exhibit an enormous increase with decreasing θ. The upper parts of the curves correspond roughly to an increase in $f(\theta)$ by a factor of 10 for an increase in θ by a factor of 4, which would make G proportional to the (log 10/log 4)th or 1.66th power of $1/\theta$; according to (110e), such a variation would result from a classical force varying as the inverse fourth power of the distance between the two molecules $(2/n = 0.66, n = 3, U \propto r^{-3}$ and the force $\propto r^{-4})$. At larger angles, however, the curve is steeper, suggesting a higher power. The continued rapid decrease of G at large angles, e.g., from 45° to 90°, is surprising. It seems unlikely that the quantum effects to be described in the next section could be large in the present case, although they would no doubt amount to something; the de Broglie wave length of the hydrogen or helium molecule should be only 1.0 or 0.8 angstrom,

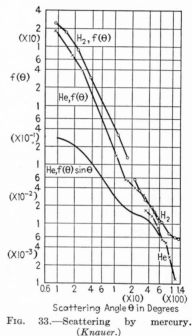

FIG. 33.—Scattering by mercury. (*Knauer.*)

respectively, as against a mean collision diameter, calculated from the viscosity data, of 3.4 or 3.2 angstroms. The final explanation of these phenomena must await the results of theoretical calculations for the actual type of collision involved, and also, perhaps, the obtaining of more accurate data in this difficult but fascinating field.

75. The Wave Mechanics of a Particle. The classical calculations of scattering coefficients that we have just made can only be regarded as a preliminary exploration of the possibilities. For any accurate treatment of molecular scattering the use of wave mechanics is essential. The general wave-mechanical theory of gases is reserved for a special chapter (Chap. X), but the approximate method that is usually employed in handling collision phenomena is simple enough so that a description of it, and of the results that have been obtained by its use, can be given here.   For the understanding of this method the material in Chap. X is not necessary.

The new mechanics starts out from radically novel conceptions concerning the fundamental properties of matter.   In classical theory it was supposed that a molecule or other particle could be imagined to move along a sharply defined path, possessing at every instant of time a definite position in space and a definite velocity, just as a thrown ball can be seen by the eye to trace out a definite curve in the air. According to the new theory, this is not so; sharply defined trajectories do not really exist, and the motion of molecules can be described accurately only in terms of probabilities.

In place of the definite position with cartesian coordinates x, y, z, which a molecule formerly was supposed to possess at a given instant t, we have in the new theory, in its nonrelativistic form with spin omitted, a probability density $P(x, y, z, t)$; this has the significance that $P(x, y, z, t)\, dx\, dy\, dz$ represents the probability that, if a very accurate observation of the molecule's position were made at the time t, this observation would reveal the molecule within the element of volume $dx\, dy\, dz$.   So long as no such observation has been made, however, we are unable to say, and mean anything physical by the statement, that the molecule is definitely at one point or another or is moving in any particular way.   We might, to be sure, repeat our observations of the position at short intervals of time in an effort to follow the molecule along a definite path, which is the method actually employed by astronomers in observing the motions of the planets; but if we did that to so small a body as a molecule, according to present knowledge each observation would disturb the motion so greatly that the path observed in this way would be an irregular zigzag devoid of significance.   It is only in dealing with much heavier bodies, or with molecules moving at much higher speeds than those of thermal agitation, that repeated observations can be imagined to reveal an approximately smooth motion along a classical trajectory.

This revolutionary change in kinematical ideas compels a corresponding change in dynamical laws.   In the place of Newton's laws of motion we have in wave mechanics a law concerning the propagation through space of the probability density.   This law is expressed by an equation of wave propagation analogous to the equations that hold for the propagation of sound or light and is most simply stated in terms, not of the probability itself, but of the so-called probability amplitude, which we shall denote by $\psi(x, y, z, t)$.   The latter is usually a complex number and the square of its absolute value equals the probability density, so that $P = |\psi|^2$, much as the energy density in a light beam is proportional to the squares of the electric and magnetic intensities. The wave equation for ψ, in the case of a particle of mass m moving in a region in which its potential energy is $U(x, y, z)$, as first proposed by Schrödinger in 1926, is

$$\frac{h}{2\pi i}\frac{\partial\psi}{\partial t} - \frac{h^2}{8\pi^2 m}\left(\frac{\partial^2\psi}{\partial x^2} + \frac{\partial^2\psi}{\partial y^2} + \frac{\partial^2\psi}{\partial z^2}\right) + U\psi = 0 \qquad (114)$$

where $i = \sqrt{-1}$ and h is Planck's constant or 6.62×10^{-27} in c.g.s. units.*

We shall not attempt here a detailed mathematical treatment of this equation but shall only describe some of the properties of its solutions. The behavior of ψ is closely similar to the behavior of ordinary waves in a dispersive medium, for simple harmonic waves of ψ having different wave lengths travel at different speeds even in free space where $U = 0$. As a result, if we attempt to localize a molecule closely by giving to ψ initial values that vanish outside of a small limited region, then the "wave packet" of values of ψ so formed rapidly spreads out, in consequence of the varying speeds of the various harmonic wave-trains into which ψ can be resolved, just as an initially concentrated disturbance on a water surface spreads out for the same reason. Such a concentrated distribution of ψ represents a molecule that is for the moment definitely localized in position but has no very definite velocity; for if we determine its position after a considerable lapse of time there is obviously a wide range of locations in which we may find it.

The only way to prevent such a spreading of the packet is to start with a very large patch of waves which are very nearly harmonic or sinusoidal in form, e.g.,

$$\psi = f(x, y, z)e^{-2\pi i\left(\nu t - \frac{x}{\lambda}\right)}$$

where ν is the frequency and λ the wave length, and the coefficient $f(x, y, z)$ is almost constant over a largish region and sinks to zero outside of it. It follows from the theory that such a wave group, like a similar group of waves on water, will keep together for a comparatively long time, moving as a unit with a fairly definite velocity v; this velocity and the corresponding momentum p are related to the

---

* Birge [*Phys. Rev.*, **49**, 204 (1936)] gives $h/e = 1.37588 \times 10^{-17}$, which with $e = 4.805 \times 10^{-10}$ (Sec. 15) makes $h = 6.618 \times 10^{-27}$. Insertion of this value of e and the derived value of m in the Rydberg constant gives $h = 6.632 \times 10^{-27}$; the discrepancy is not yet understood.

wave length λ by the de Broglie equation

$$mv\lambda = p\lambda = h. \tag{115}$$

A packet of this type thus represents the contrary case of a molecule moving with a fairly definite velocity but with a great indefiniteness of position, corresponding to the wide region throughout which ψ and the probability density $P = |\psi|^2 = |f|^2$ have appreciable values.

76. The Indetermination Principle. Intermediate sizes of wave packets correspond to intermediate degrees of indefiniteness of position and of velocity. The general principle involved here is Heisenberg's indetermination (or uncertainty) principle, which can be stated for the case in hand as follows: Let Δ_x, Δ_ξ denote the root-mean-square expectations of variation of a coordinate x and of the corresponding component of momentum ξ from their mean expectations of value, that is

$$\Delta_x = \left[\int_{-\infty}^{\infty}(x - \bar{x})^2|\psi|^2\,dx\right]^{1/2}, \qquad \bar{x} = \int_{-\infty}^{\infty}x|\psi|^2\,dx,$$

with a corresponding definition for Δ_ξ. Then

$$\Delta_x\Delta_\xi \geqq \frac{h}{4\pi}. \tag{116}$$

Let us see what is required by this principle as applied to some actual molecules. Suppose for a nitrogen molecule of mass $m = 4.65 \times 10^{-23}$ g, we allow Δ_x to be 3×10^{-9} cm or about one-thirteenth of the molecular diameter; then the least degree of indefiniteness in the x-component of velocity that we can have is

$$\Delta_v = \Delta_\xi/m = h/(4\pi m\,\Delta_x) = 3780\,\text{cm/sec}$$

or roughly one-twelfth of the mean speed of a nitrogen molecule at 15°C. For a hydrogen molecule of mass 3.35×10^{-24} g, if we make $\Delta_x = 5.4 \times 10^{-9}$ cm or a fifth of its diameter, we have

$$\Delta_v = 2.9 \times 10^4\,\text{cm/sec}$$

or a sixth of the mean speed at 15°C. Decreasing Δ_x increases Δ_v in the same ratio, and *vice versa*. Thus upon the introduction of quantum refinements the classical picture becomes definitely blurred for nitrogen and rather badly so for hydrogen. In the case of a free electron, with mass 9.12×10^{-28} g and mean speed 1.05×10^7 cm/sec at 15°C, even if we take $\Delta_x = 5 \times 10^{-8}$ cm, which exceeds the diameter of most molecules, Δ_v comes out at least equal to 1.16×10^7 cm/sec or larger than the mean speed itself; thus the classical picture fails completely for the collision of an electron with a gas molecule when moving at ordinary thermal speeds or with an energy of a few hundredths of a volt. At lower temperatures the situation is still worse, but at high temperatures, or, in other words, at higher velocities it becomes better.

These considerations make it clear that treatments of collisions in a gas by means of classical theory can possess a high degree of validity only for very heavy molecules or at very high temperatures. On the other hand, it is important to note that the general principles of the conservation of momentum and of energy still hold exactly in wave mechanics in so far as the momentum or the energy possesses a definite value under the circumstances of any particular case.

77. Wave Mechanics and Molecular Collisions. The method of treating a collision between two molecules in wave mechanics runs as follows. It turns out that the problem can be reduced, just as in classical theory, to a problem in the motion of one molecule relative to the other, the motion of their common center of mass being treated separately.

A molecule approaching another with a definite relative velocity **v** is then represented by an infinite train of plane waves of ψ having a definite wave length. This use of monochromatic wave trains corresponds exactly to the use of infinite sinusoidal wave-trains in optics, in treating such problems as the dispersion of light by a prism. In such a train of waves $|\psi|^2$ is uniform, so that equal probabilities are assigned to all positions of the molecule. This fact obviously corresponds to the assumption made concerning the beam of molecules that was employed in defining G in Sec. 68; in fact, the train of waves is usually for convenience regarded as representing such a beam rather than a single molecule, just as an infinite train of monochromatic light waves is commonly regarded as representing a continued flow of radiant energy rather than a single photon.

These incident waves are then found to be partially scattered by the second molecule in all directions, mathematically because of the term $U\psi$ in the wave equation (114); and the intensity of the waves scattered in any given direction, as compared with the intensity of the incident waves, gives the number of scattered molecules crossing unit area in that direction, as compared with the number crossing unit area in the incident beam, and so leads to a knowledge of G.

Without carrying out any calculations, many of the qualitative features of the scattering process can be inferred immediately from these facts by the same kind of reasoning about waves that succeeds so well in optics. If the molecular wave length is small compared with distances within which the scattering potential U varies appreciably, then it can be shown that the scattering follows approximately the classical laws. Thus the classical form of mechanics corresponds to geometrical optics, the classical paths being the analogue of the rays in the optical case. When, however, the wave length exceeds the limit mentioned, the process called diffraction begins to play an appreciable role, just as in the optical case; and finally for sufficiently long waves there is little of the classical picture left, just as the laws of geometrical optics fail completely for very long waves of light. Since according to (115) the wave length goes down as the momentum mv increases, heavy particles behave more nearly classically at a given speed than do light ones, and the behavior of any particle approximates to the classical type when its speed is made great enough.

The wave length associated with a molecule moving at a definite speed thus plays a decisive role in collision processes. Such wave lengths for a number of common molecules moving at their mean speed when in a gas at 15°C are given in the table in Sec. 86 below. They range from 0.1 to 1.2 in units of 10^{-8} cm. The general formula for molecules of molecular weight M moving with the mean speed $\bar{v}$ proper to a gas at absolute temperature T is

$$\lambda = \frac{h}{M m_0 \bar{v}} = \frac{2.74 \times 10^{-7}}{\sqrt{MT}} \text{ cm}$$

where $m_0 = 1.661 \times 10^{-24}$ g or the mass of a molecule with $M = 1$ [cf. eq. (23)] and $h = 6.62 \times 10^{-27}$; the numerical formula is obtained from (66a) in Sec. 30 using $R_M = 83.15 \times 10^6$ as in (20a).

78. Wave-mechanical Scattering Coefficients. Not very many scattering coefficients have as yet been calculated by wave mechanics, principally because the molecular fields are not sufficiently well known.

Some very interesting results have, however, been published recently by Massey and Mohr.* Working with assumed laws of force they found results which in part differed greatly from classical values, even in the case of hard elastic spheres; this seemed somewhat surprising at the time but might really have been anticipated from the optical analogy. A hard sphere scattering a plane beam of molecules corresponds to a sphere reflecting perfectly from its surface a plane beam of light. Now it has been known for a hundred years that there is in the center of the geometrical shadow of such a sphere a bright spot formed by waves which all meet there in phase after being diffracted around the edge. The outer boundary of this bright spot

---

* Massey and Mohr, *Roy. Soc. Proc.*, **141**, 434 (1933); **144**, 188 (1934).

occurs at an angle corresponding roughly to a retardation of one wave length between the two sides of the sphere or, approximately, at an angular distance from the center of the shadow $\theta_c = \lambda/\sigma$ in terms of the wave length λ and the diameter of the sphere σ. As the distance from the sphere is increased, θ_c remains fixed and the bright spot, therefore, spreads out, until finally it becomes much larger than the geometrical shadow itself and the latter is practically obliterated.

This phenomenon appears clearly in the results of Massey and Mohr. Figure 34 shows at A their value of G for a sphere impinging upon a dissimilar fixed sphere at a speed corresponding to a wave length $\lambda = \sigma_{12}/3$, for which $\theta_c = \lambda/\sigma_{12} = \frac{1}{3} = 19°$, σ_{12} being the mean of the diameters of the two spheres. For $\theta > \theta_c$, G approximates to the classical value, $G = \frac{1}{4}\sigma_{12}^2$ [cf. (110c)], but it exhibits oscillations

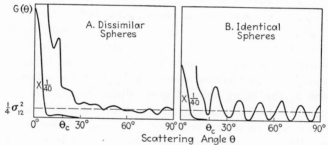

Fig. 34.—Scattering of spheres by spheres.

as θ increases, owing to interference effects; for $\theta_c < \lambda/\sigma_{12}$, on the other hand, we observe a rapid rise which continues until at $\theta = 0$ G reaches a maximum almost 500 times the classical value. The total mutual collision cross section, $S = 2\pi \int_0^\pi G \sin\theta \, d\theta$, is found to vary with λ, but it is never as small as classical theory makes it; for $\lambda = 0$ it is twice the classical value or $2\pi\sigma_{12}^2$, and then it rises to $2.6\ \pi\sigma_{12}^2$ at $\lambda = \frac{2}{5}\pi\sigma_{12}$ and finally to $4\pi\sigma_{12}^2$ at $\lambda = \infty$.

These numbers refer, however, only to spheres *dissimilar* in nature. If they are *exactly alike*, as would be the case for the molecules of a truly homogeneous gas, a curious lack of complete individuality makes itself felt and modifies the diffraction effects. The three values of S corresponding to those just cited become then $2\pi\sigma_{12}^2$, $2.4\ \pi\sigma_{12}^2$, $8.0\ \pi\sigma_{12}^2$, and for the case $\lambda = \sigma_{12}/3$ the coefficient G follows curve B in Fig. 34. Experimental verification of oscillations such as those shown by the latter curve would be extremely interesting, but it will also be difficult to obtain because in averaging the theoretical curve over a maxwellian distribution these oscillations will be effectively obliterated.

The same formulas should hold, according to theory, even for heavy masses such as billiard balls, but only under conditions sufficiently extreme to make diffraction effects appreciable. The doubled collision cross section, as compared with the classical value, for relatively short waves cannot be interpreted as meaning anything so astounding as that two billiard balls are able to deflect each other without touching; for the doubling arises from an excess of extremely minute deflections, and a ball definitely known to have missed the other one would, by the indetermination principle, necessarily have a sufficient indefiniteness in its direction of motion to prevent us from saying whether it had undergone a very minute deflection or not.

Massey and Mohr also made calculations for some force fields that fall off rapidly but extend nominally to infinite distances, and showed that wave mechanics leads in all cases to a finite value for the cross section. The analogous optical phenomenon is that an infinite pane of glass, in which the refractive index rises (or falls off) continuously but more and more slowly in every direction away from a certain point, must, according to geometrical optics, cast an infinite shadow at infinity, whereas physical optics shows that the effects of such deviations in the index will, at great distances from the pane, be largely wiped out by diffraction, and the total amount of darkening in the shadow will therefore be finite. It seems doubtful, however, whether either this finiteness of the cross section in general or the doubling of the cross section for spheres possesses any real significance for kinetic theory because, as has been said, they represent effects of very small deflections.

The applications that Massey and Mohr made of these results to the theory of viscosity will be discussed in connection with that topic.

CHAPTER IV

VISCOSITY, THERMAL CONDUCTION, DIFFUSION

In the preceding chapters we have dealt almost exclusively with a gas which from the macroscopic viewpoint is in complete equilibrium. In the present chapter we shall now take up some of the principal phenomena exhibited by gases under circumstances such that, while they may perhaps be in a steady state, yet they are not in equilibrium in the strict sense of the term. The topics of *gaseous viscosity*, the *conduction of heat*, and *diffusion* will be taken up in order. The methods of handling these three phenomena are so similar that they are most conveniently discussed as a group; they are often referred to under the name of *transport phenomena*. The conduction of electricity through gases is another very similar topic, but it involves so many novel features that it is best reserved for a special chapter.

Throughout the discussion we have kept a double goal in view. On the one hand, we endeavor to derive known properties of gases from simple and broad theoretical assumptions, and such must always be the primary goal in the development of any theory. On the other hand, the comparison of the results of theory with experimental data has also yielded much information concerning molecular magnitudes. The combination of these two viewpoints is especially characteristic of kinetic theory and we shall encounter many more examples of it. During the past century the theory was on trial, and every new explanation of a gaseous property constituted a fresh triumph and a welcome addition to the evidence for its truth. During the present century, however, such a wealth of direct evidence has been secured in favor of the basic assumptions that the theory is now universally regarded as well established and the emphasis in research has definitely shifted to the problem of discovering the properties of the molecules. It is still useful, nevertheless, to consider in what way the general properties of gases arise as consequences of the properties and motions of the molecules, and it will always be worth while, as fresh data accumulate, to make sure that no contradiction develops anywhere between the theoretical conclusions and the experimental facts such as might force a radical revision of our fundamental ideas.

A. VISCOSITY

79. Viscosity. The phenomenon of viscosity occurs in a fluid when it is undergoing shearing motion. To start with the simplest case possible, suppose the gas is in mass motion with a velocity everywhere the same in direction but varying in magnitude from point to point, and let this spatial variation of the magnitude be most rapid in a certain direction perpendicular to that of the velocity itself, while over any plane perpendicular to this direction of most rapid variation the velocity is constant. The maximum rate of variation is then called the velocity gradient. Under these conditions it is found experimentally that the stress which acts in the gas across any plane

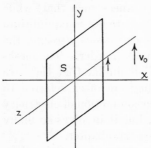

perpendicular to the direction of the velocity gradient is not of the nature of a simple pressure normal to the plane but contains also a tangential or shearing component, whose direction is always such as to tend to equalize the velocities at different points; and when the effect is small, as it is in all gases and in mobile liquids at not too high velocities, the shearing component of the stress is proportional to the velocity gradient.

Fig. 35.—Illustrating viscosity.

To obtain a mathematical formulation of this idea, let us take the x-axis in the direction of the assumed velocity gradient and the y-axis parallel to the direction of the velocity itself (cf. Fig. 35). Then if we draw in the fluid a plane surface perpendicular to the x-axis and therefore parallel to the velocity, the fluid lying on each side of this surface exerts a shearing force acting in a direction parallel to the y-axis upon the fluid lying on the other side of the surface. If we denote the (mass) velocity by v_0, the velocity gradient is dv_{0y}/dx; and if we then denote by P_{xy} the shearing component of force in the y-direction which the medium on the side of the surface toward $+x$ exerts upon each unit area of that on the side toward $-x$, this force being called positive when it acts toward $+y$, we can write

$$P_{xy} = \eta \frac{dv_{0y}}{dx}. \qquad (117)$$

The factor of proportionality η in this equation is called the coefficient of viscosity of the fluid or, for short, its viscosity.

At the same time, of course, by Newton's third law the fluid lying beyond the plane toward $-x$ exerts a force $-P_{xy}$ per unit area on the fluid lying on the side toward $+x$.*

The problem for kinetic theory is then to infer the value of the coefficient η and the nature of its properties from the assumed or known fundamental properties of the molecules. Before taking up this subject, however, it may be worth while to interject a short discussion of fluid stresses in general; the uninterested reader can easily omit this and pass at once to the following section.

80. Fluid Stresses in General.   If a small plane be drawn anywhere in a medium which for the purpose in hand can be treated as continuous, and if one side of this plane be labeled positive and the other negative, then the medium lying on the positive side of the plane will be exerting a certain vector force upon the medium lying on the negative side; the amount of this force per unit of area is called the *traction* across the plane.   At the same time, of course, the medium on the negative side exerts an exactly equal but opposite vector force upon that on the positive side.   The traction can in all cases be resolved into one component acting perpendicular to the plane and a second "tangential" component acting in a direction parallel to it. In general, both components vary as the orientation of the plane is altered; but it can be shown that if the values of the traction are known for any three mutually perpendicular positions of the plane the traction can be expressed in terms of these three values when the plane has any other orientation.

Now it is characteristic of a fluid, as opposed to a solid, that when it is at rest the traction across any plane in it is wholly normal to the plane and is thus of the nature of a pressure, either positive or negative; and furthermore, that this pressure at a given point in the fluid is independent of the orientation of the surface across which it acts, which is commonly expressed by saying that the pressure is equal in all directions.

On the other hand, when the fluid is moving, the stresses become altered in consequence of the relative motion of its parts.   Even the normal component of the traction now varies, in general, as the test

* It is not generally remarked in treatises on kinetic theory that tangential stress forces of equal magnitude must likewise act in the x-direction across surfaces drawn perpendicular to the y-axis; if they did not, a cube of fluid with faces perpendicular to these two directions would obviously be set into rotation.   The interested reader will find it an excellent exercise to construct the theory of these stresses, in parallel with the treatment of the others that is here given.

plane is rotated; so that the pressure is no longer equal in all directions, although, of course, it is always the same in each of two diametrically opposite directions.   An analysis of the most general type of continuous motion shows, however, that the motion can be resolved, in the neighborhood of any point, into three shearing motions in three perpendicular planes, plus a motion of compression or dilatation occurring at an equal rate in all directions.   The differences in pressure referred to above and the tangential stresses then arise as the sum of the three tangential shearing stresses, each related to one of the shearing components of the motion in terms of the viscosity η as described above, together with a positive or negative component of pressure proportional to the rate of compression or dilatation.   The constant of proportionality for this latter part of the stress constitutes a second frictional constant characteristic of the moving fluid.   Nothing is known experimentally, however, in regard to its value, and theory indicates that in a gas it should be small if not actually zero; accordingly we shall give it no further consideration.

81. Simple Theory of Viscosity.   The physical explanation of viscosity in a gas becomes obvious at once if, returning to the case

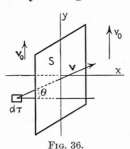

FIG. 36.

described in Sec. 79 we consider the vector momentum carried by the molecules across a macroscopically small plane surface S drawn perpendicular to the x-axis, i.e., to the direction of the velocity gradient (cf. Fig. 36).   In the first chapter, when we made our calculation of the pressure we considered only the component of the momentum that is normal to S; now we turn our attention to the component tangential to S.   We shall suppose, as usual, that the molecules influence each other only when extremely close together, so that we can neglect, for the present, those short-lived situations in which there is mutual force-action between two molecules situated on opposite sides of the plane.

Suppose, for definiteness, that dv_0/dx is positive.   Then molecules crossing S from left to right come from regions where the mass velocity v_0 is less than it is in the region into which they go and so tend to arrive in their new positions with less than the proper amount of y-momentum, whereas at the same time those crossing to the left come from regions where v_0 is greater and so tend to carry out an excessive share of such momentum.   In this way the gas lying to the right of S tends on the whole to suffer a loss of y-momentum, and this is equivalent to the action of a force on it directed toward $-y$, while the gas on the left tends similarly to gain momentum and so experiences a force toward $+y$.

In order to develop this idea quantitatively we need to know how much momentum is carried by the molecules. Now the velocity of a molecule is determined as a result of its last collision. We are led therefore to consider the distribution of velocities among those molecules which collide in a given element of volume $d\tau$. A natural assumption to make, and the one that was universally made in the early days of the theory, is that these molecules have an average velocity after their collisions in $d\tau$ equal to the mass velocity of the gas at that point. If x denotes the distance of $d\tau$ from S and v_{0s} the value of the mass velocity at S, its value at $d\tau$ can be written $v_{0s} + xv_0'$, where v_0' stands for the value of dv_c/dx at S, provided we may suppose v_0' to vary only inappreciably over a distance comparable with the molecular mean free path. Let us suppose that the molecules all have mass m. Then those that collide in $d\tau$ carry away from it, according to the assumption just made, an average y-momentum of amount $m(v_{0s} + xv_0')$. The total momentum carried toward $+x$ across unit area of S per second will therefore be obtained if we take the average of this expression for all molecules that cross toward $+x$, and multiply this average by the number of molecules that cross in this direction, which is given by (72a) in Sec. 37. The resulting expression for the momentum is

$$\tfrac{1}{4}\, n\bar{v}m(\overline{v_{0s} + xv_0'}) = \tfrac{1}{4}\, n\bar{v}m(v_{0s} + \bar{x}v_0').$$

Here n is the number of molecules in unit volume and $\bar{v}$ their mean speed, and we have been able to write $\overline{xv_0'} = \bar{x}v_0'$ because v_0', like v_{0s}, is the same for each molecule.

We need now to find $\bar{x}$. This quantity must obviously be connected somehow with the mean free path. Now after a molecule crosses S, its chance of collision in going any given distance is the same as if its last collision had been made at S; hence the molecules must go, before colliding again, a mean distance beyond S equal to their ordinary mean free path L_v. By symmetry, however, they must also have come on the average, before reaching S, an equal distance from the point of their last collision. Thus for molecules that cross S in a direction inclined at a given angle θ to the normal drawn toward $+x$, the quantity $\bar{x}$ is simply the component of L_v perpendicular to S, and for these molecules $\bar{x} = -L_v \cos \theta$. By (71$b$) in Sec. 37 the number that cross S with given speed v and with θ in a given range $d\theta$ can be written $n' \sin \theta \cos \theta\, d\theta$ where n' is a certain number independent of θ. The average of x for all molecules that cross with speed v is therefore [cf. (63b) in Sec. 29]

$$\bar{x} = \int_0^{\pi/2}(-L_v \cos \theta)n' \sin \theta \cos \theta \, d\theta \div \int_0^{\pi/2} n' \sin \theta \cos \theta \, d\theta = -\tfrac{2}{3} L_v.$$

Let us for the present ignore the variation of L_v with speed and replace L_v by L, the general mean free path. Then $\bar{x}$ takes on the same value, $-\tfrac{2}{3} L$, for all of the molecules. Accordingly, the expression obtained just above for the rate of transfer of y-momentum by molecules crossing from left to right becomes

$$\frac{1}{4} nm\bar{v}\left(v_{0s} - \frac{2Lv_0'}{3}\right).$$

In the same way one finds that molecules crossing toward the *left* carry y-momentum *out* of the region lying on the right of S at the rate

$$\frac{1}{4} nm\bar{v}\left(v_{0s} + \frac{2Lv_0'}{3}\right);$$

and subtracting this expression from the previous one we have, finally, for the *net* transfer of y-momentum across S toward $+x$, per unit area per second,

$$-\tfrac{1}{3} nm\bar{v}Lv_0'. \tag{118}$$

By the definition of the coefficient of viscosity, e.g. as expressed in eq. (117), this net transfer must also equal $-\eta v_0'$; the absence of a minus sign in (117) is due to the fact that there P_{xy} refers to transfer toward $-x$. Hence

$$\eta = \tfrac{1}{3} nm\bar{v}L = \tfrac{1}{3} \rho\bar{v}L, \tag{119}$$

for a homogeneous gas of density ρ. This formula was obtained by Maxwell in 1860.

From a formula such as this, in which η, ρ, and $\bar{v}$ are all known, values of the molecular magnitude L can be calculated. Before proceeding to do this, however, we must first investigate the magnitude of the errors arising from the rather violent simplifications that have been introduced in the course of our deduction. It will be found that because of these errors the numerical factor $\frac{1}{3}$ requires considerable correction.

Problem. Develop the corresponding theory for a two-dimensional gas, showing that the number crossing unit length per second is $n\bar{v}/\pi$, and that $\bar{x} = \pi L/4$ and

$$\eta = \tfrac{1}{2} \rho\bar{v}L.$$

82. The Mean Free Path across a Fixed Plane. An interesting objection to the reasoning just given has sometimes been raised on the ground that, since the mean free path between two successive collisions is certainly L, the mean path from the last collision up to the plane should be, not L as we inferred it to be, but only $L/2$, leaving an equal amount $L/2$ for the mean path from the plane up to the next collision.

This reasoning rests, however, upon a tacit assumption that is not justified. Those free paths that are executed in such a position that they intersect the plane S constitute a special group selected out of all the free paths executed in the gas, and it is not safe to assume without proof that their average length will be the same as the average length of all the free paths. As a matter of fact, a long free path stands a much better chance of happening to intersect the plane than does a short one (cf. Fig. 37, in which $S'S''$ is the trace of the plane, and free paths of two different lengths are drawn). We can write for the probability that a path of length l intersects a given plane, cl, c being a factor of proportionality independent of l. Then, if $N\psi(l)\ dl$ paths are executed per second with lengths in a range dl, $cNl\psi(l)\ dl$ among these will intersect the plane, and the average length of all that intersect will be

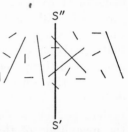

Fig. 37.—Free paths near a plane.

$$\bar{l} = \frac{\int cNl^2\psi(l)\ dl}{\int cNl\psi(l)\ dl} = \frac{\int_0^\infty l^2\psi(l)\ dl}{\int_0^\infty l\psi(l)\ dl}.$$

The average length $\bar{l}$ of paths intersecting a plane thus depends in general upon the form of their distribution function, $\psi(l)$. For molecules moving at a given speed v, according to (98b) in Sec. 59 $\psi \propto e^{-l/L_v}$, and evaluating the integrals in the formula just obtained we find $\bar{l} = 2L_v$. Thus in a maxwellian gas the mean free path of those molecules that cross a plane at given speed is just twice the mean free path for all molecules in the gas that are moving at that speed. The ratio of $\bar{l}$ to L for all molecules regardless of their speed can be written down in the form of an integral and comes out a little different from 2. In all cases, however, the mean distance to the plane, and also the mean distance traversed beyond it, are each just half of $\bar{l}$ itself.

As a more concrete example illustrative of the same principle, suppose a large bundle of straws of varying lengths is tossed high in the air and allowed to fall upon the floor in random distribution. Then the average length of those straws which happen to fall across a given crack in the floor will be greater than the average length for the whole bundle; if the lengths are distributed exponentially, it will be just twice as great.

Problems. 1. In the illustration of the straws just given, find the ratio of the average lengths of those lying across the crack to the average length of all of them, when the straws have lengths distributed equally between 0 and l_0.   *Ans.:* $\frac{4}{3}l_0$.

2. When a die is thrown, the mean number of throws (i.e., of acts of throwing) between sixes is, of course, 6. Show that, if an observer looks in at irregular intervals and watches each time until a six is thrown, he will watch on the average for 6 throws, and if he asks each time how many throws have occurred since the last six, he will learn that this six lies on the average 6 throws back, the average of the total numbers of throws between sixes as thus observed by him being 12.

83. Correction for the Velocity Spread. One of the errors in the deduction of formula (119) lies in the assumption that the mean free path is the same for molecules moving at all speeds. Let us investigate the magnitude of this error. In doing so we shall still retain the assumption concerning molecular velocities, amplifying it into the more specific assertion that those molecules which have just collided in any element of volume $d\tau$ possess for the moment the velocity distribution characteristic of a gas that is in equilibrium but moving with the mass velocity v_0.

The distribution in velocity of these molecules that have just collided is easily found. Using (61a) in Sec. 28, we have as the number of molecules that collide in a second in $d\tau$ with a speed of thermal agitation lying in a given range dv' *before* collision

$$4\pi(n\,d\tau)\Theta_{v'}Av'^2e^{-\beta^2v'^2}\,dv',$$

n being the total number of molecules per unit volume and $\Theta_{v'}$ the collision rate for molecules moving with this speed. Since we are assuming equilibrium of velocities to exist, an equal number of other molecules must in the same time acquire this speed v'. Of these latter, which according to the assumption just stated have thermal velocities equally distributed in direction, a fraction $\dfrac{\sin\theta\,d\theta\,d\varphi}{4\pi}$ will have their velocities lying in an element of solid angle $\sin\theta\,d\theta\,d\varphi$ [cf. (29)]; let the axis of polars be taken through $d\tau$ normal to S and let the reference plane from which φ is measured be taken parallel to the xy-plane (cf. Fig. 38), the mass velocity being assumed as before to have the direction of y with a gradient in the direction of x. Of these molecules again, by (98a), the fraction $e^{-\Theta_{v'}r/v'}$ will eventually cross S without having been stopped by a collision, r being the distance along the path from $d\tau$ to S. Finally, the y-component of $\mathbf{v}'$ is $v'\sin\theta\cos\varphi$,* so that, if we write again $v_{0S} + xv_0'$ for the mass velocity at $d\tau$, v_0' standing for dv_0/dx and x for the coordinate of $d\tau$ with the origin on S, the total y-momentum of a molecule is

$$mv_y = m(v_{0S} + xv_0' + v'\sin\theta\cos\varphi).$$

The product of all these quantities is

$$nmA\Theta_v v'^2 e^{-\beta^2 v'^2}(v_{0S} + xv_0' + v'\sin\theta\cos\varphi)e^{-r\Theta_{v'}/v'}$$
$$\sin\theta\,d\theta\,d\varphi\,dv'\,d\tau; \quad (120a)$$

and the integral of this expression over $0 < \varphi < 2\pi$, $0 < \theta < \pi/2$, $0 < v' < \infty$ then represents the total amount of y-momentum carried across S per second toward $+x$ by molecules whose last collision occurred in $d\tau$. If we then also integrate $d\tau$ over a cylinder of unit cross section standing normally on S, we have the total transfer per second across unit of area of S; to be sure, some molecules that actually originate within this cylinder will ultimately leave it and cross S outside of its base, but for every one that does this another one moving in the same direction will originate outside the cylinder and, after entering it, cross through its base. To carry out the specified integration over $d\tau$ it suffices to replace $d\tau$ by dx and then integrate over the range $-\infty < x < 0$, for the result of integrating with respect to φ, θ and v' is independent of y and z, and the integration over the dy and dz in $d\tau$ merely introduces the unit cross-sectional area of the cylinder. Since $r = \dfrac{(-x)}{\cos\theta}$, the complete integral thus obtained can be written in iterated form thus (v being substituted for v' in the definite integral):

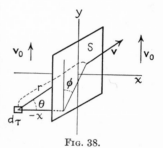

Fig. 38.

$$nmA\int_0^\infty \Theta_v v^2 e^{-\beta^2 v^2}\,dv \int_0^{\pi/2}\sin\theta\,d\theta \int_0^{2\pi} d\varphi$$
$$\int_{-\infty}^0 (v_{0S} + xv_0' + v\sin\theta\cos\varphi)e^{\frac{\Theta_v x}{v\cos\theta}}\,dx. \quad (120b)$$

---

* Resolve $\mathbf{v}$ first into $v\sin\theta$, $v\cos\theta$; then only $v\sin\theta$ has a y-component, and its magnitude is $v\sin\theta\cos\varphi$.

For the momentum carried across S in the opposite direction we then obtain an expression differing from this only in that x runs from 0 to $+\infty$ and the exponent of e is $-\Theta_v x/v \cos\theta$ because in this case $x = +r\cos\theta$. The difference between the two expressions thus obtained is then the net gain of y-momentum in the gas to the right of S, per unit area of S per second, and dividing this difference by $-v_0'$ we have the coefficient of viscosity η. Now

$$\int_{-\infty}^{0} (v_{0s} + v\sin\theta\cos\varphi)e^{\frac{\Theta_v x}{v\cos\theta}}\,dx$$

$$= \int_{0}^{\infty} (v_{0s} + v\sin\theta\cos\varphi)e^{-\frac{\Theta_v x}{v\cos\theta}}\,dx$$

simply by replacing x by $-x$; hence in the subtraction of the two expressions this part of the integral over x in (120b) cancels the corresponding term in the second expression. On the other hand,

$$\int_{-\infty}^{0} xv_0'e^{\frac{\Theta_v x}{v\cos\theta}}\,dx = -\int_{0}^{\infty} xv_0'e^{-\frac{\Theta_v x}{v\cos\theta}}\,dx$$

$$= -v_0'v^2\frac{\cos^2\theta}{\Theta_v^2},$$

so that in the subtraction this term becomes multiplied by 2. Hence, introducing the further values, $\int_{0}^{2\pi} d\varphi = 2\pi$,

$$\int_{0}^{\pi/2} \sin\theta\cos^2\theta\,d\theta = \tfrac{1}{3},$$

we find finally for η, after dividing out $-v_0'$,

$$\eta = \tfrac{4}{3}\pi nmA \int_{0}^{\infty} \frac{v^4}{\Theta_v} e^{-\beta^2 v^2}\,dv.$$

Here let us replace v by the new variable of integration $x = \beta v$ and let us also insert $A = \beta^3/\pi^{3/2}$ from (60) and $nm = \rho$, the density in grams; the result is

$$\eta = \frac{4}{3\sqrt{\pi}} \frac{\rho}{\beta^2} \int_{0}^{\infty} \frac{x^4}{\Theta_v} e^{-x^2}\,dx.$$

Let us then introduce $\bar{v} = (2/\sqrt{\pi})(1/\beta)$ or $1/\beta = \sqrt{\pi}\bar{v}/2$ from (65a) in Sec. 30, and for Θ_v let us insert its value from (104a) in Sec. 63, introducing in this latter expression $\Theta = \bar{v}/L$ from (95). The result is:

$$\eta = \frac{2}{3}\sqrt{2\pi}\rho\bar{v}L \int_{0}^{\infty} x^4 e^{-x^2}\left[e^{-x^2} + \left(2x + \frac{1}{x}\right)\int_{0}^{x} e^{-y^2}\,dy\right]^{-1}dx. \quad (121)$$

For the definite integral occurring here Boltzmann found by a numerical quadrature $0.838264/4 = 0.209566.$* Inserting this value we obtain the formula found by Boltzmann in 1881,

$$\eta = 0.350 \ \rho \bar{v} L. \tag{122}$$

This differs from the result of the simple theory as expressed in eq. (119) only in that the numerical factor is 0.350 in place of 0.333. Thus with all this work we have only changed the numerical coefficient by 5 per cent. We have here another typical example of the smallness of the correction that is required by the maxwellian distribution of velocities in those cases in which the spread of velocities merely plays the role of a disturbing element in the situation.

84. Further Correction of the Viscosity Formula. Even so, the calculation still contains another error of a very similar sort which we have not yet mentioned. We have treated the collision rate $\Theta_{v'}$ as a constant, whereas in reality it will vary during the flight of a molecule because of the variation in the mass velocity of the gas through which the molecule is passing. The necessary calculation to allow for this effect is straightforward, but it is tedious and no details of it will be given here, for a reason that will appear presently; the final result is to replace Boltzmann's formula (122) by

$$\eta = 0.310 \ \rho \bar{v} L. \tag{123}$$

This is the value of η that follows rigorously from the assumption that the velocity distribution of the molecules that have just collided at any point is maxwellian. This assumption itself is open to grave question, however. The molecules that assemble momentarily at a given point have come from regions of the gas having different mass velocities and so must exhibit some departure from a maxwellian distribution. Our own calculation indicates, in fact, that molecules which have come from a region of higher mass velocity have an average excess of velocity in that direction, and after they collide with others it is quite thinkable that they might retain some of this excess so that the transfer of y-momentum would be greater than we have found it to be.

A completely accurate theory of viscosity could undoubtedly be developed by introducing further corrections for effects of this sort. The most satisfactory theory has actually been achieved, however, by viewing the whole molecular process from quite a different standpoint. Accordingly, we shall now abandon the line of attack that we have been following and make a fresh start.

* Cf. L. Boltzmann, "Gastheorie," vol. I, p. 78.

85. New View of the Molecular Process.   If we look at the molecular processes from a certain angle, we arrive at the interesting conclusion that the force of viscosity actually has its entire origin in a certain type of departure from the maxwellian distribution of velocities.

For, if χ is any molecular magnitude whatever, the rate of transfer of χ across unit area of a plane is clearly

$$\Sigma v_\perp \chi \tag{124}$$

where $v_\perp$ is the component of the molecular velocity perpendicular to the plane, taken positive in the direction chosen as that of positive net transfer; the summation extends over all molecules in unit volume in the immediate neighborhood of the plane.   Negative values of $v_\perp$ serve automatically in the sum to subtract the amount of χ that is carried backward.   (Cf., e.g., our first deduction of η in Sec. 81, or the calculation of the pressure in Sec. 5.)   In (124) we have a general expression for the rate of transfer of any molecular magnitude.

To obtain the viscosity, we have then only to substitute in (124), in our previous notation, $\chi = mv_y$ and $v'_\perp = v_x$; if we also suppose the velocity gradient to be unity, the rate of transfer of momentum thus obtained is numerically equal to the coefficient of viscosity η.   We thus obtain

$$\eta = \Sigma m v_x v_y. \tag{125}$$

This sum would obviously vanish owing to the symmetry of $f(\mathbf{v})$ if the distribution were exactly maxwellian!

The viscosity can be calculated at once from (125) if we can find out what the distribution of velocities actually is in a shearing gas. Now this distribution must be a certain type of steady solution of the Boltzmann differential equation, as represented by eq. (87) above. Accordingly, Boltzmann himself attempted to solve this equation for the case of a shearing gas; and a feasible method of doing this by means of successive approximations has been elaborated by Enskog.* A somewhat different method of approach, initiated by Clausius and Maxwell, seems, however, to be easier to follow and has been carried through by Chapman.   For obtaining accurate results these methods are so far superior to the free-path line of attack that the latter might well be relegated to the status of a historical curiosity, were it not that it throws a peculiarly vivid light upon the complexity of molecular phenomena in a gas; furthermore, simple calculations like our

---

* ENSKOG, "Kinetische Theorie der Vorgänge in mässig verdünnten Gasen," Dissertation, Upsala, 1917.

first one often serve a good purpose because they indicate quickly the order of an effect and the quantities upon which it depends.

In our treatment of heat conduction we shall actually employ an approximate form of the Maxwell-Chapman method. The necessary calculations are rather lengthy, however, and the features of the method are less well brought out in the case of viscosity; for these reasons the application of this method to viscosity will be left as a problem (Sec. 101) for the student and only the final result will be stated here.

86. Final Viscosity Formula. Magnitudes of L and δ. The approximate form of the new method, which is equivalent to that employed in Chapman's first paper, when applied to the treatment of viscosity yields for the numerical factor in (123) above 0.491 in place of 0.310 [cf. (156b) below]. The rigorous development of the same method by means of successive approximations, as worked out by Chapman* gives, in place of (123),

$$\eta = 0.491(1 + \epsilon)\rho \bar{v} L_{vc}, \qquad L_{vc} = \frac{1}{\sqrt{2}n S_{vc}}; \qquad (126a)$$

here S_{vc} is a sort of *mean equivalent cross section for viscosity and heat conduction*, which is given in terms of the scattering coefficient by eq. (153) in Sec. 100 below, and ϵ is a number which is probably very small for any actual molecular field. For a repulsive force $\propto 1/r^n$, $\epsilon = 0$ when $n = 5$ and rises as n increases only to 0.016 for $n = \infty$; this last case corresponds to hard elastic spheres, for which accordingly we can write

$$\eta = 0.499 \, \rho \bar{v} L, \qquad (126b)$$

since for such spheres $S_{vc} = \pi\sigma^2$ and L_{vc} then becomes the ordinary mean free path L. This latter formula was found also by Enskog.† As usual, ρ is the density in grams per cubic centimeter and $\bar{v}$ is the mean molecular speed; and the results are accurate only for an indefinitely rare gas.

The reason for such a large increase in the numerical coefficient, from 0.310 to 0.499, lies in the persistence of velocities which was mentioned above. Molecules exhibit a certain average tendency to continue moving in their original direction after a collision; in the usual case of elastic spheres the average component in the original direction after collision can be shown to amount to some 40 per cent

---

* Chapman, *Phil. Trans.*, **211A**, 433 (1912); **216A**, 279 (1916); **217A**, 115 (1918).

† Enskog. *loc. cit.*

of the velocity before collision. In our analysis above we assumed that those molecules which collide in a given element of volume $d\tau$ and then move off toward the right, for example, had a transverse or y-component of velocity equal to the average y-component for all molecules in $d\tau$, but in reality these particular molecules originally entered $d\tau$ predominantly from the left and so arrived there with an average transverse velocity characteristic of a region lying to the left, and part of this difference as compared with the general average in $d\tau$ persists after collision and is carried along farther by the molecules as they move off toward the right. The effect is clearly the same as if these molecules had collided somewhere to the left of $d\tau$, and so amounts to a virtual increase in L, with a resulting increase in the transfer of momentum.

Equation (126b) is probably to be regarded as the correct formula for a rarefied homogeneous gas of elastic spherical molecules. Since everything in the equation is already known except L, we can employ the equation to calculate values of the mean free path and then from these by means of (106d), $L = 1/\sqrt{2}\pi n\sigma^2$, we can calculate values of the molecular diameter σ. We have here probably the most reliable source of information in regard to these quantities that can be obtained from the ordinary properties of gases.

Values of L and σ so calculated for a number of gases are given in the table on p. 149. They can be regarded, of course, only as *equivalent elastic-sphere* mean free paths and diameters, since no molecules really are hard spheres, but they are very useful for many sorts of approximate calculations. If the exact law of molecular force were known it might be preferable to calculate the cross section from (126a) and then to calculate from it an equivalent diameter

$$\sigma_{vc} = (S_{vc}/\pi)^{1/2},$$

but the value of the "diameter" so found would probably differ only moderately from the elastic-sphere value. The temperature has been chosen as 15°C rather than the more customary 0°C because the former lies closer to common laboratory temperatures; the only exception is Hg, for which η, L, and σ are given at 219.4°C. The power of the temperature to which η is approximately proportional near 15°C is given as n; thus $\eta \propto T^n$, $L \propto T^{n-1/2}$ at constant density, and $\sigma \propto T^{-1/2(n-1/2)}$. In all cases L refers to atmospheric pressure, being arbitrarily reduced to this pressure in the case of H_2O and Hg. The sources from which the data for η were taken are listed below the table.

87. Variation of Viscosity with Density. Our formulas predict several interesting general properties that the viscosity should have.

Some Molecular Data

	M	η	L	σ	n	λ
Unit..........		$(10^{-7}$ dyne sec/ cm)	$(10^{-6}$ cm)	$(10^{-8}$ cm)		$(10^{-8}$ cm)
H$_2$.............	2.016	871 (1)(2)(16)	11.77	2.74	0.69	1.136
H$_2^2$ (heavy hyd.)	4.027	871 (17)	11.77	2.74	0.69(?)	0.8040
Helium........	4.002	1943 (3)	18.62	2.18	0.64	0.8065
CH$_4$ (methane)	16.03	1077 (1)	5.16	4.14	0.88	0.4030
NH$_3$..........	17.03	970 (4)	4.51	4.43	1.09	0.3910
H$_2$O..........	18.02	926*(14)	4.18	4.60	(1.07)	0.3801
Neon.........	20.18	3095 (3)(12)	13.22	2.59	0.67	0.3592
N$_2$.............	28.02	1734 (3)(5)	6.28	3.75	0.77	0.3048
C$_2$H$_4$ (ethylene)	28.03	998 (4)	3.61	4.95	0.95	0.3048
C$_2$H$_6$ (ethane)..	30.05	900 (1)	3.15	5.30	0.97	0.2943
O$_2$.............	32.00	2003 (1)(6)	6.79	3.61	0.81	0.2852
HCl...........	36.46	1397 (15)	4.44	4.46	(1.07)	0.2672
Argon.........	39.94	2196 (3)(7)	6.66	3.64	0.86	0.2553
CO$_2$...........	44.00	1448 (3)(8)(16)	4.19	4.59	0.95	0.2432
Krypton......	82.9	2431 (9)	5.12	4.16	(.85)	0.1772
CH$_3$Br (methyl bromide)....	94.94	1310 (10)	2.58	5.85	1.10	0.1656
Xenon........	130.2	2236 (18)	3.76	4.85	0.92	0.1414
Hg............	200.6	4700 (13) (219.4°C)	8.32 (219.4°C)	4.26 (219.4°C)		0.1139
Air...........	28.96	1796 (11)	6.40	3.72	0.79	0.2998
Electron.......	5.490 $\times$ 10^{-4}					68.86

* Calculated from a measurement on saturated vapor.

M = molecular weight, η = viscosity, L = mean free path at atmospheric pressure, σ = elastic-sphere equivalent diameter of the molecule, λ = molecular wave length at the mean speed $\bar{v}$; n is the exponent in: $\eta \propto T^n$, $L \propto T^{n-\frac{1}{2}}$ at constant density or $L \propto T^{n+\frac{1}{2}}$ at constant pressure, $\sigma \propto T^{-\frac{1}{2}(n-\frac{1}{2})}$, near 15°C. The temperature is 15°C except for η, L, σ for Hg.

Sources of material:

(1) Trautz and Sorg. *Ann. Physik*, **10**, 81 (1931); 2) Trautz and Stauff, *ibid.*, **2**, 737 (1929); (3) Trautz and Zink, *ibid.*, **7**, 427 (1930); (4) Trautz and Heberling, *ibid.*, **10**, 155 (1931); (5) Trautz and Baumann, *ibid.*, **2**, 733 (1929); (6) Trautz and Melster, *ibid.*, **7**, 409 (1930); (7) Trautz and Binkele, *ibid.*, **5**, 561 (1930); (8) Trautz and Kurz, *ibid.*, **9**, 981 (1931); (9) Nasini and Rossi, *Gazz. chim. ital.*, **58**, 433 (1928); (10) Titani, *Bull. Chem. Soc. Japan*, **5**, 98 (1930); (11) Kellström, *Nature*, **136**, 682 (1935); (12) Edwards, *Roy. Soc. Proc.*, **119**, 578, 1928; (13) Braune, Basch and Wentzel, *Zeits. phys. Chem.*, (A) **137**, 447 (1928); (14) Braune and Linke, *ibid.*, (A) **148**, 195 (1930); (15) Jung and Schmick, *ibid.*, (B) **7**, 130 (1930); (16) Sutherland and Maass, *Canad. Jour. Res.*, **6**, 428 (1932); (17) Van Cleave and Maass, *ibid.*, **12**, 57 (1935); (18) Trautz and Heberling, *Ann. Physik*, **20**, 118 (1934).

Suppose we keep the *temperature constant*. Then $\bar{v}$ remains constant, and so does ρL, according to our conclusions in Sec. 58. Hence our formulas indicate that, for a rarefied gas composed of molecules interacting only when very close together, the *viscosity* should be *independent* of the *density*. This result, contrasting strongly with our natural expectation that less gas ought to mean less viscous drag, was deduced from theory by Maxwell in 1860 and was found actually to be confirmed in some careful experiments that he performed upon air. In its day this constituted a particularly striking success for kinetic theory. Later work indicates that this law holds for the viscosity of all gases which are sufficiently rare, but it fails, naturally, at high densities; for example, the viscosity of CO_2 at 40°C is 1.57×10^{-4} c.g.s. units at 1 atmosphere and rises only to 1.69×10^{-4} at 23.8 atmospheres, but thereafter it increases more and more rapidly up to 4.83×10^{-4} at 100 atmospheres, being not far from proportional to ρ at this latter pressure. Theoretical treatments of the variation at considerable densities do not yet exist.

As the density is made vanishingly low, however, the effects of viscosity must eventually decrease, and it is easy to see under what conditions this should occur. When the mean free path finally becomes comparable with the spatial dimensions of the phenomenon under observation, the basis of our calculation fails and departures from our formulas may be expected to set in. When the density is made so extremely low that intermolecular collisions are actually infrequent, the effects of the individual molecules must be simply additive, and the viscosity should then be directly proportional to the density; we shall return to this subject in a special chapter on low-pressure phenomena (Chap. VIII) and shall find that the theoretical prediction is confirmed.

88. Variation of Viscosity with Temperature. Suppose now, on the other hand, we keep the density constant and vary the temperature. Under these conditions, as we have seen in Sec. 58, the mean free path L should be a constant, provided the gas is rare and composed of molecules that interact only when close together. The mean speed $\bar{v}$, however, is proportional to the square root of the absolute temperature T. Hence, in such a gas, according to our approximate formulas (119) or (123), the coefficient of viscosity should be proportional to $T^{\frac{1}{2}}$; and according to (126b) the fully corrected formula leads to the same conclusion at least for hard elastic spheres.

Now it is a fact that the viscosity of gases does rise in all cases with a rise of temperature; and this qualitative confirmation of the theory is particularly interesting because the viscosity of liquids is observed to change in exactly the opposite direction, and a decrease is what we might naturally expect as a result of the increased mobility of the molecules at higher temperatures. The increase is in all gases more rapid than the square root of T, however. In Fig. 39 are plotted values of η against T for six common gases, and in Fig. 40 log η is plotted against log T for the same gases.   If it were true that $\eta \propto T^{1/2}$,

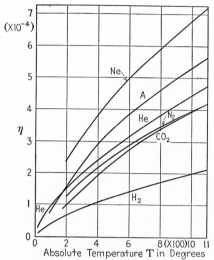

Fig. 39.—Viscosity η vs. absolute temperature T.

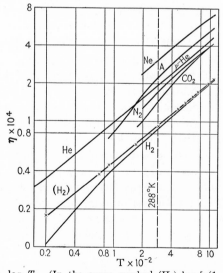

Fig. 40.—Log η vs. log T.   (In the curve marked (H₂) log $[\eta(1 + 14/T)]$ is plotted against log T.)

the latter curves would be straight lines with a slope of $\frac{1}{2}$; but in reality the curves everywhere slope upward more steeply than this.

It is not surprising, however, that a theory based on hard-spherical molecules should predict the right variation of viscosity with density but not with temperature; for lowering the density does not change the character of the collisions but only lengthens the intervening free paths, whereas raising the temperature increases the violence of the impacts and so may easily alter their effect upon the molecular motions. A more rapid increase in η with rising temperature than that indicated by the hard-sphere theory is in fact just what we should expect if the molecules were in reality somewhat soft, the repulsive force in a collision developing at a rapid but finite rate as two of them approach each other; for then as the velocities become greater, a molecule approaching another along a given path will be less deflected upon striking. The net result of a rise in temperature must therefore be an increase in the persistence of velocities and a resulting increase in the numerical factor that occurs in the formula for the viscosity.

89. Viscosity and Temperature with an Inverse-power Force. Further quantitative progress toward a theory of the variation with temperature can be made only on the basis of a new assumption concerning the molecular fields. In the absence of definite knowledge a favorite assumption has been that the force action between two molecules is proportional to some inverse power of their distance r apart, say to r^{-s}. It happens that in this case the variation of viscosity with temperature can be found by the method of similitude (or by the nearly equivalent but more abstract* method of dimensions, in terms of which the result was first obtained by Lord Rayleigh in 1900). It is possible to do this because we know already that the viscosity is a function of the temperature alone.

To apply the method of similitude, consider a particular motion that is executed by the molecules, and imagine this motion to be modified in such a way that the molecular paths retain their shape but have their linear dimensions all changed in the same ratio λ, and suppose that the times taken to traverse corresponding parts of the paths are likewise changed but in some other ratio τ. Then if we compare this modified motion with the original one we see that *velocities* at corresponding points of the molecular paths have been changed in the ratio λ/τ, and the accelerations and the *forces* necessary to produce these have, therefore, been changed in the ratio λ/τ^2, the masses being unaltered. The factor r^{-s}, however, to which the molecular forces are assumed to be proportional, has now been changed in the ratio λ^{-s}.

---

* In using dimensions, a special argument is necessary to show that η must be proportional to a *power* of T; cf. P. T. BRIDGMAN, "Dimensional Analysis."

Hence the modified motion will be a dynamically possible one only provided $\lambda/\tau^2 = \lambda^{-s}$, i.e., provided

$$\tau = \lambda^{(1+s)/2}. \tag{127}$$

It is now readily seen that the *energy* has been changed in a definite ratio depending only upon λ and τ and so has been changed in value to that characteristic of some other temperature. Accordingly, by modifying in this way all of the motions executed at temperature T we obtain the gas moving at a new temperature. Let us find out in what ratio the temperature and the viscous forces have been changed. In the modified motion, because of the changes in the velocities, times and linear dimensions, we have λ/τ times as much momentum transferred in a time τ times as long, across an area λ^2 times as great; and the velocity gradient is obviously $(\lambda/\tau)/\lambda = 1/\tau$ times as great. Hence, from the definition of the viscosity in terms of momentum transfer divided by velocity gradient, we see that η has been changed in the ratio $[(\lambda/\tau)/\tau\lambda^2]/(1/\tau) = 1/\lambda\tau$, or, by (127), in the ratio

$$\lambda^{-3/2-s/2}.$$

On the other hand, $T \propto \overline{v^2}$ and so has been changed in the ratio λ^2/τ^2 or

$$\lambda^{1-s}.$$

Now it is easily seen by multiplying out that

$$-\frac{3}{2} - \frac{s}{2} = \left(\frac{1}{2} + \frac{2}{s-1}\right)(1-s).$$

Hence, if we set

$$n = \frac{1}{2} + \frac{2}{s-1}, \tag{128}$$

T^n has been changed in the same ratio as has η. Accordingly we may conclude that $\eta \propto T^n$ with this value of n. It is immaterial to this conclusion whether the force be attractive or repulsive.

According to (128) η should vary as a power n of T somewhat higher than $\frac{1}{2}$ and log η should plot against log T as a straight line with a slope equal to this higher power. The experimental data plotted in Fig. 40 above actually show good agreement with this conclusion for helium and neon except at high temperatures, the best values of n being 0.64 and 0.67, respectively, and the agreement for hydrogen is fair between 200°K and 500°K with $n = 0.69$; but the data for argon, N_2, and CO_2 can be fitted to such an equation only over short ranges of temperature. The values of n just stated, and the best values near $288°K$ for the other three gases, are collected in a table at the end of the next section opposite the heading n', together with the approximate corresponding values of s as calculated from (128), listed opposite the heading s'.

The success of eq. (128) for helium, neon, and hydrogen seems at least to justify the conclusion that in these gases the forces between two molecules drop off very rapidly with distance; the variation is doubtless not exactly according to any power of the distance, but it can probably be concluded that in making other theoretical calculations we may reasonably expect to obtain approximately correct results by assuming the power to be the value of n given in the table. The much higher values of n obtained for the other three gases mentioned may perhaps be taken as an indication that these molecules depart much more widely than do the other three from the properties of hard spheres. Not very much significance can be attached, however, to the agreement over a limited range of the experimental curve for η with some power of T, since any analytical curve whatever can be fitted to some power of the independent variable as accurately as desired over a sufficiently short range of values.

90. Viscosity and Temperature on Sutherland's Hypothesis. Quite a different hypothesis in regard to the molecular forces was proposed by Sutherland.* He retains the assumption of hard spheres but adds a weak attraction between them, falling off rather rapidly with distance.

Such an attraction acts in two ways to produce shortening of the mean free path. In the first place, molecules which pass each other at close range without actually touching experience a small deflection, and this obviously has much the same effect upon the molecular motion as would a glancing collision. In the second place, this deflection will also cause some molecules to come into actual contact when they would otherwise have passed by each other without touching, and will thus increase the actual collision rate. Some possible paths of the center of mass of one molecule relative to another according to these conceptions are indicated roughly in Fig. 41. Of the two effects, Sutherland supposes that the second is much the more important, and he actually neglects the first entirely; apparently no simple justification for this discrimination can be given, but it has been justified subsequently in certain cases by the more complete analyses of Chapman and Enskog.

---

* SUTHERLAND, *Phil. Mag.*. **36**, 507 (1893).

The increase in contact collisions is easily calculated by utilizing some of the results obtained relative to the coefficient of scattering. To do this, let us select for consideration two groups of molecules moving with vector velocities $\mathbf{v}_1$ and $\mathbf{v}_2$, and consider the motion of the first group relative to the second, in the manner of the analysis in Sec. 71. If a molecule of the first group approaches one of the second group along an initial line distant b from the second molecule, the distance between their centers at the instant when they are closest together will be r_0, as given by eq. (109) in Sec. 69, with m replaced by $m_1 m_2 / (m_1 + m_2)$, as explained in Sec. 71, provided they do not collide; if, however, r_0 as given by this equation is less than the mean diameter of the two molecules or $\sigma_{12} = \frac{1}{2}(\sigma_1 + \sigma_2)$, a collision must

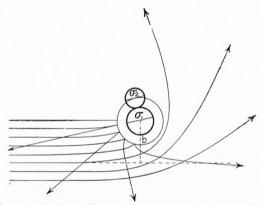

Fig. 41.—Sutherland's hypothesis of molecular interaction.

occur before r sinks to r_0. Now, for an attractive force ($U < 0$) that falls off with increasing r, or for any sufficiently weak force, according to (109), r_0 and b vary in the same sense. Hence all values of b result in collision up to that limiting value $b = b_0$, which makes $r_0 = \sigma_{12}$. The mutual collision cross section is thus $S = \pi b_0^2$, or, putting $b = b_0$ and $r_0 = \sigma_{12}$ in (109), we have

$$S = S_0\left[1 - 2(m_1 + m_2) \frac{U(\sigma_{12})}{m_1 m_2 v^2} \right], \qquad (129a)$$

where $S_0 = \pi r_0^2 = \pi \sigma_{12}^2$ and denotes the cross section as it would be if the field were absent. If both molecules have the same diameter σ and the same mass m

$$S = S_0\left[1 - 4 \frac{U(\sigma)}{mv^2} \right]. \qquad (129b)$$

This result shows that for hard spheres an attractive force-field ($U < 0$) increases the collision cross section, whereas a repulsive force ($U > 0$) decreases it.

If *all* molecules had the *same speed*, we could now at once substitute S from (129b) in (102a) in Sec. 61 and obtain for the mean free path in a homogeneous gas an expression of the form

$$L = \frac{3}{4nS} = \frac{L_0}{1 + \dfrac{C}{T}}, \tag{130}$$

where $L_\nu = 3/(4nS_0)$, T is the absolute temperature, and C stands for the constant quantity $-4U(\sigma)\,\dfrac{T}{mv^2}$; and then for the viscosity we should have, by comparison with (126a, b) in Sec. 86,

$$\eta = \frac{a_1 \rho \bar{v} L_0}{1 + (C/T)} = \frac{aT^{\frac{1}{2}}}{1 + (C/T)}, \tag{131}$$

in which a_1 has a value at least very close to its value of 0.499 in (126b), and the numerator can be written $aT^{\frac{1}{2}}$ in terms of a new constant a provided we assume that ρL_0 is constant.

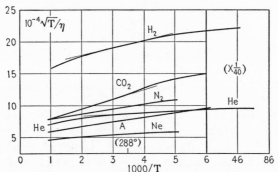

FIG. 42.—Test of Sutherland's formula.

(For $1000/T > 6$ both scales are reduced in the ratio $1:40$, but with a separate origin for each curve.)

In a *maxwellian* gas it is easily shown that a result of the same form must hold, but perhaps with some change in the value of C. This is so because, in the first place, the relative distribution of the molecules as to velocity is the same at all temperatures, and, in the second place, each group contributes independently to the collision rate.

Equation (131) is known as *Sutherland's formula*. It is found to hold, when suitable empirical values of a and C are inserted, for many gases over a considerable range of temperature; it is, in fact, more widely useful than a formula like (128), containing a power of T. The data require in all cases a positive C corresponding to an attractive field. Of course, the equation necessarily holds also as a two-constant empirical formula for all gases over any sufficiently short range of temperature, the necessary values of C varying with the choice of the range; but this latter fact, of course, proves nothing in regard to molecular forces. When the observations are extended over the full range of temperature that is available in modern experimentation, the formula fails badly in all cases, for either high or low temperatures or both.

A straight-line test of Sutherland's formula is readily made by plotting $T^{1/2}/\eta$ against $1/T$. In Fig. 42 a plot of this sort is shown for the same data that are plotted in another way in Figs. 39 and 40. It is at once apparent that the formula is hopeless for hydrogen and is useful only over limited ranges for the others. The values of C that correspond to the three straight lines that are drawn on the plot and to corresponding tangents at 288°K drawn to the other three curves are given in the table below, opposite the heading C'.

Constants in the Viscosity Formulas

	Helium	Neon	Argon	H_2	N_2	CO_2
n'	0.64	0.67	0.86	0.69	0.77	0.95
s'	15	13	6.6	11.5	8.4	5.4
C'	38	56	141	61	104	269
n	0.654	0.601	......	0.628	0.503	......
C	0.5	19	......	14	103	......

For n' and s' see Sec. 89, for n and C, Sec. 91. C' is described just above.

91. Viscosity and Temperature: Other Hypotheses. In attempting to obtain an expression for the variation of viscosity with temperature that will give a still better fit with observation, we can proceed either empirically or theoretically. An obvious empirical step would be to combine the features of both (128) and (131) into the modified formula*

$$\eta = \frac{aT^n}{1 + (C/T)}. \tag{132}$$

Since this formula contains three disposable constants, a, n, and C, it can necessarily be made to fit more closely, or over a much wider range, than can either of the original formulas. In order to test it,

* Cf. Trautz and Binkele, *Ann. Physik*, **5**, 561 (1930).

the same data for six gases that are plotted in Fig. 39 were employed; a good value of C was determined by trial and then $\log\left[\eta\left(1 + \dfrac{C}{T}\right)\right]$ was plotted against $\log T$, and when a fair straight line had been secured in this way, the value of n was taken from the slope of the line. The line obtained in this way for hydrogen is drawn in Fig. 40, points being shown by crosses. The values of n and C thus obtained are collected in the table on p. 157. The formula can be fitted within about 1 per cent over the entire range for helium, neon, hydrogen, and nitrogen, but even this three-constant formula cannot be fitted satisfactorily to the data for argon and carbon dioxide.

Further progress can hardly be made except by introducing more specialized assumptions concerning the molecular fields. Formula

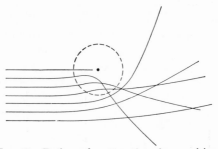

Fig. 43.—Paths under attraction plus repulsion.

(132) may be regarded as corresponding roughly to the conception that actual molecules possess both the attractive field postulated by Sutherland and, at small distances, a softness similar to that to which a repulsive field gives rise; the relative paths would then be as suggested in Fig. 43 rather than as in Fig. 41. A simple form of such a field would be one in which the force that is exerted by one molecule on the other when their centers are a distance r apart, and the corresponding potential energy U, have the values

$$F = \frac{\lambda_n}{r^n} - \frac{\lambda_m}{r^m}, \qquad U = \frac{\lambda_n}{(n-1)r^{n-1}} - \frac{\lambda_m}{(m-1)r^{m-1}}, \qquad (133)$$

λ_n and λ_m being constants. Calculations using such a field, taking $m = 3$ for reasons of mathematical convenience, were made by Jones,[*] with the result that for a relatively weak attracting field

$$\eta = \frac{aT^{1/2}}{T^{-2/(n-1)} + (S/T)}. \qquad (134)$$

* JONES, Roy. Soc. Proc., **106**, 441 (1924).

This is a three-constant formula but is somewhat different in form from the empirical formula (132).   Jones showed that with suitable values of the constants it represents the viscosity of argon within 0.6 per cent from $-183°C$ to $+183°C$; the fit was found to be equally good, however, either with $n = 21$ and $S = 62.45$ or with $n = 14\frac{1}{3}$ and $S = 38.62$, so that no very definite conclusion could be drawn in regard to the molecular forces.

It seems doubtful whether much further progress can be made by trying to invent arbitrary force-fields that will reproduce such data as those on viscosity.   The possible forms of field are too many, the necessary mathematical labor is too extensive, and the precision in the experimental data that is required in order to distinguish between different hypotheses is too hard to secure.   More interest, perhaps, will attach in the future to attempts at calculation of the viscosity in terms of universal constants by means of wave mechanics without the introduction of special postulated constants, or to attempts to correlate viscosity with other molecular properties.

A few calculations by wave mechanics have been made by Massey and Mohr with interesting results.*   They first work out the case of an artificial model, assuming the molecules to be small elastic spheres. In this case the enormous number of small deflections due to diffraction of the molecular waves, which was described above in connection with molecular scattering (Sec. 78), simulate in their effect a force-field, for with rising temperature and increasing molecular velocity these deflections are confined progressively to smaller angular ranges and so have less effect.   As a result of this phenomenon the elastic-sphere model gives a variation of η with temperature that is more rapid than $T^{\frac{1}{2}}$; by assuming the right diameter for the sphere, the experimentally observed variation could actually be reproduced rather well in the case of helium, and somewhat less successfully for hydrogen.

In a second paper† Massey and Mohr apply to helium an approximate form of the *fundamental* method of wave mechanics, in which everything is deduced without fresh hypothesis from the basic properties of electrons and nuclei.   A good approximation to the field of a helium atom is known from Slater's work; it is stated in eqs. (177a) and (177b) in Sec. 121 below.   Using this field the authors calculate a cross section for viscosity Q_η, which is $\frac{2}{3}$ of our S_{vc}, and, substituting its value in their equivalent of our eq. (126a) in Sec. 86 above, they obtain the value of the viscosity.   Comparing their results with observed values they find:

---

* Massey and Mohr, *Roy. Soc. Proc.*, **141**, 434 (1933).

† Massey and Mohr, *Roy. Soc. Proc.*, **144**, 188 (1934).

T (abs.)	15.0°	20.2°	88.8°	203.1°	294.5°
η (obs.)	29.46	35.03	91.8	156.4	199.4
η (calc.)	36	43	98	165	213

The unit of viscosity employed here is the micropoise or 10^{-6} c.g.s. unit. Such a degree of agreement between theory and experiment would not ordinarily be considered very good, but it must be remembered that in this case the theoretical calculations themselves are only approximate, and the agreement becomes really impressive when we further recall that in all of the theoretical work no special assumptions referring to helium are introduced except that its nucleus is much heavier than an electron and carries a charge numerically twice as great.

92. Viscosity of Mixed Gases. Up to this point the gas has been assumed to be homogeneous. We must now consider how the theory is to be extended to a gas consisting of several kinds of molecules. When a rarefied gas composed of several different kinds of molecules is set in shearing motion, the viscous transfer of momentum across any plane will be the simple sum of the transfers by the different groups of molecules. The analysis of the "simple theory" in Sec. 81, if valid for a pure gas, should accordingly be applicable to each group separately. We are thus led to write for the viscosity, as a generalization of (119) in Sec. 81,

$$\eta = \frac{1}{3}\sum_i \rho_i \bar{v}_i L_i' = \sum_i \frac{\eta_i L_i'}{L_i},$$

the sums extending over the various sorts of molecules; L_i' stands for the mean free path of kind i in the mixed gas, whereas L_i is what the mean free path of this kind would be if it alone were present at its actual density ρ_i, and $\eta_i = \frac{1}{3}\rho_i L_i$ or the viscosity of kind i according to (119). Taking L_i from (106b) in Sec. 64 and L_i' from (105c), we have

$$\frac{L_i'}{L_i} = \frac{\sqrt{2}n_i S_i}{\sum_j n_j S_{ij}[1 + (M_i/M_j)]^{\frac{1}{2}}}$$

in which M_i is the molecular weight of molecules i and S_i the equivalent cross section for collisions of these molecules with each other, while S_{ij} is the mutual cross section when they collide with kind j. The expression for η can then be thrown into the form

$$\eta = \sum_i \frac{\eta_i}{1 + \sum_{j \neq i} \zeta_{ij} \frac{n_j}{n_i}}, \qquad \zeta_{ij} = \frac{S_{ij}}{S_i} \frac{[1 + (M_i/M_j)]^{\frac{1}{2}}}{\sqrt{2}}, \qquad (135a)$$

in which the η_i represent the viscosities of the separate pure constituents and the coefficients ζ_{ij} should be independent of the composition; n_i and n_j can be interpreted, if desired, as concentrations by volume, or in terms of moles per unit volume. In the case of a binary mixture this becomes

$$\eta = \frac{\eta_1}{1 + \zeta_{12} \frac{n_2}{n_1}} + \frac{\eta_2}{1 + \zeta_{21} \frac{n_1}{n_2}}. \qquad (135b)$$

The complete analysis of Chapman shows, however, that so simple a formula cannot be quite accurate, presumably because the persistence of velocities is different for the different kinds of molecules and in different types of collisions; he obtains for a binary mixture a formula that can be summarized in the form*

$$\eta = \frac{\eta_1 a_1 n_1^2 + \eta_{12} n_1 n_2 + \eta_2 a_2 n_2^2}{a_1 n_1^2 + b n_1 n_2 + a_2 n_2^2}, \qquad (136a)$$

η_{12}, a_1, a_2, and b being four new constants depending on the molecular masses, the law of force, and the temperature.

Chapman fitted† a quadratic formula of this last type to some observations made by Schmitt‡ on mixtures of argon and helium and of oxygen and hydrogen and found good agreement (mostly within 1 per cent); the data and the theoretical curves are shown in Fig. 44, abscissas representing per cents of the lighter gas in the mixture. Schmitt himself, however, had found good agreement of his extensive results with Thiesen's formula, which is equivalent to our (135b). More recent work by Trautz and his collaborators§ is in agreement with the double-quadratic type of formula, eq. (136a), but it is not clear how definitely the simpler form (135b) is ruled out. For a given pair of gases formula (136a), regarded as an empirical one, has four disposable constants in addition to the viscosities of the pure constituents, as against only two in (135b), and very precise work is

* CHAPMAN, *Phil. Trans.*, **217A**, 115 (1918).
† CHAPMAN, *Phil. Trans.*, **211A**, 433 (1912).
‡ SCHMITT, *Ann. Physik*, **30**, 393 (1909).
§ TRAUTZ et al., *Ann. Physik*, **3**, 409 (1929); **7**, 409 (1930); **11**, 606 (1931).

necessary in order to show definitely that all four are needed.   For practical purposes the simple quadratic expression,

$$\eta = \eta_1\left(\frac{n_1}{n}\right)^2 + \frac{\eta_{12}n_1n_2}{n^2} + \eta_2\left(\frac{n_2}{n}\right)^2, \tag{136b}$$

in which η_{12} is a new constant to be determined empirically and n_1/n, n_2/n are the fractional densities in terms of volumes or moles, appears to suffice.

So far as we can see in advance without knowing the relative values of the constants, the viscosity for a given mixture might lie either between its values for the pure constituents, or above or below both of the latter.   Cases are actually known in which the addition of a gas

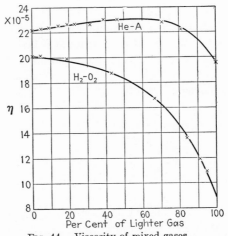

Fig. 44.—Viscosity of mixed gases.

with smaller viscosity raises the viscosity of the mixture; an example is furnished by Schmitt's data for helium and argon as shown in Fig. 44 above, according to which, for example, the substitution of about 40 per cent of helium for an equal amount of argon raises η from 2.22×10^{-4} for pure argon to a maximum of 2.30×10^{-4}, from which it then sinks to 1.97×10^{-4} for pure helium.   In other cases, however, the viscosity of the mixture has an intermediate value for all compositions.

B. CONDUCTION OF HEAT

93. The Kinetic Theory of Heat Conduction.   When inequalities of temperature exist in a gas, heat is transferred by molecular action from hotter regions to colder; this process is called conduction and is independent of any transfer of energy that may be going on simultaneously by means of radiation. The heat flows in the direction in which the temperature falls most rapidly; the maximum rate of decrease of temperature is called the temperature gradient. The amount of heat conducted in a given time is found by experiment to be accurately proportional to the temperature gradient so long as the latter is sensibly uniform over any distance equal in length to a molecular mean free path; and the amount of heat that is transferred per second across unit area of any small plane drawn perpendicular to the direction of heat flow, divided by the temperature gradient, is called the *thermal conductivity* of the gas. We shall denote the conductivity by K. The gas is assumed to be at rest and in a steady state (although, of course, not in complete equilibrium). If the x-axis is taken so as to be parallel to the direction that the temperature gradient has at any given point in the gas, then across a small plane drawn through that point perpendicular to the x-axis an amount of heat H will pass per unit area per second given by

$$H = -K \frac{dT}{dx},$$

T being the temperature.

The qualitative explanation of this phenomenon in terms of kinetic theory is obvious. Molecules moving from warmer regions into colder ones carry with them more heat energy than those moving in the opposite direction, and the consequence is a net transfer of heat toward the colder regions. To calculate the conductivity, therefore, we need to study the energy carried from place to place by the molecules, just as in treating the pressure and the viscosity we studied various components of their momentum.

94. Simple Theory of the Conductivity. For a first simple attempt at a theory, we can utilize the calculation already made for viscosity merely by substituting in it the average heat energy $\bar{\epsilon}$ of a molecule in place of mv_0, the y-momentum of mass motion. If we do this throughout in the argument leading up to eq. (118) in Sec. 81, we obtain at once for the stream density H of heat energy, in analogy with that equation,

$$H = -\frac{1}{3} n\bar{v}L \frac{d\bar{\epsilon}}{dx},$$

n being the number of molecules per unit volume, $\bar{v}$ their mean speed, and L their mean free path. This equation, in comparison with the one written down just above, shows us that, since

$$\frac{d\bar{\epsilon}}{dx} = \frac{d\bar{\epsilon}}{dT}\frac{dT}{dx},$$

$$K = \frac{1}{3} n\bar{v}L \frac{d\bar{\epsilon}}{dT}.$$

Now $d\bar{\epsilon}/dT$ is connected with the specific heat of the gas; for when it is heated at constant volume all of the heat supplied must go into an increase in the energy of the molecules, so that $nd\bar{\epsilon}/dT = \rho c_V$, ρ being the density in grams and c_V the specific heat of a gram at constant volume measured in mechanical units. Hence our simple theory gives for the thermal conductivity of a homogeneous gas

$$K = \tfrac{1}{3}\rho\bar{v}Lc_V, \tag{137}$$

or, by comparison with (119) in Sec. 81,

$$K = \eta c_V. \tag{138}$$

These equations are, of course, restricted to a rarefied gas, as will be all of our results on thermal conductivity, and this for two reasons. In the first place, in calculating the transfer of heat across a surface we shall, as we have done hitherto in treating the momentum, consider only bodily convection by molecules that actually cross the surface, ignoring all force-actions between two molecules while lying on opposite sides of it. In the second place, the heat energy can be expressed as the sum of the heat energies of the separate molecules or as $n\bar{\epsilon}$ only so long as there is not on the average an appreciable amount of mutual molecular energy.

Equation (138) is interesting and important, both because it involves nothing but directly observable quantities, and also because it predicts on the basis of theory a relation between physical magnitudes of two different sorts, mechanical and thermal, which we might have expected to be quite unrelated. To test the equation, the experimental value of the ratio $K/\eta c_V$ for a number of gases is given in the table in Sec. 103 below. In expressing K and c_V it is obviously immaterial what unit of heat is employed so long as the same unit is employed for both. A glance at the table shows that the predicted relation is in agreement with the data at least as regards order of magnitude, the maximum value of $K/\eta c_V$ being only 2.5. Equation (138) constitutes, therefore, a distinct success for the theory, and it is reasonable to hope that further refinement of the calculation will introduce a numerical factor into it which will lead to a good agreement with observation.

In refining the theory we might now follow the trail blazed by O. E. Meyer some sixty years ago and proceed to introduce corrections for Maxwell's law, etc., as we did for the viscosity. The result, however, is even less satisfactory here than it was there, for the reason that conduction is a distinctly more complicated process. Accordingly, we shall shift at once to the viewpoint required by the other method of attack, which was initiated by Clausius and Maxwell and finally carried through to completion by Chapman. Incidentally we shall be able to insert for trial the assumption made by Meyer and obtain thereby his result as well, for the sake of comparison.

95. Thermal Conductivity of Symmetrical Small-field Molecules. First Step. Let us consider as usual a rarefied gas composed of small-field molecules, which act upon each other only when they come very close together. Let us suppose also that they possess energy of translation only, so that the energy of a molecule is $\epsilon = \frac{1}{2} mv^2$. This condition requires that whenever two of them do interact the forces must pass through their centers of mass; this can also be expressed by describing the molecules as spherically symmetrical. Small, hard elastic spheres obviously constitute a special case satisfying these requirements.

A general expression for the flow of heat in such a gas is obtained from (124) in Sec. 85 if we substitute in that expression

$$\chi = \frac{1}{2} mv^2.$$

Let us also change $v_\perp$ to v_x, the x-axis being taken in the direction of the temperature gradient. We obtain thus for the amount of energy transferred by molecular convection across unit area per second, which also equals $-K \, dT/dx$ by the definition of the thermal conductivity K,

$$H = -K \frac{dT}{dx} = \sum \frac{1}{2} mv_x v^2, \tag{139}$$

the sum extending over all molecules in unit volume (more precisely, over all in a given volume, the result being then divided by the volume). In the special case of a homogeneous gas containing n molecules in unit volume each of mass m, this equation becomes

$$-K \frac{dT}{dx} = \frac{1}{2} m \sum v_x v^2 = \frac{1}{2} nm \int v_x v^2 f(\mathbf{v}) \, d\kappa, \tag{140}$$

where $f(\mathbf{v})$ is the distribution function for velocities and $d\kappa = dv_x \, dv_y \, dv_z$ and the integral extends over all velocities.

The conduction of heat in a homogeneous gas thus depends directly upon the value of the quantity $\Sigma v_x v^2$ summed over all molecules in the neighborhood of a given point. If the distribution were exactly maxwellian, this sum would be zero, in consequence of the symmetry of f, and there would be no conduction at all. The new method which we shall follow consists, accordingly, in seeking that slightly modified form of f which comes into existence in consequence of the temperature gradient; from this we then calculate the value of $\Sigma v_x v^2$, and from this in turn the value of K is obtained.

For convenience let us split up f visibly into a maxwellian term and a correction term, thus:

$$f(\mathbf{v}) = f_0(\mathbf{v}) + f_s(\mathbf{v}), \qquad f_0(\mathbf{v}) = Ae^{-\beta^2 v^2}, \qquad (141a, b)$$

where A and β^2 are so chosen that

$$\int f_0 \, d\kappa = \int f \, d\kappa = 1, \qquad \int v^2 f_0 \, d\kappa = \int v^2 f \, d\kappa,$$

the last integral representing $\overline{v^2}$. Thus $f_0(\mathbf{v})$ represents that maxwellian distribution which would correspond to the temperature of the gas as determined by its actual value of $\overline{v^2}$, whereas $f_s(\mathbf{v})$ represents a small correction term. By inserting f from (141a) into the last two equations we can also obtain equations equivalent to them in a form containing f_s alone, thus:

$$\int f_s \, d\kappa = 0, \qquad \int v^2 f_s \, d\kappa = 0. \qquad (142)$$

Furthermore, to make the mass velocity zero, as it is assumed to be in defining the conductivity, we must have, as an additional condition upon f, $\int \mathbf{v} f \, d\kappa = 0$ or, in terms of components and of f_s,

$$\int v_x f_s \, d\kappa = \int v_y f_s \, d\kappa = \int v_z f_s \, d\kappa = 0. \qquad (143)$$

Finally, when we substitute f from (141a) in (140) f_0 cancels out of the integral by symmetry, and we are left with

$$-K \frac{dT}{dx} = \frac{1}{2} m \sum v_x v^2 = \frac{1}{2} nm \int v_x v^2 f_s \, d\kappa. \qquad (144)$$

This equation expresses K in terms of the correction term f_s alone.

For the determination of f we have now the Boltzmann equation, (87) in Sec. 51, in which we put $\mathbf{F} = 0$ here because we are dealing with the simple force-free case, also $\partial(nf)/\partial y$, $\partial(nf)/\partial z$ because conditions are here assumed to vary only in the direction of x, and $\partial(nf)\partial t$ because by assumption we are dealing with a steady state of heat flow. The equation thus reduces here to two terms only and can be written, after inserting f from (141a),

$$v_x \frac{\partial}{\partial x}(nf_0) + v_x \frac{\partial}{\partial x}(nf_s) = \left[\frac{\partial(nf)}{\partial t}\right]_{coll},$$

the term in square brackets representing the effect of collisions.

In this equation, moreover, the term in nf_s can be dropped in comparison with the one in nf_0, since nf_s is a small quantity of the same order as the temperature gradient; nf_s will probably vary with x because the temperature does, but the rate of this variation will again be small as compared with nf_s itself and $\frac{\partial(nf_s)}{\partial x}$ will, therefore, be a small quantity of the second order, whereas $\frac{\partial(nf_0)}{\partial x}$ is of the first. The dropping of this term is required, as a matter of fact, for the sake of consistency, for the whole theory as ordinarily developed is limited to the first-order effects of the temperature gradient. On the right side of the equation, on the other hand, we can replace f or $f_0 + f_s$ by f_s alone; for the collisions can alter neither the total number of molecules nor, in consequence of the conservation of energy, the value of $\overline{v^2}$, and so have no tendency to change the value of f_0, as is at once evident from our definition of it. Accordingly, the equation reduces for our purpose to the following:

$$\left[\frac{\partial(nf_s)}{\partial t}\right]_{coll} = v_x \frac{\partial}{\partial x}(nf_0). \tag{145}$$

If we then insert f_0 from (141b), the second member of (145) becomes

$$v_x \frac{\partial}{\partial x}(nf_0) = v_x\left(A \frac{dn}{dx} + n\frac{dA}{dx} - nAv^2 \frac{d}{dx}\beta^2\right)e^{-\beta^2 v^2}.$$

But $\beta^2 \propto 1/T$ [cf. eq. (56)] and $A \propto \beta^3$ [cf. eq. (60)]; hence*

$$\frac{1}{\beta^2}\frac{d}{dx}\beta^2 = -\frac{1}{T}\frac{dT}{dx}, \qquad \frac{1}{A}\frac{dA}{dx} = \frac{3}{2}\frac{1}{\beta^2}\frac{d}{dx}\beta^2 = -\frac{3}{2}\frac{1}{T}\frac{dT}{dx}.$$

Furthermore, since the pressure must be uniform in order to leave the gas at rest, nT must be independent of x and so

$$\frac{1}{n}\frac{dn}{dx} = -\frac{1}{T}\frac{dT}{dx}.$$

Inserting all these values into (145) and noting that n is unaffected by collisions and so can be taken outside of the square bracket on the left, we find finally

* E.g., $\log \beta^2 = -\log T + \text{const.}$, and differentiation yields the result stated.

$$\left[n \frac{\partial f_s}{\partial t} \right]_{\text{coll}} = -\frac{nAv_x}{T}\left(\frac{5}{2} - \beta^2 v^2 \right)e^{-\beta^2 v^2}\frac{dT}{dx}. \qquad (146)$$

This equation is now to be solved for f_s.

96. Thermal Conductivity on Meyer's Assumption. Proceeding from this point, we can obtain Meyer's result if we now assume with him that those molecules which collide during each element of time have a distribution after collision of the maxwellian type. This assumption implies that all molecules after collision pass into the distribution represented by f_0, none of them entering that represented by f_s. The quantity $[n\, \partial f_s/\partial t]_{\text{coll}}$ thus contains no gains but only losses. In estimating these losses, moreover, we can ignore collisions of the f_s distribution with itself because their effect is a small quantity of the second order in the temperature gradient. Hence, using Meyer's assumption, we can write for the left-hand member of eq. (146) $- \Theta_v n f_s$, where Θ_v is the collision rate for a molecule moving at speed v through the maxwellian gas represented by nf_0. If we then solve the resulting equation for f_s, we find

$$f_s = \frac{Av_x}{T\Theta_v}\left(\frac{5}{2} - \beta^2 v^2 \right)e^{-\beta^2 v^2}\frac{dT}{dx}.$$

This value of f_s can now be substituted in (144), and the resulting integral can then be evaluated by numerical integration, Θ_v being taken from eq. (104a). The final result of doing this can be written, if for comparison that value of the viscosity is brought forward which was derived above on the basis of Meyer's assumption, i.e.,

$$\eta = 0.310\, \rho \bar{v} L,$$

as given in eq. (123) in Sec. 84:

$$K = 1.10\, \eta c_V.$$

This equation agrees scarcely better with the experimental data than does eq. (138) obtained from the simple theory.

A serious objection to the procedure here outlined, however, lies in the fact that the form employed for f_s does not make the net flow of molecules vanish, as is readily discovered by evaluating $\int v_x f_s\, d\kappa$. There would thus be a thermal-transpiration effect, manifesting itself by a mass flow of the gas in one direction. Now there may well be a tendency for such a mass flow to be set up as a consequence of inequalities of temperature, but the absence of mass motion which is specified in the definition of the conductivity, and which is actually enforced upon the gas by the experimental arrangements when a measurement of the conductivity is made, requires that any such mass motion resulting from molecular diffusion must be exactly offset by an equal mass flow in the opposite direction.

In his pioneer calculation Meyer himself followed a procedure different in one respect from that just indicated; he brought the net flow of molecules to zero by making a suitable choice of the value of dn/dx, instead of choosing this latter quantity so as to secure uniformity of pressure. Had we done this we should have obtained $K = 1.540\eta c_V$, a much better result and almost the same as Meyer's own final one, $K = 1.603\eta c_V$. The equality of pressure seems, however, to be an absolute essential in order to keep the gas at rest, and Meyer's procedure, therefore, can scarcely be defended. The net flow of molecules must in nature be balanced out in consequence of the existence of a form of f_s different from the one that we have here assumed.

We shall return, therefore, to our differential equation for f_s and seek a solution of it that keeps the net flow of molecules zero.

97. Thermal Conductivity: Second Step. The most direct procedure in attempting to solve eq. (146) for f_s would be to insert in it the value of $[\partial f/\partial t]_{\text{coll}}$ given by eq. (43) in Sec. 25 and then to endeavor to solve the resulting integrodifferential equation for f_s. This rather formidable undertaking has seldom been attempted, however. The Maxwell-Chapman method proceeds by a sort of flank attack.

The expression in the right-hand member of (145) or of (146) represents, as is clear from its origin in the process of deriving the original differential equation for nf, a steady inflow of molecules distributed in velocity in the manner exhibited by that expression in (146); thus, molecular convection is continually tending to build up a distribution of the form

$$nf'_s = av_x(\tfrac{5}{2} - \beta^2 v^2)e^{-\beta^2 v^2}, \tag{147}$$

a being a constant of proportionality. Here negative values of f'_s can be regarded simply as representing missing molecules that would have been there had the distribution been uniform and maxwellian throughout. This distribution is then at the same time being continually transformed by collisions in the direction of a maxwellian one, and the existing steady form of f_s is that form for which these two opposing influences are in balance.

Now Enskog showed* that we could infer a good deal in regard to the final form that f_s must assume, from the nature of the inflow

* ENSKOG, *loc. cit.*

distribution f'_s and from the symmetries of the situation. The function f'_s is of the type

$$f'_s = v_x F(v^2),\qquad (148a)$$

and we can show that under the influence of collisions this type of function is invariant except for a possible change in the form of the function F.

To show this, consider the way in which collisions between the f'_s and the maxwellian f_0 distributions change the distribution of velocities during a time dt; collisions of f'_s with itself need not be included because f'_s is small. Select any element $d\kappa'$ in velocity space about a velocity $\mathbf{v}'$ making an angle α' with the v_x-axis (cf. Fig. 45) and another

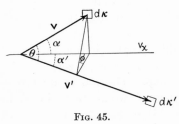

FIG. 45.

element $d\kappa$ about a velocity $\mathbf{v}$ making an angle α with v_x and an angle θ with $\mathbf{v}'$. Then the latter element $d\kappa$ will contain $nf'_s\, d\kappa$ molecules out of the f'_s distribution, and their collisions with f_0 will throw into $d\kappa'$ during dt a number of molecules which will be proportional to $nf'_s\, d\kappa$, to $d\kappa'$ and to dt, but which will otherwise depend, because of the properties of the scattering process, only upon the magnitudes of the velocities $\mathbf{v}$ and $\mathbf{v}'$ and upon the angle θ between their directions. Let us write for the number thus thrown into $d\kappa'$

$$nf'_s\, g(v,\, v',\, \theta)\, d\kappa'\, d\kappa\, dt.$$

The total number of molecules thrown out of f'_s into $d\kappa'$ by all collisions will then be

$$dN = n\, d\kappa'\, dt \int f'_s\, g(v,\, v',\, \theta)\, d\kappa$$

integrated over all values of $\mathbf{v}$.

We wish now to show that the new distribution represented by $dN/d\kappa'$ as a function of $\mathbf{v}'$ is again of the form $(148a)$. Let us introduce polars with the direction of $\mathbf{v}'$ as their axis and write in terms of these $d\kappa = v^2 \sin\theta\, d\theta\, d\varphi\, dv$. In expression $(148a)$ for f'_s we can write $v_x = v \cos\alpha$; and by projection we readily find that, if the polar azimuth is measured from the plane containing $\mathbf{v}'$ and the v_x-axis, $\cos\alpha = \cos\theta\cos\alpha' + \sin\theta\cos\varphi\sin\alpha'$. Hence

$$dN = n\, d\kappa'\, dt \int\int\int v^3(\cos\theta\cos\alpha' + \sin\theta\cos\varphi\sin\alpha')$$
$$F(v^2)\, g(v,\, v',\, \theta)\sin\theta\, d\theta\, d\varphi\, dv$$

integrated over all of velocity space. The φ integration gives at once $\int_0^{2\pi} \cos \varphi \, d\varphi = 0$, $\int_0^{2\pi} d\varphi = 2\pi$, whence

$$dN = n \, d\kappa' \, dt \cos \alpha' \iint v^3 \, F(v^2) \, g(v, v', \theta) \sin \theta \cos \theta \, d\theta \, dv.$$

The integral now represents a function solely of v'; and we can write $\cos \alpha' = v_x'/v'$. Thus dN has the form, v_x' times a function of v', and, accordingly, has the same general form as had f_s'. We may conclude, therefore, that collisions may at most tend to change the form of the function $F(v^2)$.

A plausible first guess is now that perhaps there is, after all, no change even in $F(v^2)$, and that the final form of f_s is the same as that of the inflow distribution f_s' itself, which is given by (147). If this is so, we can write

$$f_s = C v_x(\tfrac{5}{2} - \beta^2 v^2) e^{-\beta^2 v^2}, \tag{148b}$$

where C is a constant to be determined. Such a value of f_s satisfies the requirement that the net flow of molecules must vanish, for with this form of f_s

$$\int v_x f \, d\kappa = \int v_x f_s \, d\kappa = C \int v_x^2(\tfrac{5}{2} - \beta^2 v^2) e^{-\beta^2 v^2} \, d\kappa = 0$$

(cf. table of integrals at the end of the book).

In the hope of obtaining a good approximate value let us calculate the conductivity using this assumption for f_s. The constant C we shall choose so as to secure the best approximate fit to eq. (146), which is the equation determining f_s.

The novel feature in Chapman's work was the method of making such an approximate fit by multiplying the equation through by a suitable function and then integrating over all velocity space; this procedure greatly facilitated the handling of the left-hand member. For this purpose it is natural to employ the same function, $v_x v^2$, whose sum determines the conduction of heat [cf. (140)]. Treated in this way the left-hand member of (146) becomes

$$\int v_x v^2 \left[n \frac{\partial f_s}{\partial t} \right]_{\text{coll}} d\kappa.$$

This expression is easily seen to represent the rate of change by collision of $\Sigma v_x v^2$ summed over all molecules in unit volume, which can also be written $\int v_x v^2 f \, d\kappa$ or $\int v_x v^2 f_s \, d\kappa$; this rate of change we shall denote by $D\Sigma v_x v^2$. The entire integrated equation can then be written

$$D\Sigma v_x v^2 = -\frac{nA}{T}\frac{dT}{dx}\int v_x^2 v^2\left(\frac{5}{2} - \beta^2 v^2\right)e^{-\beta^2 v^2}\,d\kappa. \qquad (149)$$

This equation may be regarded as a special case of a general transport equation worked out by Maxwell for any molecular magnitude Q, in analogy with the Boltzmann differential equation for f itself, and Chapman's method was originally developed with that equation of Maxwell's in mind. Its general form, for a gas at rest and free from external force, is

$$\frac{\partial}{\partial t}(n\bar{Q}) + \frac{\partial}{\partial x}(n\overline{v_x Q}) + \frac{\partial}{\partial y}(n\overline{v_y Q}) + \frac{\partial}{\partial z}(n\overline{v_z Q}) = \left[\frac{\partial}{\partial t}(n\bar{Q})\right]_{coll};$$

the bar denoted an average for all molecules in the neighborhood of any given point. In our case $Q = v_x v^2$.

In order to proceed we have now to calculate $D\Sigma v_x v^2$.

98. Effect of One Collision upon $\Sigma v_x v^2$. In calculating $D\Sigma v_x v^2$ we can ignore collisions between any two molecules of the f_0 distribution; for such collisions, being the same as the collisions in a maxwellian gas, can have no tendency on the whole to alter $\Sigma v_x v^2$, which remains permanently zero in the maxwellian case. Collisions between two molecules both belonging to f_s, moreover, can likewise be ignored as a second-order effect. Thus there remain for consideration only collisions between f_s and f_0.

Let us begin by considering a single collision between a molecule of f_s moving with velocity $\mathbf{v}_1$ and one of f_0 moving with velocity $\mathbf{v}_2$ and find the effect of this collision upon the contribution made by these two molecules to $\Sigma v_x v^2$.

To obtain general expressions for the components of velocity of these two molecules after the collision, let us introduce the velocity of their common center of mass $\mathbf{u}$ and write $\mathbf{w}$ for the vector relative velocity between the first and the second. We shall assume for the moment that the molecules have unequal masses m_1 and m_2, in order to make the formulas useful in other connections. Then

$$\mathbf{u} = \mu_1\mathbf{v}_1 + \mu_2\mathbf{v}_2, \qquad \mathbf{w} = \mathbf{v}_1 - \mathbf{v}_2,$$

$$\mu_1 = \frac{m_1}{m_1 + m_2}, \qquad \mu_2 = \frac{m_2}{m_1 + m_2}, \qquad (150)$$

in terms of which (cf. Fig. 46)

$$\mathbf{v}_1 = \mathbf{u} + \mu_2\mathbf{w}, \qquad \mathbf{v}_2 = \mathbf{u} - \mu_1\mathbf{w}. \qquad (151a)$$

The effect of a collision is now merely to rotate the relative velocity **w** through some angle θ into a new position **W** without changing its magnitude, while **u** remains unaltered.   Hence for the new velocities after collision we can write

$$\mathbf{V}_1 = \mathbf{u} + \mu_2\mathbf{W}, \qquad \mathbf{V}_2 = \mathbf{u} - \mu_1\mathbf{W}; \qquad W = w. \qquad (151b)$$

(Cf. Secs. 23 to 24.   Of course, **W** is usually not in the same plane with **v**₁, **v**₂, and **w**.)

The results of squaring **V**₁ and **V**₂ can now be handled more neatly if we employ the notation of vector analysis.   For this purpose we need only the *scalar product*, which for two vectors **A** and **B** is denoted by **A** · **B** and defined thus:

$$\mathbf{A} \cdot \mathbf{B} = AB \cos (A, B) =$$
$$A_xB_x + A_yB_y + A_zB_z,$$

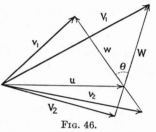

Fig. 46.

A and B denoting the magnitudes of **A** and **B** and (A, B), the angle between their directions; the last expression is obtained by noting that if $l\ m\ n$, $l'\ m'\ n'$ are the direction cosines of the directions of **A** and **B**, respectively, then

$$\cos (A, B) = ll' + mm' + nn',$$

and $lA = A_x$, $l'B = B_x$, etc.   As special cases $\mathbf{A} \cdot \mathbf{A} = A^2$ and

$$(\mathbf{A} + \mathbf{B})^2 = (\mathbf{A} + \mathbf{B}) \cdot (\mathbf{A} + \mathbf{B}) = A^2 + B^2 + 2\mathbf{A} \cdot \mathbf{B}.$$

The change in $\Sigma v_x v^2$ produced by the collision is then, obviously,

$$\Delta \Sigma v_x v^2 = V_{1x}V_1^2 + V_{2x}V_2^2 - v_{1x}v_1^2 - v_{2x}v_2^2.$$

Substituting from (151a) and (151b), in which we now put $m_1 = m_2$ because we are at present dealing with a homogeneous gas, and then multiplying out and using the vector formulas, we obtain from the last equation for the effect of one collision

$$\Delta \Sigma v_x v^2 = (u_x + \tfrac{1}{2} W_x)(\mathbf{u} + \tfrac{1}{2} \mathbf{W})^2 + (u_x - \tfrac{1}{2} W_x)(\mathbf{u} - \tfrac{1}{2} \mathbf{W})^2$$
$$- (u_x + \tfrac{1}{2} w_x)(\mathbf{u} + \tfrac{1}{2} \mathbf{w})^2 - (u_x - \tfrac{1}{2} w_x)(\mathbf{u} - \tfrac{1}{2} \mathbf{w})^2$$

or

$$\Delta \Sigma v_x v^2 = W_x \mathbf{u} \cdot \mathbf{W} - w_x \mathbf{u} \cdot \mathbf{w}.$$

99. Average of the Effect on $\Sigma v_x v^2$.   As the next step in the calculation we can now conveniently average the expression just obtained for $\Delta \Sigma v_x v^2$ over all positions of the plane containing the angle θ between **w** and **W**.   All positions of this plane are equally probable when **v**₁ and $\mathbf{v}_2$ and hence $\mathbf{w}$ have given values, in consequence of the symmetry of the scattering process. Let us write

$$\mathbf{W} = \mathbf{w} \cos \theta + \mathbf{r}$$

where $\mathbf{r}$ is perpendicular to $\mathbf{w}$ (cf. Fig. 47).   Then we can imagine the average in question to be taken as the vector $\mathbf{r}$ revolves at a uniform rate in a plane perpendicular to $\mathbf{w}$ while retaining the constant magnitude $r = W \sin \theta = w \sin \theta$.

Inserting the value just written for W, we have as the effect of one collision

$$\Delta \Sigma v_x v^2 = (w_x \cos \theta + r_x)\mathbf{u} \cdot (\mathbf{w} \cos \theta + \mathbf{r}) - w_x \mathbf{u} \cdot \mathbf{w}$$
$$= -w_x \mathbf{u} \cdot \mathbf{w} \sin^2 \theta + r_x \mathbf{u} \cdot \mathbf{w} \cos \theta + w_x \mathbf{u} \cdot \mathbf{r} \cos \theta + r_x \mathbf{u} \cdot \mathbf{r}$$

after multiplying out.   Here the second and third terms on the right average to zero because any component of $\mathbf{r}$ does.   The last term,

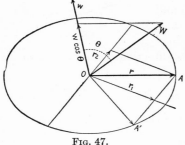

$r_x \mathbf{u} \cdot \mathbf{r}$, is quadratic in $\mathbf{r}$, however, and requires special study.

Let us resolve $\mathbf{r}$ into two rectangular components in fixed directions perpendicular to $\mathbf{w}$, writing

$$\mathbf{r} = \mathbf{r}_1 + \mathbf{r}_2;$$

then

$$r_x \mathbf{u} \cdot \mathbf{r} = r_{1x}\mathbf{u} \cdot \mathbf{r}_1 + r_{1x}\mathbf{u} \cdot \mathbf{r}_2 + r_{2x}\mathbf{u} \cdot \mathbf{r}_1 + r_{2x}\mathbf{u} \cdot \mathbf{r}_2.$$

Fig. 47.

Now for a given value of r_{1x} negative and positive values of $\mathbf{r}_2$ occur in pairs with equal frequency (e.g., OA and OA' in Fig. 47), and similarly for r_{2x} and $\mathbf{r}_1$; hence the middle two terms average again to zero. Furthermore, if we denote by u_1, u_2 components of $\mathbf{u}$ in the directions of $\mathbf{r}_1$ and $\mathbf{r}_2$, respectively, and by l_1, l_2 the cosines of the angles between these directions and the x-axis,

$$r_{1x}\mathbf{u} \cdot \mathbf{r}_1 = r_{1x}r_1 u_1 = l_1 r_1^2 u_1;$$

and $r_1^2 = r^2 \cos^2 (r, r_1) = w^2 \sin^2 \theta \cos^2 (r, r_1)$ and averages $\frac{1}{2} w^2 \sin^2 \theta$ as $\mathbf{r}$ revolves (since as an angle φ varies uniformly the average of $\cos^2 \varphi$ is $\int_0^{2\pi} \cos^2 \varphi \, d\varphi / \int_0^{2\pi} d\varphi = \frac{1}{2}$).   The term $r_{2x}\mathbf{u} \cdot \mathbf{r}_2$ can be similarly treated.   Hence the average of $r_x \mathbf{u} \cdot \mathbf{r}$ reduces to

$$\tfrac{1}{2} w^2 (l_1 u_1 + l_2 u_2) \sin^2 \theta.$$

This expression can be converted back into cartesian components in the following way.   If u_w denotes the component of $\mathbf{u}$ in the direction of $\mathbf{w}$ and l_w the cosine of the angle between this direction and the x-axis,

$$u_x = l_1 u_1 + l_2 u_2 + l_w u_w*$$

whence

$$l_1 u_1 + l_2 u_2 = u_x - l_w u_w;$$

and

$$w l_w = w_x, \qquad w u_w = w u \cos (u, w) = \mathbf{u} \cdot \mathbf{w}.$$

For the average of $r_x \mathbf{u} \cdot \mathbf{r}$ we have, therefore,

$$\tfrac{1}{2} w^2 (l_1 u_1 + l_2 u_2) \sin^2 \theta = \tfrac{1}{2} (u_x w^2 - w_x \mathbf{u} \cdot \mathbf{w}) \sin^2 \theta.$$

Thus, finally, writing $\overline{\Delta \Sigma v_x v^2}$ for the average of $\Delta \Sigma v_x v^2$ as the result of a collision between molecules of velocity $\mathbf{v}_1$ and $\mathbf{v}_2$, we have

$$\overline{\Delta \Sigma v_x v^2} = (\tfrac{1}{2} u_x w^2 - \tfrac{3}{2} w_x \mathbf{u} \cdot \mathbf{w}) \sin^2 \theta.$$

100. Total Effect of Collisions on $\Sigma v_x v^2$.

The next step is to sum $\overline{\Delta \Sigma v_x v^2}$ over all collisions between the f_s and f_0 distributions. Of the f_s molecules, $n f_s(\mathbf{v}_1) \, d\kappa_1$ in unit volume have velocities lying in a range $d\kappa_1$ about $\mathbf{v}_1$, and of the f_0 ones $n f_0(\mathbf{v}_2) \, d\kappa_2$ lie around $\mathbf{v}_2$; of the former, $n w f_s(\mathbf{v}_1) \, d\kappa_1$ cross unit area per second in their motion relative to the second group. Hence in terms of the scattering coefficient G defined in Sec. 68 above [cf. eq. (107a)] there are

$$2 \pi n^2 w \, G(w, \theta) f_s(\mathbf{v}_1) f_0(\mathbf{v}_2) \sin \theta \, d\kappa_1 \, d\kappa_2$$

collisions in unit volume between f_s and f_0 molecules which result in a rotation of the relative velocity through an angle between θ and $\theta + d\theta$; $G(w, \theta)$ is written here because G will in general depend upon the relative velocity. Multiplying this expression by $\overline{\Delta \Sigma v_x v^2}$ and integrating the result over $\mathbf{v}_1$ and $\mathbf{v}_2$ and over θ, we have then for the total change in $\Sigma v_x v^2$ made by all collisions in a second:

$$D \Sigma v_x v^2 = 2 \pi n^2 \int \int \int_0^\pi w(\overline{\Delta \Sigma v_x v^2}) \, G(w, \theta) f_s(\mathbf{v}_1) f_0(\mathbf{v}_2) \sin \theta \, d\theta \, d\kappa_1 \, d\kappa_2.$$

$$(152a)$$

This integral is most easily evaluated if we change variables from $\mathbf{v}_1$ and $\mathbf{v}_2$ to $\mathbf{u}$ and $\mathbf{w}$. From (151a), in which again we put $\mu = \tfrac{1}{2}$,

$$v_{1x} = u_x + \tfrac{1}{2} w_x, \qquad v_{2x} = u_x - \tfrac{1}{2} w_x, \text{ etc.;}$$

* If we think for the moment in terms of new axes in the directions of $\mathbf{r}_1$, $\mathbf{r}_2$ and $\mathbf{w}$, a unit vector in the original x-direction has components l_1, l_2, l_w, hence its scalar product with $\mathbf{u}$, which equals the old u_x, also equals $l_1 u_1 + l_2 u_2 + l_w u_w$.

hence

$$v_1^2 = \mathbf{v}_1 \cdot \mathbf{v}_1 = u^2 + \tfrac{1}{4} w^2 + \mathbf{u} \cdot \mathbf{w}, \qquad v_2^2 = u^2 + \tfrac{1}{4} w^2 - \mathbf{u} \cdot \mathbf{w},$$

and in any integral $dv_{1x}\, dv_{2x} = |J|\, du_x\, dw_x$, where J stands for the Jacobian

$$J\begin{pmatrix} v_{1x}, & v_{2x} \\ u_x, & w_x \end{pmatrix} = \begin{vmatrix} 1 & \tfrac{1}{2} \\ 1 & -\tfrac{1}{2} \end{vmatrix} = -1.$$

A similar result holds for the y- and z-components. Hence, inserting also the value found above for $\overline{\Delta}\Sigma v_2 v^2$ and the expressions for f_s and f_0 obtained by changing $\mathbf{v}$ to $\mathbf{v}_1$ in (148b) and to $\mathbf{v}_2$ in (141b),

$$D\Sigma v_x v^2 = 3\pi n^2 C A \int\int\int\int\int\int\int_0^\pi w[\tfrac{1}{3} u_x w^2 - w_x(u_x w_x + u_y w_y + u_z w_z)]$$
$$[u_x + \tfrac{1}{2} w_x][\tfrac{5}{2} - \beta^2(u^2 + \tfrac{1}{4} w^2 + u_x w_x + u_y w_y + u_z w_z)]$$
$$G(w,\, \theta) e^{-\beta^2(2u^2 + \frac{1}{2}w^2)} \sin^3 \theta\, d\theta\, du_x\, du_y\, du_z\, dw_x\, dw_y\, dw_z, \qquad (152b)$$

$\mathbf{u} \cdot \mathbf{w}$ being here written out in cartesians. The reduction of this septuple integral is a straightforward but somewhat lengthy process and we shall omit most of the details. After separating it into simple parts by multiplying out, those few terms which do not at once go to zero by symmetry are easily integrated with respect to $\mathbf{u}$ with the help of the table of integrals in the back of the book. The resulting expressions can then be reduced to an integration over the two variables w and θ by introducing in place of w_x, w_y, w_z polar coordinates in $\mathbf{w}$ space, w, θ', φ', and then carrying out the integrations over θ' and φ'.

The whole integral thus finally comes to depend upon a single irreducible one, which we shall write in the form

$$S_{vc} = \frac{\pi}{16}\beta^8 \int_0^\infty \left[\int_0^\pi G(w,\, \theta) \sin^3 \theta\, d\theta \right] w^7 e^{-\frac{1}{2}\beta^2 w^2}\, dw$$
$$= \pi \int_0^\infty \left[\int_0^\pi G\left(2\sqrt{\frac{kT}{m}}\, x,\, \theta\right) \sin^3 \theta\, d\theta \right] x^7 e^{-x^2}\, dx \qquad (153)$$

in terms of $x = \beta w/\sqrt{2} = \tfrac{1}{2}\, (m/kT)^{1/2} w$. The constant factor has been so chosen in defining S_{vc} that for similar elastic spheres, for which $G = \tfrac{1}{4}\, \sigma^2$ as in (110c) in Sec. 70, S_{vc} reduces to the ordinary collision cross section, $\pi\sigma^2$. This quantity, which also occurs in the analogous treatment of viscosity but not in that for diffusion, might be called the *equivalent cross section for viscosity and heat conduction*. It can be calculated if $G(w,\theta)$ is known.

The final result obtained in this manner, after inserting $A = \beta^3/\pi^{3/2}$, is

$$D\Sigma v_x v^2 = \frac{4}{3}\frac{\pi\sqrt{2}}{\beta^8} n^2 S_{vc} C. \tag{154a}$$

It is interesting to compare with this rate of destruction of $\Sigma v_x v^2$ the value of the latter quantity itself; as found from (144) and (148b) this is

$$\Sigma v_x v^2 = nC \int v_x^2 v^2 \left(\frac{5}{2} - \beta^2 v^2\right) e^{-\beta^2 v^2} d\kappa = -\frac{5}{4}\frac{\pi^{3/2}}{\beta^7} nC.$$

If we insert the mean speed $\bar{v} = 2/(\sqrt{\pi}\beta)$ we have, therefore,

$$\frac{D\Sigma v_x v^2}{\Sigma v_x v^2} = -\frac{16}{15\sqrt{2}} n\bar{v}S_{vc} = -\frac{8}{15}\frac{\bar{v}}{L_{vc}}, \tag{154b}$$

where $L_{vc} = 1/(\sqrt{2}nS_{vc})$ and would represent the mean free path if S_{vc} had the significance of an ordinary collision cross section.

According to this last equation, if the quantity $\Sigma v_x v^2$ underwent no change except by collision, and if f_s retained always the form that we have assumed for it, then $\Sigma v_x v^2$ would die out exponentially, about half of it disappearing in a time $L_{vc}/\bar{v}$ or roughly the time taken for each molecule to make one collision. Maxwell showed that in the special case of molecules repelling according to the inverse fifth power of the distance $\Sigma v_x v^2$ would decay at the rate just found regardless of the form of f_s. In any case this result serves to give us some idea of the great rapidity of the process discussed in Sec. 32 in Chap. II, by which departures from Maxwell's law are ordinarily smoothed out. As an example, in air at 15°C and 1 atmosphere ($L = 6.40 \times 10^{-6}$ cm, $\bar{v} = 4.59 \times 10^4$ cm/sec) equilibrium is practically restored in a billionth of a second, but at a pressure of 10^{-3} cm Hg nearly a thousandth of a second is required, and at 10^{-6} cm Hg nearly a second.

101. Thermal Conductivity: Final Approximate Formula. The value which $D\Sigma v_x v^2$ must have to keep the state of the gas a steady one is given by eq. (149). This equation contains the same integral as occurs in the expression just given for $\Sigma v_x v^2$ and so reduces to

$$D\Sigma v_x v^2 = \frac{5}{4}\frac{\pi^{3/2}}{\beta^7}\frac{nA}{T}\frac{dT}{dx}. \tag{154c}$$

Insertion of this value of $D\Sigma v_x v^2$ in (154a) would now give us C, but our main objective is reached more quickly if we insert it into (154b) and so obtain, after putting $A = \frac{\beta^3}{\pi^{3/2}}$,

$$\Sigma v_x v^2 = -\frac{75}{64}\frac{\sqrt{2}}{\beta^4 \bar{v} S_{vc} T}\frac{dT}{dx}.$$

This value of $\Sigma v_x v^2$ can then finally be inserted in (140) in order to obtain the value of the thermal conductivity K. In doing this it is convenient also to replace one factor, $1/\beta^2$, by $(\sqrt{\pi}\bar{v}/2)^2$ in terms of the mean speed $\bar{v}$ and the remaining $1/\beta^2$ by $2\bar{v^2}/3$ [cf. eq. (65b) in Sec. 30]. If we wish, we can also go farther and eliminate T, as we did previously, by means of the fact that the specific heat at constant volume of the monatomic gas under consideration is simply its mean translatory energy per gram divided by the absolute temperature or $c_V = \frac{1}{2}\,\bar{v^2}/T$; and it may also be interesting to insert again

$$L_{vc} = \frac{1}{\sqrt{2}nS_{vc}}$$

which would be the mean free path if the molecules were spheres. In this way may be obtained the following expressions for the conductivity:

$$K = \frac{25\pi}{128\sqrt{2}} \frac{m\bar{v}\bar{v^2}}{S_{vc}T} = \frac{25\pi}{64}\,\rho\bar{v}L_{vc}c_V, \tag{155a}$$

where $\rho = nm$, the density in grams. Comparing this value of K with that obtained for the viscosity η by the same approximate method, which is stated in eq. (156b) below, we find also:

$$K = \tfrac{5}{2}\,\eta c_V. \tag{155b}$$

These formulas may now be compared with those furnished by the simple theory of heat conduction. The numerical factor in (155a) has the value 1.23 as against $\frac{1}{3}$ in (137) in Sec. 94 above, so that our value of K is nearly four times that furnished by the simple theory (provided we may overlook the difference between L and L_{vc}, which would be identical for hard elastic spheres anyhow). In a similar way (155b) differs from (138) in Sec. 94 by a factor of $\frac{5}{2}$. Part of the latter increase is clearly due to greater persistence of $\Sigma v_x v^2$ after collision than of the quantity $\Sigma v_x v_y$, upon which viscosity depends, for the coefficient in the "relaxation rate" is only $\frac{8}{15}$ in eq. (154b) above as against $\frac{4}{5}$ in eq. (156a) below. The remainder of the increase up to $\frac{5}{2}$ appears to be due to correlation between high values of the kinetic energy, $\frac{1}{2}\,mv^2$, and high rates of convection for high values of v.

Problem. Apply the preceding method to the treatment of viscosity. The principal equations obtained in doing this are given below, each preceded by the number of its analogue in brackets:

[140] $$-\eta\,\frac{dv_{0y}}{dx} = m\Sigma v_x v_y;$$

[146]
$$\left[n \frac{\partial f_s}{\partial t} \right]_{\text{coll}} = 2nA\beta^2 v_x v_y e^{-\beta^2 v^2} \frac{dv_{0y}}{dx}$$

at a point where $v_{0y} = 0$—elsewhere v_y must be replaced by $(v_y - v_{0y})$ in this and the following equation;

[148b]
$$f_s = C v_x v_y e^{-\beta^2 v^2},$$
$$\Delta \Sigma v_x v_y = \tfrac{1}{2} (W_x W_y - w_x w_y),$$
$$\overline{\Delta} \Sigma v_x v_y = -\tfrac{3}{4} w_x w_y \sin^2 \theta,$$

[154b]
$$\frac{D \Sigma v_x v_y}{\Sigma v_x v_y} = -\frac{4}{5} \sqrt{2} n \bar{v} S_{vc} = -\frac{4}{5} \frac{\bar{v}}{L_{vc}}; \qquad (156a)$$

$$\eta = \frac{5\pi}{32\sqrt{2}} \frac{m\bar{v}}{S_{vc}} = \frac{5\pi}{32} \rho \bar{v} L_{vc}. \qquad (156b)$$

Here η is the coefficient of viscosity, ρ the density, and $\bar{v}$ the mean molecular speed, whereas $L_{vc} = 1/(\sqrt{2} n S_{vc})$ and S_{vc} is the collision cross section for viscosity and heat conduction as defined in terms of the scattering coefficient by eq. (153) above. The value of the coefficient in (156b) is $5\pi/32 = 0.491$.

102. Final Correction of the Conductivity Formula. The formulas just obtained represent still only a first approximation to the correct ones, since we employed a special assumption as to the modified velocity distribution, using f_s as given in (148b) instead of the more general form given in (148a). The error arising from this assumption was examined by Chapman in a later paper.* His method was equivalent to expanding $F(v^2)$ in powers of v^2, then substituting the form of f_s thus obtained in eq. (146), and finally integrating this equation after multiplying it in turn by various functions, whose individual rates of destruction by collisions were calculated much as we did that for $\Sigma v_x v^2$. In this way he obtained an infinite number of linear equations for the determination of the coefficients in the expansion of $F(v^2)$, as a generalization of our single equation for the determination of C. The final result of his rather laborious calculations was only to replace our (155a, b) by

$$K = (1 + \alpha) \frac{25\pi}{128\sqrt{2}} \frac{m\bar{v}\overline{v^2}}{S_{vc}T} = (1 + \delta) \frac{5}{2} \eta c_V, \qquad (155c)$$

where α and δ are very small numbers. In the case of repulsion according to the inverse fifth power of the distance, which by mathematical luck is easy to handle and was exactly solved long ago by Maxwell, α and δ are both exactly zero, so that in this case our

---

* CHAPMAN, *Phil. Trans.*, **A 216**, 279 (1916).

approximate formulas are exactly right; for repulsion according to higher powers α and δ are small positive constants, rising for hard elastic spheres to their maximum values: $\alpha = 0.026$, $\delta = 0.010$ (0.009 according to Enskog). It seems safe, therefore, to conclude that (155c) will hold with very small positive values of α and δ for classical point-mass molecules having any type of field that is likely to occur in nature. In all cases, therefore, our own approximate values as given in (155a) and (155b) must themselves be very nearly correct.

103. Comparison with Observed Conductivities. It remains now to compare these formulas with the results of experiment. Accordingly, observed values of the quantities involved are given for a number of gases in the table below. Some of the viscosity values are extrapolated from data in the sources cited under the table following Sec. 86 the remainder and the other data are taken from various tables. The temperature is in all cases 0°C. Except where stated, c_V is calculated as c_p/γ.

	η	K	c_V	γ	$\dfrac{K}{\eta c_V}$	$\dfrac{1}{4}(9\gamma - 5)$
Unit.................	$(10^{-7}$ c.g.s.)	10^{-3} cal ⎯⎯⎯⎯⎯ cm sec deg	cal ⎯⎯ g deg			
Helium...............	1875	0.344	0.753	1.660	2.44	2.485
Neon.................	2986	0.1104	0.150	1.64	2.47	2.44
Argon...............	2100	0.0387	0.0763	1.67	2.42	2.51
H_2..................	840	0.416	2.40	1.410	2.06	1.92
N_2..................	1664	0.0566	0.178	1.406	1.91	1.91
O_2..................	1918	0.0573	0.156	1.395	1.92	1.89
H_2O at 100°C..........	1215	0.0551	0.366	1.32	1.24	1.72
CO_2.................	1377	0.0340	0.151	1.31	1.64	1.70
NH_3.................	915	0.0514	0.401	1.32	1.40	1.72
CH_4, methane.........	1027	0.0718	0.400	1.31	1.75	1.70
C_2H_4, ethylene.........	948	0.0404	0.282	1.25	1.51	1.56
C_2H_6, ethane..........	854	0.0428	0.325	1.23	1.54	1.52

η = viscosity, K = thermal conductivity, c_V = specific heat at constant volume, $\gamma = c_p/c_V$, c_p = specific heat at constant pressure, all at 0°C except in the case of H_2O.

We note at once that the ratio $K/\eta c_V$ is close to the approximate theoretical value of 2.500 for the three monatomic gases mentioned in the table. The discrepancy in the case of argon, however, probably exceeds the experimental error, although in the case of the conductivity this error may be rather large. Argon seems to deserve further experimental and perhaps theoretical study.

For all other gases $K/\eta c_v$ is much less than 2.5. A possible cause of its departure from this value presents itself immediately, however, in the fact that the energy of complex molecules must include other forms than mere kinetic energy of translation. This point we shall proceed at once to investigate.

104. Conduction of Heat by Complex Molecules. In the theory of conductivity as developed up to this point account has been taken only of the translatory energy of the molecules. Now if the internal energy always stood in a fixed ratio to the translatory, our final formula for thermal conductivity as expressed in terms of the specific heat by eq. (155b) or (155c) ought still to hold, since the presence of the internal energy would raise both the heat energy and the conductive flow of heat in the same proportion and would therefore have the effect of multiplying K and c_v by the same factor. Closer consideration of the processes involved in heat conduction raises doubts on this score, however; for we have found the conductivity to be greatly enhanced by the fact that those molecules which move about most actively are also the ones that carry the largest amount of translatory energy, but it is by no means certain that they will also carry more than an average share of internal energy. It might well be that the internal energy is propagated at a less rapid rate than is the translatory, and any difference of this sort would obviously have the effect of lowering the conductivity without altering the specific heat.

The question can be settled theoretically only by investigating the rapidity with which collisions produce the interchange of energy between its various forms. Not much progress has been made as yet, however, along such lines. The theory of conduction has scarcely advanced beyond a simple suggestion made by Eucken[*] in 1913.

Starting from the observation that the ratio of the rate of propagation of energy in the conduction of heat to the rate of propagation of momentum in the production of viscosity might well have different values for the different types of molecular energy, Eucken suggested that we might perhaps come close to the truth if we assumed the ratio of these rates for the internal energy to have the value predicted for it by the simple theory of both phenomena, in which no allowance is made for persistence of velocities, whereas for the translatory part of the energy the more elaborate theory should hold.

To develop this idea in quantitative form, let us divide the specific heat at constant volume c_v into a part c_{vt} representing changes in the translational energy and a part c_{vi} arising from the internal energy; we can divide K into two corresponding terms representing the respec-

[*] EUCKEN, *Phys. Zeits.*, **14**, 324 (1913).

tive rates of transmission of these two kinds of energy. Then, according to Eucken, for the internal part of K eq. (138) in Sec. 94 should hold, at least approximately, with c_V replaced by c_{Vi}, whereas for the translational part eq. (155b) should be very nearly true with c_V replaced by c_{Vt}, and for the total conductivity we should have

$$K = (\tfrac{5}{2} c_{Vt} + c_{Vi})\eta.$$

Now, $c_{Vi} = c_V - c_{Vt}$, and we shall find later that for a perfect gas $c_{Vt} = \tfrac{3}{2} R$ [cf. (203) in Sec. 142 below]; hence we can also write $K = (\tfrac{9}{4} R + c_V)\eta$. But for a perfect gas $R = c_p - c_V = (\gamma - 1)c_V$ in terms of γ, the ratio of the specific heats at constant pressure and at constant volume (cf. Sec. 141). Hence, according to Eucken,

$$K = \tfrac{1}{4} (9\gamma - 5)\eta c_V. \tag{157}$$

To test this formula values of $\tfrac{1}{4} (9\gamma - 5)$ are shown in the table of conductivities on page 180, in the column after the observed values of $K/\eta c_V$. The agreement in general is surprisingly good, in view of the crudeness of our reasoning, and seems to justify the conclusion that there must be a great deal of truth in Eucken's assumption.

105. Properties of the Conductivity. The first value of K given in eq. (155a) indicates that at a *given temperature* the conductivity should, like the viscosity, be *independent of the density*, for S_{vc} should not vary with the frequency of the collisions so long as their individual character remains unaltered. The complete theory of Chapman and Enskog leads to the same result.

This rather surprising conclusion was drawn from the theory by Maxwell in 1866 and was soon verified by Stefan (1872) and others. It cannot be expected to hold at high pressures, of course, and it must fail when the pressure becomes so low that the mean free path is comparable with distances in which the temperature gradient varies appreciably, or with the dimensions of the gas-filled space. The range of pressure allowed by such conditions is sufficient, however, to make the fact of importance in some types of vacuum work. In a 10-cm tube containing air, for example, the pressure must be reduced to less than 0.001 mm to obtain much benefit in the way of diminished loss of heat by conduction through the air.

On the other hand, all of our results predict an *increase* of the conductivity *with temperature*. In the case of monatomic gases, in fact, the first expression given for K in (155a) or (155c) suggests that it should vary in exactly the same way as does the viscosity, since in those expressions $\overline{v^2}/T$ is constant and the remaining variables are the same as the ones that appear in the first expression given in (156b) for the viscosity. In a monatomic gas, therefore, the thermal conductivity and the viscosity should be proportional to each other. Now the experimental study of conductivity at various temperatures has not been carried out to the same extent as has that of viscosity, because of the greater difficulty of making reliable measurements, but the existing data do indicate a fairly close parallelism between the temperature coefficients of these two quantities. The conductivity of all gases increases, therefore, like their viscosity, at least more rapidly than the square root of the absolute temperature.

For example, the observations of S. Weber on neon[*] yielded the result that within 2 per cent its thermal conductivity is proportional to $T^{0.7}$ between $-181°C$ and $106°C$, whereas the viscosity, according to the value of n' in the table at the end of Sec. 90 above, is roughly proportional to $T^{0.67}$ over a similar range. Rather extensive observations of conductivities at various temperatures were made by Eucken;[†] some of his results and some values of interesting ratios given by him are shown in the table on page 184. If the conductivity K and the viscosity η varied in the same way with the temperature, the ratio $K_T \eta_{273}/K_{273}\eta_T$ would be unity. According to Eucken's data this ratio shows some variation with T, even for the monatomic gas helium, but the variation in the ratio is at least much less than the total changes in K and η themselves. The same statement holds for the ratio $K/\eta c_V$.

Finally, if we turn to the *conductivity of a mixture* of different kinds of gas, we readily reach the conclusion that the simple theory suggests formulas which can be obtained from (135a) or (135b) in Sec. 92 merely by replacing η by K throughout. In the fully corrected theory of monatomic gases these formulas are replaced by very complicated expressions which we shall not write down. For a mixture of polyatomic molecules no accurate theory exists. Perhaps all practical needs can be met by a simple quadratic expression, which for a binary mixture can be written

$$K = K_1\left(\frac{n_1}{n}\right)^2 + K_{12}\frac{n_1 n_2}{n^2} + K_2\left(\frac{n_2}{n}\right)^2$$

in terms of the conductivities K_1, K_2 of the two constituent gases when pure, n_1/n and n_2/n being their fractional concentrations in terms of volume or moles and K_{12} a new constant to be determined empirically.

Experimentally it is found that in many cases the still simpler mixture rule holds, $K = K_1\frac{n_1}{n} + K_2\frac{n_2}{n}$; but in other cases it does not.

[*] Weber, Commun. Leiden Suppl., no. 42a (1918).
[†] Eucken, *Phys. Zeits.*, **12**, 1101 (1911); **14**, 323 (1913).

Gas	T (abs.)	$\dfrac{K_T}{K_{273^\circ}}$	$\dfrac{K_T \eta_{273^\circ}}{K_{273^\circ}\eta_T}$	$\dfrac{(K/\eta c_V)_T}{(K/\eta c_V)_{273^\circ}}$
He	373°	1.193	0.961	
	194.6	0.788	0.983	
	81.5	0.441	0.930	0.93
	21.0	0.155	0.843	0.84
Ar	373	1.311	1.008	
	194.6	0.750	1.007	
	90.6	0.364	1.034	1.03
H_2	194.6	0.774	0.980	1.07
	81.5	0.335	0.754	1.15
	21.0	0.0813	0.760	1.21
N_2	373	1.264	0.996	
	194.6	0.758	1.003	
	81.6	0.322	0.965	1.04
O_2	373	1.303	1.006	
	194.6	0.745	0.988	1.02
	81.6	0.302	0.900	(0.91)
CO_2	373	1.495	1.109	
	194.6	0.656	0.88	1.02
CH_4 (methane)	194.6	0.702	0.912	0.99
	91.5	0.314	0.924	1.01
C_2H_4 (ethylene)	200	0.626	0.803	
C_2H_6 (ethane)	200	0.631	0.825	

Eucken's data: K = conductivity, η = viscosity, c_V = specific heat at constant volume; the subscript specifies the absolute temperature T.

For example, mixtures of ammonia and air or of steam and air may have a thermal conductivity 5 to 10 per cent above that given by the simple mixture rule.*

C. DIFFUSION

106. Diffusion. When a gas contains two or more different kinds of molecules whose relative densities vary from point to point, a process called diffusion is observed to occur in such a way as continually to diminish the inequalities of composition. The explanation of this phenomenon by kinetic theory is immediately obvious: in consequence

---

* Gruss and Schmick, *Wiss. Abh. Siemens-Konzern,* **7,** 202 (1928).

of thermal agitation more molecules of a given kind travel from regions rich in that kind to regions of scarcity, than travel in the opposite direction, and this process tends to smooth out inequalities of distribution. The net flow of each kind of molecule will obviously occur in the direction of its negative density gradient, i.e., in the direction in which the density decreases most rapidly.

In preparation for a theoretical investigation of this phenomenon we shall first review briefly the customary manner of describing it in quantitative terms. We shall confine ourselves, however, to binary mixtures containing just two kinds of molecules. To express the rate of diffusion it might be thought that, in general, two coefficients would be necessary, each having reference to the motion of one constituent; for example, in a mixture of hydrogen and carbon dioxide, the hydrogen would be expected to diffuse much more rapidly through the carbon dioxide than does the latter through the hydrogen because the hydrogen molecules have thermal velocities more than four times greater. From one point of view this expectation is perfectly correct. If, however, nothing more than these two processes were involved in the phenomenon of diffusion, a greater volume of hydrogen would be transferred in one direction than of carbon dioxide in the opposite, and the gas would thereby be caused to move bodily toward one side. The experimental conditions under which diffusion is studied usually preclude such bodily motion of the whole gas; and in other cases it is more convenient to treat such a mass motion as a separate phenomenon, to be handled by the usual methods of hydrodynamics.

Accordingly, a pure case of *gaseous diffusion* is arbitrarily defined to be one in which any tendency of either constituent to move with excessive rapidity toward one side is offset by a mass current of the whole in the opposite direction, this current being of such a magnitude that the total net transfer of gas, as measured in terms of volume, is zero. The mass velocity of the gas as a whole is then considered to be zero. The transfer of *volume* is thus balanced out by definition, but there will usually be a net transfer of *mass* in one direction. In defining the mass velocity of a diffusing gas we are compelled to choose between a criterion in terms of volume and one in terms of mass, and the advantage seems to lie with the former.

107. The Coefficient of Diffusion. In perfect gases, to which our attention will be confined, volume and number of molecules are proportional to each other by Avogadro's law, so that zero transfer of volume means zero net transfer of molecules by number. Accordingly it is convenient to define the coefficient of diffusion for a mixture of two gases in the following way.

Let the numbers of the two kinds of molecules per unit volume be n_1 and n_2, respectively, and the total number in unit volume, $n = n_1 + n_2$. Then for equilibrium the pressure, and hence n, must be uniform. Accordingly, if the x-axis be drawn in the direction of the concentration gradient, we must have

$$\frac{dn_1}{dx} = -\frac{dn_2}{dx}, \qquad \frac{1}{m_1}\frac{d\rho_1}{dx} = -\frac{1}{m_2}\frac{d\rho_2}{dx},$$

ρ_1 and ρ_2 being the densities in grams of the two constituent gases and m_1, m_2 their molecular masses. A simple case of this sort is exhibited graphically in Fig. 48.

Now let Γ_1, Γ_2 denote the (algebraic) net number of molecules of each kind that pass per second toward $+x$ across unit area of a macroscopically small plane drawn perpendicular to the concentration gradient, and let the conditions be such that $\Gamma_2 = -\Gamma_1$. (If the gas is not perfect it would perhaps be more convenient to require that the ratio of the numbers transferred in the two directions should be such as to produce equal increases in volume on the two sides of the plane. This distinction is scarcely of experimental importance, however.) Then the *coefficient of diffusion* D for the mixture of these two gases is defined by the equations

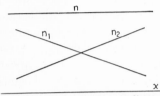

Fig. 48.—Concentration gradients.

$$\Gamma_1 = -D\frac{dn_1}{dx}, \qquad \Gamma_2 = -D\frac{dn_2}{dx}. \tag{158}$$

In these equations the diffusion current densities Γ_1, Γ_2 can also be expressed in terms of *volume* of gas under standard conditions provided we understand n_1, n_2 to denote concentrations expressed in those terms. The numbers of *grams* of the two constituents transferred across unit area per second, on the other hand, are $m_1\Gamma_1$ and $m_2\Gamma_2$, respectively, and in general these quantities are not equal.

In solving problems in diffusion, however, these equations are not usually employed directly; it is generally advantageous to pass at once from the current densities Γ, which are not directly observable, to a differential equation containing the concentrations only. The method of doing this is similar to that employed in Sec. 51 in obtaining the differential equation for nf. In the simple case in which the concentrations vary only in the direction of x, let Γ_1 and $\Gamma_1 + (\partial\Gamma_1/\partial x)\,dx$ represent the values of the stream density of the first gas at points on two planes perpendicular to the x-axis and separated by a distance dx.

Then this kind of gas is accumulating between the planes at a rate equal to the negative difference between these two expressions, or at the rate of

$$-\frac{\partial \Gamma_1}{\partial x}\, dx = \frac{\partial}{\partial x}\left(D\, \frac{\partial n_1}{\partial x}\right) dx$$

molecules per second per unit area of the planes, by (158). This rate of accumulation is also represented, however, by $(\partial n_1/\partial t)\, dx$, the volume of the space included between the planes being dx for each unit of the area. Hence we have

$$\frac{\partial n_1}{\partial t} = \frac{\partial}{\partial x}\left(D\, \frac{\partial n_1}{\partial x}\right),$$

or, if D is constant or practically so

$$\frac{\partial n_1}{\partial t} = D\, \frac{\partial^2 n_1}{\partial x^2}.$$

When n_1 varies in three dimensions, the latter equation takes the more general form

$$\frac{\partial n_1}{\partial t} = D\left(\frac{\partial^2 n_1}{\partial x^2} + \frac{\partial^2 n_1}{\partial y^2} + \frac{\partial^2 n_1}{\partial z^2}\right).$$

In all cases there exists likewise a similar equation for n_2. The diffusion coefficient D is often defined as the coefficient that occurs in these differential equations, under such conditions that the net transfer of molecules in any direction vanishes, just as the thermal conductivity is sometimes defined as the constant that occurs in the analogous and mathematically identical equation for the temperature in an unequally heated body.

Problems. 1. Show that if D_1 denotes the coefficient of single diffusion of one gas through another and D_2 that of the second through the first (i.e., $-D_1\dfrac{dn_1}{dx}$ is the number of molecules of the first gas crossing unit area per second under such circumstances that on the whole none of the second gas crosses at all), then

$$D_1 = \frac{n}{n_2}\, D, \qquad D_2 = \frac{n}{n_1}\, D.$$

2. A slender jar has some alcohol in the bottom while across the top a light breeze blows gently enough so as not to disturb the air inside the jar but rapidly enough to keep the density of alcohol vapor practically zero at the top. The temperature is 40°C, the pressure is 1 atmosphere. Find the rate at which the surface of the alcohol will

sink in consequence of evaporation and diffusion of the vapor upward, when its surface lies 20 cm below the top of the jar. Assume the air to be saturated just over the alcohol. Vapor pressure of alcohol at 40°C, 134 mm; density of the saturated alcohol vapor, 3.15×10^{-4} g/cc, of liquid alcohol, 0.772 g/cc; coefficient of diffusion, D, of alcohol vapor and air through each other at 40°C, 0.137 in c.g.s. units (variation with concentration to be neglected). *Ans.* The stream density of alcohol vapor is uniform and given by $\Gamma = \left(\dfrac{nD}{h}\right) \log \left(1 - \dfrac{n_{10}}{n}\right)$, where n_1 = molecular density of the alcohol vapor, n_{10} its value just above the liquid, n = density of the mixture of air and vapor, $h = 20$ cm;

$$n_1 = n\left[1 - \left(1 - \frac{n_{10}}{n}\right)^{1-\frac{x}{h}}\right], \quad x = \text{height above the surface. The}$$

alcohol sinks 2.7 mm a day.

108. Simple Theory of Diffusion. Just as we obtained a simple theory of heat conduction by making the proper substitution in the treatment of viscosity as given in Sec. 81, so by another suitable modification we can obtain at once a simple theory of diffusion.

For this purpose we assume that in a mixture of two gases equilibrium exists in all respects, except that the densities of the two constituents vary in a certain direction, which we take to be that of the x-axis. Then if n_1 denotes the density of the first constituent at a surface S drawn perpendicular to the x-axis (cf. Fig. 36), its density in an element of volume $d\tau$ located at a small distance x from S will be $n_1 + x \, dn_1/dx$ and thus greater than the density at S in the ratio $1 + (x/n_1)(dn_1/dx)$. The number of molecules of this constituent gas that collide in $d\tau$ and thereafter cross S will accordingly be increased, as a result of the density gradient, in the same ratio, and the total number crossing unit area of S per second toward $+x$ will be, not $\frac{1}{4} n_1 \bar{v}_1$ as given by eq. (72a) in Sec. 37, but

$$\frac{1}{4} n_1 \bar{v}_1\left[1 + \frac{\bar{x}}{n_1} \frac{dn_1}{dx}\right] = \frac{1}{4} n_1 \bar{v}_1 + \frac{1}{4} \bar{v}_1 \bar{x} \frac{dn_1}{dx},$$

$\bar{v}_1$ denoting as usual the mean molecular speed for this kind of molecule and $\bar{x}$ standing for the average value of x at their last point of collision. We then insert $\bar{x} = -\frac{2}{3} L_1$, as in Sec. 81, L_1 being the mean free path of the molecules of the first kind in the mixed gas, and then subtract the corresponding expression for the molecular stream that crosses toward $-x$, in which $\bar{x} = +\frac{2}{3} L_1$; the result is an expression analogous to eq. (118) in Sec. 81 for the net molecular stream density of the first kind of gas: $\Gamma_1' = \frac{1}{2} \bar{v}_1 \bar{x} \dfrac{dn_1}{dx}$ or

$$\Gamma_1' = -\frac{1}{3} \bar{v}_1 L_1 \frac{dn_1}{dx}.$$

For the second kind of molecule we find similarly

$$\Gamma_2' = -\frac{1}{3} \bar{v}_2 L_2 \frac{dn_2}{dx};$$

and it must be remembered that, as noted above, uniformity of pressure requires that $dn_2/dx = -dn_1/dx$.

Since, however, $\Gamma_1' \neq \Gamma_2'$ in general, to have the standard conditions for pure diffusion we must now superpose upon this molecular process the mass motion of the whole gas that was mentioned in the last section. The mass velocity v_{0x} must be such that there will be no net flow of molecules across S, or such that

$$\Gamma_1' + \Gamma_2' + n v_{0x} = 0,$$

where $n = n_1 + n_2$ and denotes the total number of molecules in unit volume, the term $n v_{0x}$ representing the flow of molecules due to the mass motion. Using previous equations, we thus find

$$v_{0x} = \frac{1}{3n} (\bar{v}_1 L_1 - \bar{v}_2 L_2) \frac{dn_1}{dx} = \frac{1}{3n} (\bar{v}_2 L_2 - \bar{v}_1 L_1) \frac{dn_2}{dx}.$$

The total numbers of molecules of the separate kinds crossing unit area of S per second, taken positive when they cross toward $+x$, are then, since $\left(1 - \dfrac{n_1}{n}\right) = \dfrac{n_2}{n}$,

$$\Gamma_1 = \Gamma_1' + n_1 v_{0x} = -\frac{1}{3} \left(\frac{n_2}{n} \bar{v}_1 L_1 + \frac{n_1}{n} \bar{v}_2 L_2 \right) \frac{dn_1}{dx},$$

$$\Gamma_2 = \Gamma_2' + n_2 v_{0x} = -\frac{1}{3} \left(\frac{n_1}{n} \bar{v}_2 L_2 + \frac{n_2}{n} \bar{v}_1 L_1 \right) \frac{dn_2}{dx};$$

and comparing these equations with (158) on page 186, we have for the coefficient of diffusion

$$D = \frac{1}{3} \left(\frac{n_2}{n} \bar{v}_1 L_1 + \frac{n_1}{n} \bar{v}_2 L_2 \right). \tag{159}$$

This is often called Meyer's formula for the diffusion coefficient; in his book, however, he gives the factor as $\pi/8$ instead of $\frac{1}{3}$ after including a correction for Maxwell's law.* The formula predicts substantial variation of the diffusion coefficient with the composition of the gas,

* O. E. MEYER, "Kinetic Theory of Gases" (transl. pub. by Longmans, Green, 1899).

which is represented by the relative values of n_1 and n_2, for the quantities $\bar{v}_1 L_1$ and $\bar{v}_2 L_2$ are likely to be quite different if the molecular masses differ greatly because lighter molecules will both move faster and tend to have longer free paths. Experiment shows, on the contrary, that the coefficient of diffusion is almost independent of composition.

The simple free-path theory thus fails badly in this instance. Accordingly we shall pass at once without further comment to an approximate treatment of diffusion by the Maxwell-Chapman method.

109. Approximate Coefficient of Diffusion for Spherically Symmetrical Molecules. The calculation of the coefficient of diffusion by the method of correcting the velocity distribution function parallels so closely the calculation already made for thermal conductivity in Secs. 95 to 101 that we may save space here by leaning heavily upon that treatment; it will suffice, in fact, merely to indicate the differences.

The quantity which determines the net flow of the molecules themselves in one direction, in the same way as $\Sigma v_\perp v^2$ determines the flow of their translatory energy, is obviously simply $\Sigma v_\perp$, $v_\perp$ denoting the component of the molecular velocity $\mathbf{v}$ perpendicular to the plane across which the flow is being calculated. Hence, if we take the x-axis in the direction of the composition gradient in a binary mixture of gases, the stream densities of the two kinds of molecules can be written, as an amplification of (158),

$$\Gamma_1 = -D\frac{dn_1}{dx} = \Sigma v_{1x}, \qquad \Gamma_2 = -D\frac{dn_2}{dx} = \Sigma v_{2x}, \qquad (160a, b)$$

the sums extending over all molecules of the appropriate kind in unit volume. We proceed to study these sums.

Resolving the distribution function for each kind of molecule into a maxwellian part plus a small correction term, we write

$$f_1(\mathbf{v}_1) = f_{01} + f_{s1}, \qquad f_{01} = A_1 e^{-\beta_1{}^2 v_1{}^2},$$
$$f_2(\mathbf{v}_2) = f_{02} + f_{s2}, \qquad f_{02} = A_2 e^{-\beta_2{}^2 v_2{}^2}.$$

We then obtain differential equations for f_{s1} and f_{s2} in analogy with (145) and (146) in Sec. 95, of which the first is

$$\left[\frac{\partial(n_1 f_{s1})}{\partial t}\right]_{\text{coll}} = v_{1x}\frac{\partial}{\partial x}(n_1 f_{01}) = A_1 v_{1x} e^{-\beta_1{}^2 v_1{}^2}\frac{dn_1}{dx}, \qquad (161)$$

since we assume the temperature to be constant and the gas to be at rest, so that only n_1 and n_2 vary with x. The right-hand member of this equation then suggests as approximate forms for the correction terms

$$f_{s1} = C_1 v_{1x} e^{-\beta_1{}^2 v_1{}^2}, \qquad f_{s2} = C_2 v_{2x} e^{-\beta_2{}^2 v_2{}^2},$$

as a result of which

$$\Sigma v_{1x} = n_1 C_1 \int v_{1x}^2 e^{-\beta_1^2 v_1^2} d\kappa_1 = \frac{\pi^{3/2}}{2} \frac{n_1 C_1}{\beta_1^5}, \qquad \Sigma v_{2x} = \frac{\pi^{3/2}}{2} \frac{n_2 C_2}{\beta_2^5}.$$

To prevent net flow of the gas, we must have $\Sigma v_{1x} + \Sigma v_{2x} = 0$. Hence C_1 and C_2 must satisfy the relation

$$\frac{C_2}{C_1} = -\frac{n_1 \beta_2^5}{n_2 \beta_1^5}. \tag{162}$$

Finally, multiplying the differential equation (161) through by v_{1x} and integrating over $\mathbf{v}_1$, we have as the condition for a steady state, in analogy with (149),

$$D\Sigma v_{1x} = A_1 \frac{dn_1}{dx} \int v_{1x}^2 e^{-\beta_1^2 v_1^2} d\kappa_1 = \frac{1}{2\beta_1^2} \frac{dn_1}{dx}, \tag{163}$$

since $A_1 = \beta_1^3/\pi^{3/2}$. Here $D\Sigma v_{1x}$ represents the rate of change of Σv_{1x} by collisions; and there is a corresponding equation for $D\Sigma v_{2x}$.

Turning then to the calculation of $D\Sigma v_{1x}$, we first make the interesting observation that collisions of the molecules of the first kind with each other can have no effect whatever upon Σv_{1x} because they leave unaltered the total x-component of the momentum of these molecules, which is $m_1 \Sigma v_{1x}$. We can thus say that each kind of gas is hindered in its diffusing motion only by the other gas. This observation was made long ago by Stefan, who developed upon this basis a theory which predicted no variation of the diffusion coefficient with composition and so agreed much better with the facts than did Meyer's theory. Maxwell adopted Stefan's theory but seems to have failed to explain its true basis in such a way as to make it generally understood.

The formulas for $\mathbf{v}_1$, $\mathbf{v}_2$, $\mathbf{V}_1$, $\mathbf{V}_2$ in Sec. 98 are, accordingly, to be applied only to collisions between a molecule of the first kind and one of the second; and we must now retain in them μ_1 and μ_2 with the values given by (150). One finds at once that in a single collision the change in Σv_{1x}, averaged over φ, is

$$\Delta \Sigma v_{1x} = V_{1x} - v_{1x} = \mu_2(W_x - w_x).$$

Writing then, as in Sec. 99, $\mathbf{W} = \mathbf{w} \cos \theta + \mathbf{r}$, we note next that the average of $\mathbf{r}$ will vanish as before because of the symmetry of the scattering process, and accordingly the average of $\Delta \Sigma v_{1x}$ per collision will be simply

$$\overline{\Delta} \Sigma v_{1x} = -\mu_2 w_x(1 - \cos \theta)$$

in terms of the angle θ through which the relative velocity $\mathbf{w}$ is turned.

In summing over all collisions between unlike molecules, then, we can omit those that occur between the maxwellian distributions f_{01} and f_{02}, which because of their symmetry cannot affect Σv_{1x}, and also those between f_{s1} and f_{s2}, whose effect must be of the second order in the concentration gradient and therefore negligible; there remain thus only collisions between f_{s1} and f_{02} and between f_{01} and f_{s2}. For the contribution of the former to the rate of change of Σv_{1x} we find easily, in analogy with (152a) and (152b) in Sec. 100,

$$D_1 \Sigma v_{1x} = 2\pi n_1 n_2 \iiint_0^\pi w(\bar{\Delta} \Sigma v_{1x}) \, G(w, \, \theta) \, f_{s1}(\mathbf{v}_1) \, f_{02}(\mathbf{v}_2) \sin \theta \, d\theta \, d\kappa_1 \, d\kappa_2,$$

or

$$D_1 \Sigma v_{1x} = -2\pi n_1 n_2 \mu_2 C_1 A_2 \iiint \iiint \int_0^\pi w_x w(u_x + \mu_2 w_x)$$
$$G(w, \, \theta) e^{-\beta_1^2 v_1^2 - \beta_2^2 v_2^2}(1 - \cos \theta) \sin \theta \, d\theta \, du_x \, du_y \, du_z \, dw_x \, dw_y \, dw_z.$$

To express the exponent of e in this expression in terms of $\mathbf{u}$ and $\mathbf{w}$, we note first that, by (56) in Sec. 28 and (150) in Sec. 98,

$$\mu_2 \beta_1^2 = \mu_1 \beta_2^2 = \frac{m_1 m_2}{2(m_1 + m_2)kT}, \tag{164}$$

whence, by (151a) in Sec. 98,

$$\beta_1^2 v_1^2 + \beta_2^2 v_2^2 = (\beta_1^2 + \beta_2^2)u^2 + (\mu_2^2 \beta_1^2 + \mu_1^2 \beta_2^2)w^2,$$

and here, since by (164) $\beta_2^2 = \mu_2 \beta_1^2 / \mu_1$ and by (150) $\mu_1 + \mu_2 = 1$,

$$\beta_1^2 + \beta_2^2 = \frac{\beta_1^2}{\mu_1}, \qquad \mu_2^2 \beta_1^2 + \mu_1^2 \beta_2^2 = \mu_2 \beta_1^2.$$

Thus

$$e^{-\beta_1^2 v_1^2 - \beta_2^2 v_2^2} = e^{-\beta_1^2 (u^2/\mu_1 + \mu_2 w^2)}.$$

The integral now can be reduced easily; the term in u_x contributes nothing by symmetry, w_x is handled in terms of polars as in reducing (152b), and (164) is used. The result is:

$$D_1 \Sigma v_{1x} = -\frac{4}{3} \pi n_1 n_2 \sqrt{\mu_2} C_1 \frac{S_d}{\beta_1^6}$$

where

$$S_d = 2\pi \mu_2^3 \beta_1^6 \int_0^\infty \left[\int_0^\pi G(w, \, \theta)(1 - \cos \theta) \sin \theta \, d\theta \right] w^5 e^{-\mu_2 \beta_1^2 w^2} \, dw \tag{165a}$$

or

$$S_d = 2\pi \int_0^\infty \left[\int_0^\pi G\left(x \sqrt{\frac{m_1 + m_2}{m_1 m_2} 2kT}, \, \theta\right)(1 - \cos \theta) \sin \theta \, d\theta \right] x^5 e^{-x^2} \, dx. \tag{165b}$$

The effect of f_{01} colliding with f_{s2} will clearly be represented by the same expressions with C_2A_1 replacing C_1A_2 and v_{2x} or $u_x - \mu_1 w_x$ replacing $v_{1x} = u_x + \mu_2 w_x$; hence it will simply be equal to $D_1 \Sigma v_{1x}$ multiplied by

$$-\frac{C_2A_1\mu_1}{C_1A_2\mu_2} = \frac{n_1\beta_2^5}{n_2\beta_1^5} \frac{\beta_1^3\mu_1}{\beta_2^3\mu_2} = \frac{n_1}{n_2}$$

by (162) and (164). The total value of $D\Sigma v_{1x}$ is thus $\left(1 + \dfrac{n_1}{n_2}\right)$ or $\dfrac{n}{n_2}$ times the value of $D_1\Sigma v_{1x}$ or

$$D\Sigma v_{1x} = -\frac{4}{3}\pi n_1 n \sqrt{\mu_2} C_1 \frac{S_d}{\beta_1^6}.$$

We can eliminate C_1 now by dividing this expression by the value of Σv_{1x} as found in the beginning, which gives

$$\frac{D\Sigma v_{1x}}{\Sigma v_{1x}} = -\frac{8}{3}\frac{n\sqrt{\mu_2}}{\sqrt{\pi}\beta_1} S_d = -\frac{4}{3}\sqrt{\mu_2} n \bar{v}_1 S_d$$

in terms of the mean speed $\bar{v}_1 = 2/(\sqrt{\pi}\beta_1)$. It is the presence of the factor $\sqrt{\mu_2}$ in this expression that prevents the occurrence of a great variation in the diffusion coefficient with composition, such as was predicted by Meyer's free-path theory in the case of molecules of very unequal masses. If m_1/m_2 is very large the heavy molecules sweep the others out of their way and tend to keep on going, thereby building up sizable amounts of Σv_{1x} in spite of their more sluggish motion.

Finally, if we solve the last equation for Σv_{1x} and, after substituting for $D\Sigma v_{1x}$ from (163), insert the value so found for Σv_{1x} in (160a), we obtain as our approximate value of the coefficient of diffusion

$$D = \frac{3}{8}\frac{1}{\sqrt{\mu_2} n \bar{v}_1 \beta_1^2 S_d}$$

or, after substituting $1/\beta_1^2 = \pi \bar{v}_1^2/4$,

$$D = D_{12} = \frac{3\pi}{32}\frac{\bar{v}_1}{\sqrt{\mu_2} n S_d} = \frac{3\pi}{32}\frac{\bar{v}_2}{\sqrt{\mu_1} n S_d}, \tag{166}$$

since $\bar{v}_1\sqrt{m_1} = \bar{v}_2\sqrt{m_2}$. Here $\mu_1 = m_1/(m_1 + m_2)$, $\mu_2 = m_2/(m_1 + m_2)$, and n is the total number of molecules per unit volume.

A formula equivalent to (166) was obtained by Langevin in 1905. According to our assumptions the formula is restricted to low densities and to small values of the composition gradient. By inserting the value of μ_2 and the value of $\bar{v}_1$ from (66a) in Sec. 30 we can also write it in the more symmetrical form

$$D_{12} = \frac{3}{8}\sqrt{\frac{\pi}{2}}\frac{1}{nS_d}\left[\frac{m_1 + m_2}{m_1 m_2}kT\right]^{\frac{1}{2}} =$$

$$\frac{3}{8}\sqrt{\frac{\pi}{2}}\frac{1}{nS_d}\left[\frac{M_1 + M_2}{M_1 M_2}R_M T\right]^{\frac{1}{2}}. \quad (166a)$$

Here $k = 1.381 \times 10^{-16}$ or $R_M = 83.15 \times 10^6$ in c.g.s. units and M_1, M_2 are the molecular weights.

The new molecular constant S_d that appears in the formula for D and is defined in terms of the scattering coefficient G for any relative speed by eq. (165a) or (165b) obviously functions as an equivalent mutual cross section of these two kinds of molecules for diffusion. We have so defined it that it reduces in the case of classical spheres of diameters σ_1 and σ_2 to the usual cross section, $S_d = S = \dfrac{\pi(\sigma_1 + \sigma_2)^2}{4}$ [cf. (110d) in Sec. 70].

110. Self-diffusion. The case in which $M_1 = M_2$ is of special interest. The formula for this case can be applied to the diffusion of a gas through itself. Such a phenomenon could be realized in the laboratory if we could mark in some way part of the molecules of a homogeneous gas and then observe the diffusion of the marked ones among the unmarked. Now according to present atomic theory such marking is essentially impossible unless the physical nature of the molecules is changed in some way; accordingly, strict self-diffusion has in reality become a notion devoid of physical meaning. There are, however, several ways of modifying molecules without appreciably affecting their outer fields, for example, by bombarding them with neutrons and thereby altering the nucleus of an atom without changing the nuclear charge, and the formula for self-diffusion should then hold for the diffusion of such modified molecules among the normal ones. Ordinary gaseous *ions* behave, of course, like a different gas, because of their strong fields.

If all molecules have the same mass, $\mu = \frac{1}{2}$; hence we can write for the coefficient of self-diffusion in a homogeneous gas, as a first approximation, from (166),

$$D_{11} = \frac{3\pi}{16\sqrt{2}}\frac{\bar{v}}{nS_d} = \frac{6}{5}\frac{S_{vc}}{S_d}\frac{\eta}{\rho} \quad (167a)$$

where $\rho = nm$ and represents the density in grams, and the second of the two expressions given is got by comparing the first with the corresponding approximate value of the viscosity as given in eq. (156b) in Sec. 101.

For the special case of hard spheres $S_d/S_{vc} = 1$, both cross sections reducing to $S = \dfrac{\pi(\sigma_1 + \sigma_2)^2}{4}$; in the case of repulsion according to the inverse fifth power of the distance Maxwell's results show that $S_d/S_{vc} = 0.778$. The forms of (167a) for these two types of molecules are,[*] respectively:

$$D_{11} = 1.200\,\frac{\eta}{\rho}; \qquad D_{11} = 1.543\,\frac{\eta}{\rho}. \qquad (167b, c)$$

111. The Corrected Diffusion Coefficient. According to the result of our approximate calculation as expressed in eq. (166) the coefficient of diffusion in a mixture of two gases should be entirely independent of the proportions of the mixture, for n_1 and n_2 do not occur separately in the formula but only the combination $n_1 + n_2 = n$. In this feature our new result goes to the opposite extreme from that of the simple theory as developed in Sec. 108 and agrees with the formulas obtained by Stefan and Maxwell.

When, however, we turn to the fully corrected theory as worked out by Chapman[†] and by Enskog,[‡] we find that in general there really should be a small variation of D_{12} with composition. There is none, however, if the molecular masses are equal; and this fact facilitates the application of the formula to the phenomenon of self-diffusion, for it makes the coefficient the same whether we contemplate the diffusion of a large group or a small one among the rest. Furthermore, in the mathematically simple case of gases in which two unlike molecules repel as the inverse fifth power of their distance apart, which was solved exactly by Maxwell, D_{12} again comes out independent of the composition of the mixture; and in this latter case our values of D_{12} and D_{11} as stated in eqs. (166) and (167a) agree with Maxwell's formulas and hence are actually exact.

For the general case it is convenient to write these equations in the slightly more general forms,

$$D_{12} = (1 + \lambda_{12})\,\frac{3}{8}\sqrt{\frac{\pi}{2}}\,\frac{1}{n\,S_d}\left(\frac{m_1 + m_2}{m_1 m_2}\,kT\right)^{1/2}, \qquad (168a)$$

---

[*] The coefficient is given as 1.504 in Jeans' "Dynamical Theory of Gases," but the formulas and numbers there given, and also those in Maxwell's paper, "Scientific Papers" vol. II, p. 26, lead to the value 1.543.

[†] Chapman, *Phil. Trans.*, **217A**, 115 (1918).

[‡] Enskog, "Kinetische Theorie der Vorgänge in mässig verdünnten Gasen," Dissertation, Upsala, 1917.

$$D_{11} = (1 + \lambda_{11}) \frac{3\pi}{16\sqrt{2}} \frac{\bar{v}}{nS_d} = C \frac{\eta}{\rho}, \qquad (168b)$$

in the first of which S_d refers as before solely to collisions between unlike molecules.

The result of the corrected theory as regards D_{11} can then be stated at once by saying that λ_{11} is a small positive number, which vanishes for the inverse-fifth-power law of force and reaches a maximum for hard elastic spheres; this maximum value Chapman estimates at 0.017 within a thousandth or so. The quantity λ_{12} is likewise positive and is also, of course, zero for the inverse fifth power, but it can rise to a maximum value of $32/9\pi - 1 = 0.132$ for hard spheres of extremely unequal mass, a limiting case in which, as it happens, the modified distribution function can actually be found by solving the Boltzmann differential equation for nf. In other cases than these two, λ_{12} varies somewhat with composition and usually in such a direction that the rate of diffusion increases as the lighter gas is made scarcer. The formulas exhibiting this variation are extremely complicated, however, and none of them will be written down here. The theoretical variation in most practical cases is small, and if a formula is needed for practical use, and a linear one will not answer, an empirical one of quadratic type such as

$$D_{12} = a_{11}n_1^2 + a_{12}n_1n_2 + a_{22}n_2^2$$

will probably be found to meet all requirements.

The coefficient C in (168b) is shown by Chapman to have a magnitude lying between the value 1.200 for hard spheres, which just happens to agree to this number of places with the approximate value that we obtained above, and the value 1.543 for inverse-fifth-power repulsion.

112. Experiments on the Variation with Composition. The conflict between Meyer's theory, on the one hand, predicting large variation in the diffusion coefficient with changes in the relative concentration of the mixed gases, and the Maxwell-Chapman-Enskog theory, on the other, predicting no change at all, stimulated a series of careful observations at Halle designed to settle the question experimentally.* The method of experiment as finally perfected was to fill one half of a long uniform vertical tube with a pure gas and the other half with a mixture of this gas and another one, the denser of the two resulting masses of gas being put below the other, and then to open a stopcock and allow diffusion to go on for a known number of hours; the composition of that gas which had been pure at the start was then determined, either by chem-

---

* Cf. Lonius, *Ann. Physik*, **29**, 664 (1929).

ical analysis or by weighing it in order to find its density. With this arrangement, when the stopcock is opened, the concentration at the middle of the tube promptly changes to a value halfway between the two initial concentrations and thereafter remains at this value; the observational result, interpreted with the help of the usual one-dimensional theory of diffusion, thus furnishes a value of D corresponding to this intermediate value of the concentration.

These experiments demonstrated beyond a doubt that some variation of D with composition does occur, but the variation is always small and is hard to observe unless the molecular masses are very unequal. The most interesting of the results obtained are shown in the table below; the observer is named in each case just under the names of the gases, and the fractional part which the heavier gas formed of the mixture in each case is given in the second column. The temperature was 15°C, the pressure approximately atmospheric. The values given under D_1 are the original ones, expressed in terms of meters and hours; under D are given corresponding values in terms of centimeters and seconds, obtained by dividing the original numbers by 0.36. In his last paper Chapman made theoretical calculations from his formulas to fit these experimental cases, adjusting the mean value of D arbitrarily in each case to fit the observed mean; values of the molecular diameters were calculated from the known viscosities. His theoretical values are given in the last column. The agreement is probably to be considered satisfactory and thus serves to confirm the theory.

DIFFUSION DATA

Gases	$\dfrac{n_1}{n_1 + n_2}$	D	D_1 obs.	D_1 theor.
O_2-H_2 (Deutsch)	0.25	0.767	0.276	0.276
	0.50	0.778	0.280	0.282
	0.75	0.803	0.289	0.289
CO_2-H_2 (Deutsch)	0.25	0.592	0.213	0.212
	0.50	0.606	0.218	0.222
	0.75	0.633	0.228	0.226
Ar-He (Lonius)	0.273	0.678	0.244	0.248
	0.315	0.694	0.250	0.250
	0.677	0.711	0.256	0.257
	0.763	0.731	0.263	0.259

113. Diffusion at Various Pressures and Temperatures. The theoretical results indicate that at a *given temperature* the coefficient of diffusion should be *inversely proportional* to the total *density* and so proportional to the mean free path, which is as we should expect. This is shown clearly by our approximate formulas, in which the molecular density n occurs in the denominator and S_d should depend only on the violence of the collisions but not on their frequency; and Chapman showed that the same conclusion should hold with precision. This property of the diffusion coefficient was verified in certain cases by Loschmidt in 1870. Accepting it as universally valid at sufficiently low densities, we can write $D = F(T)/p$, where p is the pressure and $F(T)$ is a function of the absolute temperature T alone.

At *constant pressure*, on the other hand, our formulas (166) and (167a) predict that $D \propto T^{3/2}$, since $\bar{v} \propto T^{1/2}$ and at constant pressure $1/n \propto T$, provided S_d is independent of T, as it would be for hard spheres. According to statements made in tables of physical data, the observed rate of variation is greater than this, D being roughly proportional to T^n where n is around 1.75 for the more permanent gases but around 2 for the more condensable ones.

The latter values of n are roughly greater by unity than the corresponding values for the viscosity η of the same gases, so that for these gases $D/\eta T$ or $\rho D/\eta$ ($\rho = $ density) must be nearly independent of the temperature at constant pressure. Such a relation is suggested by our approximate formulas; it follows, for instance, from eq. (167a), expressing the coefficient of self-diffusion, provided the ratio S_{vc}/S_d is independent of temperature, or at once from (167b) or (167c) in the case of hard spheres or the inverse-fifth-power law of force. Further experiments to test the variation of $\rho D/\eta$ with temperature would be of interest.

An increase of D more rapid than as $T^{3/2}$, resulting from a decrease in S_d with rising temperature, is just what we should expect in accordance with the considerations brought forward above in order to explain the rapid variation of the viscosity.

For molecules repelling as the inverse sth power of the distance the method of similitude can be employed, as was done in dealing with the viscosity in Sec. 89. In that section modified motions were contemplated in which all lengths were changed in the ratio λ and all times in the ratio

$$(t:) \qquad \tau = \lambda^{\frac{1+s}{2}}.$$

It was then shown that the absolute temperature T is changed in the ratio

$$(T:) \qquad \lambda^{1-s}.$$

Now D, being the ratio of molecular flow over unit area per second to a molecular density gradient, will be changed in the ratio

$$(1/\lambda^2 \tau)/([1/\lambda^3]/\lambda)$$

or

$$(D:) \qquad \lambda^{\frac{3-s}{2}}.$$

But we saw that we could write $D = \dfrac{F(T)}{\rho}$. Here, the masses being unaltered, ρ is changed in the ratio $1/\lambda^3$; hence $F(T)$ or ρD must be changed in the ratio

$$\frac{\lambda^{(3-s)/2}}{\lambda^3} = \lambda^{-\frac{3+s}{2}},$$

or like T^n, where $n = -\dfrac{3+s}{2(1-s)}$. Accordingly,

$$D \propto \frac{1}{\rho} T^n, \qquad n = \frac{1}{2} + \frac{2}{s-1}.$$

This is the same value of n that is given in eq. 128 in Sec. 89 for the variation of the viscosity with temperature for molecules repelling as the inverse sth power of the distance. Accordingly, for this type of molecule $D \propto \eta/\rho$, or $\rho D/\eta$ is constant, as was suggested by our general formulas.

As an alternative, there is Sutherland's theory in which the molecules are assumed to be hard elastic spheres surrounded by weak attractive fields. This theory we found to have considerable success in dealing with the viscosity. Sutherland showed that it gives for the coefficient of diffusion

$$D = \frac{aT^{3/2}}{1 + (C_{12}/T)}$$

in which a and C_{12} are constants. This equation he found to hold satisfactorily in certain cases. It must be recognized, however, that the diffusion coefficient has not yet been investigated over a sufficiently wide range of temperatures to make possible an adequate test of such formulas as these, and it seems pretty certain that when accurate data are obtained all formulas of such simple type will be found to fail for diffusion just as they did for the viscosity.

114. Numerical Values of the Diffusion Coefficient. Our formulas for the diffusion coefficient as expressed in eq. (166) or (168a) contain still another new molecular characteristic, the equivalent mutual collision cross section for diffusion denoted by S_d and defined in terms of the scattering coefficient by (165a) or (165b). For this reason these formulas cannot be tested very exactly in terms of other known magnitudes but serve rather to enable us to calculate values of S_d from diffusion data. In general S_d is not quite the same as the quantity S_{vc} which controls viscosity and heat conduction and which is defined in terms of the scattering coefficient by eq. (153) in Sec. 100. These two quantities, however, must be at least of the same order of magnitude; in the case of hard spheres moving classically they are, of course, actually identical and equal to the ordinary mutual cross section.

Instead of calculating values of S_d itself from the formulas it is probably more convenient to calculate for reference what may be called the *equivalent classical mean hard-spherical diameter* for the two kinds of molecules in question, defined as $\sigma_d = (S_d/\pi)^{1/2}$; this is the mean diameter of hard spheres which, moving classically, would exhibit the same diffusion. If we had available for this purpose data on *self-diffusion*, such values of σ_d might then be compared directly with the values of σ calculated previously from viscosity data. Unfortunately, however, very few data exist on anything approximating to self-diffusion. An alternative idea would be to calculate values of an equivalent σ_{vc} from data on the viscosity of the diffusing mixtures themselves for comparison with their values of σ_d. The significance of such a comparison would not be too clear, however, for the diffusion is controlled almost entirely by interaction between dissimilar molecules, whereas the viscosity is influenced also in part by interaction between similar molecules, and neither theory nor experiment has progressed to a point where these two kinds of influence upon the viscosity can be estimated separately from the data with much accuracy.

In view of this situation we shall, for the purpose of testing our formulas, merely calculate S_d and σ_d from D_{12} for several mixtures of gases by means of eq. (166a), in which $n = n_0\dfrac{T_0}{T}$ and is known, omitting for this purpose the small and uncertain correction term λ_{12} which is added in (168a). The values of n_0, T_0, and R_M are given in eqs. (22), (19), and (20a). Values of $\sigma_d = (S_d/\pi)^{1/2}$ calculated in this way for a number of pairs of gases at 15°C are shown in the following table. For comparison with them, values of $\sigma_{av} = (\sigma_1 + \sigma_2)/2$ are also shown for the same pairs of gases in terms of the equivalent hard-sphere diameters for viscosity as given under "σ" in the table following Sec. 86 above. The table contains also observed values of n in the approximately valid formula, $D = D_0(T/T_0)^n(p_0/p)$, where p = pressure. The values placed in parentheses are less reliable.

DIFFUSION DIAMETERS

Gases	n	σ_d (unit, 10^{-8} cm.)	σ_{av}	Gases	n	σ_d (unit, 10^{-8} cm.)	σ_{av}
H_2-CH_4	(1.75)	3.15	3.44	He-Ar	1.75	3.04	2.91
H_2-H_2O	(1.75)	2.86	3.67	CH_4-CO_2	(1.75)	3.97	4.36
H_2-Ne	1.71	3.02	2.66	H_2O-air	(1.75)	3.36	4.16
H_2-C_2H_6	(1.75)	3.62	4.02	H_2O-CO_2	(2.0)	4.06	4.60
H_2-O_2	1.75	2.95	3.18	O_2-N_2	1.80	3.40	3.68
H_2-CO_2	1.74	3.29	3.66	Air-CO_2	(2.0)	3.76	4.16

A glance at the table shows that there is a rough agreement between the values of σ_d and σ_{av}, probably as close an agreement as ought to be expected in view of the theoretical difference between the two effective cross sections. In most cases, however, σ_{av} is somewhat the larger. Such a difference would be expected in view of the difference between the ways in which the angle of deflection θ enters into the expressions for S_d and S_{vc} as given in eqs. (165a), (165b), and (153). The factor $(1 - \cos \theta)$ in the integral causes S_d to depend more upon large-angle deflections than upon small ones, whereas the corresponding factor $\sin^2 \theta$ in the case of S_{vc} is symmetrical about $\theta = \pi/2$, and with any reasonable type of molecular field except the rigid-body type small deflections must predominate over large. Thus we should expect to find $S_d < S_{vc}$. The physical reason for the difference can be said to be this, that momentum and energy can be transferred in a collision from one molecule to another, and the effect of deflections respectively greater and smaller than $\pi/2$ may therefore be much the same, whereas the inner nature of a molecule cannot be transferred, and consequently, while a small deflection will retard diffusion but little, a deflection near 180° actually reverses the diffusing motion.

The general situation is accordingly very satisfactory for the theory.

115. Forced Diffusion. Up to this point we have dealt with concentration gradients as the sole cause of diffusion. Any influence, however, which affects the rate of flow of molecules across a surface might conceivably cause a differential flow that would constitute a phenomenon essentially of the same nature.

A case that occurs very commonly in vacuum-tube work is that of the drifting motion caused by forces acting selectively upon certain molecules, such as the forces exerted by an electric field upon ions. This case is readily connected with the process of ordinary diffusion by the following argument and may be regarded as a sort of forced diffusion.

Let each molecule of a certain sort be acted upon by a steady external force F, and let there be n_1 such molecules per unit volume with the distribution function $f_1(\mathbf{v}_1)$. Let the gas be uniform in composition, and at rest and in equilibrium except for the forces F.

Then if the x-axis be taken in the direction of F, the Boltzmann differential equation (87) in Sec. 51, applied to n_1, becomes

$$v_{1x}\frac{\partial}{\partial x}(n_1 f_1) + \frac{F}{m_1}\frac{\partial}{\partial v_{1x}}(n_1 f_1) = \left[\frac{\partial}{\partial t}(n_1 f_1)\right]_{\text{coll}},$$

terms in t, y, and z disappearing under the conditions assumed. Let us write, as in Sec. 109, $f_1 = f_{10} + f_{1s}$, where

$$f_{10} = A_1 e^{-\beta_1^2 v_1^2} = A_1 e^{-\beta_1^2(v_{1x}^2 + v_{1y}^2 + v_{1z}^2)},$$

A_1 and β_1^2 being independent of x because the temperature is uniform. Then in the last equation we can, as in that section, replace f_1 by f_{1s} in the collision term on the right, and by f_{10} elsewhere; accordingly

$$\frac{\partial}{\partial v_{1x}}(n_1 f_1) = -2\beta_1^2 v_{1x} n_1 f_{10}$$

and, inserting $\beta_1^2 = m_1/2kT$ from (56) in Sec. 28, we have

$$v_{1x}\left(\frac{dn_1}{dx} - \frac{n_1 F}{kT}\right)A_1 e^{-\beta_1^2 v_1^2} = \left[\frac{\partial}{\partial t}(n_1 f_{1s})\right]_{\text{coll}}.$$

This equation has exactly the same form as eq. (161) in Sec. 109, which formed the basis of the theory of diffusion, except that dn_1/dx is here replaced by the quantity

$$P = \frac{dn_1}{dx} - \frac{n_1 F}{kT}.$$

We may conclude that a uniform steady force F acting on each one of a group of molecules of density n_1 per unit volume has the same tendency to cause diffusion as has a density gradient of those molecules of magnitude

$$\left(\frac{dn_1}{dx}\right)_{\text{equiv}} = -\frac{n_1 F}{kT}, \tag{169a}$$

k being as usual the gas constant for one molecule and T the absolute temperature.

The remainder of the theory of diffusion as we have developed it will now apply and we can utilize its results to obtain an expression for the mean rate of drift of the selected molecules.

One other circumstance must first receive attention, however. If other forces were acting in the opposite direction upon other molecules in such a way as to make the total force equal to zero, we could assume that $dn_1/dx = 0$. As it is, the total force n_1F per unit volume can only be balanced by a force arising from a pressure gradient dp/dx of such magnitude that

$$\frac{dp}{dx} = n_1F$$

(cf. the reasoning in Sec. 45); since the pressure equals nkT in terms of the total molecular density n, this requires a gradient $\dfrac{dn}{dx} = \dfrac{1}{kT}\dfrac{dp}{dx}$, from which we find, since the composition is assumed uniform,

$$\frac{dn_1}{dx} = \frac{n_1}{n}\frac{dn}{dx} = \frac{n_1}{n}\frac{1}{kT}\frac{dp}{dx} = \frac{n_1^2}{n}\frac{F}{kT}.$$

The quantity P defined above thus becomes

$$P = \frac{n_1^2 F}{nkT} - \frac{n_1 F}{kT} = -\frac{n_1 n_2}{n}\frac{F}{kT},$$

where $n_2 = n - n_1$ and represents the density of the remaining molecules. We find also that

$$\frac{dn_2}{dx} = \frac{n_2}{n}\frac{dn}{dx} = \frac{n_1 n_2}{n}\frac{F}{kT} = -P.$$

The mathematical equations for both kinds of molecules thus take on the same form as in Sec. 109, where the two gradients were equal and opposite. Accordingly, we obtain the stream density of the molecules on which F is acting by substituting P for dn_1/dx in (160a), which gives for it

$$\Gamma_1 = D\frac{n_1 n_2}{n}\frac{F}{kT}, \tag{169b}$$

D being the ordinary coefficient of diffusion for molecules of the selected sort diffusing through the gas.

The average velocity of drift u of the selected molecules under the action of the force F is then Γ_1 divided by their density n_1 or

$$u = \frac{n_2}{n}\frac{D}{kT}F. \tag{170a}$$

The ratio u/F, representing the drift velocity with a unit force acting on each molecule, might be called the *dynamical mobility* U_f of these molecules in the gas; it satisfies the relation,

$$\frac{D}{U_f} = \frac{n}{n_2} kT. \tag{170b}$$

In most practical cases, however, n_1 is relatively very small; then the last two equations take on the simpler approximate forms

$$u = \frac{D}{kT} F, \qquad \frac{D}{U_f} = kT. \tag{170c, d}$$

Even ordinary diffusion can be interpreted as a kind of forced diffusion, the equivalent force per molecule being from (169a)

$$F_d = -kT \frac{1}{n_1} \frac{dn_1}{dx}.$$

The total equivalent force on the n_1 molecules in unit volume is then $n_1 F_d = -kT \frac{dn_1}{dx} = -\frac{dp_1}{dx}$, where $p_1 = n_1 kT$ and represents the partial pressure due to these molecules. Diffusing molecules can thus be regarded as being driven by their partial-pressure gradients, a view of the process that is often illuminating.

116. Thermal Diffusion. Another case of diffusion arising from causes other than a concentration gradient was predicted theoretically by Chapman (1916) and later revealed by experiment. He showed that a temperature gradient in a mixed gas might well give rise to a slight flow of one constituent relative to the gas as a whole, producing an effect that he called "thermal diffusion."*

Our approximate theory of heat conduction does not lead to this conclusion, since the approximate correction term that we introduced into the velocity distribution as given in eq. (148b) in Sec. 97 was such as to give rise to no net flow of molecules. The more complete analysis of heat conduction leads, however, to the contrary conclusion that collisions between different types of molecules in a mixed gas should usually give rise to a small differential diffusion. The effect vanishes for Maxwell's molecules repelling as r^{-5}, and for this reason was not discovered by him. It possesses a peculiar interest for theory as being one of the very few phenomena in gases which depend for their bare existence upon the particular form of the law of force; experiments upon thermal diffusion might be expected for this reason to throw a particularly valuable light upon the nature of the molecular forces.

The theoretical formulas obtained by Chapman are again too complicated to quote, so only a few illustrative figures will be men-

* CHAPMAN, *Phil. Trans.*, **217A**, 115 (1918).

tioned. Let k_T denote the relative effectiveness of a temperature
gradient in promoting diffusion as compared with a composition
gradient, being defined as the ratio of the two resulting diffusive flows
when $(1/T)(dT/dx)$ in the one case is numerically equal to
$(1/n)(dn_1/dx)$ in the other, n_1 being the density in molecules per unit
volume of one constituent and n that of the whole gas. Then, according to Chapman, if the molecules were hard spheres, k_T should not
exceed 1 per cent or so in a mixture of two similar molecules like oxygen
and nitrogen, but when the masses are very different, as in an argon-
helium or oxygen-hydrogen mixture, it might range up to something
like 0.13. For molecules having softer force-fields k_T is less, and it
vanishes of course for pure repulsion as r^{-5}. Usually the direction is
such that the heavier molecules tend to diffuse toward the colder
region.

The simplest case to study experimentally probably would be that
of a steady flow of heat through a layer of gas; there thermal diffusion
would result eventually in setting up a steady composition gradient
parallel to the temperature gradient of such magnitude that the resulting transport of molecules by ordinary diffusion in one direction would
just balance the transport by thermal diffusion in the other. Actual
experiments of this sort were performed in collaboration with Chapman
by Dootson* and the expected effect was shown to exist. Two bulbs
connected by a tube containing a stopcock were filled with the mixture
of gases to be studied, and then with the stopcock open the bulbs were
held at different constant temperatures for a number of hours in order
to allow the steady state to be set up; the stopcock was then closed and
the gas in each bulb was analyzed. As an example of the results, a
mixture of nearly equal parts by volume of hydrogen and carbon
dioxide, after the bulbs had been held at 200 and 10°C, respectively, for
4 hours, showed a concentration of hydrogen in the hot bulb exceeding
that in the cold one by 2.2 per cent of the total concentration; a mixture
of hydrogen and sulfur dioxide in the ratio 3:2 gave a difference in the
same direction of 3.5 per cent. The theoretical values for these two
cases as calculated from Chapman's formulas for hard spherical
molecules were 7.1 and 9.1 per cent, respectively. The difference
between these theoretical numbers and the experimental values might
easily be ascribed to the softness of the molecules and can probably
be taken as a direct indication that some softness exists, but probably
not so much as would result from an inverse-fifth-power repulsion.

* Chapman and Dootson, *Phil. Mag.*, **33**, 248 (1917).

CHAPTER V

THE EQUATION OF STATE

For our next topic we may conveniently return once more to the consideration of gases in equilibrium; but we shall now drop the assumption that the gas is practically perfect. The principal effect of the intermolecular forces in causing departures from the behavior of perfect gases is manifested in the relation between pressure and volume, and to this effect the present chapter will be devoted.

117. The Equation of State. In the theory of a fluid the general relation between the *pressure*, the *volume*, and the *temperature* is of fundamental importance. An equation expressing this relation is called the *equation of state* of the fluid. For a perfect gas we have found for it the simple familiar form, $pV = RT$; and it has been remarked that according to experiment all gases follow this equation more and more closely as the pressure is decreased, so that it can be accepted as the universal equation of state for a gas in the limit of vanishing density.

As the density is raised, on the other hand, departures from the perfect-gas law would be expected and actually occur; at extremely high densities all gases become, in fact, only slightly compressible and in general take on the properties that we commonly associate with liquids. In this chapter we shall survey the principal attempts that have been made to arrive at an equation of state that will hold for real gases at all densities, or at least over a considerable range.

The problem is susceptible of attack along two fundamentally different lines. We may endeavor to refine our physical assumptions in regard to the properties of molecules in the hope of obtaining a theoretical equation that will agree better with the facts; or, on the other hand, we may seek by trial and error to construct an empirical equation to fit the observations. Progress has actually been made along both lines; the earliest steps taken consisted mostly of modifications in the assumed properties of molecules, but during the last two decades the empirical method has received the greater share of attention. The ultimate theoretical solution should, of course, come out of wave mechanics, but as yet little has been accomplished in this direction.

118. The Equation of van der Waals. The most important of the earlier attempts at an improved equation of state was the proposal

made by van der Waals in 1873.*   The following is a paraphrase of the
argument by which he arrived at his new equation.

   In a real gas there must be cohesive forces acting between the
molecules; in the liquid or solid state this is shown very obviously by
their clinging together, and it is natural to assume that such forces act
at least slightly, however far apart the molecules may be.   Consequently, a molecule near the wall of the containing vessel must experience a net average force due to the attraction of the other molecules
tending to draw it away from the wall.   The pressure of the gas on the
wall will be diminished thereby, and, since the amount of the pull on
the gas will be proportional to the number of molecules pulled and also
to the number that pull on each one, the diminution of pressure should
be proportional to the square of the density of the gas; this diminution
can accordingly be written in the form, a/V^2, where a is a constant
depending on the exact law of attraction.

   On the other hand, the pressure will be affected also by the finite
size of the molecules.   Each one is compelled at least to remain
outside of all the others, and the space available for it to move in
is reduced in consequence; the impact rate of the molecules on each
other must thereby be increased.   Now each molecule should reduce
the available space by a definite constant amount, hence the total
reduction for a given number of them will have some definite constant value; let us denote its magnitude for a gram by b.   The effect
of molecular size will then be to increase the pressure caused by
molecular motion, which otherwise would have the value RT/V,
in the ratio of the whole volume V to the available volume, or in
the ratio $V/(V - b)$.

   Combining these two effects, we thus obtain for the net pressure
upon the wall of the vessel

$$p = \frac{RT}{V - b} - \frac{a}{V^2}. \qquad (171a)$$

This is the new equation of state, usually written in the form,

$$\left(p + \frac{a}{V^2}\right)(V - b) = RT, \qquad (171b)$$

and commonly known as "van der Waals' equation."   It is one of the
most famous equations in all kinetic theory.

   * VAN DER WAALS, "Essay on the Continuity of the Liquid and Solid States"
(in Dutch; Leiden, 1873).   Translated in Threlfall and Adair, "Physical Memoirs"
(Taylor and Francis, 1890).

Perhaps the remark may be added that, like every important advance in physics, the equation had forerunners which went a long way toward accomplishing the same thing. Clausius, for example, introduced the term b, and Hirn wrote $p + a$ for p. The advance made by van der Waals over his predecessors was twofold: first of all, he made the change from a to a/V^2, and then he discussed the equation in comparison with experimental data and showed that in certain cases it fitted well. Both of these steps were important. We can probably say with safety, however, that, if van der Waals had not proposed the equation, some one else presently would have done so; it was, so to speak, in the air. In scientific work in general the individual scientist seems to determine when and in what form an advance shall come rather than to determine what advances shall ultimately be made.

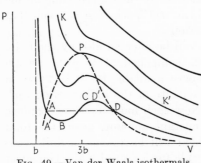

FIG. 49.—Van der Waals isothermals.

119. The van der Waals Isothermals.

The most interesting properties of van der Waals' equation lie in a region beyond the reach of present-day kinetic theory and will be mentioned here only briefly; a fuller discussion may be sought in books on heat or on the properties of matter.*

The general character of the isothermal curves on the p, V diagram as predicted by the equation is shown in Fig. 49. All isothermals corresponding to temperatures above a certain limit, which is called the *critical temperature*, slope downward toward increasing volume, and at high temperatures they approximate to the hyperbolas that are characteristic of a perfect gas. Below the critical temperature each theoretical isothermal exhibits a maximum and a minimum, between which there is a rising segment (e.g., BC). The critical isothermal KK', corresponding to the critical temperature, is merely horizontal at one point, called the *critical point* (P in the figure). All isothermals rise to infinity as V approaches the value b.

Now the p, V diagrams of all substances actually show a region of this general sort, with one important modification. Instead of ascending segments on the isothermals, there is a polyphase region, outlined by the dotted curve in Fig. 49, within which the substance, when in equilibrium, is separated into at least two phases; one of the coexistent phases is a saturated vapor, the other or others are liquid or solid.

* E.g., B. C. McEwen, "Properties of Matter," 1923, especially Chap. VI.

This region touches the critical isothermal at the critical point.   An isothermal of the homogeneous substance can be followed experimentally only a short distance into the polyphase region, as from A to A' (superheated liquid) or from D to D' (supercooled vapor), and the substance is then not stable.   It is easy to see why no point on an ascending segment BC can be realized with the substance all in one phase; for it would then be highly unstable toward small inequalities of density, any slight rarefaction tending to increase without limit. The actual isothermals for the substance in equilibrium pass, therefore, horizontally through the polyphase region, as illustrated by the dotted line AD.

In many cases there exist other polyphase regions representing states in which two or more liquid or solid phases coexist, but with these we are not concerned.

Particular interest attaches to the *critical point.*   The corresponding temperature and volume, as given by van der Waals' equation, can be found as follows.

Differentiating (171a) with T kept constant, we have

$$\frac{\partial p}{\partial V} = -\frac{RT}{(V-b)^2} + \frac{2a}{V^3}. \tag{172}$$

Thus $\partial p/\partial V = 0$ when

$$\frac{2a}{RT} = \frac{V^3}{(V-b)^2}. \tag{173}$$

Now the right-hand member of this equation is infinite both for $V = b$ and for $V = \infty$; it has therefore a minimum when its derivative vanishes, i.e., for such a value of V that

$$\frac{3V^2}{(V-b)^2} - \frac{2V^3}{(V-b)^3} = \frac{V^2(V-3b)}{(V-b)^3} = 0$$

or when $V = 3b$.   At this value of V we have $\partial V/\partial p = 0$, provided, according to (173), $RT = 8a/27b$; with this value of RT but any other value of V, the right-hand member of (173) is larger than the left and $\partial p/\partial V < 0$, so that the corresponding isothermal is horizontal at just one point.   Also, for any larger value of T the left-hand member of (173) is always the smaller, and hence $\partial p/\partial V$ cannot vanish anywhere, the isothermal sloping downward toward the right throughout its course.

The pair of values of V and T thus found refer, therefore, to the critical point.   Calling them the *critical volume V_c* and *critical tempera-*

ture T_c, and adding the corresponding *critical pressure* p_c, calculated from (171a), we have thus for the critical constants:

$$V_c = 3b, \qquad p_c = \frac{1}{27}\frac{a}{b^2}, \qquad RT_c = \frac{8}{27}\frac{a}{b}. \qquad (174a, b, c)$$

Special interest attaches also to the *critical ratio* RT_c/p_cV_c, which is a pure number and represents the ratio of the volume as given by the perfect-gas law at the critical pressure and temperature to the actual volume V_c (or the ratio of the perfect-gas pressure at the critical volume and temperature to the actual pressure, or the ratio of the critical temperature to the perfect-gas temperature at the critical pressure and volume). The van der Waals value of this ratio is, from (174a, b, c),

$$\frac{RT_c}{p_cV_c} = \frac{8}{3} = 2.67. \qquad (175)$$

120. Quantitative Tests of van der Waals' Equation. When we turn from its qualitative features to a quantitative comparison of van der Waals' equation with the data for actual gases, we find very soon that it really does not fit the data very well.

The easiest quantitative feature to test is the critical ratio RT_c/p_cV_c, for which the equation predicts a value of $\frac{8}{3}$, as stated in eq. (175). In the following table are shown experimental values of the critical constants for a number of gases and the corresponding experimental value of the critical ratio. It will be noted that the experimental values are uniformly larger than the theoretical value of 2.67, lying near 3.5 for the gases shown, except that it is above 4 for water, whose critical density

CRITICAL DATA

Substance	t_c, °C	p_c, atm	$d_c = 1/V_c$, g/cc	RT_c/p_cV_c
Hydrogen	−240°	12.8	0.0310	3.27
Helium	−267.9°	2.26	0.069	3.26
H_2O	374°	218	$\begin{cases} 0.4 \ \ (?) \\ 0.329(?) \end{cases}$	5.40 4.45
Neon	−228°	25.9	0.484	3.42
Nitrogen	−147°	33.5	0.311	3.43
Oxygen	−119°	49.7	0.430	3.42
HCl	52°	86	0.42	3.48
Argon	−122°	48.0	0.53	3.42
CO_2	31.1°	73.0	0.46	3.57
Ethyl ether, $C_4H_{10}O$	194°	35.6	0.262	3.82

t_c = critical temperature, p_c = critical pressure, V_c = critical volume.

is hard to determine accurately.   Dieterici collected similar data for 23 other substances, all organic, and found values of the ratio mostly below 4 but ranging from 3.67 to 5.   Probably, however, large as the discrepancy is, the fact that it is not even larger furnishes some ground for believing that there must be a considerable measure of truth in the reasoning leading up to van der Waals' equation.

Difficulties of a similar order are encountered when an attempt is made to fit van der Waals' equation to a set of actual isothermals.

It must be recognized, however, that in using the equation near the critical point we are taxing very heavily the general validity of its theoretical foundations.   The equation might be expected to succeed better, although less spectacularly, at much lower densities.   Such a test of its validity will be made later in connection with the discussion of the second virial coefficient.   First, however, let us see how the theoretical foundations themselves can be improved.

121. More Exact Theory of the Pressure in a Dense Gas.   The argument by which we arrived at van der Waals' equation above was distinctly sketchy and needs to be replaced by a precise analysis of the process by which the pressure is produced in a dense gas.   Such an analysis will now be given.

The changes that were made in our hypotheses concerning molecular properties when we abandoned the assumption of a perfect gas amounted to allowing the molecules to exert appreciable forces upon each other while their centers of mass are still at considerable distances apart.   To find the effect of such forces upon the pressure, let us consider as in Sec. 5 the flow of normal momentum across a small plane area drawn anywhere in the gas (cf. Fig. 50 below).

In order to locate the molecules definitely with respect to this plane, let us define the position of any one to be the position of its center of mass, so that by definition a molecule "crosses" the plane at the instant when its center of mass crosses.   The mean molecular density, which now means the density of centers of mass, is then simply the ordinary number of molecules per unit volume.   Furthermore, according to classical statistical mechanics, the distribution of velocities is quite unaffected by the presence of intermolecular forces (cf. Sec. 205).   Accordingly, the entire elementary calculation made in Sec. 5 of the rate of convection of momentum across the plane by molecules that actually cross it still holds, and we have for the part of the pressure that is due to this cause, which we shall denote by p_k and call the *kinetic pressure*, simply the perfect-gas value

$$p_k = \frac{RT}{V},$$ (176)

in which V is the volume of a gram of the gas and $R = R_M/M$ and denotes its gas constant calculated just as if it were perfect (R_M = universal gas constant, M = molecular weight).

In addition to this convective flow of momentum, however, we now have an additional transfer through the agency of forces acting between molecules that lie momentarily on opposite sides of the plane, as at B and C in Fig. 50, irrespective of whether they themselves ever actually cross it or not. This part of the pressure, measured by the total force that acts across unit area, we shall call the *dynamic pressure* and denote by p_d. A definite expression can be

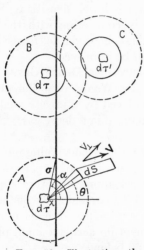

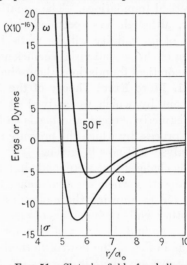

Fig. 50.—Illustrating the effect of molecular forces and finite size upon the pressure in a gas.

Fig. 51.—Slater's field for helium. ω = potential energy; F = force; r = interatomic distance; and σ = molecular diameter from viscosity.

obtained for it only from a knowledge of the law of intermolecular force, but the following qualitative analysis possesses a certain interest.

All that we know about molecules points toward the conclusion that the intermolecular force is usually of the nature of an attraction which rises as two molecules approach each other, reaches a maximum, and then quickly sinks and turns into a repulsion; the latter then increases rapidly as the molecules come close together. As an illustration, the actual curve for the force F, measured positively when repulsive, and its associated potential energy $\omega = \int_r^\infty F\, dr$, for two helium atoms as obtained from an approximate treatment by wave mechanics* is shown in Fig. 51; the equations for the two curves are

* SLATER and KIRKWOOD, *Phys. Rev.*, **37**, 682 (1931).

$$\omega = \left[7.7 \, e^{-2.43 \frac{r}{a_0}} - \frac{0.68}{(r/a_0)^6} \right] \times 10^{-10} \text{ erg,} \qquad (177a)$$

$$F = -\frac{d\omega}{dr} = 0.354 \, e^{-2.43 \frac{r}{a_0}} - \frac{0.0771}{(r/a_0)^7} \text{ dyne,} \qquad (177b)$$

where $a_0 = 5.29 \times 10^{-9}$ cm (the Bohr radius) and $r =$ distance between atomic centers. Conceivably the force might also oscillate more than once between attraction and repulsion, and in most cases it must depend a good deal upon the orientation of the molecules.

In any case, we can at any moment classify all of the forces that are actually acting across the plane between various pairs of molecules into the two types of attraction and repulsion, and we can in thought imagine each type to contribute its proper component to the pressure. The component due to attractive forces may be called the *cohesive pressure* and we shall denote it by p_c; it is often called the "internal" or "intrinsic" pressure. The component due to repulsive forces will be called the *repulsive pressure*, denoted by p_r. These two components together then make up what we have called the dynamic pressure p_d; and adding to this the kinetic part as given by (176), we have as the total pressure

$$p = p_k + p_d = \frac{RT}{V} + p_d, \qquad p_d = p_c + p_r. \qquad (178a, b)$$

It is interesting to note that the analysis up to this point would hold according to classical theory for a liquid or solid as well as for a gas. The kinetic pressure in a liquid or solid is, of course, enormous; the dynamic pressure is almost as great and is, of course, negative, the algebraic sum of the two equaling the external pressure.

Further quantitative progress along these lines cannot be made without additional information in regard to the molecular forces. Furthermore, it must be recognized that the introduction of wave mechanics blurs the sharpness of the distinctions that we have introduced here; even in a rarefied gas the distinction between repulsive and cohesive components cannot be so sharply drawn as in classical theory, and as the density increases, even the distinction between dynamic and kinetic pressures progressively loses physical significance until probably it scarcely retains any validity at all for the liquid or solid states. Moreover, wave mechanics furnishes an additional source of pressure in the "exchange" effects which are characteristic of the new theory and have no analogue in the old. Since, however, the latter effects are appreciable only for very light particles, or at enormous densities, or at minutely low temperatures, and so are as yet of importance only in the electron theory of metals, and since little is really known that is quantitative in regard to molecular forces, and accurate calculations are in any case necessarily complicated, we shall follow the usual procedure of working out by classical theory a simplified ideal case as a sort of model. The conceptions that are developed in doing this have at least some value as qualitative modes of thought in reasoning about the internal state of an actual gas.

Problem. Calculate the kinetic and dynamic pressures in water at 15°C and under 1 atmosphere of pressure. *Ans.:* 1,312 and −1,311 atmosphere. (Estimates of the cohesive pressure by itself run to 10,000 or 20,000 atmospheres.)

122. Hard Attracting Spheres: The Repulsive Pressure. Let us suppose that the molecules are all of one kind and that they

(a) are hard spheres of diameter σ obeying classical mechanics, and

(b) attract each other with a weak force that depends only upon their distance apart and effectively vanishes at distances several times as great as σ. Let us also restrict the density of the gas to be low enough so that the effect of these additional features upon the pressure is a small one; i.e., we seek only a first-order correction to the perfect-gas law. These are the assumptions that underlay the first quantitative calculation by van der Waals and others relative to his equation.

Let us begin by calculating the repulsive pressure p_r. With molecules of the type assumed, repulsive forces will act across the plane introduced in the last section only when a molecule lies part way across it and is struck by another whose center lies on the other side. Thus p_r arises here entirely from the finite size of the molecules.

To calculate the total effect of such impacts, consider a particular molecule whose center is at some distance x less than σ from the plane (e.g., A in Fig. 50), and around it draw its sphere of influence of radius σ, upon which the center of another molecule must lie at the moment of collision. Consider an element dS of that part of the surface of the sphere of influence which projects across the plane. If the given molecule A has a component of velocity $v_\perp$ in the direction of the outward normal to dS, the element dS will sweep out in time dt, relative to any other molecule moving with corresponding component $v_\perp'$, a volume $(v_\perp - v_\perp')dS\,dt$, independently of any transverse component of the motion of either molecule.

Now the density of molecules with a component within $dv_\perp'$ of $v_\perp'$ is, by (62) in Sec. 28, $n(\beta/\sqrt{\pi})e^{-\beta^2 v_\perp'^2}dv_\perp'$; hence the chance that another molecule has its center in the volume swept out by dS and so gets struck is

$$n(v_\perp - v_\perp') \, \frac{\beta}{\sqrt{\pi}} \, e^{-\beta^2 v_\perp'^2} \, dv_\perp' \, dS \, dt.$$

If such an impact occurs, according to the laws of elastic collisions an amount $m(v_\perp - v_\perp')$ of momentum in the direction of the normal to dS is transferred to the second molecule, m being the mass of each one, and a component of momentum normal to the plane of magnitude

$$m(v_\perp - v_\perp') \cos \theta$$

is thereby transmitted across the plane, θ being the angle between the normal to dS and the normal to the plane.

On the other hand, the chance that a molecule lies within a volume element $d\tau$ surrounding the position assumed for the first molecule and has also a component within $dv_\perp$ of $v_\perp$ is

$$n \, \frac{\beta}{\sqrt{\pi}} \, e^{-\beta^2 v_\perp^2} \, dv_\perp \, d\tau.$$

The total normal momentum transmitted across the plane by such collisions in time dt is then the product of these three expressions integrated over all possible velocities and all positions of dS and $d\tau$ or

$$n^2 m \, \frac{\beta^2}{\pi} \, dt \int \int \int \int (v_\perp - v_\perp')^2 e^{-\beta^2(v_\perp^2 + v_\perp'^2)} \cos \theta \, dv_\perp \, dv_\perp' \, dS \, d\tau.$$

This expression divided by dt and by the area of the plane then equals the repulsive pressure. Instead of dividing the whole integral by the area, however, we may also simply confine the integration over $d\tau$ to the space contained in a cylinder standing perpendicularly on a unit area of the plane; for each such cylindrical portion of space contributes an equal part to the whole. We can also imagine the integration over the two variables y and z running parallel to the plane to be carried out at once, the result of this integration being simply unity since the integrand is independent of y and z; we have left then only an integration over x perpendicular to the plane.

Accordingly, the repulsive pressure p_r will be given by the last expression with $d\tau$ replaced by dx, the limits for x being 0 and σ since no molecule can lie farther than σ cm from the plane and still collide with another beyond it. Let us transform the integral by writing $dS = \sigma^2 \sin \theta \, d\theta \, d\varphi$ in terms of polars with axis normal to the plane. Then, introducing obviously appropriate limits of integration, we have

$$p_r = n^2 m \sigma^2 \frac{\beta^2}{\pi} \int_0^\sigma dx \int_0^{2\pi} \int_0^\alpha \sin\theta \cos\theta \, d\theta \, d\varphi \int_{-\infty}^\infty dv_\perp$$

$$\int_{-\infty}^{v_\perp} (v_\perp - v_\perp')^2 e^{-\beta^2(v_\perp{}^2 + v_\perp{}'^2)} \, dv_\perp',$$

in which α is the value of θ at the circle along which the plane cuts the sphere of influence, and so depends upon the value of x, and the upper limit for $v_\perp'$ is $v_\perp$ because faster molecules could not be overtaken by the first one.

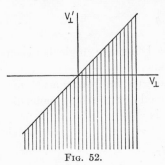

$v_\perp'$

$v_\perp$

FIG. 52.

The double integral over $v_\perp$, $v_\perp'$ can, however, be simplified. We can extend the integration over the entire $v_\perp$, $v_\perp'$-plane and then divide by 2, since the integrand is symmetric in $v_\perp$ and $v_\perp'$; the original region of integration is that which is shaded in Fig. 52, but the integrand has the same value at any two points that are symmetrically situated relative to the line $v_\perp = v_\perp'$. Doing this, we find

$$\int_{-\infty}^\infty dv_\perp \int_{-\infty}^{v_\perp} (v_\perp - v_\perp')^2 e^{-\beta^2(v_\perp{}^2 + v_\perp{}'^2)} \, dv_\perp' = \frac{1}{2} \int_{-\infty}^\infty \int_{-\infty}^\infty (v_\perp{}^2 +$$

$$v_\perp{}'^2) e^{-\beta^2(v_\perp{}^2 + v_\perp{}'^2)} \, dv_\perp \, dv_\perp' = \int_{-\infty}^\infty \int_{-\infty}^\infty v_\perp{}^2 e^{-\beta^2(v_\perp{}^2 + v_\perp{}'^2)} \, dv_\perp \, dv_\perp'$$

$$= \int_{-\infty}^\infty x^2 e^{-\beta^2 x^2} \, dx \int_{-\infty}^\infty e^{-\beta^2 x^2} \, dx = \frac{\pi}{2\beta^4},$$

the term in $v_\perp v_\perp'$ that arises from the expansion of $(v_\perp - v_\perp')^2$ giving zero by symmetry. (Cf. table of integrals at the end of the book.)

The remaining integrations are then easily carried out with the help of the obvious relation, $\cos\alpha = x/\sigma$, giving, since $\int_0^{2\pi} d\varphi = 2\pi$,

$$\int_0^\alpha \sin\theta \cos\theta \, d\theta = \frac{1}{2}\sin^2\alpha = \frac{1}{2}\left(1 - \frac{x^2}{\sigma^2}\right), \int_0^\sigma dx = \sigma, \int_0^\sigma x^2 \, dx = \frac{1}{3}\sigma^3,$$

$$p_r = n^2 m \sigma^2 \frac{\beta^2}{\pi} \left(\frac{\pi}{2\beta^4}\right) 2\pi \left(\frac{1}{3}\sigma\right)$$

or, after inserting $nm = 1/V$ and $\beta^2 = 1/(2RT)$ by (56) in Sec. 28,

$$p_r = \frac{2\pi}{3} \frac{n}{V} \sigma^3 RT.$$

For the repulsive pressure we can accordingly write

$$p_r = b\frac{RT}{V^2}, \qquad b = \frac{2}{3}\pi n V\sigma^3, \qquad (179a, b)$$

in which V is the volume of a gram.

123. Equation of State for Hard Attracting Spheres. On the other hand, the cohesive pressure, arising from the assumed attraction, is easily found merely by restating the brief argument of Sec. 118 in more precise terms. Because of the low density, the molecular distribution will be very nearly the same as in a perfect gas, i.e., each molecular center is as likely to be in one position as in another and the various molecules are distributed independently. Accordingly, the chance of a molecule's being in any element $d\tau$, say at B in Fig. 50, is simply $n\,d\tau$ where n is the number of molecules per unit volume; the chance of another's being in another element $d\tau'$ at some point such as C across the plane is similarly $n\,d\tau'$; and the chance that both are in these positions simultaneously is $n^2\,d\tau\,d\tau'$. The expectation of a resulting contribution to the cohesive pressure p_c can thus be written $n^2 F_\perp\,d\tau\,d\tau'$ where $F_\perp$ denotes the component of force normal to the plane that one molecule exerts upon the other and so is some function of the positions of $d\tau$ and $d\tau'$. Similar considerations apply to all elements of volume. Hence the total cohesive pressure is $n^2\int\int F_\perp\,d\tau\,d\tau'$ or

$$p_c = -a'n^2 = -\frac{a}{V^2},$$

where a' or a is a small constant.

For the total pressure we have then finally, inserting our values of p_c and p_r in (178a, b) above,

$$p = p_k + p_c + p_r = \frac{RT}{V}\left(1 + \frac{b}{V}\right) - \frac{a}{V^2}. \qquad (180)$$

Here R is the gas constant for a gram computed as for a perfect gas (e.g., $R = R_M/M$).

This equation agrees for small values of b/V with that obtained from van der Waals' equation, which can be expanded in powers of b as follows [cf. (171a) in Sec. 118]:

$$p = \frac{RT}{V}\left(1 + \frac{b}{V} + \frac{b^2}{V^2} + \cdots\right) - \frac{a}{V^2}. \qquad (181)$$

Our analysis thus furnishes a rigorous deduction of van der Waals' equation for the type of molecules under consideration, but only for the case in which the effect of molecular size is relatively small. The question as to the validity of the equation at higher densities is left untouched.

124. The Value of b. In the last section we obtained a connection between our constant b, which at low densities is the same as van der Waals' b, and the size of the molecules, for the case in which the latter are hard spheres. The value given by (179b),

$$b = \tfrac{2}{3}\pi n V \sigma^3,$$

is equal to four times the actual volume of the molecules in a gram of the gas. In our original rough analysis, on the other hand, b was introduced as representing a diminution in the space available for the molecules to move around in, and since each molecule excludes the centers of all others from its sphere of influence, we might perhaps have expected b to equal the total volume of all the spheres of influence, which would be eight times the sum of the actual molecular volumes, or twice as great as the value just found. The reduction from eight to four undoubtedly arises from the interpenetration of these spheres, of which an example is illustrated by molecules B and C in Fig. 50, where the spheres of influence are represented by dotted circles; but only a detailed calculation could show that the ratio of reduction is exactly ½.

It must not be forgotten that even the value obtained above for b has reference only to rarefied gases, i.e., it applies to the first-order correction to the perfect-gas law. If we assign this value to the constant b in van der Waals' equation and then suppose the equation to hold even up to very high densities, a curious consequence results, since as $V \to b$ the pressure becomes infinite; this ought to mean that when $V \to b$ the molecules become tight-packed, but if they were, the volume of the gas ought to be less than twice rather than four times the actual volume of the molecules themselves. This consideration alone is sufficient to show that van der Waals' equation cannot be correct at all densities for an attracting-sphere gas. The equation might conceivably be found to hold closely for some actual gas even up to very high densities; but then we could infer that the molecules of that gas at least were not hard, weakly attracting spheres, and the empirical constant b appearing in the equation would then of necessity possess some other significance than that which we have found here.

125. Other Equations of State. Many attempts have been made to obtain an equation of state agreeing more closely with the behavior of actual gases.   Besides efforts to improve the precision of calculations similar in type to that which we have just made, various other lines of approach have been tried, varying from strictly theoretical arguments to purely empirical procedures.

Boltzmann, for example, carried the calculation for hard spheres a step farther by considering the effect of "triple encounters," or cases in which a third molecule lies close enough to have an influence upon the probability of a collision between two given molecules. In our calculation we assumed that the chance of finding a second molecule in an element of volume $d\tau$ near another one (e.g., near A in Fig. 50) has the value $n \, d\tau$ in which n is the number of molecules in unit volume.   This is certainly the *average* number in $d\tau$ during the whole time.   We must recognize, however, that a second molecule can have its center in an element only when the latter is not over-lapped by the sphere of influence of some third molecule.   Now, if $d\tau$ is assumed to lie just outside the sphere of influence of a molecule A, the range of positions in which a third molecule might lie with its sphere of influence overlapping $d\tau$ is easily seen to be restricted by the presence of A, and hence it is easier for a second molecule to get into such an element than into one that is out in the open. Thus in an element near the sphere of influence of a molecule the mean density of molecular centers is somewhat greater than n, the excess being itself proportional to n so long as n is small.   (A similar enhancement of the mean density near the wall of the containing vessel actually serves to account for the entire increase in the pressure on the wall corresponding to p_r, not merely for the second-order term which we are now discussing.)

The resulting effect on the pressure can be calculated;* Boltzmann finds that it changes the parenthesis in (180) from $\left(1 + \dfrac{b}{V}\right)$ to

$$\left(1 + \frac{b}{V} + \frac{5b^2}{8V^2}\right).$$

The added term goes part way toward supplying the term $\dfrac{b^2}{V^2}$ in the expansion of van der Waals' equation; but the behavior of the equation at the critical point is found not to be improved.   The calculation could be extended further so as to allow for encounters of four or more molecules, but this is scarcely worth while because the assumption of hard spheres is, after all, pretty wide of the truth.

* Cf. also Ursell, references at end of Sec. 129.

In a more general way, both van der Waals himself and others have proposed to treat a and b in his equation as variables, either replacing one or both of them by some expression containing additional unknown constants, or simply regarding them as functions of V and T. A better fit with experiment can, of course, be attained in this manner, but it must be noted that the original form of van der Waals' equation loses all significance if a and b are allowed to vary without restriction; for in this sense any relation whatever between p, V, and T can be written in the van der Waals form (or, for that matter, in the simpler perfect-gas form $pV = RT$, by allowing R to stand for a suitable function of V and T!).

Of the various other equations of state containing a limited number of disposable constants that have been proposed from time to time we shall mention only two.

In 1899 Dieterici proposed the equation*

$$p = \frac{RT}{V - b}\, e^{-\frac{a}{RTV}},$$

in which a and b are new constants whereas R is, as usual, the perfect-gas constant. The equation rests theoretically on the assumption that the cohesive forces are on the whole equivalent to a force-field acting upon molecules in the surface layer of the gas in such a way as to tend to draw them back into the interior, with the result that the density is less at the surface in proportion to the Boltzmann factor, $e^{-\omega/kT}$. It would be natural, then, to complete the argument by saying that we should expect ω to be proportional simply to the density of the gas or to $1/V$; but such a statement would be open to serious question, since the force-field at the surface must owe its origin largely to those molecules which are in the rarefied surface layer itself, and accordingly its mode of variation with the density is not obvious after all. In any case, Dieterici himself adopted the assumption that $\omega \propto 1/V$ as a result of empirical trial, and his equation therefore rests on a half-empirical basis. It fits rather well in certain cases, and in particular it makes $RT_c/p_cV_c = \frac{1}{2}\,e^2 = 3.695$, which lies right among the observed values, in contrast to the van der Waals value of 2.67 (cf. the table in Sec. 120).

The most ambitious attempt at a closed equation of state is perhaps that of Beattie and Bridgman:†

* Dieterici, *Ann. Physik*, **69**, 685 (1899).

† Beattie and Bridgman, *Jour. Amer. Chem. Soc.*, **49**, 1665 (1927); **50**, 3133 and 3151 (1928); *Zeits. Physik*, **62**, 95 (1930).

$$p = \frac{RT}{V^2}\left(1 - \frac{c}{VT^3}\right)\left(V + B_0 - \frac{bB_0}{V}\right) - \frac{A_0}{V^2}\left(1 - \frac{a}{V}\right).$$

By suitably choosing the five disposable constants in this equation (*R* being the ideal gas constant), the authors show that the data can be fitted within 0.5 per cent over a wide range of pressures and temperatures, even near the critical point, for at least 14 gases including all the common ones. Some theoretical justification for the equation can be given, but its chief interest seems to lie in its possible utility, since, as the authors point out, its algebraic form facilitates its use in · thermodynamical calculations.

Problem. Show that the equation of Dieterici obeys the law of corresponding states, and gives at the critical point $V_c = 2b$,

$$\frac{RT_c}{p_c V_c} = \frac{1}{2}\,e^2 = 3.695.$$

126. Series for pV; Virial Coefficients. The difficulties encountered in seeking a satisfactory equation of state in closed form led Kammerlingh Onnes* in 1901 to turn to simple expansions in series, and this procedure has been widely adopted. The most usual form is an expansion of the product *pV* in powers of the density or reciprocal of the volume, thus,

$$pV = A + \frac{B}{V} + \frac{C}{V^2} + \cdots, \tag{182a}$$

or else, as preferred by many, in powers of *p*,

$$pV = A + B_p p + C_p p^2 + \cdots. \tag{182b}$$

Forms such as

$$pV = A\left(1 + \frac{B'}{V} + \frac{C'}{V^2} + \cdots\right)$$

are also frequently employed; and *d* is sometimes written for $1/V$. It is quite common to take as the unit for *V* the volume under standard conditions, or sometimes the ideal or perfect-gas volume under standard conditions, which is, of course, slightly different; if the perfect-gas unit for *V* is employed $A = 1$, whereas if the actual volume is taken as the unit *A* differs slightly from unity.

The coefficients $A, B \cdots$ or $A, B_p \cdots$ are functions of the temperature which were called by Onnes first, second, etc., "virial

* KAMMERLINGH ONNES, Commun. Leiden, 71 (1901); *K. Akad. Amsterdam, Proc.*, **4**, 125 (1900).

coefficients." In all equations we must have $A = RT$ to make the perfect-gas law hold at zero density or pressure; and B, $C \cdot \cdot \cdot$, often written B_v, C_v, $\cdot \cdot \cdot$ are related to B_p, $C_p \cdot \cdot \cdot$ by the equations

$$B = AB_p = RTB_p, \qquad C = A(B_p^2 + AC_p), \text{ etc.,} \qquad (182c)$$

as is easily shown by substituting the value of p from (182a) in the right-hand member of (182b) and equating the coefficients of powers of $1/V$ in the result to those in the right-hand member of (182a).

127. The Second Virial Coefficient. Much interest has been taken lately in the experimental determination of the second virial coefficient B as a function of temperature, and the results are of considerable

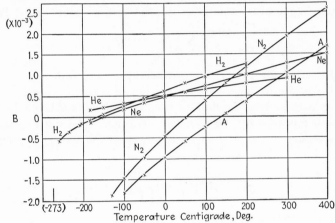

FIG. 53.—The second virial coefficient B. (p in atmospheres, V in terms of the standard volume.)

theoretical interest. This is done by running isothermals at different temperatures, i.e., determining values of pV for a series of pressures at each temperature and then fitting a series to the observations. Equation (182b) often fits exceedingly well with only the three terms that we have written, and even C tends to be small.

Experimental values of B for several gases are plotted against the absolute temperature T in Fig. 53, p being expressed in atmospheres and pV being made unity under standard conditions. The data were taken from papers listed below, values of B_p being multiplied by $T/273.1*$ to get values of B, and Holborn and Otto's being multiplied by 0.76 to convert from meters Hg to atmospheres.†

* This is not absolutely correct when pV is made unity under standard conditions rather than at infinity, but the difference is negligible for our purpose.

† WHITELAW, *Physica*, **1**, 749 (1934); HOLBORN and OTTO, *Zeits. Physik*, **23**, 77 (1924), **33**, 1 (1925), **38**, 359 (1926).

The *sign* of B tells us the initial direction of the variation of the product pV with density. If $B < 0$, $\dfrac{\partial(pV)}{\partial(1/V)} < 0$ at $p = 0$, and the first change in pV with rising density is a slight decrease. In all such cases, however, the subsequent terms of the series are such that pV passes through a minimum at a certain density and thereafter increases, finally attaining large values under pressures of the order of 10,000 or 20,000 atmospheres. All known gases exhibit this type of behavior at sufficiently low temperatures. As the temperature is raised, however, B eventually becomes positive in all cases shown in the figure, and probably this is true for all gases; at such temperatures, pV rises with increasing density from the start.

The temperature at which B changes sign is called the *Boyle temperature*. It is more often called the Boyle *point*, but this term might better be applied in a more general way to any point on the volume-temperature diagram at which pV passes through a minimum along a given isothermal, so that in the immediate neighborhood of that point Boyle's law holds; the Boyle temperature is then that temperature at which the Boyle point on the corresponding isothermal occurs at density zero and above which no Boyle points occur at all. Holborn and Otto give the following Boyle temperatures (centigrade) for six common gases; these values agree approximately with the temperatures at which $B = 0$ in Fig. 53.

He	H_2	Ne	N_2	A	O_2	Air
$-254°$	$-167°$	$-139°$	$50°$	$137°$	$150°$	$74°$

For most gases the Boyle temperature lies above 0°C.

128. The Second Virial Coefficient and van der Waals' Equation. The behavior of B as a function of temperature furnishes a very convenient test of van der Waals' equation at low densities, for comparison of (181) in Sec. 123 with (182a) above shows that according to van der Waals' equation

$$B = bRT - a. \tag{183}$$

The same value of B follows from eq. (180), representing the result given by the theory of hard attracting spheres. Thus, according to these equations of state, B should be a linear function of T, and the slope and intercept of the line representing B plotted against T should give us at once the values of the constants a and b. If $B_p = B/RT$

is employed in place of B, we have $B_p = b - \dfrac{a}{RT}$, and B_p should therefore approach a constant value equal to b at high temperatures.

Now, the curves for B in Fig. 53 do approximate roughly to straight lines, showing again that the ideas of van der Waals must contain a good deal of truth; but they all show some curvature. Their convexity upward suggests the equivalent of a decrease of b with rising temperature; the latter is what would be expected if the molecules are not hard spheres but interact by means of extended force-fields.

Apparent values of a and b can be calculated from the curves by drawing tangent lines at some point and assuming these lines to obey eq. (183). With our choice of units the values so found are also the values in terms of any units of the dimensionless quantities $a/p_0 V_0^2$ and b/V_0, p_0 and V_0 standing for the standard pressure and volume; these quantities give an immediate idea of the degree of departure from the perfect-gas law at 0°C and 1 atmosphere pressure, and the general van der Waals equation can be written in terms of them if desired, thus:

$$pV\left(1 + \frac{p_0 V_0^2}{pV^2}\frac{a}{p_0 V_0^2}\right)\left(1 - \frac{V_0}{V}\frac{b}{V_0}\right) = RT.$$

Values of $a/p_0 V_0^2$ and of b/V_0 so derived from tangents at 0°C drawn in Fig. 53 are given in the following table. For comparison, values of the same quantities are also shown calculated from the critical data by means of formulas (174b) and (174c) in Sec. 119, these two formulas being preferred because they do not contain V_c; such values are distinguished by a subscript c. Finally, we have added for comparison with b/V_0 values of this quantity calculated by inserting in

VAN DER WAALS TERMS
(Unit in all cases, 10^{-3})

	$a/p_0 V_0^2$	b/V_0	$a_c/p_0 V_0^2$	b_c/V_0	$\frac{2}{3}\pi n_0\sigma^3$
H_2	0.34	0.95	0.48	1.18	1.16
He	−0.04	0.46	0.07	1.06	0.58
Ne	0.30	0.77	0.44	0.80	0.98
N_2	3.07	2.55	2.68	1.72	2.97
O_2	3.60	2.60	2.70	1.42	2.65
Ar	3.04	2.06	2.68	1.44	2.71
H_2O	......	.....	10.9	1.36	5.48
CO_2	(17.5)	(9.9)	7.17	1.91	5.44
$C_4H_{10}O$ (ethyl ether)	......	.....	34.6	6.01	

the hard-sphere expression for it, or $\frac{2}{3}\pi n_0\sigma^3$ as given by eq. (179b) in Sec. 122, the values of σ obtained from the viscosity at 15°C, which would be only slightly different at 0°C (cf. table in Sec. 86); $n_0 =$ molecules per cubic centimeter under standard conditions.

A broad agreement between the values of $a/p_0 V_0^2$ and b/V_0 derived from these different sources is at once evident. Assuming the data sufficiently reliable, we have here another indication that there is a good deal of truth in van der Waals' ideas but that his equation fails in the finer details. The values of b/V_0 derived from viscosity data (last column) agree on the whole distinctly better with those obtained from the virial coefficients (b/V_0) than do values calculated from the critical data (b_c/V_0), as would be expected. The values from viscosity are, however, all 2 to 32 per cent larger than the virial-coefficient values, except in the case of CO_2, for which precise data on B do not seem to exist; this uniform difference may well correspond to the difference in the molecular processes involved in the production of viscous forces and of pressure, and it at least serves to indicate again that the molecules do not behave quite like hard spheres.

129. Theory of the Second Virial Coefficient, B. The value of B that follows from classical mechanics for any spherically symmetrical type of molecular field is readily obtained in the form of an integral by making suitable modifications in the calculation given in Sec. 122.

Let us write $\omega(r)$ for the mutual potential energy of two molecules when their centers are a distance r apart; the force on each, taken positive as a repulsion, is then $-\omega' = -d\omega/dr$. Probably the value of ω will be negative at moderate distances, but as r approaches zero it will become positive and rise with tremendous rapidity, somewhat after the fashion of the example plotted in Fig. 51. We must still assume the density to be very low, since B refers only to the first-order effect of increasing density, but we need make no restriction upon the numerical magnitude of ω other than to assume that it vanishes at least faster than $1/r^3$ as $r \to \infty$, in order to secure convergence of certain integrals.

Resuming then our usual procedure of calculating the pressure as the rate of transfer of momentum across a small plane of reference drawn in the gas, consider the force due to a molecule, such as A in Fig. 54, acting upon other molecules lying on the opposite side of the plane. The chance that, when A is in the position assumed, a given other molecule simultaneously has its center in any element $d\tau'$ distant r from the center of A is $Ce^{-\frac{\omega}{kT}}d\tau'$ by (94a) in Sec. 55, provided all others are far away. Then $C\int e^{-\frac{\omega}{kT}}d\tau'$, integrated for all possible positions of the second molecule in the whole volume V of the gas, must be 1. The integral itself in this expression is practically equal to V, however, since the region in which ω differs appreciably from 0 is negligibly small as compared with V itself; hence we can write as a first approximation $C = 1/V$. Because of the assumed rarity of the gas we can also neglect all encounters except binary ones and so can as usual treat the occurrences of molecules in $d\tau'$ as independent events. Accordingly, we can write for the probability that some other molecule has its center in $d\tau'$ the product of $Ce^{-\frac{\omega}{kT}} d\tau'$ by the total number nV of molecules in the gas, or

$$ne^{-\frac{\omega}{kT}} d\tau',$$

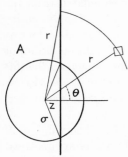

Fig. 54.

n being the number of molecules in unit volume. In Sec. 122 we wrote simply $n\, d\tau$ for this probability because there by hypothesis ω was necessarily small.

If, now, a second molecule does lie in $d\tau'$, A will exert upon it a component of force normal to the plane of magnitude $-\omega' \cos \theta$, θ being the angle between the line joining the centers of the two molecules and the normal to the plane; and there are on the average $n\, dz$ such molecules as A lying at a distance between z and $z + dz$ from a given unit area of the plane. The total normal component of force exerted by the latter on all molecules beyond the plane is, therefore,

$$-n^2\, dz \int (\omega' \cos \theta) e^{-\frac{\omega}{kT}} d\tau'$$

integrated over the whole space beyond the plane.

The integral of this expression from $z = 0$ to $z = \infty$ then gives the dynamic pressure p_d. Putting $d\tau' = 2\pi r^2 \sin \theta\, d\theta\, dr$ with the polar axis perpendicular to the plane and introducing appropriate limits of integration (cf. Fig. 54), we thus find

$$p_d = -2\pi n^2 \int_0^\infty dz \int_z^\infty \omega' e^{-\frac{\omega}{kT}} r^2\, dr \int_0^{\cos^{-1}\frac{z}{r}} \cos \theta \sin \theta\, d\theta$$

$$= -2\pi n^2 \int_0^\infty r^2 \omega' e^{-\frac{\omega}{kT}} dr \int_0^{\frac{\pi}{2}} \cos \theta \sin \theta\, d\theta \int_0^{r \cos \theta} dz$$

or

$$p_d = -\tfrac{2}{3} \pi n^2 \int_0^\infty r^3 \omega' e^{-\frac{\omega}{kT}} dr \qquad (184a)$$

since $\int_0^{\frac{\pi}{2}} \cos^2 \theta \sin \theta \, d\theta = \frac{1}{3}$.   We can also write for this last integral in r

$$\int_0^\infty kTr^3 \frac{d}{dr}\left(1 - e^{-\frac{\omega}{kT}}\right) dr,$$

in which we have inserted the 1 to secure convergence at infinity; and if we then integrate it by parts, the integrated term vanishes at both limits, reducing at infinity to $r^3\omega$, and hence to zero according to our assumption as to the smallness of ω there.   We thus obtain the alternative expression:

$$p_d = 2\pi n^2 kT \int_0^\infty r^2\left(1 - e^{-\frac{\omega}{kT}}\right) dr. \tag{184b}$$

Now, from (178a) in Sec. 121, we have

$$pV = RT + p_d V;$$

and comparison of this with (182a) in Sec. 126, in which $A = RT$, shows that at low densities

$$B = p_d V^2.$$

Hence, inserting in this equation either of the values of p_d just found and writing N for the number of molecules in the mass of gas whose volume is V, which can be chosen arbitrarily, and R for the perfect-gas constant appropriate to this chosen mass, so that $nV = N$ and $Nk = R$, we obtain finally:

$$B = -\frac{2}{3}\pi N^2 \int_0^\infty r^3 \frac{d\omega}{dr} e^{-\frac{\omega}{kT}} dr = 2\pi NRT \int_0^\infty r^2\left(1 - e^{-\frac{\omega}{kT}}\right) dr. \tag{185}$$

This value of B may be contrasted with that for hard, weakly attracting spheres as stated in eq. (183) in the last section.   The expression obtained here is more general, not only because of substitution of a general potential-energy function ω for the hard-sphere assumption, but also because we have here employed the Boltzmann distribution formula in place of the more restrictive assumption that the distribution is sensibly uninfluenced by ω.

From the last expression for B given in eq. (185) it is evident that positive values of ω result in positive contributions to B, and negative to negative.   We can say, therefore, that a positive value of B implies a predominance of repulsion between the molecules, whereas a negative value implies a predominance of attraction.

By employing still more precise forms of the Boltzmann formula it is possible to take account of ternary and higher orders of encounters and thereby to obtain corresponding expressions for the higher virial coefficients. General formulas of this sort have been worked out by Ursell employing a direct approach on the basis of statistical mechanics,* but as yet not much use has been made of them in the discussion of experimental results.

Problem. Assuming that in (185) $\omega = \infty$ for $r < \sigma$ and ω is small for $r > \sigma$, obtain the van der Waals expression for B as given in (183) with $b = \frac{2}{3} N\pi\sigma^3$ as usual and $a = -2\pi N^2 \int_\sigma^\infty \omega r^2 \, dr$.

130. Nature of Molecular Forces. The formulas just obtained can be utilized for calculating B only if we know the law of molecular force. Upon this latter question the modern theory of the atom has thrown a great deal of light. It appears that molecular forces arise from several distinct sources and are correspondingly varied in their spatial distribution; each of the following types probably occurs at least with some molecules:

1. Relatively huge electrostatic forces varying as $1/r^2$ between ionized and therefore charged molecules.

2. Electrostatic forces varying as $1/r^5$ between an ion and a neutral molecule polarized by the field of the ion.

3. Electrostatic forces varying as $1/r^4$ between dipoles or molecules possessing permanent electric moments, such as those of steam.

4. Electrostatic forces varying as $1/r^3$ between electric dipoles and ions.

5. Electrostatic forces varying as $1/r^7$ between the dipole moment of one molecule and a second molecule possessing no natural moment but polarized by the field of the first.

6. Attractive forces ultimately proportional to $1/r^7$ due to distortion of one molecule under the influence of another which possesses neither a net charge nor a dipole moment, arising from the complicated interaction between the electrons and the nuclei.

7. Forces of quantum origin chiefly due to the "exchange" effect in the electron shells, falling off rapidly and roughly exponentially with r.

In each of these cases r denotes the distance between molecular centers of mass and the potential energy ω varies as an inverse power of r one less than that stated for the force. In cases 3 to 5, at least, the force varies greatly with the orientation of the molecule and is accompanied by a torque tending to produce rotation.

Forces of type 7, originating chiefly in the exchange phenomenon in the electron shells, are now believed to account, on the one hand,

---

* Ursell, *Camb. Phil. Soc. Proc.*, **23.** 685 (1927); R. H. Fowler, "Statistical Mechanics," 1929, p. 129

for the formation of chemical compounds through primary or satiable valence and, on the other hand, for the observed impenetrability of atoms. The impenetrability was always difficult to explain in terms of the classical conception of an atom composed solely of electric charges; spherically symmetrical shells of charge about a nucleus, for instance, should pass right through each other, the effect of such a shell on any element of charge outside it being the same as if the whole shell were concentrated at its center (and on an element of charge inside it, nothing at all), so that no special repulsion would develop when two shells came into contact.

Forces of type 6, on the other hand, are believed to account for the van der Waals attraction in most of the commoner gases; the chemical combination by "secondary" or nonsatiable valence is believed to be an enhanced effect of the same sort. Permanent moments when present must also contribute, however, to the van der Waals attraction; if the dipoles were oriented at random their effect would vanish, as must the mean electric field due to any distribution that is electrically neutral as a whole, but the Boltzmann factor results in a slight preponderance of molecular positions having less potential energy and so gives rise to an average attractive effect.

The force-action between actual molecules may, of course, and no doubt commonly does, represent a combination of several of the elementary types listed above.

131. B with an Inverse-power Force. When the force is both spherically symmetrical and proportional to a simple power of the intermolecular distance, the variation of B with temperature is easily found. Suppose that the mutual potential energy ω of two molecules is proportional to $1/r^s$. Then we can write $\omega/kT = c/(r^sT)$, where c is a constant, and, if we take r^sT as a new variable x, so that $r = T^{-1/s}x^{1/s}$ and $r^2\,dr = (1/s)T^{-3/s}x^{3/s-1}\,dx$, we find from the last expression in eq. (185)

$$B = \frac{2\pi}{s}\,NRT^{1-\frac{3}{s}}\int_0^\infty x^{\frac{3}{s}-1}(1 - e^{-\frac{c}{x}})\,dx.$$

Before drawing conclusions from this formula, however, we must first discuss the integral in relation to the value of s. It diverges at the upper limit unless $s > 3$, so that a value of s equal to 3 or less, corresponding to spherically symmetrical forces decreasing at best as rapidly as $1/r^4$, would lead to a pressure arising mostly from distant parts of the gas and therefore depending upon the shape of the containing vessel. Now, of the forces listed in the last section, types 3 and 4, arising from dipole moments, fail to diminish with distance more rapidly than $1/r^4$; but, on the other hand, for random orientation of the molecules they average to zero. Their only effect thus arises from the Boltzmann factor; it is found to diminish much more rapidly with distance. Forces of type 1 due to simple electrostatic charges, on the other hand, are spherically symmetrical, and they actually fall off only as $1/r^2$ (ω as $1/r$). Such forces must occur between ions in a gas. Accordingly, if a gas were composed of just one kind of ion, the pressure would undoubtedly depend upon the shape of the mass of the gas, which would then simply be regarded as acting according to the usual laws of electrostatics upon its own space charge. This must be true of an electron gas, for instance, only its pressure in actual cases is too small to be measured. In most cases, however, ions of opposite sign occur with practically equal amounts of charge per unit volume; the net effect is then a differential one and the difficulty in question does not arise.

When one of these conditions is met, the integral has a definite numerical value; and the equation then shows that $B \propto T^{1-\frac{3}{s}}$. For $s > 3$ this is a far slower variation of B with T than is shown in any of the six curves in Fig. 53, with the exception perhaps of that for helium, which shows B not far from proportional to T itself, as might happen if s were very large. For the other five gases we may conclude, therefore, that the assumption that the whole of ω is proportional at all distances to a single power of the distance must be wide of the truth. This is scarcely surprising, of course, for these molecules undoubtedly exhibit repulsion at some distances but attraction at others.

132. Classical Calculations of B. For several laws of molecular force, which combine two simple types such as those listed in Sec. 130, detailed calculations of B have been made in terms of classical mechanics. Keesom, in 1912, found B for rigid spheres attracting as $1/r^m$; he also worked out the case of spheres containing quadrupoles, including the associated polarization effects, which requires rather complicated analysis because a summation must be made over various orientations.

A much better hypothesis to try is the two-power force for which calculations were made by Lennard-Jones and his coworkers.* Assuming spherical symmetry, they write the force exerted by one molecule on another at a distance r, measured positively as a repulsion, in the form

---

* Lennard-Jones and Cook, *Roy. Soc. Proc.*, **112**, 214 (1926); Jones, *Roy. Soc. Proc.*, **106**, 463 (1924); R. H. Fowler, "Statistical Mechanics," Cambridge, 1929, chapter by Lennard-Jones, p. 227.

$$\frac{\lambda}{r^n} - \frac{\mu}{r^m}.$$

By adjusting the four positive constants λ, μ, n, m they were able to secure agreement with such accurate observations on B as have been made. The theoretical results were, however, found to be extraordinarily insensitive to the values assumed for n and m; for simplicity they merely always set $m = 5$ and made n integral, or sometimes, for mathematical convenience, equal to $14\frac{1}{3}$.

The approximate best values thus found for n and the corresponding values of the force constants λ and μ are shown in the table below. To give a better idea of the spatial extent of the corresponding molecular fields, we give also under the heading σ', as a sort of equivalent diameter, the distance of closest approach of two molecules which approach each other at speeds each equal to the root-mean-square speed at 15°C and along coplanar lines inclined at 45° to the line joining their centers. The distance r_0 at which the force itself vanishes, calculated from the equation $\lambda/r_0^n = \mu/r_0^m$ is also given; it is of course much larger than σ'. Finally, values of the equivalent hard-sphere diameter σ_{vc} as obtained from viscosity data (cf. table in Sec. 86) are appended for comparison.

	n	m	λ (c.g.s.)	μ (e.g.s.)	σ' (unit 10^{-8} cm)	r_0 (unit 10^{-8} cm)	σ_{vc} (unit 10^{-8} cm)
Helium.........	$14\frac{1}{3}$	5	2.35×10^{-115}	2.33×10^{-45}	2.04	3.17	2.18
H$_2$.............	11	5	7.38×10^{-89}	1.98×10^{-44}	2.52	3.94	2.74
Neon...........	11	5	4.38×10^{-89}	1.72×10^{-44}	2.39	3.70	2.59
N$_2$.............	9	5	1.58×10^{-72}	1.82×10^{-43}	3.49	5.43	3.75
Argon..........	$14\frac{1}{3}$	5	1.64×10^{-112}	1.13×10^{-43}	3.25	4.21	3.64

The agreement between σ' and σ_{vc} is quite good enough to be satisfactory. Of course a much better test would be actually to calculate the viscosity using the law of force in question. This was done by Lennard-Jones and Cook only in the case of hydrogen, where the attractive field has relatively little effect upon the viscosity; excellent agreement was obtained, the values found for λ being 7.19×10^{-89} from viscosity and 7.38×10^{-89} from the virial coefficient.

Revised calculations of this sort are described by Lennard-Jones in the second edition of R. H. Fowler's "Statistical Mechanics," published in 1936. The above discussion serves, however, to give a general idea of what can be accomplished in this manner.

If such a field yields theoretical values both of B and of the viscosity agreeing with experiment, we can perhaps conclude that it gives us some rough idea of the actual field. The significance of the agreement must not be overestimated, however, for two reasons. In the first place, the assumed law of force contains, after all, four adjustable constants, and any formula containing so many can be made to fit a considerable range of experimental data unless the experimental values are much more accurate than are the existing ones for B and the viscosity. In the second place, and this is even more important, classical mechanics is undoubtedly inadequate to give anything better than rough qualitative results in dealing with forces between molecules that are close together; accurate results can be obtained only by means of wave mechanics. To this we shall now turn.

133. Calculations of B by Wave Mechanics. In applying wave mechanics to the interaction of molecules there is a choice between two different starting points, and the significance of the results is decidedly different according to the choice that is made.

We may start out from some arbitrary assumption as to the law of molecular force, as in the classical calculations just described, and then try to fit the data by assigning suitable values to certain disposable constants. If agreement with the data can be secured, such agreement then constitutes evidence in favor of the assumed law of force, and the results will possess significance chiefly in proportion to the extent to which the same law can be made to explain different phenomena.

On the other hand, in wave mechanics it is also possible to approach the problem along much more fundamental lines. The simple general principles of the theory are believed to be adequate for the deduction, by mathematical calculation alone, of all of the properties of atoms and molecules and so even of matter in bulk. The fundamental equations contain four universal constants, i.e., Planck's h, the speed of light, and the charge and mass of the electron; to these we need add only the atomic number and the nuclear mass of any particular atom in order to be able to deduce all of its properties.

Unfortunately, however, the purely mathematical difficulties in the way of carrying out this latter program are prodigious, and in the particular field of molecular properties little has as yet been accomplished by this method. In regard to the equation of state, little has been done beyond a few calculations of the second virial coefficient B, and these calculations, besides employing very rough methods of approximation, have been limited to helium. The results obtained by Kirkwood,[*] however, possess real interest because of the fact that

---

[*] Kirkwood, *Phys. Zeits.*, **33**, 39 (1932).

they were reached along the more fundamental of the two lines of approach.

Kirkwood employs the approximate expression for the mutual potential energy of two helium atoms which is stated in eq. (177a) in Sec. 121 and also plotted in Fig. 51. This curve for ω drops so low at the deepest that there is room for one discrete quantum state for the pair of atoms, at an energy $\epsilon_1 = -0.5 \times 10^{-16}$ erg. This means that a pair of helium atoms can form a sort of molecule, loose but stable, in a quantum state of energy ϵ_1; the center of mass of the pair can then also be moving with any positive amount of kinetic energy. The only other states in which a pair of helium atoms can exist are states in which they are moving with positive energy of relative motion and will eventually separate completely, perhaps after first approaching and undergoing something like a collision.

The method of approximate calculation which Kirkwood follows amounts to assuming that so long as the energy of the relative motion is positive, classical theory holds nearly enough and the probability for spatial position in $d\tau$ and velocity in $d\kappa$ is

$$Ce^{-\omega/kT - mv^2/2kT} \, d\tau \, d\kappa$$

[cf. (88) in Sec. 52]; whereas, on the other hand, the probability of the occurrence of the discrete state of negative energy ϵ_1 is $Ch^3 e^{-\frac{\epsilon_1}{kT}}$ [cf. (93a) in Sec. 54].* An indirect method of obtaining the pressure must then be employed, since our simple geometrical analysis of it fails when quantization has to be introduced.

The resulting values of B/RT for helium are shown in the following table in comparison with the observed values, the units being cubic centimeters per mole:

T (abs.)	15°	20°	25°	35°	100°	200°	250°	300°	350°
B/RT (obs.)	−14.00	−4.00	0.80	4.80	10.95	11.95	11.95	11.80	11.60
B/RT (calc.)	−15.10	−5.14	0.17	4.44	10.80	11.62	11.37	11.16	10.82

In view of the rough approximation involved in the method, the agreement shown by these figures is surprisingly good. Even the slight drop at high temperatures in the values of the ratio B/RT, which according to the hard-sphere equation should approach a con-

---

* When a system is imagined to be capable of existing either in one of a series of discrete quantum states or in a condition to which classical theory applies, the classical element of phase space $dp \, dq$ is to be replaced for each quantum state by h^n, n being the number of coordinates needed to describe the motion (cf. Sec. 233).

stant value, is given by the theory. Such a theoretical success is particularly interesting as an example illustrating the general remark made above, because in the entire calculation, including the obtaining of the formula for ω, no special quantity is introduced referring specifically to helium except its atomic number 2 (and the fact that its nucleus is very much heavier than an electron).

An improved method has been worked out by Kirkwood in which the use of classical methods as an approximation is entirely avoided,* but this method is hard to handle and numerical results have not yet been published.

134. B for Mixed Gases. When several different kinds of molecules are present, there will be interaction not only between the molecules of a given type but also between those of one type and those of another. It is immediately obvious that at low pressures the effects of these interactions will be simply additive in the dynamic pressure p_d and also, therefore, in the second virial coefficient B.

Accordingly, when just two kinds of molecules are present with respective densities n_1, n_2, the expression for p_d will consist of three terms each of the form of (184b) in Sec. 129 but containing, respectively, n_1^2, $n_1 n_2$, and n_2^2 as factors and ω_{11}, ω_{12}, or ω_{22} in place of ω, ω_{ij} denoting the mutual potential energy of a molecule of type i in the presence of one of type j. If we write for convenience $n_1 = \gamma_1 n$, $n_2 = \gamma_2 n$, where $n = n_1 + n_2$, so that γ_1 and γ_2 represent the fractional concentrations of the two kinds of gas in terms of molecules and $\gamma_1 + \gamma_2 = 1$, it is easily seen that the resulting expression for B can be written, as a generalization of (185),

$$B = (\gamma_1^2 B_{11} + 2\gamma_1 \gamma_2 B_{12} + \gamma_2^2 B_{22}),$$

where

$$B_{ij} = 2\pi NRT \int_0^\infty r^2 \left(1 - e^{-\frac{\omega_{ij}}{kT}}\right) dr,$$

N denoting as usual the total number of molecules and R the value of the gas constant for the whole mass of gas.

For a *binary* mixture B should thus be a quadratic function of the molecular concentrations. Now for a mixture of oxygen and nitrogen the observed relationship seems, rather, to be linear in γ_1, γ_2;† this can happen, however, if $B_{12} = \frac{1}{2}(B_{11} + B_{22})$, which is very plausible in the case mentioned since the molecular fields of oxygen and nitrogen

---

* KIRKWOOD, *Phys. Rev.*, **44**, 31 (1933); **45**, 116 (1934).

† HOLBORN and OTTO, *Zeits. Physik*, **10**, 367 (1922).

are probably quite similar. For hydrogen mixed with nitrogen* or helium,† on the other hand, a quadratic curve fits the data very well. The original data on these latter mixtures had reference to $B_p = B/RT$; the values of B_{pij} that were found to secure the best fit with the data were

	N_2-N_2	N_2-H_2	H_2-H_2	H_2-He	He-He
20°C	−2.80	6.10	6.50		
25°C	.....	....	6.59	7.00	5.10

The unit is 10^{-4} in terms of atmospheres and the standard volume at 0°C.

These results are interesting as indicating that repulsion predominates over attraction, as shown by the positive sign, not only between the molecules of hydrogen itself but also between the molecules of hydrogen and those of nitrogen, and, furthermore, that the repulsive effect is a little greater between a molecule of hydrogen and one of helium than it is when both molecules are of the same kind.

135. The Virial Theorem. In place of the treatment of the pressure in a real gas that we have given in Sec. 121, the argument can be rearranged in a more abstract but very neat form known as the virial theorem of Clausius. The discussion of the equation of state will be closed with a deduction of this theorem.

Let x, y, z denote the cartesian components of the center of mass of a molecule, and let us write down the equation expressing Newton's second law as applied to its x-coordinate and then multiply this equation through by x. We thus obtain

$$m \frac{d^2x}{dt^2} = X, \qquad mx \frac{d^2x}{dt^2} = xX,$$

in which X is the total x-component of force on the molecule. The second of these equations can also be written

$$\frac{d}{dt}\left(mx \frac{dx}{dt}\right) - m\left(\frac{dx}{dt}\right)^2 = xX.$$

Now these equations must hold at all times; hence the average values of the two members of the last must be equal. Let us take such averages over a very long time and denote them by a bar.

Then the average of the first term in the last equation is simply the total change in $mx\, dx/dt$ divided by the total time. Now, dx/dt does

* VERSCHOYLE, *Roy. Soc. Proc.*, **111**, 552 (1926).
† GIBBY, TANNER, and MASSON, *Roy. Soc. Proc.*, **122**, 283 (1934).

not increase without limit; x may do so, but the theory of the Brownian motion (q.v.) shows that it increases only as the square root of the time. Hence the average of the first term will ultimately be zero. The average of the second term is minus one third the average of

$$m\left[\left(\frac{dx}{dt}\right)^2 + \left(\frac{dy}{dt}\right)^2 + \left(\frac{dz}{dt}\right)^2\right] = mv^2,$$

provided we assume the motion to be on the average isotropic, hence by (25b) in Sec. 15 it equals kT. Thus in the long run

$$-kT = \overline{xX}.$$

A similar equation holds for the y- and z-coordinates and the corresponding force components, Y and Z.

We can also sum up these equations for all N molecules in a given mass of gas and write as our result

$$NkT = -\Sigma\overline{xX} = -\Sigma\overline{yY} = -\Sigma\overline{zZ}; \tag{186a}$$

or, adding these three equations and again inserting $\frac{1}{3}m\overline{v^2} = kT$, we have the double result that

$$3NkT = \Sigma m\overline{v^2} = -\Sigma(\overline{xX} + \overline{yY} + \overline{zZ}). \tag{186b}$$

The right-hand member of the last equation divided by 2 was called by Clausius the "virial" of the forces, and it is this latter form of statement that is usually called the virial theorem; it can be expressed in words by saying that the mean translatory kinetic energy of the molecules is equal to the virial of all the forces that act upon them.

If we can evaluate the virial, the equation of state can be written down at once. The forces consist in part of forces exerted on the molecules by the walls of the containing vessel and the term representing their contribution to the virial introduces the pressure into the equation. This term is most simply calculated if we give to the vessel a rectangular form with its faces perpendicular to the axis; then if x_1 and x_2 are the values of x at the two faces perpendicular to the x-axis, x_2 being the greater, the contribution at the first face to $\Sigma\overline{xX}$ can be written $x_1\Sigma\overline{X} = x_1 S_x p$ where S_x is the area of this face and p is the macroscopic pressure on it; the contribution at the second face is similarly $-x_2 S_x p$; and the sum of the two contributions is

$$-(x_2 - x_1)S_x p = -Vp,$$

where V is the volume of the vessel.

If the gas is perfect, there are no other contributions to the virial, and (186a) then gives at once the perfect-gas equation, $pV = NkT$. Otherwise, wherever two molecules interact, the equal and opposite forces on the two act at points for which, in general, x has different values. The calculation of the resulting term in $\Sigma \overline{xX}$, in case the density is sufficiently low so that only binary encounters need be considered, differs only in nonessentials from the calculation given in Sec. 129 above in obtaining an expression for B. If enough knowledge of the molecular motion were available so that $\Sigma \overline{xX}$ could be calculated at all densities, we could at once find the complete equation of state. The same can be said, however, of the methods employed above, so that the virial theorem does not seem to be of much real use in kinetic theory.

Problem. Making the same physical assumptions as in Sec. 129, calculate the contribution to $\Sigma \overline{xX}$ in (186a) that arises from intermolecular forces and so obtain the expression for B given in eq. (185).

CHAPTER VI

ENERGY, ENTROPY, AND SPECIFIC HEATS

The physical state of a given mass of gas that is in equilibrium and subjected to ordinary conditions (e.g., not subject to any force-field) is completely fixed when we assign values to any two of the three variables p, V, T (pressure, volume, temperature). These three variables are connected by the equation of state, which was the subject of discussion in the last chapter, and by solving this equation any one of the three can be obtained as a function of the other two.

In addition to these three there are other quantities that are characteristic of a gas in equilibrium. Especially important are the *energy* and the *entropy*, and, connected with the derivatives of these, the *specific heats*. These might be called collectively *thermal* magnitudes. They will form the subject of discussion in the present chapter.

The laws of thermodynamics require certain connections to exist between the thermal quantities and the equation of state. This connection is such that if we know the equation of state and either of the two quantities, energy and entropy, we can calculate the other one; furthermore, it is sufficient to know one of these quantities merely for the gas in its perfect state of vanishing density. Our discussion of the thermal quantities in terms of kinetic theory can accordingly be greatly restricted; it can be limited to the problem of the energy of a perfect gas.

In preparation for this discussion, however, it is advantageous first to survey the conclusions that are furnished by thermodynamics. Of course, the general validity of the laws of thermodynamics is also itself one of those properties of gases which it is the object of kinetic theory to explain as a consequence of the fundamental properties of the molecules; such an explanation of the second law of thermodynamics we shall, in fact, undertake in the chapter on Statistical Mechanics. The explanation there obtained is so abstract, however, and our confidence in the validity of these laws is so great, that it is best at this point simply to assume their truth and to direct our principal efforts toward developing a theory that shall supply the other half of the information which thermodynamics cannot furnish.

The preliminary thermodynamic investigation of the relations between thermal quantities and the equation of state is necessarily rather mathematical and abstract. Any reader who is interested primarily in the contributions of kinetic theory to the subject and prefers to take the thermodynamics on faith can without difficulty omit the next six sections entirely and pass at once to Sec. 142.

INFORMATION OBTAINABLE FROM THERMODYNAMICS

136. Some Definitions and Basic Principles. Let U denote the internal or intrinsic energy of a gram of gas, i.e., that part of its energy which is neither kinetic nor due to an external force-field. For simplicity it will be assumed that energy of these latter sorts is entirely absent, and hereafter for brevity we shall refer to U simply as the energy (or specific energy, since we are dealing with a gram). In books on physical chemistry the mass is often taken to be a gram molecule, but the advantage in physics seems to lie in the direction of the gram as the unit. In any case, all of the formulas in this chapter will hold for a gram molecule, provided all quantities, even the specific heats, are understood to refer to that unit of mass.

Then U can change only through exchange of energy between the gas and its surroundings; and this exchange may occur in either of two ways which from the thermodynamic standpoint are fundamentally different. Energy may pass into the gas by thermal conduction, or by some process equivalent to this so far as its effects on the gas are concerned (such as the absorption of infrared radiation); energy so passing into a body is called *heat*. On the other hand, the gas may lose energy by doing mechanical *work*.

These three quantities are related by a simple formula expressive of the conservation of energy. During some slight change let the gas absorb heat dQ, undergo a change of energy dU, and do work dW. Then $dQ = dU + dW$. Under ordinary conditions, however, a gas does work only by expanding while exerting pressure. Confining ourselves hereafter to such cases, we have $dW = p \, dV$, V being the volume (or specific volume) and p the pressure; thus

$$dQ = dU + p \, dV. \tag{187}$$

To this equation, expressing the "first law" of thermodynamics, the second law then adds the proposition, already noted in Sec. 13, that if the heat dQ is imparted reversibly, we can write

$$dQ = T \, dS, \tag{188}$$

where T and S are two other definite functions of the state of the gas, i.e., functions of whatever pair of independent variables are being employed to specify its state. From (188) and (187) we have then also

$$T \, dS = dU + p \, dV. \tag{189}$$

This equation was, in effect, employed in Sec. 13 in setting up the thermodynamic temperature scale, and in accordance with the procedure followed there, we can interpret T to stand for the absolute temperature, the new function S then representing the entropy.

Connections between U and S, on the one hand, and the equation of state on the other, are now arrived at by seeking the mathematical consequences of the equations just written down, especially when taken in conjunction with the fact that both U and S are, by assumption, definite differentiable functions of the independent variables.

Equation (189) shows that if the equation of state is known, so that, say, p is known as a function of V and T, then S can be found from U, or, alternatively, U can be found from S, by a process of simple integration; for example,

$$S = \int \frac{dU}{T} + \int \frac{p}{T} \, dV. \tag{189a}$$

It is sufficient, therefore, to discuss in detail only one of these two quantities. Experimentally, S is the more important one of the two, but U is more interesting from the point of view of kinetic theory; accordingly we shall select U for further consideration here.

137. Differential Equations for the Energy U. Taking as independent variables V and T, we can write

$$dU = dU(V, T) = \left(\frac{\partial U}{\partial V}\right)_T dV + \left(\frac{\partial U}{\partial T}\right)_V dT.$$

Then (189) can be written

$$dS = \left[\frac{1}{T}\left(\frac{\partial U}{\partial V}\right)_T + \frac{p}{T}\right] dV + \frac{1}{T}\left(\frac{\partial U}{\partial T}\right)_V dT.$$

In writing partial derivatives here we have indicated in each case by a subscript the variable that is being kept constant.

Now this expression for dS is of the form $dS = H \, dV + K \, dT$; if we make $dT = 0$, $dS/dV = (\partial S/\partial V)_T$ by definition of the partial derivative, while if we make $dV = 0$, $dS/dT = (\partial S/\partial T)_V$; hence

$$H = \left(\frac{\partial S}{\partial V}\right)_T, \qquad K = \left(\frac{\partial S}{\partial T}\right)_V.$$

But, since S is a definite function of V and T (and if we may assume its second derivatives to be continuous),

$$\frac{\partial}{\partial T}\left(\frac{\partial S}{\partial V}\right)_T = \frac{\partial^2 S}{\partial T\,\partial V} = \frac{\partial^2 S}{\partial V\,\partial T} = \frac{\partial}{\partial V}\left(\frac{\partial S}{\partial T}\right)_V.$$

Hence

$$\left(\frac{\partial H}{\partial T}\right)_V = \left(\frac{\partial K}{\partial V}\right)_T.$$

In the case before us this means that

$$-\frac{1}{T_2}\frac{\partial U}{\partial V} + \frac{1}{T}\frac{\partial^2 U}{\partial T\,\partial V} + \frac{\partial}{\partial T}\frac{p}{T} = \frac{1}{T}\frac{\partial^2 U}{\partial V\,\partial T},$$

whence

$$\left(\frac{\partial U}{\partial V}\right)_T = T^2\left(\frac{\partial}{\partial T}\frac{p}{T}\right)_V = T\left(\frac{\partial p}{\partial T}\right)_V - p. \tag{190a}$$

As an alternative, we might employ p and T as independent varia bles.   We need then only to replace dV in (189) by

$$dV = \left(\frac{\partial V}{\partial p}\right)_T dp + \left(\frac{\partial V}{\partial T}\right)_p dT$$

and dU by a similar expression, so that, divided through by T, (189) takes the form

$$dS = \left[\frac{1}{T}\left(\frac{\partial U}{\partial p}\right)_T + \frac{p}{T}\left(\frac{\partial V}{\partial p}\right)_T\right]dp + \left[\frac{1}{T}\left(\frac{\partial U}{\partial T}\right)_p + \frac{p}{T}\left(\frac{\partial V}{\partial T}\right)_p\right]dT.$$

Then, by similar reasoning, we obtain

$$\left(\frac{\partial U}{\partial p}\right)_T = -p\left(\frac{\partial V}{\partial p}\right)_T - T\left(\frac{\partial V}{\partial T}\right)_p. \tag{190b}$$

Both (190a) and (190b) obviously rest for their validity in part upon the second law of thermodynamics.

When the relation between p, V, and T is known, either (190a) or (190b) constitutes a partial differential equation for U.   The two equations are mathematically equivalent, of course, for from (190a) one can pass back to the conclusion that $(\partial H/\partial T)_V = (\partial K/\partial V)_T$ with H and K defined as above, and then by a simple mathematical theorem it follows that $H\,dV + K\,dT$ is a perfect differential, or the differential of some definite function of the independent variables, for which we can write dS; one then finds easily that $T\,dS = dU + p\,dV$, as in (189), and from this we can then deduce (190b) as before. In a similar way we can pass in the reverse direction from (190b) to (190a).

From (189), which is reached on the way in either case, one can also pass by the conservation of energy to (187) and (188), which latter expresses the second law. It is therefore evident that any form of the function U that satisfies one of the differential equations just obtained will automatically be in complete harmony with thermodynamic requirements.

The solution of any partial differential equation contains, however, a large degree of arbitrariness. Additional information is necessary, therefore, for the complete determination of U.

The same situation exists as regards the entropy.

Problems. 1. Show that thermodynamics requires similarly that the entropy S satisfy the following differential equations (constituting two of what are called the "thermodynamic relations"):

$$\left(\frac{\partial S}{\partial V}\right)_T = \left(\frac{\partial p}{\partial T}\right)_V, \qquad \left(\frac{\partial S}{\partial p}\right)_T = -\left(\frac{\partial V}{\partial T}\right)_p. \qquad (191a, b)$$

2. Show that if U is a function of T alone, then p/T is a function of V only; and, conversely, if the equation of state has the form $p = Tf(V)$, then U is a function of T only and the heat of free expansion vanishes.

138. Experimental Measurement of Energy and Entropy; the Specific Heats. According to (187) and (188), the energy U and the entropy S of a gas can be found from the integrals

$$U = \int dQ - \int p \, dV, \qquad S = \int \frac{dQ}{T},$$

in which T is the absolute temperature and dQ is the heat absorbed by the gas during a small reversible change in its state. Since, however, an integral necessarily contains an arbitrary constant of integration, values of U and S must be assigned arbitrarily to some convenient base state of the gas, e.g., the state at some point A_0 on the pV diagram (cf. Fig. 55); in other words, it is only changes of U and S that possess physical significance.* We might then determine U and S in any other state A by carrying the gas along any reversible path from A_0 to A, such as A_0BA, and observing the successive elements of heat dQ and of work $p \, dV$ and the values of T; from these we could then calculate the

---

* If we take the view suggested by relativistic and atomic phenomena that mass and weight are associated with all energy in a definite ratio, then U itself is physically definite. Such considerations, however, lie entirely outside the range of kinetic theory.

increases in U and in S. In practice, however, the thermal observations are usually interpreted as yielding values of the specific heats, and the other necessary data are taken from observations on the equation of state.

The *specific heats* are very simply related to U and S. When the gas is kept at constant volume, so that it does no external work, $dQ = dU = T \, dS$ (the process being assumed reversible). Hence, since we are dealing with 1 g of gas, we can write for its *specific heat at constant volume* in mechanical units

$$c_v = \left(\frac{dQ}{dT}\right)_v = \left(\frac{\partial U}{\partial T}\right)_v = T\left(\frac{\partial S}{\partial T}\right)_v. \quad (192a)$$

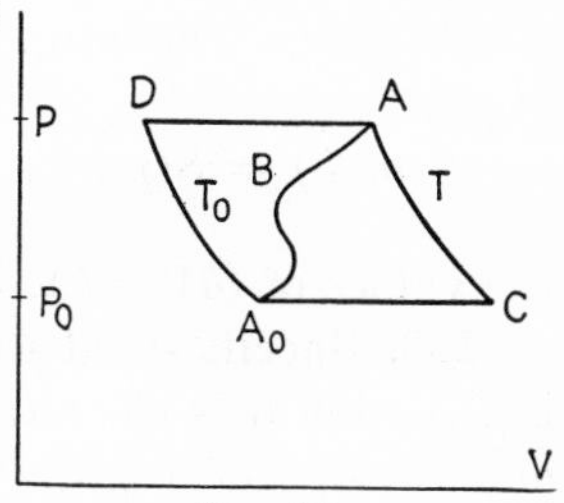

If, on the other hand, the heating is done at constant pressure, the gas does external work and $dQ = dU + p \, dV = T \, dS$; hence the *specific heat at constant pressure* in mechanical units is given by

FIG. 55.

$$c_p = \left(\frac{dQ}{dT}\right)_p = \left(\frac{\partial U}{\partial T}\right)_p + p\left(\frac{\partial V}{\partial T}\right)_p = T\left(\frac{\partial S}{\partial T}\right)_p, \quad (192b)$$

in which the value of $(\partial V/\partial T)_p$ can be found from the equation of state. Here for Q we have written a total derivative because Q is not a definite function of p and T as independent variables, but does become a function of one of them when the other is held fixed.

These formulas can be utilized in calculating U and S from observational data in the following way. To calculate the gain in energy of a gram of the gas as it passes from the base point A_0 where its pressure is p_0 and temperature T_0, up to any other point A where the pressure is p and the temperature T, let us first suppose it to be heated (or cooled, as the case may be) at constant pressure p_0 along the path A_0C to temperature T (Fig. 55). During this process the gain in energy can be written, according to (192b),

$$\int_{T_0}^{T}\left(\frac{\partial U}{\partial T}\right)_p dT = \int_{T_0}^{T}(c_p)_{p=p_0}\,dT - p_0\int_{T_0}^{T}\left(\frac{\partial V}{\partial T}\right)_p dT.$$

The last integral here represents simply the change in volume, $V(p_0, T) - V(p_0, T_0)$. Then let us compress (or expand) the gas isothermally from C to its final state A; using (190a), we can write for the increase in U along this path

$$\int\left(\frac{\partial U}{\partial V}\right)_T dV = T^2\int_{V(p_0,T)}^{V(p,T)}\left(\frac{\partial}{\partial T}\frac{p}{T}\right)_v dV.$$

If we now denote by $U(p_0, T_0)$ the assumed value of U at the base point A_0, we thus obtain finally for U at A

$$U(p, T) = U(p_0, T_0) + p_0[V(p_0, T_0) - V(p_0, T)]$$
$$+ \int_{T_0}^{T} (c_p)_{p=p_0}\, dT + T^2 \int_{V(p_0, T)}^{V(p, T)} \left(\frac{\partial}{\partial T}\frac{p}{T}\right)_V dV. \quad (193a)$$

Values of $V(p, T)$ and of $(\partial/\partial T)(p/T)_V$, the latter all being taken at the temperature T, are furnished by the equation of state.

Of course, other paths of integration may also be followed.

Problem. Show in a similar way that

$$S(p, T) = S(p_0, T_0) + \int_{T_0}^{T} \frac{1}{T} (c_p)_{p=p_0}\, dT - \int_{p_0}^{p} \left(\frac{\partial V}{\partial T}\right)_p dp, \quad (193b)$$

the values of $(\partial V/\partial T)_p$ being taken at the temperature T.

139. Specific-heat Relations. From the equations obtained in the last section it is clear that in order to be able to ascertain the energy and entropy of a gas, all that we need in addition to the equation of state is a knowledge of the specific heats. There exist, in turn, a number of relations between the latter and certain mechanical quantities which serve to simplify the problem still further.

In the first place, we may note the familiar relationship that

$$\gamma = \frac{c_p}{c_V} = \frac{(\partial p/\partial V)_S}{(\partial p/\partial V)_T} \quad (194)$$

or the *ratio* of the specific heats γ equals the ratio of the adiabatic and the isothermal elasticities.* The proof of this equation requires only a straightforward application of the conservation of energy, but we shall refer for it to other books.†

In the second place, an important expression for the *difference* of the specific heats can be deduced by means of thermodynamical reasoning. From (192a, b)

$$c_p - c_V = T\left(\frac{\partial S}{\partial T}\right)_p - T\left(\frac{\partial S}{\partial T}\right)_V.$$

Now

$$dS = \left(\frac{\partial S}{\partial p}\right)_T dp + \left(\frac{\partial S}{\partial T}\right)_p dT, \qquad dp = \left(\frac{\partial p}{\partial V}\right)_T dV + \left(\frac{\partial p}{\partial T}\right)_V dT,$$

∴

$$dS = \left(\frac{\partial S}{\partial p}\right)_T\left(\frac{\partial p}{\partial V}\right)_T dV + \left[\left(\frac{\partial S}{\partial p}\right)_T\left(\frac{\partial p}{\partial T}\right)_V + \left(\frac{\partial S}{\partial T}\right)_p\right] dT.$$

---

* As usually defined, these elasticities are, of course, $-V(\partial p/\partial V)_S$, $-V(\partial p/\partial V)_T$.

† Cf. Poynting and Thomson, "Heat," 9th ed., 1928, p. 288; also, E. Edser, "Heat," 1936, p. 367, where the proof is indirect.

Hence

$$\left(\frac{\partial S}{\partial T}\right)_V = \left(\frac{\partial S}{\partial T}\right)_p + \left(\frac{\partial S}{\partial p}\right)_T \left(\frac{\partial p}{\partial T}\right)_V,$$

and accordingly

$$c_p - c_V = -T\left(\frac{\partial S}{\partial p}\right)_T \left(\frac{\partial p}{\partial T}\right)_V,$$

or, by (191b), which latter rests upon the second law,

$$c_p - c_V = T\left(\frac{\partial p}{\partial T}\right)_V \left(\frac{\partial V}{\partial T}\right)_p = -T\left(\frac{\partial p}{\partial V}\right)_T \left[\left(\frac{\partial V}{\partial T}\right)_p\right]^2; \qquad (195)$$

the second and perhaps more useful form here results from the mathematical relations*

$$\left(\frac{\partial V}{\partial p}\right)_T \left(\frac{\partial p}{\partial T}\right)_V = -\left(\frac{\partial V}{\partial T}\right)_p, \qquad \left(\frac{\partial V}{\partial p}\right)_T = \frac{1}{(\partial p/\partial V)_T}.$$

The values of the derivatives in (195) are all obtainable from the equation of state.

We thus reach the important conclusion that separate observations of both specific heats are unnecessary if the equation of state is known.

As a matter of fact, (194) and (195) together could be employed to calculate the specific heats themselves from mechanical data alone, γ being known from the velocity of sound in the gas and the value of the right-hand member of (195) from the equation of state. Certain *qualitative* information of a nonmechanical sort would still be required, however, for we should need to know what constitutes an *adiabatic* compression, and this is not a purely mechanical conception. In practice, furthermore, the mechanical data are scarcely complete enough at present to make it worth while to substitute them for direct observations upon one of the specific heats.

140. Variation of the Specific Heats. The experimental or theoretical study of one specific heat which thus remains to be made can be reduced further by means of yet a third connection with the equa-

---

* These can be obtained by writing

$$dV = \left(\frac{\partial V}{\partial p}\right)_T dp + \left(\frac{\partial V}{\partial T}\right)_p dT = \left(\frac{\partial V}{\partial p}\right)_T \left(\frac{\partial p}{\partial V}\right)_T dV + \left[\left(\frac{\partial V}{\partial p}\right)_T \left(\frac{\partial p}{\partial T}\right)_V + \left(\frac{\partial V}{\partial T}\right)_p\right] dT,$$

in which $(\partial V/\partial p)_T \, (\partial p/\partial V)_T = 1$ and hence the last term equals zero; dividing out dT we have then the equation stated.

tion of state. For by differentiating the first and last members in (192a) and (192b) with T constant, and then substituting for $\partial^2 S / \partial V \, \partial T$ and $\partial^2 S / \partial p \, \partial T$ from (191a, b), we find

$$\left(\frac{\partial c_V}{\partial V}\right)_T = T\left(\frac{\partial^2 p}{\partial T^2}\right)_V, \qquad \left(\frac{\partial c_p}{\partial p}\right)_T = -T\left(\frac{\partial^2 V}{\partial T^2}\right)_p. \qquad (196a, b)$$

In view of these equations it is clear that we need add to the equation of state only a knowledge of c_V as a function of temperature *at a single volume*, or of c_p *at a single pressure*, in order to be in a position to calculate all values of the specific heats, and then from these the energy and the entropy. It is sufficient, for instance, to determine in some way either c_V or c_p for the perfect-gas limiting case of vanishing density. To a theoretical study of the latter problem we shall accordingly devote the major part of this chapter, tarrying only to note the special forms which some of the preceding equations take in certain simple cases.

141. Thermodynamics of Perfect and van der Waals Gases. If a gas obeys the perfect-gas law,

$$pV = RT,$$

we have at once

$$\left(\frac{\partial p}{\partial T}\right)_V = \frac{R}{V} = \frac{p}{T}, \qquad \left(\frac{\partial V}{\partial T}\right)_p = \frac{R}{p} = \frac{V}{T},$$

and hence, by (190a) in Sec. 137,

$$\left(\frac{\partial U}{\partial V}\right)_T = 0.$$

The energy U is, therefore, a function of the temperature alone. The reasoning here constitutes the inverse of that in Sec. 13, where we started from the assumption that, for a perfect gas, U is a function of the temperature only and then proceeded to show that the equation of state must have the form, $pV = RT$. If we know the function $U(T)$, we can evaluate both integrals in eq. (189a) in Sec. 136, the second giving $\int \frac{p}{T} dV = R \int \frac{dV}{V} = R \log V$; we find thus for the entropy of a gram of a perfect gas, writing $dU = c_V \, dT$ from (192a),

$$S = \int c_V \frac{dT}{T} + R \log V = \int c_V \frac{dT}{T} + R \log (RT) - R \log p.$$

Furthermore, it follows from (195) that

$$c_p - c_V = R, \qquad (197)$$

so that or a perfect gas this difference is a constant, representing a constant work difference between the two specific heats equal to the gas constant R. From this equation we have, in terms of the specific-heat ratio, $\gamma = c_p/c_V$,

$$c_V = \frac{R}{\gamma - 1}, \qquad c_p = \frac{\gamma R}{\gamma - 1}. \qquad (198a, b)$$

Differentiating further, we find also that

$$\left(\frac{\partial^2 p}{\partial T^2}\right)_V = 0, \qquad \left(\frac{\partial^2 V}{\partial T^2}\right)_p = 0,$$

and hence by (196a, b)

$$\left(\frac{\partial c_V}{\partial V}\right)_T = 0, \qquad \left(\frac{\partial c_p}{\partial p}\right)_T = 0.$$

Thus, for a perfect gas both specific heats and likewise their ratio γ are, like U, functions of the temperature alone.

The actual forms of the functions $U(T)$, $c_V(T)$, or $c_p(T)$ are not fixed by any general principle but depend upon the special properties of the molecules.

As a special case, if we know, or are willing to assume, that c_V is independent of temperature and so is completely constant, we can at once integrate (192a) to find U and so obtain

$$U = c_V T + \text{const.}; \qquad (199)$$

then, the above equation for S takes the form

$$S = c_V \log T + R \log V + \text{const.}, \qquad (200a)$$

or

$$S = c_p \log T - R \log p + \text{const.}, \qquad (200b)$$

since $V = RT/p$ and by (197) $c_V + R = c_p$. The two constants of integration differ, if S is the same, by $R \log R$. One of these formulas is often written as the general formula for the entropy of a perfect gas, but strictly speaking the constancy of c_V hardly forms part of the perfect-gas idea; there is no reason why c_V should become *independent of temperature* as the molecules of the gas get farther and farther apart and the gas therefore takes on perfect-gas properties.

Experimental results, in so far as they exist, seem to show that actual gases approximate to the perfect gas in their thermal behavior under the same circumstances and to about the same degree as they do in regard to their equation of state. The specific heats and γ all increase, however, when the density becomes considerable; they may ultimately become much larger than at low densities, especially near the critical point.

Problem. Obtain the following equations for the van der Waals gas, valid also at low densities for a gas of weakly attracting hard spheres, and compare them with the equations for the perfect gas:

$$c_p - c_V = \frac{R}{\left[1 - \frac{2a}{RVT}\left(1 - \frac{b}{V} \right)^2 \right]}, \qquad \left(\frac{\partial c_V}{\partial V} \right)_T = 0; \qquad (201)$$

$$\left(\frac{\partial U}{\partial V} \right)_T = \frac{a}{V^2}, \qquad U = U_0(T) - \frac{a}{V},$$

$$S = \int \frac{dU_0}{T} + R \log (V - b).$$

Thus for small values of a/RVT and b/v

$$c_p - c_V = R + \frac{2a}{VT}. \qquad (202)$$

SPECIFIC HEAT OF THE PERFECT GAS

We shall now complete our study of the energy and related magnitudes of a gas by taking up the fundamental problem of its energy and specific heat at vanishing density, when it becomes perfect.

It is instructive to consider first the conclusions that are indicated by classical theory, which contain a great deal of truth, and then to correct and amplify these results by introducing wave mechanics.

142. Molecular Energy. The energy of a gas, regarded as the energy of its molecules, can be divided more or less definitely into a number of different parts, as follows:

a. Translatory kinetic energy.

b. Rotational kinetic energy.

c. Energy of vibration of the atoms relative to the center of mass of the whole molecule, partly kinetic and partly potential in nature (at least in classical theory).

d. Mutual potential energy of the molecules as wholes.

e. Internal atomic energy.

Even in classical theory the distinction between these different types cannot always be drawn sharply, but it is sufficiently definite to make the classification helpful.

At very low densities the mutual energy, type (*d*), becomes negligible, and hence it will not further concern us here; its effect is, in fact, covered by the various connections with the equation of state that we have deduced from thermodynamics. The translatory kinetic energy of the molecules moving as wholes is likewise quite distinct at low densities from the other forms. The remaining types, which we have been lumping together and calling internal molecular energy, are much more closely interrelated; both classical and quantum theory indicate, however, that they can be distinguished clearly enough so long as they are of quite different orders of magnitude, and such is the case at least when the temperature is sufficiently low.

Each of these types of energy is a definite function of the coordinates and momenta, and if the form of this function is known, the average value of this part of the energy can be found by the methods of statistical mechanics. For one type of energy classical theory furnishes an extremely simple general rule: According to the famous principle of the *equipartition of energy*, if any part of the energy of a system is simply proportional to the square of a coordinate or of a component of velocity or momentum, then, when the system is in thermal equilibrium at temperature T, the mean value of this part of the energy is $\frac{1}{2} kT$, k being the gas constant for one molecule (cf. Sec. 206).

Now the *translatory energy* of a molecule is the sum of three such terms, corresponding to its three degrees of translational freedom; it can be written, for instance, $(p_x^2 + p_y^2 + p_z^2)/2m$ in terms of the cartesian components of momentum, p_x, p_y, p_z. The mean translatory energy of a molecule should accordingly be $\frac{3}{2} kT$, in agreement with the usual elementary result. Multiplying this value by the number of molecules, we have therefore for the translatory energy of a gram

$$U_t = \tfrac{3}{2} RT, \tag{203}$$

R being as usual the gas constant for a gram.

143. The Classical Theory of Specific Heat. We can conceive of molecules that possess no other form of energy than translational. This would be true, for instance, if they were simple mass points incapable of rotation, or if they were smooth spheres initially devoid of rotation and having the center of gravity at the geometrical center, so that their state of rotation could never be changed by any molecular impact. For a gas composed of such molecules the total energy would be $U = U_t$; the specific heat at constant volume would accordingly be, by (203), $c_V = (\partial U/\partial T)_V = \frac{3}{2} R$, and, since for a perfect gas $c_p - c_V = R$ [cf. (197)], the specific heat at constant volume would be $c_p = \frac{5}{2} R$, and for the ratio of the two we should have $c_p/c_V = \frac{5}{3}$. If the gas constant R_M for a gram molecule or mole is substituted for R we have $\frac{3}{2} R_M$ as the specific heat in terms of moles; substituting

$R_M = 83.15 \times 10^6$ and dividing by 4.186×10^7, we find for this 2.98 cal per mole. This result is often cited as a specific heat of about 3 cal per mole for a monatomic gas.

Since any internal energy that the molecules may possess is almost certain to increase rather than to decrease with a rise of temperature, its presence should increase not only U but also the specific heats. Accordingly, we are led to expect all real gases at low pressures to satisfy the following inequalities:

$$U \geqq \tfrac{3}{2} RT, \qquad c_V \geqq \tfrac{3}{2} R, \qquad c_p \geqq \tfrac{5}{2} R, \qquad \gamma \leqq \tfrac{5}{3}. \qquad (203a, b, c, d)$$

The last two of these is based upon the assumption that $c_p - c_V = R$.

The next simplest type, after the simple mass point, would be a *dumbbell*, or two atoms rigidly united into a molecule possessing a single axis of symmetry. Such a molecule would be incapable of any change in rotation about this axis; it would have, therefore, two degrees of rotational freedom, corresponding to independent rotations about two axes perpendicular to each other as well as to the axis of symmetry. The principle of equipartition also asserts that the mean kinetic energy associated with each of these degrees of rotational freedom would have an average value of $\tfrac{1}{2} kT$ (cf. Sec. 206). Accordingly, the molecules in a gram would possess, in addition to U_t, rotational energy of magnitude

$$U_r = RT$$

and we should have $U = U_t + U_r = \tfrac{5}{2} RT$, $c_V = \tfrac{5}{2} R$, $c_p = \tfrac{7}{2} R$, $\gamma = \tfrac{7}{5}$.

If, on the other hand, the molecule were *rigid* but possessed *no axis* of symmetry, as would almost certainly be the case if it were composed of three or more atoms not lying on the same line, all three degrees of rotational freedom would take up their share of kinetic energy and we should have

$$U_r = \tfrac{3}{2} RT;$$

hence $U = 3RT$ and $c_V = 3R$, $c_p = 4R$, $\gamma = \tfrac{4}{3}$.

Another possibility is that the atoms may *vibrate* relative to each other. If these vibrations are of rather small amplitude, they should be very nearly harmonic; the expression for the corresponding potential energy would then be of the squared form to which the principle of equipartition applies, e.g., $\tfrac{1}{2} aq^2$, where q is a coordinate and a a constant, and so would likewise average $\tfrac{1}{2} kT$. The total mean energy, kinetic and potential, associated with each mode of vibration would then be kT, and the total amount of this kind of energy in a gram would be RT.   A gas composed of dumbbell molecules in which the atoms can vibrate along the line joining their centers would thus have energy $U = U_t + U_r + RT = \frac{7}{2} RT$, so that $c_V = \frac{7}{2} R$, $c_p = \frac{9}{2} R$, $\gamma = \frac{9}{7}$.

A general formula can easily be worked out for an asymmetric molecule containing any number τ of atoms which are capable of relative vibration in simple harmonic motion.   We require 3τ coordinates to specify the positions of the atoms, but three combinations of these represent the position of the center of mass of the whole molecule and three more are accounted for by the three possible independent rotations; hence there are only $3\tau - 6$ independent modes of vibration. Thus there will be in a gram $U_v = (3\tau - 6)RT$ ergs of vibrational energy, $U_r = \frac{3}{2} RT$ of rotational and $U_t = \frac{3}{2} RT$ of translational, or a total of $U = 3(\tau - 1)RT$ ergs: consequently $c_V = 3(\tau - 1)R$, $c_p = (3\tau - 2)R$, $\gamma = \dfrac{(3\tau - 2)}{3(\tau - 1)}$.   The specific heats in an actual case might be smaller than these values if some of the atoms were rigidly bound together; or, if some of the modes of vibration were anharmonic, the specific heats might even exceed the values stated, but probably not by a great deal.

The classical results thus worked out are summarized in the following table, the column headed U/U_t giving in each case the ratio of the total energy to the translatory energy alone:

Molecular type	U/U_t	c_V/R	c_p/R	γ
Spherically symmetrical	1	$\frac{3}{2}$	$\frac{5}{2}$	$\frac{5}{3} = 1.667$
Dumbbells	$\frac{5}{3}$	$\frac{5}{2}$	$\frac{7}{2}$	$\frac{7}{5} = 1.400$
Rigid nonsymmetrical	2	3	4	$\frac{4}{3} = 1.333$
Diatomic, vibrating S.H.	$\frac{7}{3}$	$\frac{7}{2}$	$\frac{9}{2}$	$\frac{9}{7} = 1.286$
τ atoms vibrating S.H. (nonsymmetric, $\tau > 2$)	$2(\tau - 1)$	$3(\tau - 1)$	$3\tau - 2$	$1 + \dfrac{1}{3(\tau - 1)}$

144. Comparison with Actual Specific Heats.   For comparison with the theoretical formulas the principal thermal data for the commoner gases and a few organic ones under ordinary conditions are collected in the annexed table on p. 252.

Under the heading γ is given the ratio of the two specific heats, mostly determined from the velocity of sound, and under the heading c_p' is given the specific heat at constant volume stated in terms of calories per gram for convenience in comparing with other specific heats; c_p' must, therefore, be multiplied by the mechanical equiavalent of the calorie, $J = 4.186 \times 10^7$ ergs, to obtain the quantity c_p that occurs above in our formulas.   In the fourth column are shown val-

SPECIFIC HEATS

Gas	γ	c_p'	$\dfrac{c_p - c_V}{R}$	$\dfrac{c_V}{R}$
Helium..........................	1.659 (18°)	1.252 (18°)	1.001	1.519
Neon............................	1.64 (19°)			
Argon...........................	1.66$_8$	0.125	1.008	1.509
Krypton.........................	1.68 (19°)			
Xenon...........................	1.66 (19°)			
H$_2$............................	1.410	3.39$_3$	.9995	2.438
HCl.............................	1.40 (20°)	0.194	1.02	2.54
N$_2$...........................	1.404	0.247$_5$	1.005	2.448
CO..............................	1.404	0.248	1.005	2.488
O$_2$...........................	1.401	0.218$_0$	1.004	2.504
NO.............................	1.400	0.233$_1$	1.005	2.512
Cl$_2$..........................	1.36	0.115	1.09	3.02
H$_2$O..........................	1.32 (100°)	0.48 (100°)	1.06	3.3
H$_2$S..........................	1.32 (18°)	0.253	1.05	3.29
CO$_2$..........................	1.304	0.199	1.027	3.38
SO$_2$..........................	1.29	0.152	1.10	3.79
NH$_3$..........................	1.31	0.524	1.06	3.42
C$_2$N$_2$......................	1.25$_6$	0.205	1.09	4.27
CH$_4$ (methane)................	1.31	0.529	1.01	3.25
C$_2$H$_4$ (ethylene)...........	1.25$_5$	0.360	1.03	4.04
C$_2$H$_6$ (ethane).............	1.22	0.386	1.05	4.78
C$_2$H$_6$O (ethyl alcohol).....	1.13 (90°)	0.454 (100°–223°)	1.21(?)	9.3(?)
C$_4$H$_{10}$O (ethyl ether)....	1.08 (35°)	0.445 (35°)	1.23	15.4

The data are for 1 atmosphere pressure and, unless otherwise stated, 15°C.

c_p and c_V are in mechanical units, c_p in calories per gram.

ues of the ratio $\dfrac{(c_p - c_V)}{R}$ calculated as $\dfrac{(\gamma - 1)c_p'J}{\gamma R}$ or mostly as $(\gamma - 1)C_p \times 10^7/\gamma R_M$, R_M being the molar gas constant or 8.315 joules per degree and C_p, the heat capacity of a gram molecule in joules per degree. The fifth column contains values of c_V/R, c_V being calculated as $c_p'J/\gamma$. The data were taken largely from the International Critical Tables, where the values given are mostly those of C_p, from which c_p' was found by dividing by 4.186 and by the molecular weight.

A glance at the table shows at least that inequalities (203b) and (203d) are always satisfied. It is really sufficient to discuss only one of the two quantities c_V and γ, since, as we have seen, the other is determined in terms of it by means of relations obtained from thermodynamics, but as a matter of interest we shall discuss both.

We note that for five gases γ lies close to the theoretical value of $\frac{5}{3}$ that was found in the last section for mass points; and for two of these

c_V/R is known and lies close to the theoretical value of 1.5.   These are the rare gases, whose molecules are believed to consist of single atoms. When these gases were first discovered, to be sure, their monatomic character was actually inferred from observations on γ and the interpretation in the light of kinetic theory, for the reason that these gases scarcely enter into chemical combination, but modern atomic theory has now lent strong support to the conclusion that they have monatomic molecules.

There follows next a group from H_2 to NO for which γ is close to 1.4 and c_V/R fairly close to 2.5, which are the theoretical values for rigid dumbbell molecules.   Since there are abundant chemical reasons for believing these gases to be diatomic, classical theory was able to explain their values of γ and c_V very nicely by supposing the two atoms to be bound rigidly together in the molecule and hence incapable of vibration. The next gas in the table, however, Cl_2, is also certainly diatomic, yet it has $\gamma = 1.36$ and $c_V/R = 3.02$.   These values do not correspond exactly to any simple classical type; if the explanation of the departure lay in a classical vibration of the atoms, which is the most attractive supposition, we ought to have $\gamma = 1.286$ and $c_V/R = 3.5$ (cf. table at end of preceding section), whereas if the dumbbell were rigid but somehow asymmetric we should have $\gamma = 1.333$ and $c_V/R = 3.0$.   The latter number agrees well with the experimental value, but the value of γ definitely does not; such an assumption is, moreover, very improbable. Thus in this case classical theory fails.

All of the gases in the table with more than two atoms in the molecule have γ less and c_V/R greater, respectively, than the theoretical values $\frac{4}{3}$ and 3 for rigid asymmetric molecules.   This much is satisfactory, since their molecules all contain at least three atoms; and we note also that c_V/R never exceeds the value $3(\tau - 1)$, which is the maximum that could be accounted for by allowing all of the τ atoms in a molecule to execute classical simple harmonic motions.   No definite progress can be made, however, using classical ideas, toward accounting for the data in detail.

It is interesting to note that the classical results were supposed to be applicable to *liquid* and *solid* phases as well to gases.   In the case of pure elementary substances the molecule was commonly thought to be monatomic in condensed phases, the individual atoms moving independently.   If we then assume that in a solid the atoms of such a substance vibrate approximately in simple harmonic motion, we arrive at the conclusion that the heat content should be just twice that of a monatomic gas, the energy averaging half kinetic and half potential, and the specific heat should accordingly be $3R$.   The heat capacity of a mole would then be $3R_M$ or $3 \times 83.15 \times 10^6/4.186 \times 10^7 = 5.96$ or about 6 cal per mole.

Now, it is a fact that for most solid elements at ordinary temperatures the specific heat is not far from 6 cal per mole. There are a few notable exceptions, however, such as diamond. Furthermore, later work has shown that the specific heat of all substances drops eventually if the temperature is lowered sufficiently, apparently tending toward 0 at $T = 0$. The first satisfactory explanation of these facts was given by Debye in 1912, but it lies outside the scope of this book.*

145. The Specific-heat Difference. The values of $(c_p - c_v)/R$ are in quite a different status from those of γ or c_v, since the value of $c_p - c_v$ is fixed by eq. (195) above in terms of quantities derivable from the equation of state. Departures of $(c_p - c_v)/R$ from the perfect-gas value of unity thus serve as an indication in thermal data of a departure from the behavior of a perfect gas, and some interest attaches to them for this reason.

For the first eight gases for which values are given, with the exception of HCl, and for methane, $(c_p - c_v)/R$ is actually within 1 per cent of unity; these are all gases whose critical temperature lies below 0°C (even that of methane being -82.5°C). The remaining gases in the table all have critical points above 0°C and would be expected to show greater departures from the perfect gas. We found above that a gas composed of hard weakly attracting spheres, or a van der Waals gas, should obey eq. (202) in Sec. 141; since a is, according to its theoretical origin, necessarily positive, for such a gas $(c_p - c_v)/R$ should exceed unity. This is uniformly the case for actual gases except for hydrogen, where the slight defect in the ratio may easily represent experimental error.

146. The Problem of the Internal Energy. It is obvious from our discussion that classical theory was unable to deal in any satisfactory way with the internal energy of the molecules. The worst feature of the situation was that classical statistics indicated a mean value of $\frac{1}{2} kT$ for the kinetic energy associated with each degree of freedom, and the nature of atomic spectra pointed very clearly to the existence of many internal modes of vibration even within a single atom; it was necessary to assume that for some unknown reason these modes did not contribute appreciably to the specific heat.

The difficulty was not quite so serious in the present connection as in the theory of radiation, where the degrees of freedom of the electromagnetic field were actually infinite in number, and where the

---

* Cf. F. K. RICHTMYER, "Introduction to Modern Physics," 1934, p. 280.

difficulty had in 1900 led to Planck's invention of the quantum theory; but as time went on, matters became worse instead of better.

The success of the Rutherford atom in 1912 was the last straw; for the concentration of the positive charge into a minute nucleus opened up a deep hole in which, according to the classical Boltzmann formula, the electrons would be completely swallowed up. The potential energy of an electron of charge e at a distance r from a nucleus of positive charge $-Ze$ being $\omega = -Ze^2/r$, the probability, according to the Boltzmann formula $(92a)$ in Sec. 55, that the electron is in an element $d\tau$ of space is $C_{mq}e^{\frac{Ze^2}{rkT}}\,d\tau$, and the chance that it lies at a distance between r and $r + dr$ from the nucleus is, therefore,

$$P_r\,dr = 4\pi r^2 C_{mq}e^{\frac{Ze^2}{rkT}}\,dr;$$

the total chance of its lying within a distance r_1 of the nucleus is then

$$\int_0^{r_1} P_r\,dr = 4\pi C_{mq}\int_0^{r_1} r^2 e^{\frac{Ze^2}{rkT}}\,dr = 4\pi C_{mq}\int_{1/r_1}^{\infty} e^{\frac{Ze^2\mu}{kT}}\,\frac{d\mu}{\mu^4}.$$

This is infinite unless $C_{mq} = 0$, in which case the electron would have to be right on top of the nucleus. Any departure from the Coulomb law that could reasonably be assumed did not help matters much.

The first step toward a solution of such difficulties was the partial substitution of quantum for classical ideas in the atomic theory proposed by Bohr in 1913. Accordingly we shall turn now to the treatment of the internal energy that is furnished by modern wave mechanics.

147. Quantum Theory of the Specific Heat. The different parts into which the molecular energy can be divided, as described above in Sec. 142, fare differently in wave mechanics. As regards the *translatory kinetic* energy, it can be shown (cf. Chap. X) that in practically all cases the classical expression is correct within the limits set by experimental error, and in those special cases in which perceptible deviations of quantum origin can occur, the effects of molecular forces are sufficiently great to mask the quantum effects. Furthermore, in the limiting case of indefinitely low density the quantum effects disappear entirely. Hence we can write with complete accuracy for the translatory energy of a gram of indefinitely rare and therefore perfect gas

$$U_t = \tfrac{3}{2}\,RT,$$

as in eq. (203) above.

The *internal energy*, on the other hand, requires radically different handling, as was explained in Sec. 54. If for simplicity we suppose the various fundamental quantum states of a molecule to be numbered off in a single series, then for statistical purposes we may imagine the molecule to spend a fraction P_j of its time in each quantum state of energy ϵ_j, where P_j has the value given in eq. (93b), viz.,

$$P_j = e^{-\frac{\epsilon_j}{kT}}/Z, \qquad Z = \sum_j e^{-\frac{\epsilon_j}{kT}}, \qquad (204a, b)$$

the sum in Z extending over all fundamental quantum states. The mean internal energy of such a molecule will thus be

$$\bar{\epsilon} = \sum_j \epsilon_j P_j = \sum_j \epsilon_j e^{-\frac{\epsilon_j}{kT}}/Z \qquad (205)$$

and the internal energy of a gram of gas containing N such molecules will be

$$U_i = N\sum_j \epsilon_j e^{-\frac{\epsilon_j}{kT}}/Z = RT^2 \frac{d}{dT} \log Z \qquad (206)$$

where $R = Nk$ or the gas constant for a gram.

The quantity $Z(T)$ which thus plays an important role in the theory was called by Planck the *state sum* (in German, "Zustandssumme"); it has also been called the "partition function." We could equally well include in it by definition the factor N, so that it would have reference to a gram. If we know the energies ϵ_j of the molecular quantum states, we can calculate Z and U_i as functions of the absolute temperature T; the specific heat at constant volume can then be calculated as

$$c_V = \frac{d}{dT} (U_t + U_i). \qquad (207)$$

The quantum states for a given molecule ordinarily fall naturally into a number of distinct groups corresponding to the fact that the energy can be separated approximately into rotational energy of the whole molecule, vibrational energy of the atomic nuclei, and electronic energy, and for this reason it is customary to number them by means of not one but three quantum numbers; the latter are often denoted by n, v, J, being assigned so that changes of J imply chiefly changes in the rotational motion, of v, in the relative motions of the nuclei, and of n, in the electronic configuration. The change in energy involved in a jump of one of the quantum numbers from its lowest value to the next higher, which is the most important jump from our standpoint, is of a different order of magnitude in the three cases; expressed in terms of kT_{15}, the value of kT at 15°C or two thirds of the mean kinetic energy of a molecule at that temperature, the first step in rotation or in J requires about 0.15 to 0.3 kT_{15} ergs, whereas the first step in vibration or in v requires 1 to 10 kT_{15}, and the first step in electronic excitation or in n usually requires at least 100 kT_{15}.

A further multiplicity due to the nuclei must often be allowed for, either by the use of additional quantum numbers or by the introduction of suitable statistical weights or multiplicity factors into formulas such as (205) or (206).   (Cf. Sec. 54.)   This is illustrated in the discussion of hydrogen below.

148. Variation of Specific Heat with Temperature.   In the light of the facts just stated the general course of the specific heat as a function of temperature can at once be predicted.   If we first go to extremely low temperatures, the probability P_j of the state in which the internal energy ϵ_j has its lowest value ϵ_1 is very much larger than is P_j for any other state, and the molecules remain, therefore, nearly all of the time in this lowest state; all terms in the series for U_i in (206) are then extremely small in comparison with the first term, in which $\epsilon_j = \epsilon_1$, and the series for Z in (204b) likewise reduces to its first term alone. Thus $U_i = N\epsilon_1$ and is independent of temperature, and the specific heat reduces to $dU_t/dT = 3R/2$, just as for a gas of mass points.

If we then gradually raise the temperature, in the case of polyatomic molecules the higher rotational states eventually begin to be occupied; and a little consideration shows that when kT comes to exceed the sum of the first few energy steps between these states, there will be an approximation to the classical value of the rotational energy.   This condition can often be met before the higher vibrational states begin to occur with appreciable frequency; in such a case there may be a considerable range of temperature over which c_V has its classical value, including the part that represents rotational energy but nothing more.

When the temperature is raised sufficiently, however, vibrational energy will begin to occur in appreciable amounts, and c_V will then increase further: Electronic excitation, on the other hand, can occur in appreciable amount only at temperatures of the order of a hundred times normal, or above, say, 20,000°.   It should be noted that in the electronic energy there is included all energy of rotation of monatomic molecules, and also, in the case of molecules with collinear nuclei, the energy of rotation about the axis through the nuclei.

The general shape thus predicted for the specific-heat curve of a perfect gas with polyatomic molecules is shown in Fig. 56.   In the case of the more permanent gases there is evidence to show that the curve actually has such a form, the gas at ordinary temperatures being on the flat part of the curve between A and B; only in hydrogen, however, does the drop at A occur at easily accessible temperatures. The success of the classical theory in dealing with these gases is thus accounted for. Most gases are at B or still farther to the right.

In order to construct a quantitative theory, we might now adopt some simple model for the molecule and try to adjust its assumed moments of inertia and vibrational properties in such a way as to make the theoretical values of c_V at different temperatures fit the experimental data. Several attempts to do this were made in the case of simple molecules such as hydrogen, but for various reasons complete success was never achieved. A much better procedure, in general, is probably to make use of the rich material concerning molecular energy levels that is furnished by the study of band spectra and to leave the theoretical interpretation of the levels themselves as a problem for the theoretical spectroscopist. The labor involved even in this procedure is considerable, and it is increased by a peculiar complication due to nuclear spin; but several cases have been worked out. As an example the famous case of hydrogen will be discussed in detail presently; but first it will be worth while to consider briefly an ideal case that can easily be treated completely.

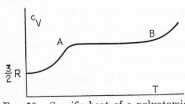

FIG. 56.—Specific heat of a polyatomic gas.

149. The Case of Harmonic Oscillators. As a special case, suppose the molecules can vibrate harmonically in some way with a definite frequency ν. Then there will be some coordinate q that can vary sinusoidally with the time and can be written $q = a \sin 2\pi\nu(t + \delta)$, and there will be a corresponding term in the energy of the form $\frac{1}{2}(\alpha\dot{q}^2 + \beta q^2)$ where $\dot{q} = dq/dt$ and α and β are constants. In such a case wave mechanics predicts a series of quantum states whose energies are of the form $(n + \frac{1}{2})h\nu$, n being a positive integer or zero.

The state sum for such an oscillator is easily calculated. We have only to establish first the mathematical formulas

$$\sum_{j=0}^{\infty} e^{-ix} = \frac{1}{1 - e^{-x}} = \frac{e^x}{e^x - 1},$$

$$\sum_{j=0}^{\infty} je^{-ix} = -\frac{d}{dx}\sum_{j=0}^{\infty} e^{-ix} = \frac{e^{-x}}{(1 - e^{-x})^2} = \frac{e^x}{(e^x - 1)^2}.$$

Putting $x = h\nu/kT$ in these formulas and $\epsilon_j = (j + \frac{1}{2})h\nu$ in (204b) and (205), we obtain at once for the state sum Z and the mean energy

$\bar{\epsilon}$ per oscillator

$$Z = e^{-\frac{h\nu}{2kT}} \sum_{j=0}^{\infty} e^{-\frac{jh\nu}{kT}} = \frac{e^{\frac{h\nu}{2kT}}}{e^{\frac{h\nu}{kT}} - 1}, \tag{208a}$$

$$\bar{\epsilon} = h\nu e^{-\frac{h\nu}{2kT}} \sum_{j=0}^{\infty} j \, e^{-\frac{jh\nu}{kT}}/Z + \frac{1}{2} h\nu e^{-\frac{h\nu}{2kT}} \sum_{j=0}^{\infty} e^{-\frac{jh\nu}{kT}}/Z$$

or

$$\bar{\epsilon} = \frac{h\nu}{e^{\frac{h\nu}{kT}} - 1} + \frac{1}{2} h\nu. \tag{208b}$$

N molecules in a gram, each containing such an oscillator, would then contribute $N\bar{\epsilon}$ to U_i, and to the specific heat c_V the amount

$$c_{V\nu} = \frac{d}{dT} N\bar{\epsilon} = \frac{Rh^2\nu^2}{4k^2T^2} \Big/ \sinh^2 \frac{h\nu}{2kT} \tag{209}$$

in terms of $R = Nk$ and $\sinh x = (e^x - e^{-x})/2$.

In Fig. 57 are plotted $\bar{\epsilon}/h\nu$ and $c_{V\nu}/R$ against the temperature T. For large T or, more exactly, for small $h\nu/kT$, these quantities approach the classical values, kT and 1; for, if we expand the exponential that occurs in (208b) or (209), we obtain the series:

$$\bar{\epsilon} = kT\Big(1 + \frac{1}{12}\frac{h^2\nu^2}{k^2T^2} \cdots \Big),$$

$$c_{V\nu} = R\Big(1 - \frac{1}{12}\frac{h^2\nu^2}{k^2T^2} \cdots \Big).$$

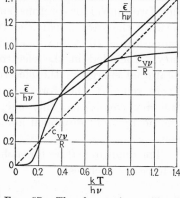

Fig. 57.—The harmonic oscillator. $\bar{\epsilon}$ = mean energy.

For small T, on the other hand, $c_{V\nu}$ sinks exponentially to 0. It might have been anticipated that at some intermediate temperature it would rise above the classical value in order to make up the deficit in energy that should exist at low temperatures, but no such rise occurs; according to present theory, there is really not a deficit but an excess of energy, due to the zero-point energy or the constant term $\frac{1}{2} h\nu$ in $\bar{\epsilon}$. The physical significance of this term is not too clear, however; if it were missing, as in the older quantum theory, the energy at high temperatures would simply remain permanently below the classical value by the amount $\frac{1}{2} h\nu$.

To give some idea of numerical magnitudes, we may note that at 15°C the specific heat $c_{V\nu}$ would be 1 per cent below R for a frequency $\nu = 0.346 = kT_{15}/h = 2.08 \times 10^{12}$, corresponding to a radiant wave length $3 \times 10^{10}/2.08 \times 10^{12}$ cm or 0.14 mm. As the frequency rises, the difference between $c_{V\nu}$ and R increases. For the normal oxygen molecule the second vibrational level lies above the first at a height equivalent to a frequency of 1,556 cm^{-1} or $\nu = 4.67 \times 10^{13}$. If we treat this as a simple harmonic mode of vibration, which is certainly justifiable at ordinary temperatures, we find from (209) that it contributes to the specific heat $c_{V\nu} = 0.026R$. This is just appreciable. Chlorine, on the other hand, has a first vibrational frequency of about 560 cm^{-1}, for which at 15°C, $c_{V\nu} = 0.542$. This is just about right to account for the observed excess of $0.52R$ above the dumbbell value, $c_V = 2.5R$.*

In hydrogen and nitrogen the vibrational frequencies lie too high to affect the specific heat at ordinary temperatures. The hydrogen molecule, on the other hand, has such a small moment of inertia that the drop in its rotational energy occurs at a moderately low temperature. The behavior of this gas will accordingly be discussed in detail.

150. Hydrogen. The hydrogen molecule consists of two electrons and two nuclei or protons so tightly bound by the force-actions between the various particles that, as already remarked, at ordinary temperatures the vibrational and electronic energy practically never vary. Included in the electronic energy is also the equivalent of rotational energy of the electrons about the line joining the nuclei. There remains, therefore, as internal energy that does vary under ordinary conditions, only energy of rotation of the molecule as a practically rigid dumbbell about an axis perpendicular to the nuclear line.

The quantum states for such a rotation are shown in wave mechanics to have the energies

$$\epsilon_J = \frac{h^2}{8\pi^2 I} J(J + 1), \tag{210}$$

where J is a positive integer or zero, h is Planck's constant, and I is the moment of inertia of the molecule about an axis perpendicular to the nuclear line.†

In the case of hydrogen the moment of inertia arises almost entirely from the large masses of the nuclei, the electrons being 1,821 times lighter and so negligible; and its value is known from the spacing in

---

* Cf. also Trautz and Ader, *Zeits. Physik*, **89**, 15 (1934).

† Cf. Condon and Morse, "Quantum Mechanics," 1929, p. 69.

band spectra to be $I = 4.67 \times 10^{-41}$ c.g.s. units.* The factor $h^2/8\pi^2 I$ in (210) has thus the value,

$$\frac{(6.62 \times 10^{-27})^2}{8\pi^2 I} = 1.19 \times 10^{-14} \text{ erg} = 0.30 \, kT_{15},$$

so that only about the first three states $(J = 0, 1, 2)$ would be well represented at ordinary temperatures; hence appreciable deviation of the specific heat ought to set in upon a moderate lowering of the temperature.

The first attempts at a quantitative theory of the specific heat of hydrogen failed, however, because two important principles of quantum theory were unknown until about 1927. In the first place, nuclei as well as electrons exhibit the phenomenon called *spin*, or something equivalent to it. One aspect of the spin is an internal angular momentum, whose total value in the case of a simple particle like a proton or electron never changes but whose component along any chosen axis when quantized can take on only one of two possible values, either $\frac{1}{2}$ or $-\frac{1}{2}$ times $h/2\pi$. For two protons we should accordingly expect four times as many independent quantum states as there would be without spin; in the absence of interaction between the protons, the corresponding wave functions would be obtained by taking each allowed function in terms of the spatial coordinates and assigning the spin $\frac{1}{2}$ or $-\frac{1}{2}$ in succession to each proton separately.

But then a reduction in the number of quantum states occurs in consequence of the second of the two new principles, the Fermi-Dirac-Pauli *exclusion principle*, which applies to any set of identically similar particles. When we have obtained any wave function for such a set, we can always form another one corresponding to the same energy merely by interchanging in the given function the coordinates of any two particles. The exclusion principle now asserts that, for some reason as yet unknown, only those quantum states occur in nature for which the new function thus obtained is merely the old one changed in sign, and so does not represent a new quantum state. Functions having this property are said to be *antisymmetrical* in the coordinates of the particles.

As a consequence of the exclusion principle, in the case of the dumbbell rotator, rotational quantum states with *even* J would not occur at all if there were no spin, for the wave-functions of these states without spin are symmetrical in the particles, only those with odd J being

---

* Hori, *Zeits. Phys.*, **44**, 834 (1927).

antisymmetrical.* When spins are introduced, however, it turns out that the functions for even J can be made antisymmetrical in the spins and so can be used. Those for *odd* J, on the other hand, can be made symmetrical in the spins and so antisymmetrical on the whole; and it happens that this can be done in three different independent ways, in two ways with the spins parallel and in one way with them anti-parallel, so that we obtain three different functions of this type for each odd value of J, as against only one for each even value.

Thus there are two distinct types of hydrogen molecules. One type, which is called *parahydrogen*, has wave-functions antisymmetric in the nuclear spins and rotates always with an *even* value of J, including the state of no rotation at all with $J = 0$; the other type, called *ortho-hydrogen*, has wave-functions symmetric in the nuclear spins and rotates with an *odd* value of J. The para molecules have $2J + 1$ quantum states for each value of J, corresponding to $2J + 1$ different possible quantized values of the component of angular momentum about any chosen axis, or, the statistical weight or multiplicity of the multiple state J is $2J + 1$; but the ortho molecules have three times as many states or a multiplicity of $3(2J + 1)$.

151. Para-, Ortho-, and Equilibrium Hydrogen. The first treatment of the specific heat of hydrogen in which allowance was made for these new features of quantum theory was that of Hund,† but his results did not fit the facts. Hund assumed that individual molecules would pass freely back and forth between the two types. Dennison then pointed out that,‡ since the process of conversion from one type to the other ought theoretically to be an extremely slow one, the proportion of the two types would probably not change appreciably during the time in which the gas changes temperature in an ordinary measurement of specific heat. Hydrogen should therefore behave like a mixture of two gases which can transform into each other at a slow rate and so will come to a definite equilibrium of relative concentration when the gas is allowed to stand long enough, but which will not remain in equilibrium when a change of temperature is made quickly. In ordinary experiments on specific heat we are dealing, therefore, with a mixture that is practically fixed in composition. The equilibrium

---

* Polar angles θ, φ can be used to describe the rotation, with the axis drawn from one particle to the other; then the wave-functions for even J are of such forms as 1, 3 $\cos^2 \theta - 1$, $e^{i\varphi} \sin \theta \cos \theta$ [i.e., $e^{im\varphi} P_l^m (\cos \theta)$ with even l], and such functions retain their value if we substitute in them $\varphi + \pi$ for φ and $\pi - \theta$ for θ to represent an interchange of the cartesian coordinates of the particles, whereas the functions for odd J or odd l, such as $\cos \theta$, $e^{2i\varphi} \cos \theta$, etc., change sign.

† Hund, *Zeits. Physik*, **42**, 93 (1927).

‡ Dennison, *Roy. Soc. Proc.*, **115**, 483 (1927).

composition itself will, however, vary with the temperature at which the equilibrium is established, because of the differences in the Boltzmann factors for even and odd J.

This extraordinary theoretical conclusion has been confirmed by experiment. A good description of the relevant facts is contained in a recent book by Farkas.* At 20°K the molecules tend to crowd into the lowest state of no rotation, and in consequence equilibrium hydrogen at this temperature, according to eq. (212) below, is 99.8 per cent pure parahydrogen. It has been found that the process of conversion from the ordinary mixture into this form, which would take three years to go only halfway under standard conditions, can be catalyzed by adsorbing the gas on charcoal, so that at 20°K the process goes practically to completion in at most a few hours. If the temperature is then raised, the gas remains in its new form for a long time. Thus practically pure parahydrogen can be prepared and experimented upon; by comparison of its properties with the ordinary mixture, the properties of pure orthohydrogen can then be inferred indirectly. In most respects the two forms differ very little, but in specific heat and in related properties, such as thermal conductivity, as also in their band spectra, they differ decidedly.

An exact expression for the composition of equilibrium hydrogen at any temperature can easily be obtained from the Boltzmann probabilities. The relative numbers of molecules in the various quantum states are given by (204a) in Sec. 147 with ϵ_j replaced by ϵ_J as given in (210) above or

$$\epsilon_J = J(J + 1)xkT, \qquad x = \frac{h^2}{8\pi^2 I} \frac{1}{kT} = \frac{84.8}{T}. \qquad (211a, b)$$

For convenience we may, as explained in Sec. 54, group together states having the same energy and hence simply write for the probability of any multiple J state $P_J = \dfrac{(2J + 1)e^{-\frac{\epsilon_J}{kT}}}{Z}$ for even J and

$$P_J = \frac{3(2J + 1)e^{-\frac{\epsilon_J}{kT}}}{Z}$$

for odd J. The fractional part of the equilibrium gas that is in the para form will then be ΣP_J summed for even J beginning with 0, divided by ΣP_J summed for all J, or

* Farkas, "Orthohydrogen, Parahydrogen and Heavy Hydrogen," 1935.

$$\frac{1 + 5e^{-6x} + 9e^{-20x} + \cdots}{1 + 3 \times 3e^{-2x} + 5e^{-6x} + 3 \times 7e^{-12x} + 9e^{-20x} + \cdots}. \quad (212)$$

This formula gives for the per cent of parahydrogen in the equilibrium mixture: 99.8 per cent at 20°K, 88.6 per cent at 40°, 38.5 per cent at 100°, 25.7 per cent at 210°, 25.13 per cent at 273°K. Thus at room temperature the ratio of para to ortho has practically its limiting value of 1:3; this latter conclusion is confirmed by the distribution of the intensity in the band spectra of ordinary hydrogen.

152. Specific Heat of Hydrogen. In a similar way, by inserting ϵ_J from (211a, b) for ϵ_j in (206) and (204b) in Sec. 147, we obtain the following expression for the rotational energy of a gram of *equilibrium* hydrogen containing N molecules:

$$U_{Je} = RT^2 \frac{d}{dT} \log Z_e = -\frac{Nh^2}{8\pi^2 I} \frac{d}{dx} \log Z_e,$$

$$Z_e = 1 + 3 \times 3e^{-2x} + 5e^{-6x} + 3 \times 7e^{-12x} + 9e^{-20x} + \cdots,$$

in which x is given by (211b) whereas $R = Nk$ and represents the gas constant. If the temperature were now changed so slowly that the hydrogen remained continuously in equilibrium, its rotational specific heat at constant volume would be

$$c_{Je} = \frac{dU_{Je}}{dT} = Rx^2 \frac{d^2}{dx^2} \log Z_e.$$

Corresponding expressions for para- and orthohydrogen are obtained by including only terms for even or odd values of J, respectively, thus:

$$c_{Jp} = Rx^2 \frac{d^2}{dx^2} \log Z_p, \qquad Z_p = 1 + 5e^{-6x} + 9e^{-20x} + \cdots,$$

$$c_{Jo} = Rx^2 \frac{d^2}{dx^2} \log Z_o, \qquad Z_o = 3e^{-2x} + 7e^{-12x} + \cdots.$$

Finally, if a mixture containing fractional parts γ_p and γ_o of para- and orthohydrogen, respectively, is changed in temperature with ordinary rapidity so that its composition has no time to change appreciably, its *apparent* rotational specific heat will be

$$c_{Vr} = \gamma_p c_{Jp} + \gamma_o c_{Jo}.$$

In all cases the total specific heat at constant volume is obtained by adding to these values the translational term $\frac{3}{2} R$. The series given above do not represent any ordinary functions, but fortunately they converge rapidly at room or lower temperatures.

In Fig. 58 are shown data obtained by several observers on hydrogen subjected to various preliminary modes of treatment, and also the theoretical curve for that mixture which gave the best fit with the data, the assumed percentage of parahydrogen being given near

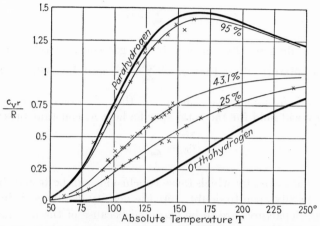

Fig. 58.—Rotational specific heat c_{v_r} of hydrogen. $R = 0.985$ cal per g.

each curve.* The ordinates represent in terms of R the rotational specific heat at constant volume, obtained by subtracting $\frac{3}{2} R$ from the total specific heat c_V. The uppermost curve is almost that for pure parahydrogen, and it shows an interesting maximum, well above the classical value, at about 160°K. The curve marked 25 per cent is for the ordinary mixture. Theoretical curves for pure parahydrogen and orthohydrogen are also drawn; and in Fig. 59 is shown the total specific heat c_V for these two forms and for ordinary hydrogen.

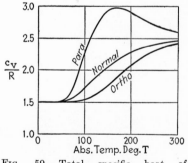

Fig. 59.—Total specific heat of hydrogen.

From these curves it appears that the modern theory is completely successful in accounting for the specific heat of hydrogen at ordinary or low temperatures.

153. Specific Heats of Mixed Gases. The heat capacity at constant volume of a rarefied or perfect gas composed of different kinds of molecules will be the sum of the heat capacities of the separate kinds;

* Cf. Eucken and Hiller, *Zeits. phys. Chemie*, **4(B)**, 142 (1929); Clusius and Hiller, *ibid.*, 158.

for at low densities interaction can be neglected and the energies of the molecules are simply additive. Accordingly, if molecules of kind ν form a fraction γ_ν by weight of the whole and have specific heat $c_{V\nu}$, the specific heat of the mixture at constant volume will be

$$c_V = \sum_\nu \gamma_\nu c_{V\nu} .$$

Since according to (20c) in Sec. 14 the gas constant obeys the same "law of mixtures," so that $R = \sum_\nu \gamma_\nu R_\nu$, and by (197) in Sec. 141 $c_{p\nu} = c_{V\nu} + R_\nu$ and for the heats of the mixture $c_p = c_V + R$, the same law will hold for the total specific heat at constant pressure:

$$c_p = \sum_\nu \gamma_\nu c_{p\nu}.$$

Few data exist by which these conclusions can be tested, but their truth is hardly open to doubt. As the density of the gas is increased, however, departures are to be expected because of the mutual energy of the molecules, and in the case of c_p also because of departures from the perfect-gas law.

CHAPTER VII

FLUCTUATIONS

In the preceding chapters we have dealt with gases in mass, confining our attention to physical phenomena on such a large scale that the gas behaves like a continuous medium. In developing a molecular theory of such phenomena we continually averaged molecular quantities until we smoothed out all irregularities due to the particular behavior of individual molecules. In marked contrast with such phenomena there exist others in which molecular irregularities themselves give rise to observable effects; the most famous case of this sort is the irregular dancing about or "Brownian motion" of small particles suspended in a fluid. This chapter will be devoted to the discussion of such phenomena, which are often grouped together under the collective name of *fluctuations*.

These phenomena possess great theoretical interest as constituting direct and striking manifestations of the molecular structure of matter; they are likewise increasing in importance as a nuisance for the observing physicist. Most of the cases of practical importance do not involve gases, to be sure, but the appropriate methods of treatment and the nature of the phenomena have so largely the special character peculiar to kinetic theory that it seems natural to step a little outside of our principal range of subject matter at this point.

The methods that have been developed for the theoretical treatment of phenomena of this sort fall into two rather distinct classes. In one type of method the attempt is made to obtain results as consequences of the assumed properties of the molecules themselves; in the other type, only broad features of the molecular motion are made use of and a connection is sought with some mass property of the gas, such as its viscosity or its coefficient of diffusion. The latter method is the safer and more widely useful one, but the former, more fundamental method does lead directly to a few observable results, and it also assists greatly in forming a lively picture of the chaos in the molecular world; so we shall include one or two examples illustrating this method as well.

The fluctuations themselves can also be divided roughly into two classes, phenomena of dispersion and fluctuations about an average. We begin with the former.*

* An extensive study of fluctuations is contained in R. Fürth's "Schwankungserscheinungen in der Physik," 1920. Cf. also the excellent book by T. C. Fry,

PHENOMENA OF DISPERSION

154. The Simple Random Walk. The essence of all problems of molecular dispersion is contained in the simple one-dimensional problem sometimes called that of the "random walk." A vivid and completely typical form of this problem is the following. A man takes steps of equal length either forward or backward at random. Where will he probably be after taking N steps?

To solve this problem, we note first that under the conditions stated each individual step is equally likely to be taken forward or backward quite independently of the directions of the others. All possible sequences of steps, each taken in a definite direction, are thus equally probable; and the probability of any given sequence is $(\frac{1}{2})^N$, for the probability that the first step is taken in an assigned direction is $\frac{1}{2}$, similarly for the second independently of the direction of the first, and so on through the N steps.

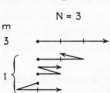

Now the only way in which the man can arrive, in the end, just m steps away from his starting point in the positive direction, is by his taking on the whole N_1 positive and N_2 negative steps, where N_1

Fig. 60.—The various groupings of three steps.

and N_2 have such magnitudes that $N_1 - N_2 = m$ and $N_1 + N_2 = N$; it follows that $N_1 = \dfrac{N}{2} + \dfrac{m}{2}$, $N_2 = \dfrac{N}{2} - \dfrac{m}{2}$. Clearly m can only be even if N is even, and odd if N is odd. But only certain sets of steps can result in any particular value of m (cf. Fig. 60); the number of such sets is obviously the number of combinations of N things taken either N_1 at a time or N_2 at a time, and so is equal to $N!/(N_1!N_2!)$. Multiplying this number by $(\frac{1}{2})^N$, the probability that any particular set occurs, we have, therefore, as the probability for the occurrence of any particular value of m

$$P_m = \frac{N!}{\left(\dfrac{N}{2} + \dfrac{m}{2}\right)!\left(\dfrac{N}{2} - \dfrac{m}{2}\right)!}\,(\tfrac{1}{2})^N. \tag{213}$$

This result is easily seen to hold for negative values of m as well.

We may note in passing that if the probability of a positive step were p instead of $\frac{1}{2}$, and that of a negative one, therefore, $q = 1 - p$,

---

"Probability and its Engineering Uses," 1928, and R. A. Fisher's "Statistical Methods for Research Workers."

the same expression would be obtained except that $(\frac{1}{2})^N$ would be replaced by $p^{\frac{N}{2}+\frac{m}{2}} q^{\frac{N}{2}-\frac{m}{2}}$.

In kinetic theory we shall be concerned chiefly with very large values of N. In any such case (213) can be replaced by an approximate expression that is easier to handle by means of Stirling's formula, which reads:

$$n! = (2\pi n)^{\frac{1}{2}}\left(\frac{n}{e}\right)^n \qquad (214a)$$

within $9/n$ per cent for integral $n > 0$ (the *numerical* error increasing, however, with increasing n), or

$$\log n! = (n + \tfrac{1}{2}) \log n - n + \tfrac{1}{2} \log (2\pi) \qquad (214b)$$

with an error less than $0.09/n$.

Using the latter form, we can write, approximately,

$$\log P_m = \left(N + \frac{1}{2}\right) \log N - \left(\frac{N}{2} + \frac{m}{2} + \frac{1}{2}\right) \log \left(\frac{N}{2} + \frac{m}{2}\right)$$
$$- \left(\frac{N}{2} - \frac{m}{2} + \frac{1}{2}\right) \log \left(\frac{N}{2} - \frac{m}{2}\right) - \frac{1}{2} \log (2\pi) - N \log 2.$$

Now let us use the series, $\log (1 + x) = x - \dfrac{x^2}{2} \cdots$, so that

$$\log \left(\frac{N}{2} \pm \frac{m}{2}\right) = \log \left[\frac{N}{2}\left(1 \pm \frac{m}{N}\right)\right] = \log N - \log 2 \pm \frac{m}{N} - \frac{m^2}{2N^2} \cdots$$

Then, dropping powers of $1/N$ beyond the first, we obtain

$$\log P_m = -\frac{1}{2} \log N + \log 2 - \frac{1}{2} \log (2\pi) - \frac{m^2}{2N} \cdots$$

and

$$P_m = \sqrt{\frac{2}{\pi N}}\, e^{-\frac{m^2}{2N}} \qquad (215a)$$

approximately. Here m takes on values only in steps of 2, being even or odd with N.

When N is large, it is more convenient also to introduce, in place of m as a variable, the total net displacement from the starting point, $\xi = ml$, where l is the length of a step. In practical cases l is usually small relative to distances in which we are interested; then it is convenient to treat ξ as if it were a continuous variable and to define the probability for it, P_ξ, by the statement that $P_\xi\, d\xi$ is the chance that ξ

lies in a given range $d\xi$. The number of possible values of m included in $d\xi$ is $d\xi/2l$, since m varies in steps of 2; hence $P_\xi\, d\xi = P_m\, d\xi/2l$ and $P_\xi = P_m/2l$, so that, writing

$$\lambda = l\sqrt{N},$$

we find

$$P_\xi = \frac{1}{\lambda\sqrt{2\pi}} e^{-\frac{\xi^2}{2\lambda^2}}. \tag{215b}$$

The error in (215b) as compared to (213) can be relatively large in the "tails" where $|\xi|$ is large, but this does not matter since P_ξ itself is there negligible when N is large. For the same reason we

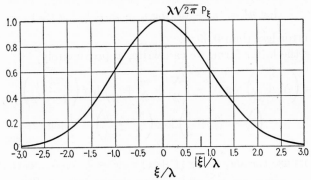

Fig. 61.—The random-walk probability curve, eq. (215b).

can also for mathematical convenience suppose ξ to range from $-\infty$ to $+\infty$. If we then evaluate the averages

$$\overline{\xi^2} = \int_{-\infty}^{\infty} \xi^2 P_\xi\, d\xi, \qquad \overline{|\xi|} = \int_{-\infty}^{\infty} |\xi| P_\xi\, d\xi = 2\int_0^{\infty} \xi P_\xi\, d\xi,$$

recalling that $\int_{-\infty}^{\infty} P_\xi\, d\xi = 1$, we find:

$$(\overline{\xi^2})^{1/2} = \lambda, \qquad \overline{|\xi|} = \sqrt{\frac{2}{\pi}}\lambda = 0.798\,\lambda. \tag{216a, b}$$

Thus λ is of the nature of a root-mean-square displacement.

The probability curve for the final displacement thus has the form of an error curve, as illustrated in Fig. 61. The most probable single net displacement, rather surprisingly perhaps, is zero; but the absolute expectation of displacement, $\overline{|\xi|}$, and the root-mean-square expectation or standard deviation, λ, both increase as $\sqrt{N}$. These expectations increase less rapidly than the numerical sum of the steps, however; the expectations for the fractional displacement, $|\xi|/Nl$ or λ/lN, *decrease* as $1/\sqrt{N}$, λ/lN being in fact equal to $1/\sqrt{N}$.

The quantity P_m or P_ξ admits, of course, of the usual double interpretation, either as a probability referring to a single instance or as a distribution function for a large number of instances. If the random walk were repeated a huge number of times the various values of ξ would be distributed (almost certainly very nearly) as indicated by P_ξ in eq. (215b), and the square root of the average of their squares would (almost certainly) lie very close to λ, and the average of their absolute values to $\overline{|\xi|}$.

155. The Varied Random Walk. The results just obtained contain the gist of the solution of all simple dispersion problems; certain generalizations of them are required, however.

First of all, suppose that the steps in a random walk vary in size but are numerous enough so that we can, without incurring appreciable error, assume that there are many of each individual size. Then formulas (215b) and (216a, b) will still hold but with a value of λ given by

$$\lambda = (\overline{l^2}N)^{\frac{1}{2}}, \tag{217}$$

where $\overline{l^2}$ denotes the mean of the squares of the variable step lengths.

To see this, consider first the simple instance of N_1 steps of length l_1 and N_2 of length l_2. Let ξ_1, ξ_2 denote the separate net displacements resulting from each kind of step. Then the probability functions for ξ_1 and ξ_2 are, by (215b),

$$P_{\xi_1} = \frac{1}{\lambda_1\sqrt{2\pi}} e^{-\frac{\xi_1{}^2}{2\lambda_1{}^2}}, \qquad P_{\xi_2} = \frac{1}{\lambda_2\sqrt{2\pi}} e^{-\frac{\xi_2{}^2}{2\lambda_2{}^3}},$$

where $\lambda_1 = l_1\sqrt{N_1}$, $\lambda_2 = l_2\sqrt{N_2}$; and what we desire is the probability for the resultant displacement, $\xi = \xi_1 + \xi_2$. Now, when ξ_1 has a certain value, ξ will lie in a given range $\delta\xi$ only if ξ_2 lies in a certain range of equal size, $\delta\xi_2 = \delta\xi$; and the chance that ξ_2 should do this is $P_{\xi_2}\,\delta\xi_2$. On the other hand, the chance that ξ_1 itself lies in a range $d\xi_1$ is $P_{\xi_1}\,d\xi_1$, independently of the probability for ξ_2 (the location of the specified range $\delta\xi_2$ shifting a little, of course, as ξ_1 shifts position in $d\xi_1$). Accordingly, the probability that simultaneously ξ_1 lies in $d\xi_1$ and also ξ in $\delta\xi$ is $P_{\xi_1}P_{\xi_2}\,\delta\xi\,d\xi_1$, and the total chance that ξ lies in $\delta\xi$ is

$$P_\xi\,\delta\xi = \int_{-\infty}^{\infty} (P_{\xi_1}P_{\xi_2}\,\delta\xi)\,d\xi_1 = \frac{\delta\xi}{2\pi\lambda_1\lambda_2}\int_{-\infty}^{\infty} e^{-\frac{\xi_1{}^2}{2\lambda_1{}^2}-\frac{\xi_2{}^2}{2\lambda_2{}^2}}d\xi_1.$$

Here $\xi_2 = \xi - \xi_1$ and is a variable, whereas ξ is to be kept constant in integrating. Evaluating the integral, we arrive again at (215b) for P_ξ, but with $\lambda^2 = N_1 l_1^2 + N_2 l_2^2 = N\overline{l^2}$, as stated in (217).

What we have proved here is a sort of addition theorem for error curves. The addition of other groups of steps can be effected in the same way; and clearly in the long run the same form for P_ξ must result if the steps are distributed continuously in length according to some definite distribution law.

In the second place, however, the steps may be taken in random directions in two or even three dimensions. In such a case the displacements in any two directions at right angles to each other are statistically independent. For, if we consider first a lot of steps whose components in two chosen directions have always one of the four sets of values (a, b) $(-a, b)$, $(a, -b)$, $(-a, -b)$, the plus and minus signs will occur at random independently for the two components, and the resultants of the two components of these steps will therefore be quite independent of each other. The same thing holds for any pair of values. Accordingly, each component will have a probability function of the same form as (215b) but with $\lambda^2 = \overline{l_1^2}N$, l_1 standing for the corresponding component of a step. If l denotes the total length of a step, we can also write, because of the obvious symmetry of the situation, either $\overline{l_1^2} = \frac{1}{2}\overline{l^2}$ or $\overline{l_1^2} = \frac{1}{3}\overline{l^2}$ and

$$\lambda^2 = \tfrac{1}{2}\overline{l^2}N \qquad \text{or} \qquad \lambda^2 = \tfrac{1}{3}\overline{l^2}N, \qquad (217a, b)$$

according as the motion occurs in two or three dimensions, N being the total number of steps.

The mean values for any component of the displacement are then given in terms of λ by (216a, b).

Since the various components are statistically independent, we can obtain the probability that a displacement ends in a given element of space merely by multiplying together the probabilities for the separate components; it is unnecessary to write down explicit formulas [but cf. (218a) below].

156. Dispersion of a Group of Molecules. The random-walk formulas could be applied at once to the motion of molecules in a gas if we could assume that each molecule after colliding with another is equally likely to move off in any direction. We could then say that a group of molecules initially in the neighborhood of a point will be distributed after a time t in such a way that an element of volume $d\xi\, d\eta\, d\zeta$, whose coordinates relative to the point of departure are ξ, η, ζ, contains a fraction $P\, d\xi\, d\eta\, d\zeta$ of them, where P is the product of three expressions such as (215b) or

$$P = \frac{1}{\lambda^3(2\pi)^{3/2}} e^{-\frac{\xi^2+\eta^2+\zeta^2}{2\lambda^2}}. \tag{218a}$$

For λ we should have, from (217b), in which $N = \bar{v}t/L$ or the number of free paths of mean length L that are executed by each molecule during the time t,

$$\lambda = \left(\overline{l^2}\,\bar{v}\,\frac{t}{3L}\right)^{1/2}, \tag{218b}$$

$\bar{v}$ being the mean molecular speed and $\overline{l^2}$ the mean of the squares of the free-path lengths.

These formulas are not accurate, however, because of the persistence of velocities that was discussed in Secs. 86 and 109. In consequence of this phenomenon, successive free paths are not statistically independent, but there is a moderate tendency for a succeeding path to favor the direction of the preceding one, and the dispersion is thereby increased. Accurate formulas for such cases are given in Fürth's book. In practical cases, however, it is better to apply the ordinary theory of diffusion; the persistence of velocities is then fully allowed for in the value assigned to the diffusion coefficient.

The formulas obtained here furnish, nevertheless, a convenient basis for a useful qualitative view of the process of dispersion, and for a rough numerical estimate in an actual case. The formulas correctly indicate that the molecules remain permanently densest near their point of departure but show a dispersion from it increasing as the square root of the time.

In using the formulas for a rough estimate, it is sufficient to set $\overline{l^2} = 2L^2$; this would be accurate if the distribution of the free paths were exponential. Equation (218b) in conjunction with (216a, b) above then gives for the mean numerical value, $\overline{|\xi|}$, and the root-mean-square value of any component of the molecular displacement

$$\overline{|\xi|} = \left(\frac{4L\bar{v}t}{3\pi}\right)^{1/2}, \qquad (\overline{\xi^2})^{1/2} = \left(\frac{2L\bar{v}t}{3}\right)^{1/2}.$$

According to these formulas, in air, where $L = 6.40 \times 10^{-6}$ cm and $\bar{v} = 45.9 \times 10^3$ cm/sec at 15°C and 1 atmosphere, $\overline{|\xi|} = 0.35\sqrt{t}$ cm, t being in seconds.

157. Molecular Scattering of Light. Another interesting case is that of the scattering of light, as in the case of scattered sunlight received from the clear sky. When a beam of light passes through a gas, each molecule is set into forced vibration and is thus caused to act as a source of radiation, and if the gas is rarefied, so that its molecules are distributed as if at random, the phase of the waves emitted by each molecule, being determined by the phase of the incident light at its position, will vary from one molecule to the next in a random manner. In certain directions the beams emitted by the different molecules nevertheless come together in a systematic manner and so give rise to the ordinary refracted beam and to the absorption of the incident beam; but in all other directions a random distribution of relative phases occurs, and the result is what we call scattered radiation. In such directions the various wave vectors combine like the steps in a random walk, and, since the energy is proportional to the squares of these vectors, the mean resultant energy comes out just equal to the sums of the energies emitted by the different molecules; just as according to (216a) the mean of ξ^2 is λ^2, and this in turn by (217) equals $N\overline{l^2}$ or the total number of steps multiplied by the mean square of their length.

It follows that the molecules of a rare gas can be treated as independent scatterers of light. Because of this fact a simple relation is easily found between the ordinary refractive index and the intensity of molecular scattering, as follows:*

According to electromagnetic theory the refractive index is

$$\mu = \sqrt{\epsilon_\nu},$$

where ϵ_ν is the effective dielectric constant for light of frequency ν; and in turn $\epsilon_\nu = 1 + 4\pi n \alpha_\nu$, where α_ν is the amplitude of electric moment induced in the molecule by unit amplitude of the electric vector in the beam, n being the number of molecules per cubic centimeter. Hence $\alpha_\nu = (\mu^2 - 1)/4\pi n$. On the other hand, electromagnetic theory gives for the number of ergs per second scattered by a molecule vibrating with moment amplitude α_ν

$$\frac{16}{3} \frac{\pi^4 \nu^4}{c^3} \alpha_\nu{}^2,$$

c being the speed of light. Multiplying this quantity by n and dividing by $c/8\pi$, which represents the mean energy incident on unit area per second in a monochromatic beam of unit amplitude, and inserting then the value just given for α_ν in terms of μ, we find for the fraction of the incident energy scattered from each cubic centimeter of the gas

---

* Cf. H. A. Lorentz, "Problems of Modern Physics," 1927, p. 60.

$$\frac{8}{3}\frac{\pi^3\nu^4}{c^4}\frac{(\mu^2-1)^2}{n^2} = \frac{32}{3}\frac{\pi^3(\mu-1)^2}{n\lambda^4},$$

since $\mu + 1 = 2$ nearly enough for a gas and $c/\nu = \lambda$, the wave length.

This formula could be used for the determination of n if better methods were not available. In optical experiments on scattering accuracy is hard to attain, but measurements of the absorption of sunlight in the earth's atmosphere, and also of scattering by pure gases in the laboratory, seem to be in satisfactory agreement with the formula. The phenomenon is of special interest because it depends essentially upon the granularity of the medium and would disappear entirely if the latter were made indefinitely fine-grained ($n = \infty$).

FLUCTUATIONS ABOUT AN AVERAGE

So far we have dealt with the dispersion of particles that start out in a group from a given initial position, or with problems that are mathematically of the same type. A rather different class of cases of great importance is characterized by the fact that a statistical equilibrium of some sort exists, and what we are interested in is the irregular local or momentary departures from it. The distribution in question may be a spatial one, such as the distribution in space of the molecules of a gas, or it may be temporal like the distribution in time of cosmic-ray impulses. More homely examples from kinetic theory are the spatial distribution of the separate molecular impulses that give rise to the pressure of a gas on the walls of its containing vessel, or the distribution of these impulses in time on a small bit of the wall. Most of the quantities encountered in physics are subject to such fluctuations, and what we ordinarily deal with is some sort of average value; even the length of the standard meter bar must be continually fluctuating to a minute extent.

Since in all such cases the basic mathematical theory is the same, we shall first develop it in the abstract and then take up special cases.

158. Theory of Fluctuations about an Average. Suppose that we have before us N elements of some sort and that they are distributed at random among s possible regions or ranges of value, which we shall for convenience call cells. The average number of elements in each cell is then N/s. Suppose, now, we ask for the probability that some particular number ν of them occur in a certain cell.

Since each of the N elements has a chance $1/s$ of falling into the given cell and a chance $\left(1 - \dfrac{1}{s}\right)$ of falling elsewhere, the chance that a particular group of ν of the elements falls into the given cell, and that at the same time all the other $N - \nu$ elements fall elsewhere, is $\left(\frac{1}{s}\right)^{\nu}\left(1 - \frac{1}{s}\right)^{N-\nu}$. Multiplying this expression by the number of different groups containing ν each that can be selected out of the N elements, each of which groups has an equal chance to be the one that falls in the given cell, we obtain as the total probability that there are just ν elements in this cell

$$P_{\nu} = \frac{N!}{\nu!(N - \nu)!}\left(\frac{1}{s}\right)^{\nu}\left(1 - \frac{1}{s}\right)^{N-\nu}. \tag{219}$$

The probability P_{ν} reaches its maximum value when ν equals $\bar{\nu}$, or whatever integer lies between $\bar{\nu} - 1 + \frac{1}{s}$ and $\bar{\nu} + \frac{1}{s}$, where $\bar{\nu} = \frac{N}{s}$ or the average number of elements per cell; if $\bar{\nu} + \frac{1}{s}$ is integral, P_{ν} takes on its maximum value both for $\nu = \bar{\nu} + \frac{1}{s}$ and for $\nu = \bar{\nu} + \frac{1}{s} - 1$. For the act of increasing ν to $\nu + 1$ multiplies P_{ν} by

$$\frac{N - \nu}{\nu + 1}\frac{1/s}{1 - \frac{1}{s}} = \frac{N - \nu}{(\nu + 1)(s - 1)} = 1 - \frac{s\left(\nu - \bar{\nu} + 1 - \frac{1}{s}\right)}{(\nu + 1)(s - 1)}$$

since $N = s\bar{\nu}$; hence $P_{\nu+1} \gtreqless P_{\nu}$ according as $\nu - \bar{\nu} + 1 - 1/s \lesseqgtr 0$ or as

$$\nu \lesseqgtr \bar{\nu} - 1 + \frac{1}{s}.$$

Now for a maximum at $\nu = \nu_m$ we must have

$$\frac{P_{\nu_m+1}}{P_{\nu_m}} \leqq 1, \qquad \frac{P_{\nu_m}}{P_{\nu_m-1}} \geqq 1.$$

Hence, according to the condition just deduced,

$$\nu_m \geqq \bar{\nu} - 1 + \frac{1}{s}, \qquad \nu_m - 1 \leqq \bar{\nu} - 1 + \frac{1}{s} \quad \text{or} \quad \nu_m \leqq \bar{\nu} + \frac{1}{s}.$$

In physical applications, however, N and s are usually so enormous that, as in the case of the random walk, a more convenient approximate formula is sufficiently accurate. Let us write (219) in the form

$$P_{\nu} = \frac{1}{\nu!}\frac{N(N - 1)\cdots(N - \nu + 1)}{s^{\nu}}\left(1 - \frac{1}{s}\right)^{N-\nu}.$$

Then, provided ν/N is negligibly small in comparison with unity, we can replace the second fraction by $N^\nu/s^\nu = \bar{\nu}^\nu$, and if $1/s$ is likewise very small we can set

$$\log\left[\left(1 - \frac{1}{s}\right)^{N-\nu}\right] = (N - \nu)\left(-\frac{1}{s} + \cdots\right) = -\frac{N}{s} = -\bar{\nu},$$

approximately. Then $\log P_\nu = -\log(\nu!) + \nu \log \bar{\nu} - \bar{\nu}$, and we have as an approximation Poisson's formula:

$$P_\nu = \frac{\bar{\nu}^\nu}{\nu!} e^{-\bar{\nu}}. \tag{220}$$

Here $\bar{\nu}$ is the average number or expectation of elements per cell; and the maximum value of P_ν still occurs at $\nu = \bar{\nu}$ or else at a value $\nu = \nu_m$ such that

$$\bar{\nu} - 1 + \frac{1}{s} \leqq \nu_m \leqq \bar{\nu} + \frac{1}{s}.$$

For practical use we require also some sort of measure of the spread of the values of ν about its average value. A convenient quantity for this purpose is the *root-mean-square* or *standard deviation*, whose value is

$$\delta \equiv [Av(\nu - \bar{\nu})^2]^{\frac{1}{2}} = \sqrt{\bar{\nu}}, \tag{221}$$

Av denoting the average value of whatever follows it. To obtain the value $\sqrt{\bar{\nu}}$ for δ, note first that

$$\sum_{\nu=0}^{\infty} \frac{\bar{\nu}^\nu}{\nu!} = e^{\bar{\nu}};$$

hence in

$$Av(\nu - \bar{\nu})^2 = \sum_{\nu=0}^{\infty} (\nu - \bar{\nu})^2 P_\nu = \sum \nu^2 P_\nu - 2\bar{\nu} \sum \nu P_\nu + \bar{\nu}^2 \sum P_\nu$$

by (220)

$$\sum_{\nu=0}^{\infty} \nu^2 P_\nu = e^{-\bar{\nu}} \sum \nu^2 \frac{\bar{\nu}^\nu}{\nu!} = e^{-\bar{\nu}} \bar{\nu} \frac{d}{d\bar{\nu}} \left(\bar{\nu} \frac{d}{d\bar{\nu}} \sum \frac{\bar{\nu}^\nu}{\nu!}\right)$$

$$= e^{-\bar{\nu}} \bar{\nu} \frac{d}{d\bar{\nu}} (\bar{\nu} e^{\bar{\nu}}) = \bar{\nu}^2 + \bar{\nu}.$$

In the same way can be obtained the otherwise obvious formulas

$$\sum_{\nu=0}^{\infty} {}' \nu P_\nu = \bar{\nu}, \qquad \sum_{\nu=0}^{\infty} {}' P_\nu = 1.$$

Hence

$$Av(\nu - \bar{\nu})^2 = \bar{\nu}^2 + \bar{\nu} - 2\bar{\nu}^2 + \bar{\nu}^2 = \bar{\nu}.$$

Thus as $\bar{\nu}$ is increased δ increases also, but the relative deviation $\delta/\bar{\nu}$ decreases as $1/\sqrt{\bar{\nu}}$; the peak of the P_ν curve at or near $\nu = \bar{\nu}$ actually broadens, but it becomes relatively narrower as compared with the magnitude of $\bar{\nu}$.

Finally, in case $\bar{\nu}$ itself is large and we are interested only in values of ν relatively close to $\bar{\nu}$, the probability for other values being practically zero, we can simplify still further by inserting the Stirling expression for log ν! from (214b).   Doing this, we obtain from (220)

$$\log P_\nu = \nu \log \bar{\nu} - \tfrac{1}{2} \log (2\pi\nu) - \nu \log \nu + \nu - \bar{\nu},$$

in which we can write

$$\nu \log \bar{\nu} - \nu \log \nu = -\nu \log \frac{\nu}{\bar{\nu}} = -\nu \log \left(1 + \frac{\nu - \bar{\nu}}{\bar{\nu}}\right)$$

$$= -\nu \left[\frac{\nu - \bar{\nu}}{\bar{\nu}} - \frac{1}{2}\left(\frac{\nu - \bar{\nu}}{\bar{\nu}}\right)^2 + \cdots \right] = -(\nu - \bar{\nu})\left[\frac{\nu - \bar{\nu}}{\bar{\nu}} - \right.$$
$$\left. \frac{1}{2}\left(\frac{\nu - \bar{\nu}}{\bar{\nu}}\right)^2 + \cdots \right] - \bar{\nu}\left[\frac{\nu - \bar{\nu}}{\bar{\nu}} - \frac{1}{2}\left(\frac{\nu - \bar{\nu}}{\bar{\nu}}\right)^2 + \cdots \right],$$

so that if we keep only the smallest power of $(\nu - \bar{\nu})$, we have

$$\log P_\nu = -\frac{1}{2}\frac{(\nu - \bar{\nu})^2}{\bar{\nu}} - \frac{1}{2}\log (2\pi\nu)$$

and

$$P_\nu = \frac{1}{\sqrt{2\pi\nu}} e^{-\frac{(\nu - \bar{\nu})^2}{2\bar{\nu}}}. \tag{222}$$

If ν is very close to $\bar{\nu}$, it can be replaced by $\bar{\nu}$ under the radical sign in this expression, and then we have a simple error curve for P_ν.

The standard deviation is, of course, still $\sqrt{\bar{\nu}}$, as given by eq. (221). From (222) it is clear again that when $\bar{\nu}$ is large P_ν has appreciable values only relatively near $\nu = \bar{\nu}$, i.e., when $(\nu - \bar{\nu})/\bar{\nu}$ is small.

In Fig. 62 are shown plots of P_ν according to (220) for $\bar{\nu} = \frac{1}{2}, 1, 2,$ and 5.   For $\bar{\nu} = 5$ the curve already shows a fair approximation to an error curve, the maximum falling at 4.5.

As a final comment, it may be remarked that the random-walk formula, (213) above, is really a special case of eq. (219), obtained by setting $s = 2$. In both cases the theory rests upon the fact that a selection occurs, guided by probability, between two alternatives. In phenomena of dispersion, however, we are interested in the differential result, the negative steps being subtracted from the positive ones; whereas in the type now under discussion we are interested only in one alternative, counting up the elements that fall into our selected cell and ignoring those that fall elsewhere.

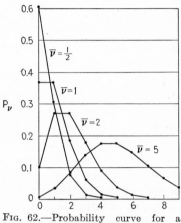

FIG. 62.—Probability curve for a fluctuation.

159. Examples of Molecular Fluctuations. The formulas just obtained can be applied at once to the distribution in space of the molecules of a gas in equilibrium. Any volume τ that is small compared with the whole volume contains on the average $\bar{\nu} = n\tau$ molecules, n being the mean density in molecules per unit volume; but momentarily it may contain any other number. The chance that it contains ν molecules is P_ν as given in (220) or (222). The root-mean-square deviation from the average value $n\tau$, according to (221), is $\delta = \sqrt{n\tau}$. As the volume is increased, the actual magnitude of the fluctuation increases as the square root of the volume, but its relative magnitude decreases in the same ratio. Equal fluctuations occur at equal values of the product of the volume under consideration into the pressure.

As a numerical illustration, a cube 1μ on edge drawn in air under standard conditions contains on the average $\bar{\nu} = 2.7 \times 10^7$ molecules, and this number fluctuates only by about $[2.7 \times 10^7]^{1/2}$ or 5,200 molecules, i.e., by $\frac{1}{52}$ per cent. If, however, the pressure is lowered to 1 mm Hg, i.e., to a Geissler vacuum, $\bar{\nu} = 3.6 \times 10^4$ and $\delta = 190$ molecules or 0.5 per cent, while at 0.001 mm, or in a cathode-ray vacuum, $\bar{\nu} = 36$ and $\delta = 6$, or 17 per cent.

Such fluctuations in density cause variations in the refractive index, and the latter may be regarded, if desired, as the cause of the molecular scattering of light by rarefied gases, a phenomenon which was treated above from an entirely different point of view. When a gas is brought close to its critical point, these fluctuations become enormously large and give rise to a characteristic opalescence; at such densities, however, the character of the phenomenon is greatly influenced by the intermolecular forces and requires other methods for its quantitative treatment.

Fluctuations in time can be similarly handled. They are most likely to lead to detectable effects in connection with molecular beams; such effects are easily observable in the case of electron emission, to which the same statistical theory applies.

Suppose, for example, that particles are emitted independently of each other at an average rate of $\bar{\nu}$ per second and that the number emitted during successive equal intervals of time is counted. Then P_ν as given by (220) represents the fractional part of these numbers that will in the long run be found to have a particular value ν. In many experiments of this sort $\bar{\nu}$ is much less than 1; this frequently happens, for example in observations with a Geiger counter upon cosmic rays. In such cases, during the majority of the intervals of time no particle at all is observed ($P_0 = e^{-\bar{\nu}} = 1$, nearly); during a small fraction P_1 or $\bar{\nu}e^{-\bar{\nu}}$ of the intervals just one is observed; during P_2, or $\frac{1}{2}\,\bar{\nu}^2 e^{-\bar{\nu}}$ of them, two (i.e., a "coincidence" occurs); etc. The factor $\frac{1}{2}$ in P_2 should be noted. It might have been thought that the chance of a coincidence would be simply P_1^2, since P_1 is the likelihood of each of the separate events; but in the train of thought leading up to this expectation each coincidence is really counted twice.

Several cases of this general sort have been studied in detail experimentally and the theoretical formulas have been shown to hold.

DIFFUSION AND THE BROWNIAN MOTION

160. The Brownian Motion. In 1828 a botanist, Robert Brown, observed that pollen grains suspended in water and viewed under the microscope showed an irregular dancing motion that never ceased. Experimenting further, he found that any kind of sufficiently small particle exhibited the same motion and concluded that the phenomenon must be due to some unknown inanimate cause. This motion is one of the most interesting phenomena in physics and is called, after its discoverer, the Brownian motion.

After various hypotheses as to its cause had been proposed, the modern view ascribing it to molecular agitation was put forward by Delsaux in 1877 and later by Gouy in 1888. Gouy showed that the motion was unaffected by variations of the intensity of the light falling on the particles, but that it increased in vigor when the viscosity of the supporting fluid was decreased. He was puzzled, however, by the fact that the apparent velocity of the particles is very much less than would be that of a gas molecule of the same mass according to kinetic theory; he did not realize that the true path of a Brownian particle is irregular on a minute scale far beyond the reach of the microscope and is, therefore, immensely longer than the apparent path that we see, which is only a sort of blur or average of the actual one.

161. Theory of the Brownian Motion. An adequate theory of the phenomenon just described was first developed by Einstein, who published in 1905 the equivalent of our eqs. (224a) and (224b) below. His method of procedure was to establish a connection between the properties of the Brownian motion and the viscosity of the medium, with a minimum use of molecular assumptions.

Let x, y, z denote the cartesian coordinates of a particle and $\dot{x}$, $\dot{y}$, $\dot{z}$, as usual, the corresponding components of its velocity. Then the ordinary viscous force on a suspended particle has the magnitude $-c\eta v$, where $v = (\dot{x}^2 + \dot{y}^2 + \dot{z}^2)^{1/2}$ while η denotes the viscosity of the medium and c is a constant depending upon the size and shape of the particle; the components of this force can be written $-c\eta\dot{x}$, $-c\eta\dot{y}$, $-c\eta\dot{z}$. Hence we can write as the equation of motion of the particle in the direction of x

$$m\ddot{x} = X - c\eta\dot{x}; \tag{223}$$

here m is its mass and X is the instantaneous x-component of force exerted upon it by the molecules of the medium over and above the ordinary viscous force $-c\eta\dot{x}$, which represents the average of the actual instantaneous forces. X will thus be highly irregular in value and as often negative as positive.

Now let us multiply this equation through by $x\,dt$ and then integrate it, thus:

$$m\int_0^t \ddot{x} x\,dt = \int_0^t Xx\,dt - c\eta \int_0^t \dot{x} x\,dt.$$

Here in the last term the differential is $\dot{x} x\,dt = d(\frac{1}{2} x^2)$, while in the first term it equals $(d\dot{x}/dt)x\,dt = x\,d\dot{x}$. Hence, if we integrate the first term once by parts, we obtain:

$$\Delta(mx\dot{x}) - m\int_0^t \dot{x}^2\,dt = \int_0^t Xx\,dt - \frac{1}{2} c\eta\Delta(x^2),$$

the symbol Δ denoting the change in a quantity from $t = 0$ to $t = t$.

In this equation the second term can be written $m\overline{\dot{x}^2}t$ and so increases ultimately in proportion to t; for $\dot{x}^2$ will have in the long run some definite average value, $\overline{\dot{x}^2}$. The first term, on the other hand, fluctuates rapidly because of the factor $\dot{x}$ in it; furthermore, since the motion must be in reality of the nature of a random walk, our general results in Sec. 155 indicate that the factor x in that term should increase only as $\sqrt{t}$. Consequently, in the long run the first term becomes negligible in comparison with the second, and can be dropped.

In $\int_0^t Xx\,dt$ the integrand Xx likewise fluctuates rapidly, and we might perhaps expect that, by the random-walk principle, this integral, also, should increase only as $\sqrt{t}$. In reality, however, the presence of the factor x causes the integrand itself, which here takes the place of the step length in the random walk, to tend to increase as $\sqrt{t}$, and the whole integral, therefore, increases at a faster rate; it must, in fact, increase as the first power of t, else the equation would furnish us with a uniform value of Δx^2 for all particles, whereas random-walk theory leads us to expect wide variations in this latter quantity.

Let us now supplement the integration just made by averaging the last equation for a large number N of different particles. This averaging process tends further to suppress the first term in the equation, which will be positive for some particles and negative for others. It also finally suppresses the third term $\int_0^t Xx\,dt$, since this term, too, must be positive for some particles and negative for others and so can only yield a random-walk residual proportional to $\sqrt{N}$ when we sum the equations, and hence a contribution to the average proportional to $1/\sqrt{N}$.

We thus obtain finally, as the result of averaging over a large number of particles,

$$-m\overline{\dot{x}^2}t = -\tfrac{1}{2}c\eta\,\overline{\Delta(x^2)},$$

$\overline{\Delta(x^2)}$ representing the average of $\Delta(x^2)$ for all particles. Now

$$m\overline{\dot{x}^2} = \tfrac{1}{3}\,m(\overline{\dot{x}^2} + \overline{\dot{y}^2} + \overline{\dot{z}^2}) = \tfrac{1}{3}\,m\overline{v^2},$$

and by the principle of the equipartition of energy the mean kinetic energy of the Brownian particle should be the same as that of a gas molecule, so that $\tfrac{1}{2}\,m\overline{v^2} = \tfrac{3}{2}\,kT$. Hence, if we assume that the particles start from the origin so that $\Delta(x^2) = x^2$, we have as the final result:

$$\overline{x^2} = \frac{2kT}{c\eta}\,t = 2kTUt. \qquad (224a)$$

Here k is the gas constant for one molecule, $U = 1/c\eta$ and represents the (dynamic) mobility* of the particle in the fluid or its steady velocity of drift under unit driving force, T is the absolute tem-

---

* Not to be confused with the mobility of an ion carrying a charge e in an electric field, as ordinarily defined, which is $|e|U$.

perature, and η is the viscosity of the medium; $\overline{x^2}$ represents the square of the x-component of the displacements during the time t, averaged either for a large number of particles moving simultaneously or for many successive displacements of a single particle.

The value of the coefficient c depends upon the shape of the particle. For a sphere whose radius a is much greater than the mean free path of the particles of the medium, $c = 6\pi a$, as first shown by Stokes; for such a particle the last equation becomes

$$\overline{x^2} = \frac{kT}{3\pi a\eta}\, t. \tag{224b}$$

The method of analysis that we have followed here gives us only $\overline{x^2}$, but not the distribution function for the separate values of x^2. Analyses more complete in detail have also been given, which start by writing down an actual integral for the equation of motion; the final result is then obtained by an application of the random-walk theory. The whole process is, however, so obviously of random-walk character that without giving such an analysis we may assert that, in accordance with the conclusions reached in Sec. 155, the probability function for the position of a Brownian particle after the lapse of a given interval is of the Gaussian error-curve form. This being granted, the actual function can then easily be written down if desired, care being taken to make it yield the correct value of $\overline{x^2}$ as given in eq. (224a). For example, we can write, as a special case of (218a) in Sec. 156, for the fraction of a group of Brownian particles starting out from the origin which after a time t lie in an element of volume $dx\,dy\,dz$, $P\,dx\,dy\,dz$, where

$$P = \frac{1}{(4\pi kTUt)^{3/2}} e^{-\frac{x^2+y^2+z^2}{4kTUt}}; \tag{225}$$

this makes $\int\int\int_{-\infty}^{\infty} P\,dx\,dy\,dz = 1$ and also

$$\overline{x^2} = \int\int\int_{-\infty}^{\infty} x^2 P\,dx\,dy\,dz = 2kTUt,$$

which agrees with (224a). Here, as we shall see in Sec. 163, kTU can also be replaced by D, the coefficient of diffusion of the particles in the supporting medium; and formulas such as (225) are, in fact, more commonly obtained by an application of the ordinary theory of diffusion.

162. Observations of Brownian Motion. Observations specifically designed to make a quantitative test of the kinetic-theory interpretation of the Brownian motion were instituted by Perrin in 1909. He worked with emulsions of gamboge or mastic made roughly uniform as to particle size by centrifugalizing.

Perrin first showed that the particles of such an emulsion did not settle entirely to the bottom of the vessel but actually remained distributed according to the law of the distribution of molecules in a force-field, as expressed by eq. (79c). A theoretical distribution similar to those observed by him is shown in Fig. 63. By counting particles at different heights h under the microscope, he verified that the mean distribution was exponential as theory requires, and assuming it to be proportional to $e^{-\frac{mgh}{kT}}$ he was able to calculate from his observations the number of particles in a gram molecule or $N_0 = R_M/k$, R_M being the gas constant for a gram molecule. In this way he found $N_0 = 6.5$ to 7.2×10^{23}. The necessary value of the mass m was obtained in several ingenious ways, as described in his interesting booklet.[*]

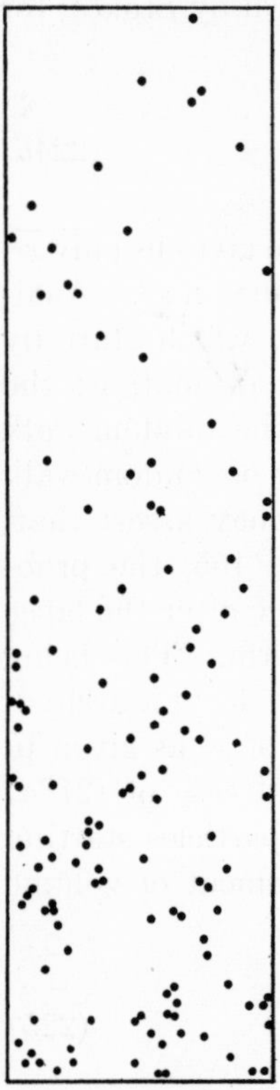

Fig. 63.—Statistical distribution under gravity (a theoretical example; cf. footnote on page 285).

Perrin then observed the motion of individual particles, projecting them for this purpose on a screen, and showed that the mean square of their horizontal displacements during a time t was approximately proportional to t, as is required by the theory that was developed in the last section; and he also showed that these displacements were distributed as nearly according to an error curve as could be expected. Finally, he measured the diameter of his particles and thereby secured, with the known viscosity of water, sufficient data for a second calculation of N_0 or R_M/k by means of the Einstein equation, (224b). The best value found in this manner was 6.8×10^{23}. Even the rotational displacements of the particles, for which a similar theory holds, could be followed in some of the drops of gamboge whose diameter was around 13 μ and which had visible spots on them; from these observations he deduced $N_0 = 6.5 \times 10^{23}$.

[*] J. B. Perrin, "Atoms," transl. by Hammick, 1916.

A theoretical track exhibiting the same general features as do some tracks actually observed by Perrin is shown in Fig. 64.* The successive positions of a particle at equal intervals of time are shown by dots; these are connected by lines in the figure, but the actual intervening path would be irregular and very complicated on a fine scale that is even beyond the reach of the microscope.

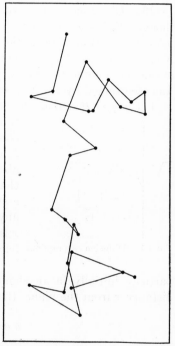

The fair agreement of Perrin's values of N_0 with those obtained by other methods, which were not very precise in his day, combined with the qualitative results that had been obtained by him and by others, completed such a striking confirmation of the kinetic theory that the last doubting Thomas seems to have been converted forthwith. Later work on the Brownian motion has yielded values of N_0 in still better agreement with what we now know to be the true value of this number; thus Pospišil (1927)† obtained from suspensions similar to those used by Perrin $N_0 = 6.22 \times 10^{23}$, as against the present value of 6.02×10^{23}.

In practice, instead of observing displacements in a given time, it is more convenient to note the time required for a particle as seen under the microscope to cross for the first time either of two parallel cross hairs, after crossing a third hair placed midway

Fig. 64.—Track of a Brownian particle (a theoretical track resembling observed ones; cf. footnote below).

between the outer two. The rather complicated analysis necessary for the interpretation of such observations was given by Fürth.‡

---

* The theoretical Brownian track was drawn as follows. First, a random sequence of 800 digits was prepared by copying the hundreds digits from the numbers in a telephone directory, taking names as they stood in alphabetical order. The row of digits was then divided into groups of three, and successive pairs of these groups were taken to represent x- and y-components of the successive displacements of the particle. The distribution shown in Fig. 63 was constructed by means of the same sequence of digits, one group being taken as the x-component of a particle, and the logarithm of the next as its y-component measured downward.

† Pospišil, *Ann. Physik*, **83**, 735 (1927).

‡ Fürth, *Ann. Physik*, **53**, 177 (1917), or his book, *loc. cit.*

The Brownian motion is also visible in the case of oil drops or other small particles suspended in a gas, and on a much larger scale than in liquids because of the lower viscosity. Several cases of this sort have been studied in detail, but the experimental difficulties are considerable, and the results have not always been entirely satisfactory from the theoretical standpoint.

163. Diffusion as a Random Walk. It is evident after a little thought that the ordinary process of diffusion must arise as a consequence of Brownian motions executed by the individual particles. A connection must exist, therefore, between quantities characteristic of this motion and the ordinary coefficient of diffusion; this connection was ascertained by Einstein in the following way.

Let $\varphi(\xi, t)\, d\xi$ denote the probability that a given particle during a

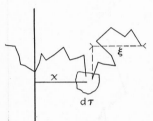

FIG. 65.—Diffusion as a random walk.

time t undergoes a displacement whose component in the x-direction lies between ξ and $\xi + d\xi$. We need assume nothing about the form of the function φ, except that $\varphi(-\xi, t) = \varphi(\xi, t)$. Then if we draw a small plane in the gas perpendicular to x, any particle starting at a positive distance x from the plane will have crossed it in the backward direction after a time t provided for this particle $\xi < -x$; and out of $n\, d\tau$

particles initially in an element of volume $d\tau$ located at a positive distance x from the plane, the number

$$n\, d\tau \int_{-\infty}^{-x} \varphi(\xi, t)\, d\xi$$

will cross the plane toward $-x$ in time t (cf. Fig. 65). The total number thus crossing unit area of the plane will be, therefore,

$$N_- = \int_0^\infty n(x)\, dx \int_{-\infty}^{-x} \varphi(\xi, t)\, d\xi = \int_0^\infty n(x)\, dx \int_x^\infty \varphi(\xi, t)\, d\xi$$

since $\varphi(-\xi, t) = \varphi(\xi, t)$. Here n has been indicated as a function $n(x)$ since we assume it to be nonuniform. Similarly the number

$$N_+ = \int_{-\infty}^0 n(x)\, dx \int_{-x}^\infty \varphi(\xi, t)\, d\xi = \int_0^\infty n(-x)\, dx \int_x^\infty \varphi(\xi, t)\, d\xi$$

cross toward $+x$. Thus, if we replace $n(x)$ by $n + x\, dn/dx$, where n now refers to the density of the particles at the plane, we find for the *net* transfer of particles toward $+x$

$$N = N_+ - N_- = -2\frac{dn}{dx}\int_0^\infty x\, dx \int_x^\infty \varphi(\xi, t)\, d\xi,$$

the terms containing n itself canceling, or, after integrating by parts with respect to x and noting that

$$\frac{d}{dx}\int_x^\infty \varphi(\xi, t)\, d\xi = -\varphi(x, t),$$

$$N = -\frac{dn}{dx}\left[x^2 \int_x^\infty \varphi(\xi, t)\, d\xi\right]\Big|_{x=0}^{x=\infty} - \frac{dn}{dx}\int_0^\infty x^2\varphi(x, t)\, dx$$

$$= -\frac{dn}{dx}\int_0^\infty \xi^2\varphi(\xi, t)\, d\xi = -\frac{1}{2}\frac{dn}{dx}\int_{-\infty}^\infty \xi^2\varphi(\xi, t)\, d\xi = -\frac{1}{2}\overline{\xi^2}\frac{dn}{dx},$$

$\overline{\xi^2}$ representing the mean squared displacement per particle in the direction of x. The integrated term vanished here because we may assume that $\int_x^\infty \varphi(\xi, t)\, d\xi$ vanishes as $x \to \infty$ faster than x^2 increases.

This number must now also equal $-tD\, dn/dx$ by the definition of the coefficient of diffusion, D. Hence $-Dt = -\frac{1}{2}\overline{\xi^2}$ or

$$\overline{\xi^2} = 2Dt. \tag{226}$$

(We need not worry about the backflow of the surrounding medium so long as the diffusing particles form only a small part of the total mass (cf. Secs. 106 to 108).)

By means of this equation either of the two quantities $\overline{\xi^2}$ or D can be calculated from observations upon the other. For example, we can calculate $\overline{\xi^2}$ for a gas molecule, whose displacements cannot be directly observed, although its value of D can be; or from the observed or theoretical value of $\overline{\xi^2}$ or $\overline{x^2}$ we can calculate the coefficient of diffusion for a Brownian particle.

The equation also shows again that the mean square of the displacement must be proportional to the time, this conclusion following here from the assumption of a constant coefficient of diffusion. If we compare the equation with $(224a)$, identifying $\overline{x^2}$ with $\overline{\xi^2}$, we obtain again the result that

$$D = kTU,$$

as was found from a different point of view in arriving at eq. $(170d)$ in Sec. 115.

164. Brownian Motion under External Force. Certain experiments involve a measurement of the rate of drift of a small particle through a fluid under the action of an external force; for example, in Millikan's determination of the electronic charge, measurements of this sort were made upon charged oil droplets suspended in air and either falling under their own weight or moving under the influence of an electric field. It is important to know what effect the Brownian motion may have upon such observations.

For such a particle we can write as the equation of motion of its x-coordinate, in place of (223) above,

$$m\ddot{x} = X - c\eta\dot{x} + F_x$$

where F_x is the component of a force F of external origin, which we shall assume to be steady. Let us change to new axes moving in such a way that, if x', y', z' are the new coordinates, we can write in terms of the time t

$$x = x' + u_x t, \qquad u_x = \frac{F_x}{c\eta},$$

with a similar equation for y and z. Then $\dot{x} = \dot{x}' + u_x$, $\ddot{x} = \ddot{x}'$, and the equation of motion for x' is

$$m\ddot{x}' = X - c\eta\dot{x}',$$

the term F_x having disappeared. This equation has now exactly the same form in terms of the new variable x' as (223) had in terms of the old one. A corresponding result is obtained for y and z. Hence we may conclude that relative to the new axes the particles will execute their usual Brownian motion unmodified by the presence of the field.

The motion of the particles is thus in general the vector sum of their ordinary Brownian motion and a uniform motion of drift under the force F at a velocity equal to $F/c\eta$ or to UF, where U is the (dynamic) mobility; one motion is simply superposed upon the other. The *average* vector displacement of a group of particles in time t is, therefore, simply UFt, unaffected by the Brownian motion, which by itself gives an average displacement of zero.

In practice, however, it is much more convenient to measure, not displacements in a given time, but rather the time required to go a given distance, for example, the time required by a particle as seen under the microscope to traverse the distance between two parallel cross hairs. If there were no Brownian motion, this time, for a distance a, would be a/UF, and so would give immediately the value of U. It is important to investigate whether the Brownian motion, which causes these times of transit to fluctuate, also alters their mean value.

The distribution of such times of transit can be inferred from results already obtained above by means of the following argument, as was shown by Schrödinger.* Suppose a group of N particles start out at time $t = 0$ from a point, which we shall take as the origin of coordinates, and drift thereafter under a constant external force F at mean speed $u = UF$ toward the geometrical plane $x = a$ (cf. Fig. 66). Then at time t the group will have become both dispersed, in conse-

* SCHRÖDINGER. *Physik. Zeits.*, **16**, 289 (1915).

quence of their Brownian motion, and also displaced a mean distance ut toward $+x$. Their density in terms of x will accordingly be $\int\int P\,dy\,dz$, where P is given by (225) in Sec. 161 with x replaced by x' or $x - ut$; it can be written

$$\rho_x = \frac{N}{(4\pi Dt)^{\frac12}}\, e^{-\frac{(x - ut)^2}{4Dt}}$$

with $D = kTU$ (cf. end of the last section). Here $\rho_x\,dx$ represents the fraction of the particles that lie in the range dx, and the value of the constant factor can be verified by showing that $\int_{-\infty}^{\infty} \rho_x\,dx = N.$

Now we can find the rate at which the particles make their first transits across the plane $x = a$ if we can find a general expression for the total number of those that at any moment have crossed it at least once; the latter we shall call for brevity "crossed" particles. Obviously all particles that lie beyond the plane at a time t have crossed at one time or another; hence at points beyond the plane the density of crossed particles is simply ρ_x, and, in particular, at the plane itself it is

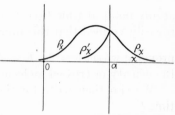

FIG. 66.—Drift plus Brownian motion.

$$(\rho_x)_a = \frac{N}{(4\pi Dt)^{\frac12}}\, e^{-\frac{(a - ut)^2}{4Dt}}.$$

There will be others, however, which after crossing toward the right, i.e., toward $+x$, subsequently crossed back to the left again; let their density be denoted by ρ'_x. Some of them may have crossed back and forth several times. We know the value of ρ'_x only at $x = a$, since there it must equal $(\rho_x)_a$; for the crossed molecules actually originate at the plane and then quickly scatter away from it in both directions, so that their density, viewed as a function of x, must be continuous at the plane. If there were no external force these particles would scatter equally in all directions, and their density at any moment would, therefore, be symmetrical on the two sides of the plane. The drift due to the force, however, disturbs this symmetry, and we are, therefore, compelled to resort to some special device in order to find a general expression for ρ'_x.

We may regard the crossed molecules to the left of the plane as having entered that region through the layer of fluid next to the plane and having undergone thereafter a combined Brownian dispersion and drift. Their density will, therefore, be uniquely determined by the values at all times of their density in the layer at the plane, together with the fact that their density is 0 at $x = -\infty$ and also vanishes everywhere at $t = 0$. If we can find a function that satisfies these requirements and also represents a distribution set up by Brownian motion under the simultaneous influence of the external force, this function will be the desired density.

Now such a function is easily guessed. A group of N' molecules starting at time $t = 0$ at a point $x = b$ would have a density

$$\rho_x' = \frac{B}{(4\pi\,Dt)^{1/2}}\, e^{-\frac{(x-b-ut)^2}{4Dt}}$$

at any point at time t (cf. the similar expression for ρ_x above); and it is easily verified that this function of x and t reduces to $(\rho_x)_a$ at $x = a$ provided we set $b = 2a,\ B = Ne^{\frac{au}{D}}$. Hence ρ_x' as so defined represents the density of crossed molecules also at points where $x < a$.

We can then write for the total number of crossed molecules at time t

$$N' = \int_{-\infty}^{a} \rho_x'\, dx + \int_{a}^{\infty} \rho_x\, dx = \frac{N}{\sqrt{\pi}} \left\{ e^{\frac{au}{D}} \int_{-\infty}^{\alpha} e^{-y^2}\, dy + \int_{\beta}^{\infty} e^{-y^2}\, dy \right\}$$

after substituting $b = 2a$ and $(x - 2a - ut)/(4Dt)^{1/2} = y$ in the first integral and $(x - ut)/(4Dt)^{1/2} = y$ in the second and writing

$$\alpha = -\frac{a + ut}{(4Dt)^{1/2}}, \qquad \beta = \frac{a - ut}{(4Dt)^{1/2}}.$$

The derivative of this expression with respect to t is then, finally, the number of particles that cross the plane for the first time in a second; it is

$$\frac{dN'}{dt} = \frac{N}{\sqrt{\pi}} \left[e^{\frac{au}{D} - \alpha^2} \frac{d\alpha}{dt} - e^{-\beta^2} \frac{d\beta}{dt} \right] = \frac{aN}{\sqrt{4\pi D}} \frac{1}{t^{3/2}} e^{-\frac{(a - ut)^2}{4Dt}}.$$

The mean time of transit from the origin to the plane is then[*]

$$\bar{t} = \frac{1}{N} \int_{0}^{\infty} t\, \frac{dN'}{dt}\, dt = \frac{a}{\sqrt{4\pi D}} \int_{0}^{\infty} \frac{dt}{\sqrt{t}}\, e^{-\frac{(a - ut)^2}{4Dt}} = \frac{a}{u}.$$

This is exactly what the mean time would be if all particles moved at the uniform drift rate u.

The presence of the Brownian motion thus requires only the making of many observations of the times of transit in order to obtain a good average, no correction in the final result itself being required.

---

[*] The integral can be reduced to $\displaystyle\int_{0}^{\infty} e^{x^2 - \frac{c^2}{x^2}}\, dx = (\sqrt{\pi}/2)e^{-2c}.$

CHAPTER VIII

PROPERTIES OF GASES AT LOW DENSITIES

In our treatment of transport phenomena we assumed the mean free path to be small compared with distances in which we are interested from the physical standpoint. Under such conditions the properties of the gas depend essentially upon the frequency and character of the intermolecular collisions.

As the pressure is lowered, however, with any given experimental arrangement, there must come a time when this condition is no longer satisfied, and a departure from the laws of high-pressure behavior would then be expected. As the density sinks, intermolecular collisions must lose their importance, and finally there must come a stage when such collisions are actually rare in comparison with collisions of gas molecules with other bodies such as the walls of the containing vessel. Each molecule will then act independently of all the others in giving rise to the properties of the gas.

A gas in this latter condition will be said to exhibit *free-molecule* behavior, in order to have a convenient term of reference. The term "molecular" has often been used in the same sense, contrasting with the "mass" or "molar" character of ordinary gaseous behavior.

Experimentally it has been found that at low densities gases actually do exhibit novel properties. As the density is lowered, the gas seems to lose its grip, so to speak, upon solid surfaces; in viscous flow it begins to slip over the surface, and in the conduction of heat a discontinuity of temperature develops at the boundary of the gas. Curious force-actions may also manifest themselves, such as are responsible for the motion of those radiometer vanes that are frequently seen spinning in the sunshine in jewelers' windows.

It is convenient to discuss the theory of all these phenomena as a group. If we knew more about the interaction of gas molecules with solid and liquid surfaces, it might be logical to begin with a study of the laws of this interaction. We know little as yet, however, concerning these laws, and hence it seems preferable to follow the historical order and to take up in succession the subject of viscosity at low density, then the conduction of heat, and finally that of thermal creep and its application to the elucidation of the radiometer. In dealing with the first two subjects, it will be convenient to take up first the initial departure from ordinary laws as the density is lowered, and then the behavior of the gas when in the free-molecule condition. Creep and the radiometer effects, on the other hand, are effectively limited to densities that are only moderately low.

MOTION IN RAREFIED GASES

165. Viscous Slip.   In 1875 Kundt and Warburg* performed a series of experiments upon the damping of a vibrating disk by a surrounding gas and found that at low pressures the damping decreased; this effect they ascribed to a slipping of the gas over the walls of the tube, such as had sometimes been supposed to occur with liquids. Their interpretation of the phenomenon has been confirmed by later work, both experimental and theoretical.

Presumably any such slipping would be proportional to the velocity gradient next to the wall of the tube, at least so long as this gradient is small.   Accordingly, if we write v_0 for that component of the mass velocity which varies and dv_0/dz for its gradient, taken positive in the direction away from the wall, the velocity of slip u relative to the wall will have the direction of v_0 and can be written

$$u = \zeta \frac{dv_0}{dz}, \qquad (227)$$

where ζ is a constant and is commonly called the *coefficient of slip*. Obviously ζ represents a length; it can be pictured by noting that the motion is the same as if the wall were displaced backward a distance ζ with the velocity gradient extending uniformly right up to zero velocity at the wall.   Kundt and Warburg found the magnitude of ζ to be of the order of the molecular mean free path in the gas, and, like the latter, inversely proportional to the pressure.

Instead of the approach that we have chosen here, the process occurring in the gas next to the wall is frequently analyzed in terms of the forces, following the procedure employed by Helmholtz in the case of liquids.   The viscous traction in the gas, which is $\eta \, dv_0/dz$ in terms of the ordinary coefficient of viscosity η, must, in steady motion, be equal to the traction or force per unit area exerted by the gas on the wall; and for the latter we can write ϵu, where ϵ is a constant called the coefficient of external friction of the gas on the wall.   Thus $\epsilon u = \eta \, dv/dz$, and by comparison with (227) we see that

$$\zeta = \frac{\eta}{\epsilon}.$$

* Kundt and Warburg. *Ann. Physik.* **155**, 337 (1875).

166. Steady Flow with Slip. Formulas pertaining to viscous phenomena are easily corrected for the existence of slip. We shall illustrate this by obtaining the correction to Poiseuille's formula for the steady flow of a gas through a long straight tube of circular cross section.*

In such a tube the velocity v of the gas across any cross section is a function of the radial distance r from the axis (cf. Fig. 67). Consider the gas inside an inner cylinder drawn coaxial with the tube and with length dx and radius r. To make steady flow possible, the net force due to the pres-

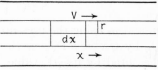

FIG. 67.—Flow along a tube.

sure p on the ends of this mass of gas must be equilibrated by the viscous drag over its sides; hence, equating forces in the x-direction along the tube,

$$-\pi r^2 \frac{dp}{dx} = -2\pi r \eta \frac{dv}{dr}, \qquad \frac{dv}{dr} = \frac{r}{2\eta} \frac{dp}{dx},$$

and by integration

$$v = \frac{r^2}{4\eta} \frac{dp}{dx} + C.$$

Now, when $r = a$, the radius of the tube, we have $v = u$, the velocity of slip, or, by (227),

$$v = \zeta \frac{dv}{dz} = -\zeta \frac{dv}{dr}.$$

Hence, according to the expression just found for dv/dr, when $r = a$, $v = -\frac{1}{2} (\zeta a/\eta) \, dp/dx$. The formula found for v reduces to this if we give to C such a value that

$$v = -\frac{1}{4\eta} (a^2 - r^2 + 2\zeta a) \frac{dp}{dx}.$$

We then obtain, after multiplying through by the density, which can be written p/RT in terms of the gas constant R for a gram and the absolute temperature T, for the total mass of gas flowing past any cross section of the tube per second,

$$Q_m = \frac{p}{RT} \int_0^a 2\pi r v \, dr = -\frac{\pi}{8} \frac{a^4 p}{\eta RT} \left(1 + 4 \frac{\zeta}{a}\right) \frac{dp}{dx}.$$

Now in the steady state Q_m must be the same at all points; and, according to Kundt and Warburg, we can write $\zeta = \zeta_1/p$, where ζ_1

---

* The flow is assumed to be slow enough to avoid turbulence.

is independent of p and so of x (the temperature being assumed uniform). Then, if we multiply the last equation through by dx and integrate along the tube, writing $\int_0^l dx = l$, the length of the tube, we obtain

$$l\,Q_m = \frac{\pi}{8}\frac{a^4}{\eta RT}\left[\frac{1}{2}(p_1^2 - p_2^2) + 4\frac{\zeta_1}{a}(p_1 - p_2)\right],$$

p_1 and p_2 being the pressures at the ends of the tube; or, if we replace Q_m by $Q_{pV} = RTQ_m$ or the amount of gas that passes per second as measured by its pV value, and if we also introduce the mean of the end pressures, $\bar{p} = (p_1 + p_2)/2$, we have

$$Q_{pV} = \frac{\pi}{8}\frac{a^4}{\eta l}\left(\bar{p} + 4\frac{\zeta_1}{a}\right)(p_1 - p_2). \tag{228}$$

Absolute units have been assumed throughout in deducing this equation, but it is obviously permissible in expressing Q_{pV} to employ any other unit for the pressure, provided the same unit is also used for $(p_1 - p_2)$.

In this formula the term $4\zeta_1/a$ may be regarded as an increment that must be added to the actual mean pressure to allow for the advantageous effects of slip. At low pressures this term may be relatively large, but the formula itself is likely to fail when the ratio ζ_1/pa or ζ/a is not small, for then normal conditions cannot develop in the central part of the tube, and, furthermore, the curvature of the wall is then likely to be of importance.

Problems. 1. In the steady flow of a gas between two parallel plane surfaces, the velocity being everywhere in the same direction, show that the amount of gas transferred per second for each unit of width perpendicular to its velocity, measured in terms of its pV value, is (except, of course, near the edges of the planes)

$$Q_{pV} = \frac{1}{12}\frac{w^3}{\eta l}\left(\bar{p} + 6\frac{\zeta_1}{w}\right)(p_1 - p_2), \tag{228a}$$

w being the distance between the surfaces and l their length in the direction of flow, η the viscosity of the gas, $\bar{p}$ its mean pressure and $p_1 - p_2$ the total drop in pressure, $\zeta_1/p = \zeta$, the slip distance at each surface; c.g.s. units are assumed.

2. If one plate is at rest and the other moving tangentially at uniform speed U, show that in the notation just defined the viscous drag upon each plate is (except near the edges, and provided the plates are relatively close together and the gas pressure uniform)

$$F = \frac{\eta U}{w + 2\zeta} \tag{229}$$

dynes per unit area. (HINT: The viscous stress must be the same across any plane parallel to the plates and hence equal to $\eta\, dv_0/dx$.)

167. Maxwell's Theory of Slip. It should be possible to calculate the magnitude of the slip distance ζ in a gas from kinetic theory. On this point the theory developed by Maxwell in 1879, although not perfect, is still the best that we have. He utilized for the purpose the results of an elaborate analysis that he had previously made of the stresses in a moving gas, but his reasoning can also be thrown into a very simple form.*

Consider the usual case of a gas having a mass velocity v_0, whose direction is everywhere the same but whose magnitude varies in some perpendicular direction; let us take the direction of the velocity as that of the y-axis and the direction of its variation as that of x. Let the gas be bounded at the left by a fixed plane surface perpendicular to x, and beyond a certain distance from this surface suppose that the velocity gradient dv_0/dx is sensibly uniform.

Then just next to the surface we can group the molecules into two streams, of which one consists of molecules that are approaching the surface, and the other of those that have just struck it and are now receding from it; and we can view the viscous drag on the surface as arising from the difference between the tangential momentum brought up by the approaching stream and that carried away by the receding one. Maxwell now makes the rather bold assumption that the approaching stream is of the same character as it is in the midst of the gas. If the same thing were true of the receding stream as well, and if the gas at the surface were on the whole at rest, it would then necessarily be true that the impinging molecules were reflected on the average with their tangential components of velocity just reversed; for it is these components that are responsible for the viscous stress, and in the midst of the gas each of the two streams gives rise to just half of this stress. Such a law of reflection is very unlikely, however. Let us accordingly make with Maxwell the more general assumption that on striking the surface the molecules give to it, on the average, the fraction f of their tangential momentum (or of their tangential momentum relative to the surface in case the latter is in motion). To restore the viscous force to its proper value, we must then allow the gas to slip over the surface. Let us, therefore, assume with Maxwell that the approaching stream exhibits a velocity gradient

---

* Cf. MILLIKAN, *Phys. Rev.*, **21**, 217 (1923).

extending uniformly up to some value $v_0 = u$ at the surface (cf. Fig. 68).

The tangential momentum brought up to unit area of the surface in a second by the approaching molecules can then be analyzed into two parts. Relative to a frame of reference moving with velocity u, momentum will be brought up equal in magnitude to that which is transmitted elsewhere in the gas by the corresponding molecular stream, or to $\frac{1}{2}\,\eta\,dv_0/dx$ per unit area per second, η being the coefficient of viscosity; to this must then be added the momentum due to the slip velocity u, of amount $\frac{1}{4}$ $nm\bar{v}u$, $\frac{1}{4}\,n\bar{v}$ representing by (72a) in Sec. 37 the number of molecules incident per second on unit area of a plane in a gas containing n molecules per unit volume whose mean speed is $\bar{v}$.

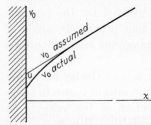

FIG. 68.—Velocity gradient near the wall.

According to our assumptions, therefore, writing $nm = \rho$, the density, and equating momentum given up to the surface to that transmitted across parallel planes in the gas, we have

$$f\left(\frac{1}{2}\,\eta\,\frac{dv_0}{dx} + \frac{1}{4}\,\rho\bar{v}u\right) = \eta\,\frac{dv_0}{dx}.$$

Hence u must have the value

$$u = 2\,\frac{2 - f}{f}\,\frac{\eta}{\rho\bar{v}}\,\frac{dv_0}{dx};$$

and for the coefficient of slip, as defined in (227), after inserting $\rho = p/RT$ and $\bar{v} = 2(2RT/\pi)^{1/2}$ from (66a) in Sec. 30, we find

$$\zeta = \frac{2 - f}{f}\,\sqrt{\frac{\pi}{2}}\,\frac{\eta}{p}\,\sqrt{RT}, \tag{230a}$$

or, if we insert $\eta = c\rho\bar{v}L$ from (126a, b) in Sec. 86,

$$\zeta = 2c\,\frac{2 - f}{f}\,L. \tag{230b}$$

Here T = absolute temperature, R = gas constant for a gram, p = pressure, L = mean free path, and c is a number lying between 0.491 and 0.499, so that very nearly $2c = 1$.

168. Discussion of the Slip Formula. According to (230b), ζ is always of the order of one mean free path and must, like the latter, vary at a given temperature in inverse ratio with the pressure, as was originally found experimentally by Kundt and Warburg.

The value of f, the transfer ratio for momentum, will presumably depend upon the character of the interaction between the gas molecules and the surface; it may vary with the temperature. We can imagine a surface that is absolutely smooth and reflects the molecules "specularly" with no change in their tangential velocities; in such a case $f = 0$ and $\zeta = \infty$, viscosity being unable to get a grip upon the wall at all. On the other hand, we can imagine the molecules to be reflected without regard to their directions of incidence and therefore with complete loss of their initial average tangential velocity. They might, for instance, be reflected diffusely according to the same cosine law that holds for the diffuse reflection of light or for the effusion of molecules from a hole [cf. (73a) in Sec. 37], being distributed, therefore, as if they came from a maxwellian gas at rest relative to the wall. In this latter case we should have $f = 1$, all of the incident momentum being given up to the wall, and

$$ \zeta = \sqrt{\frac{\pi}{2}} \frac{\eta}{p} \sqrt{RT} = 2cL, \tag{230c} $$

so that ζ is almost equal to L.

Maxwell suggested that diffuse reflection might result from free penetration of the gas molecules into interstices in the surface, where they would strike a number of times before escaping. An approach to such reflection would result also from roughness of the surface, except that at large angles of incidence chiefly the tips of elevations would be visible to an oncoming molecule and something like specular reflection should occur. Another possibility is that the molecules might condense on the surface and then re-evaporate after coming into thermal equilibrium with it; in some cases there is, in fact, definite experimental evidence for such an occurrence. In the general case, Maxwell himself interpreted a fractional value of f as meaning that a fraction f of the surface reflects diffusely and the remainder specularly; but such a special interpretation is obviously unnecessary. Even a value of f exceeding unity is conceivable, indicating that the molecules are reflected on the average with a partial reversal of their tangential velocities; for example, uniform reversal would be produced by reflection from a rectangular-zigzag surface.

In comparing (230b) and (230c) with expressions given elsewhere it must not be overlooked that L is here calculated using the modern formulas, (126a, b). So many different formulas have been used for L during the last thirty years that it is scarcely sufficient, in writing equations, to define a certain symbol as standing for the mean free path without specifying its assumed relation to the viscosity or to some other measurable quantity.

It should be remembered, furthermore, that the analysis leading up to (230a, b, c) is far from rigorous; this was, in fact, emphasized by Maxwell. At least the *returning* stream of molecules is almost certainly modified from the maxwellian form in quite a different manner than is the corresponding stream in the midst of the gas.

It may be of interest to note that the slip speed u will not usually be the same as the actual mean velocity of the gas at the wall.

169. Observations of Slip. Interesting direct measurements of slip were made by Timiriazeff,[*] using the method of two coaxial cylinders with the gas between them. In this method the inner cylinder is suspended elastically, and from its steady deflection when the outer one is revolved about it at constant speed, the viscous torque exerted upon either cylinder by the gas is calculated, and from this in turn the viscosity. In Timiriazeff's apparatus both cylinders were nickeled, and air, carbon dioxide, and hydrogen were employed in turn. He observed that as the pressure was reduced from atmospheric, the torque at first remained constant, illustrating the constancy of the ordinary viscosity; then it dropped rapidly as the slip distance ζ became comparable with the intercylinder distance w. A formula equivalent to (229) in Sec. 166 was deduced on the assumption that the narrow space between the cylinders could be treated as if bounded by planes, and this formula was found to hold closely even down to pressures at which it might be expected to fail; the observed value of ζ was comparable in magnitude to the mean free path in the gas (about 6.8, 5, and 10×10^{-6} cm at atmospheric pressure for the three gases in the order named).

The most accurate measurements of slip, however, are undoubtedly those made by Stacy[†] and by Van Dyke[†] under Millikan's supervision. They used the coaxial-cylinder method but employed the accurate formula for it; the theory usually given, which itself requires a little thought,[‡] is readily modified to allow for slip and then gives for the torque on unit length of the inner cylinder, which is suspended at rest on an elastic suspension, while the outer cylinder revolves around it at constant speed

$$\frac{8\pi^2 \eta r_1^2 r_2^2 \nu}{r_2^2 - r_1^2 + 2\zeta \dfrac{r_1^3 + r_2^3}{r_1 r_2}}$$

[*] Timiriazeff, *Ann. Physik*, **40**, 971 (1913).
[†] Stacy, *Phys. Rev.*, **21**, 239 (1923); Van Dyke, *Phys. Rev.*, **21**, 250 (1923).
[‡] Cf. Newman and Searle, "General Properties of Matter."

in terms of the viscosity η of the gas, the radii r_1 and r_2 of the cylinders, and the speed of the outer one, ν, in turns per second.

The cylinders were made of brass but could be coated with oil or shellac to obtain the slip on such surfaces as well as upon the bare metal. One observation was made at atmospheric pressure, at which the slip distance is negligible, and then another at a pressure slightly above 1 mm, which was low enough to produce a considerable drop in the torque and yet high enough to make the ordinary slip theory applicable, $[\zeta/(r_2 - r_1)$ being fairly small]; from these two observations both the value of ζ corresponding to the low pressure and the value of η could be calculated, and ζ for a pressure of 76 cm was then calculated on the assumption that it is inversely proportional to the pressure.

In a paper in the same volume of the *Physical Review** Millikan gives a table of values of Maxwell's reflection coefficient f which were calculated by substituting in the equivalent of our eq. (230a) in Sec. 167 the values of ζ obtained by the observers just mentioned and a few others. His table is repeated below, with the addition of the corresponding values of ζ/L, the ratio of the observed slip distance to the mean free path as calculated from (230b) with $2c$ set equal to 0.998. The oil referred to in the table is the watch oil that was used in Millikan's well-known oil-drop work on the electron.

	$\dfrac{f}{(\%)}$	$\dfrac{\zeta}{L}$
Air or CO_2 on machined brass or old shellac........	100	1.00
Air on mercury.................................	100	1.00
Air on oil..	89.5	1.23
CO_2 on oil......................................	92	1.17
Hydrogen on oil..............................	92.5	1.16
Air on glass....................................	89	1.24
Helium on oil..................................	87.4	1.29
Air on fresh shellac............................	79	1.53

The value, $f = 0.89$ for glass, was calculated chiefly from Knudsen's data for H_2, O_2, and CO_2 on the assumption that ζ is proportional to the mean free path. Knudsen himself, however, found no evidence of slip of these gases in the free-molecule case; and, as regards H_2, this conclusion was confirmed by Gaede. A direct study of the slip of air on glass would seem to be of interest.

Such values of f must be received with a certain caution, however. In the first place, the difference, $1 - f$, although commonly said to

---

* MILLIKAN, *Phys. Rev.*, **21**, 217 (1923).

represent specular reflection of the fraction $1 - f$ of the molecules, presumably represents in reality only a certain preponderance of forward directions in the scattering process; in the second place, Maxwell's formula for ζ cannot be said to be rigorously established until the state of the gas next to a solid boundary has been more accurately worked out. (The latter uncertainty, of course, does not affect the values of ζ/L.) As to the latter point, however, it may be noted that Blankenstein* obtained in a similar way values of f ranging from 0.98 to 1.00 for H_2, He, air, and CO_2 reflected from polished oxidized silver, and obtained values only 1 to 3 per cent lower when he repeated his observations at pressures of 0.0005 to 0.002 mm, at which the free-molecule formula (232b) should hold. Since the latter formula is not subject to the same uncertainty as is Maxwell's, this agreement of values of f obtained at high and low pressures tends to confirm Maxwell's formula for ζ at the higher pressure.

170. Free-molecule Viscosity. The concept of slip as usually understood is applicable only when the layer of gas is many mean free paths thick so that ordinary viscous motion can come into exist-

$$\xrightarrow{\quad\quad} U$$
$$\xrightarrow{\quad} u_2 \quad\quad 2$$

$$\xrightarrow{\quad} u_1$$
$$\overline{(At\ rest)} \quad\quad 1$$

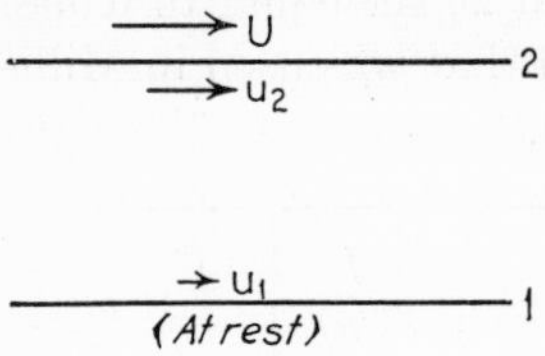

Fig. 69.—Viscous drag on a plate.

ence in the more distant part of it. When this condition is not satisfied, the phenomenon becomes more complicated; its theory has not been worked out for the general case. The situation becomes simple again, however, in the extreme free-molecule case in which the density is low enough, or the gas layer thin enough, so that the collisions of molecules with each other may be entirely neglected in comparison with their impacts upon the walls. This case is easy to treat.

As a first example, consider two parallel plates separated by a distance w that is very small as compared with the mean free path in the gas between them, and let the upper plate be moving tangentially with the velocity U (cf. Fig. 69). Under these circumstances each molecule, after striking one plate, moves at constant velocity until it strikes the other. Hence, if u_1 is the mean tangential component of velocity as the molecules leave the lower plate, this will also be their mean component as they arrive at the upper, and similarly we can write u_2 for their mean tangential component as they leave the upper or arrive at the lower.

Then, if f_1, f_2 denote the coefficients of momentum transfer at the lower and upper plates, respectively, defined as in Sec. 167, the

---

* BLANKENSTEIN, *Phys. Rev.*, **22**, 582 (1923).

momentum given to unit area of the upper plate in a second is

$$\Gamma_1 f_2 (u_1 - U), \tag{231}$$

where Γ_1 is the mass of gas that strikes unit area of the plate per second. An amount of momentum equal to this is lost by the molecules themselves, and this loss can obviously be written $\Gamma_1(u_1 - u_2)$. Hence it must be that

$$u_1 - u_2 = f_2(u_1 - U).$$

Similarly at the lower plate, which is at rest, we find

$$u_2 - u_1 = f_1 u_2.$$

From these two equations we find that

$$u_1 = \frac{f_2(1 - f_1)}{f_1 + f_2 - f_1 f_2} U, \qquad u_2 = \frac{f_2}{f_1 + f_2 - f_1 f_2} U.$$

Now let us make the usual assumption that the molecular velocities in the gas are distributed very nearly in the maxwellian manner, corresponding to some absolute temperature T. This will certainly be true so long as U is small as compared with the molecular speeds. Then, by (72b) in Sec. 37, $\Gamma_1 = p/(2\pi R T)^{\frac{1}{2}}$ in terms of the pressure p and the gas constant R for a gram; hence expression (231) for the momentum given to the upper plate per unit area per second can be written in the form $-ZU$, where

$$Z = \frac{f_1 f_2}{f_1 + f_2 - f_1 f_2} \frac{p}{(2\pi R T)^{\frac{1}{2}}}. \tag{232a}$$

The expression $-ZU$ also represents, of course, the momentum in the opposite direction that is given per second to the lower plate. If the plates are alike ($f_1 = f_2 = f$),

$$Z = \frac{f}{2 - f} \frac{p}{(2\pi R T)^{\frac{1}{2}}}. \tag{232b}$$

If $f = 1$, as for perfectly diffusing plates, this becomes simply

$$Z = \frac{p}{(2\pi R T)^{\frac{1}{2}}}. \tag{232c}$$

Here p, R and Z are all in c.g.s. units.

The coefficient Z thus defined might be called the *free-molecule viscosity* of the gas between the plates. We note that it is independent of their distance apart. A little reflection shows, in fact, that, so long as intermolecular collisions may be neglected, Z must always be independent of the magnitude of the solid bodies in contact with the gas and determined only by their relative shape. On the other hand, at constant temperature it is proportional to the pressure or the density, in contrast with the ordinary viscosity.

As a further comparison we may note that the ordinary viscous drag on unit area would be, by (229), $\eta U/(w + 2\zeta)$ or, by (126a, b) in Sec. 86, $c\rho\bar{v}LU/(w + 2\zeta)$, or, by (66a) in Sec. 30 and $p = \rho RT$, $4cpLU/(w + 2\zeta)\sqrt{2RT}$, where c is close to $\frac{1}{2}$. For $f \leqq 1$ this latter expression exceeds ZU as calculated from (232b), at least so long as $L > w$, so that, unless f exceeds unity, free-molecule viscous forces are well under those calculated by the ordinary formula.

Free-molecule viscosity was put to use by Langmuir in an instrument that he devised for the measurement of very minute pressures. He suspended a disk on a torsion fiber above a second parallel disk that was kept in constant rotation. The steady deflection of the upper disk, due to viscosity of the intervening gas, was found to be exactly proportional to the gaseous pressure, provided the mean free path was many times the distance between the disks, and this deflection served, therefore, as a measure of the pressure after the instrument had been calibrated at one known pressure.

171. Free-molecule Flow through Long Tubes. The most important type of gaseous flow for practical purposes is that through long

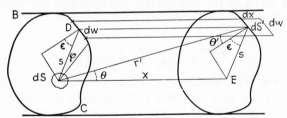

Fig. 70.—Free-molecule flow in a tube.

tubes. Let us suppose that the tube is cylindrical but has a cross section of any nonreentrant shape, and that its walls have a perfectly diffusing surface. Let the pressure be maintained at different steady values at the two ends, the temperature being uniform.

Consider the flow of molecules across a cross section BC of the tube; and consider first the flow across an element of area dS of this cross section (Fig. 70). These molecules that cross dS come from various points on the wall of the tube, where they underwent reflection; let us select those that come from an element dS' on the wall distant x from the plane of BC, and also distant r' from dS in a direction making angles θ with the normal to dS and θ' with the normal to dS', respectively. As molecules strike dS', they will leave it after diffuse reflection in the same manner as if they came from a gas in equilibrium with the density n' and mean speed $\bar{v}$ of the gas in the neighborhood of dS', and by (73a) at the end of Sec. 37

$$\frac{1}{4\pi} n'\bar{v}\, dS'\, d\omega \cos \theta'$$

of them will pass downward through dS per second; here $d\omega$ is the solid angle subtended by dS at dS' and has the value

$$d\omega = \frac{dS \cos \theta}{r'^2}.$$

Now $x = r' \cos \theta$. Furthermore, if we draw in BC a line of length s from dS to that point D on the tube which lies on the same generator as dS', and then draw the normal to the tube at D, this normal making an angle ϵ with the former line, and if we then project these lines upon the cross section through dS' as in the figure, we see from the geometry that $r' \cos \theta' = s \cos \epsilon$, since $r' \cos \theta'$ is the projection of r' and hence also the projection of the broken line $(dS\text{-}E\text{-}dS')$ upon the normal to dS'. Also, $r'^2 = s^2 + x^2$. Hence, if we write $dw\, dx$ for dS', dw being an element of the periphery of the cross section through dS', we have for the total net number of molecules passing downward through dS per second

$$\frac{\bar{v}}{4\pi} dS \int \frac{n'}{r'^2} \cos \theta \cos \theta'\, dS' = \frac{\bar{v}}{4\pi} dS \int_{-\infty}^{\infty} \frac{n'x\, dx}{(s^2 + x^2)^2} \int s \cos \epsilon\, dw,$$

the integral in dw extending around the periphery of a cross section distant x from BC but being obviously independent of x.

Now, if we limit ourselves to small density gradients, we can write

$$n' = n + x \frac{dn}{dx},$$

n representing the density at BC. Then in the last integral the term in n vanishes, whereas that in dn/dx contains the integral

$$\int_{-\infty}^{\infty} \frac{x^2\, dx}{(x^2 + s^2)^2} = \frac{1}{2} \int_{-\infty}^{\infty} \frac{dx}{x^2 + s^2} = \frac{1}{2s} \tan^{-1} \frac{x}{s} \Big|_{-\infty}^{\infty} = \frac{\pi}{2s}.$$

Furthermore, projecting dw onto dS, we see that $dw \cos \epsilon = s\, d\varphi$, where φ is the angle between s and any fixed line of reference drawn in BC through dS. Hence we have finally, for the total net number of molecules that pass through dS upward or toward $x = +\infty$ per second.

$$dN = -\frac{\bar{v}}{8} \left(\int_0^{2\pi} s \, d\varphi \right) \frac{dn}{dx} \, dS,$$

and, integrating again, for the whole number passing upward across BC per second,

$$N = -\frac{\bar{v}}{8} \left[\int dS \int_0^{2\pi} s \, d\varphi \right] \frac{dn}{dx}.$$

Let us now multiply this equation through by m, the mass of a molecule, and then introduce in it $\bar{v} = 2\sqrt{2RT/\pi}$ from (66a) in Sec. 30, and the pressure, $p = nmRT$, R being the gas constant for a gram. The result is the mass of gas passing any point of the tube per second:

$$Q_m = -\frac{1}{2} \frac{1}{(2\pi RT)^{1/2}} \left[\int dS \int_0^{2\pi} s \, d\varphi \right] \frac{dp}{dx}.$$

In the steady state Q_m must be constant along the tube; hence in the free-molecule case the pressure gradient must be uniform, in contrast to its linear variation in the high-density case of Poiseuille. We can, therefore, replace dp/dx by $(p_1 - p_2)/l$, where l is the length of the tube and $p_1 - p_2$, the difference of pressure between its ends. For practical use, however, it is more convenient also to multiply through by RT and so obtain the amount of gas passing per second measured in terms of its pV value; for this we thus find, finally,

$$Q = \frac{1}{2\sqrt{2\pi}} \frac{\sqrt{RT}}{l} \left[\int dS \int_0^{2\pi} s \, d\varphi \right] (p_1 - p_2). \tag{233a}$$

In this equation any units of pressure can be employed for p_1, p_2, and Q; R must, however, retain its c.g.s. value.

172. The Long-tube Formula. The integrals left standing in the last two equations represent quantities characteristic of the cross section of the tube, which can be calculated in any given case.

For a *circular* cross section of radius a, the calculation happens to be easy, although even here $\int_0^{2\pi} s \, d\varphi$ is not independent of the position of dS and the flow is, therefore, not quite uniform over the cross section. Writing $\int dS \int_0^{2\pi} s \, d\varphi = \int_0^{2\pi} d\varphi \int s \, dS$, and then fixing φ momentarily while we carry out the integral in dS, let us draw cartesian axes as in Fig. 71 with the origin at the center of the circle and the y-axis parallel to the line of length s. Then we can write $dS = dx \, dy$, and, x and y denoting coordinates of a point in dS,

$$\int s \, dS = \int_{-a}^{a} dx \int_{-(a^2-x^2)^{\frac{1}{2}}}^{(a^2-x^2)^{\frac{1}{2}}} [(a^2 - x^2)^{\frac{1}{2}} - y] \, dy =$$

$$2 \int_{-a}^{a} (a^2 - x^2) \, dx = \frac{8}{3} a^3.$$

Hence $\int_{0}^{2\pi} d\varphi \int s \, dS = 16\pi a^3/3$, and (233a) becomes, for a circular tube,

$$Q = \frac{4}{3} (2\pi R T)^{\frac{1}{2}} \frac{a^3}{l} (p_1 - p_2). \tag{233b}$$

This formula, like (233a), is limited in its application by the double condition that the diameter of the tube must be small in comparison both with the mean free path and with distances in which a considerable change occurs in the density of the gas. There are also end corrections which can be neglected only if the tube is very long.

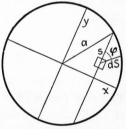

Formula (233b) was first obtained by Knudsen,* but he used an unreliable method and some of his results were wrong. Formula (233a) for the general case was obtained soon afterward by Smoluchowski,† following the reasoning that we have given. Knudsen's method was to equate the momentum imparted

Fig. 71.

to the tube by molecular impacts in a second to the difference in the pressure forces at the ends. This is correct, of course, but then in calculating the momentum, he assumed Maxwell's law to hold approximately, and as we have seen in our treatment of ordinary viscosity and heat conduction this assumption may introduce a considerable error in calculations of *differential* effects. We have ourselves employed an expression for the effusion of molecules that is appropriate only to the equilibrium state, but we were not compelled to subtract from it another quantity almost as big as itself, and the resulting error is, therefore, only of the second order in the density gradient.

In experimental work, however, the most significant thing is likely to be the rate of flow as measured by *volume*, since this controls the *relative* rate at which pressures undergo alteration. The rate of flow in these terms is, roughly, $2Q/(p_1 + p_2)$; hence, from (233b), we reach the important conclusion that for a given value of the ratio p_1/p_2 the flow in terms of volume is independent of the density of the gas.

* KNUDSEN, *Ann. Physik*, **28**, 75 (1909).
† SMOLUCHOWSKI, *Ann. Physik*, **33**, 1559 (1910).

To illustrate the order of magnitude of free-molecule flow, it may be remarked that according to the formula a bulb containing a liter of air at a pressure anywhere below 0.01 mm and connected to a high vacuum through a tube 30 cm long and 2 mm in diameter will half empty itself in a little over three minutes.   This is a fairly long time, and it indicates that at low density equalization of the pressure through small openings is a comparatively slow process.   The situation is much better, however, than if the ordinary Poiseuille equation [(228), with $\zeta_1 = 0$] held under these conditions; in that case the time required would be nearly two hours.

It was pointed out by Smoluchowski (*loc. cit.*) that the formula is easily generalized to cover the case in which only a certain fraction f of the molecules are scattered diffusely, while a fraction $1 - f$ are specularly reflected.   In that case the formula for Q becomes, in place of (233*b*),

$$Q = \frac{4}{3}\frac{2-f}{f}\,(2\pi RT)^{\frac{1}{2}}\frac{a^3}{l}\,(p_1 - p_2). \qquad (233c)$$

The new factor $(2 - f)/f$ results from the fact that the net number of molecules crossing any cross section BC, being determined by the density gradient along the tube, depends upon the mean distance from BC at which they experience their last diffuse reflection from the walls, specular reflection merely handing them on with their component of velocity along the tube unaltered, and this mean distance can be shown to be increased in the ratio $(2 - f)/f$.

173. Flow through Short Tubes.   The results just obtained are, of course, accurate only for tubes of indefinite length.   In practice the end corrections required for tubes of finite length may likewise be of interest, and in some cases, for example, in working with molecular beams, the value of the free-molecule flow through a short tube may be needed.   For such quantities only approximate values have as yet been obtained, but some discussion of these may be of interest.

Suppose two vessels containing gas in equilibrium at temperature T and at very low pressures p_1 and p_2, respectively, are connected together through a round tube of length l, which has perfectly diffusing walls, and let the radius a of this tube be very small as compared with the mean free path in the gas.   Then, when l/a is very large, the rate of flow through the tube measured in terms of pV is given by (233*b*) above and so is proportional to $1/l$.   At the opposite extreme, on the other hand, when $l = 0$, the tube reduces to a circular opening in a thin plate and, according to eq. (72*d*) in Sec. 37, the differential rate of free-molecule flow through it, measured in terms of pV, is

$$Q = a^2(\tfrac{1}{2}\pi RT)^{\frac{1}{2}}(p_1 - p_2).$$

Now it is easy to invent a formula that passes into these two forms as limiting cases. The simplest one is Dushman's formula:

$$Q = \frac{a^2(\tfrac{1}{2}\pi RT)^{\frac{1}{2}}}{1 + \tfrac{3}{8}\,(l/a)}\,(p_1 - p_2). \tag{233d}$$

For a very short tube, however, this formula is easily seen to be not quite right. A short ringlike tube, as in Fig. 72, acts to decrease the flow as compared with a plane opening of the same cross section by intercepting molecules that would otherwise pass through. The effect of this interception can be found, to the first order in l/a, by the following argument.

If the gas had everywhere the same density n_1 that it has in the left-hand vessel, then by (72a) in Sec. 37 a total of $\tfrac{1}{4}\,n_1\bar{v}_1 \times 2\pi al$ or $\tfrac{1}{2}\,\pi n_1\bar{v}_1 al$ molecules would strike the wall of the tube per second, and almost half of these would have come directly from the left-hand vessel; after striking the tube, only half of these in turn would eventually pass on into the right-hand vessel, whereas, if l were 0, all of them would do so. The presence of the tube thus decreases the number passing

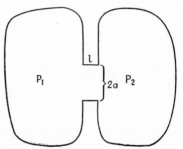

FIG. 72.—Effusion through a ring.

through by a quarter of the number that strike its wall or by $\tfrac{1}{8}\,\pi n_1\bar{v}_1 al$. On the other hand, the total number passing through in the absence of the tube is $\tfrac{1}{4}\,n_1\bar{v}_1\pi a^2$. Hence the tube reduces the flow in the ratio

$$1 - \frac{\tfrac{1}{8}\,\pi n_1\bar{v}_1\,al}{\tfrac{1}{4}\,n_1\bar{v}_1\pi a^2} = 1 - \frac{1}{2}\frac{l}{a}.$$

This result suggests as an approximate formula valid for small l/a, in place of (233d),

$$Q = \frac{a^2(\tfrac{1}{2}\pi RT)^{\frac{1}{2}}}{1 + \tfrac{1}{2}\,(l/a)}\,(p_1 - p_2). \tag{233e}$$

For large l/a, however, this formula is certainly wrong in turn, by a factor of $\tfrac{3}{4}$.

The problem of the short tube was subjected to thorough study by Clausing in his thesis.* No accurate formula could be obtained in

* P. CLAUSING, Dissertation, Amsterdam, 1918.

terms of known functions, but he works out a close approximation and also gives a table of values representing the ratio

$$Q \div a^2(\tfrac{1}{2}\pi RT)^{\frac{1}{2}}(p_1 - p_2)$$

as a function of l/a [page 130, values from his eq. (203)]. His results agree, naturally, with (233e) for small l/a; a compact empirical expression that reproduces them within 1.5 per cent for all l/a is

$$Q = \frac{20 + \dfrac{8l}{a}}{20 + \dfrac{19l}{a} + 3\left(\dfrac{l}{a}\right)^2}\, a^2(\tfrac{1}{2}\pi RT)^{\frac{1}{2}}(p_1 - p_2).$$

As compared with Clausing's values of Q, use of the shorter formula of Dushman, (233d), may incur an error of nearly 12 per cent.

174. Observations of Free-molecule Flow. The only investigations that cover the free-molecule case are the elaborate studies of the flow of gases under a pressure gradient made by Knudsen* and by Gaede.† Both of these investigators studied the molecular flow of gases through circular glass tubes, for which Knudsen developed a formula equivalent to our (233b) above. Gaede took the further precaution of freeing the tube thoroughly from adsorbed gas by preheating, and kept all water vapor frozen out in a side tube immersed in liquid air.

A critical quantity in such work is the ratio of L, the mean free path, to the radius a of the tube. Using a capillary 0.206 mm in diameter, Gaede found in the case of hydrogen agreement within 1 per cent with the theoretical formula as represented by our eq. (233b), the pressure ranging from 0.0001 mm ($L/a = 8,700$) up to 0.001 mm ($L/a = 870$), and in the case of nitrogen agreement within 2 per cent up to 0.002 mm ($L/a = 230$); but at 0.008 mm ($L/a \doteq 108$ for H_2, 58 for N_2) the observed flow was in both cases smaller by several per cent. Experimenting with less refinement, Knudsen had got a similar agreement using H_2, O_2, and CO_2; in the case of H_2 he found the formula to hold even up to pressures at which $L/a = 0.6$. Since the only special assumption made in deducing the formula, in addition to the general results of kinetic theory, is that of diffuse reflection by the walls of the tube, the latter assumption seems to be definitely confirmed by these experiments for H_2 or N_2 reflected from glass.

Both Knudsen and Gaede investigated, also, the manner in which at higher pressures the transition occurs from the free-molecule formula

* KNUDSEN, *Ann. Physik*, **28**, 75 (1909); **35**, 389 (1911).
† GAEDE, *Ann. Physik*, **41**, 289 (1913).

to that of Poiseuille.   In Fig. 73 is illustrated the general course of Q, the rate of flow measured in terms of pV, as a function of the mean pressure $\bar{p}$ for a given ratio of the pressures at the two ends of the tube. Starting out at low pressures along the free-molecule straight line FM, the curve for Q approaches asymptotically the quadratic Poiseuille curve P as the mean free path becomes less than the tube diameter. Both Knudsen and Gaede found that the curve had a form like J rather than like K, the ratio $Q/(p_1 - p_2)$ exhibiting a minimum when the mean free path became several times the tube diameter.

Finally, Gaede investigated the flow of hydrogen between two parallel plates placed only 0.004 mm apart and found $Q/(p_1 - p_2)$ to be as much as 50 per cent below the theoretical free-molecule value at a pressure of 23 mm, the mean free path L being then just about the same as the distance h between the plates.   The drop from the theoretical value began, however, at very low pressures; from 0.019 mm to 0.265 mm it amounted to 18 per cent, whereas at the latter pressure L is still about 83 times the width of the slit, and under such conditions, even if we assume every collision to remove both

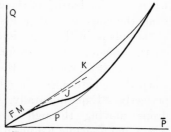

Fig. 73.—Flow through a tube.

molecules entirely from consideration and suppose, also, that the molecular paths might somehow have an effective average length of as much as three times h, we can reach only a possible theoretical drop of $\frac{3}{83}$ or 4 per cent.

The entire observed drop in $Q/(p_1 - p_2)$ below the theoretical value was ascribed by Gaede to the formation at higher pressures of an adsorbed layer of gas on the walls of the tube, which he supposed might increase the resistance to the flow.   It is hard, however, to see how an adsorbed layer could do anything except increase the amount of diffuse reflection, and the latter is already assumed to amount to 100 per cent in deducing the theoretical formula.   Further experiments on this point would seem to be worth while.

175. Stokes' Law for Spheres.   An interesting special case that deserves brief mention before we leave the subject of slip is the steady motion of a sphere through a viscous medium under the influence of a steady force, such as its weight.

Stokes showed long ago that if the ordinary laws of hydrodynamics hold, and if the velocity U of the sphere is not too large and there is no slipping of the medium over it, the force required for steady motion is

$$F = -6\pi\eta a U$$

in terms of the radius a of the sphere and the viscosity η of the medium. His deduction is easily modified to allow for the occurrence of slip;* in terms of the slip distance ζ (Sec. 165) the modified formula is

$$F = -6\pi\eta a U\left(1 - \frac{\zeta}{a}\right)$$

to the same degree of accuracy to which Stokes' law itself holds. This latter formula should be valid for a gas so long as the mean free path L is much smaller than the radius a.

The opposite extreme case of *large L/a* was studied in detail by Epstein.† He showed that in such cases the force on the sphere is

$$F = -\alpha \bar{v} \rho a^2 U,$$

where ρ is the density of the gas and $\bar{v}$ the mean speed of its molecules, while the constant α depends on the law of reflection from the surface of the sphere; if the reflection is specular (or if the molecules condense on the sphere, spread uniformly over it, and then evaporate again) $\alpha = \alpha_1 = 4\pi/3$, whereas if the reflection is diffuse α ranges from $1.442\,\alpha_1$ when the sphere does not conduct heat to $1.393\,\alpha_1$ in case it conducts perfectly. Experimentally, Millikan‡ found values for charged oil drops moving through air of very low density equivalent to $\alpha = 1.365\,\alpha_1$, while Knudsen and Weber's results for glass spheres in air correspond to $\alpha = 1.353\,\alpha_1$. Smaller values like these can be accounted for by assuming the existence of a small tendency toward specular reflection.

The *intermediate* condition in which the mean free path is of the same order of magnitude as the radius of the sphere is difficult to handle theoretically. In this region, Millikan, and also Knudsen and Weber, find that the empirical formula

$$F = -\frac{6\pi\eta a U}{1 + (L/a)(A + Be^{-ca/L})}$$

fits the data well. In terms of mean free paths calculated from eq. (126b) Millikan's data for oil drops in air require $A = 1.23$, $B = 0.41$, $c = 0.88$.

At such low pressures that L/a is large this formula becomes approximately $\dfrac{6\pi\eta a^2 U}{(A + B)L}$, so that A and B must be related to the coefficient α in the preceding formula thus: $\quad \alpha = \dfrac{6\pi\eta}{(A + B)\rho L \bar{v}}.$

---

* Cf. A. B. Bassett, "Hydrodynamics," vol. II, p. 271, 1888; H. Lamb, "Hydrodynamics," Sec. 337.

† Epstein, *Phys. Rev.*, **23**, 710 (1924).

‡ Millikan, *Phys. Rev.*, **22**, 1 (1923).

At high pressures, $(L/a \ll 1)$, on the other hand, the formula becomes $F = -\dfrac{6\pi\eta a U}{1 + \dfrac{AL}{a}}$, and comparison of this equation with one just above shows that $\zeta = AL$. The value $A = 1.23$ agrees, as a matter of fact, with the ratio $\zeta/L = 1.23$ obtained by the revolving-cylinder method and cited in the table in Sec. 169.

THERMAL CONDUCTION IN RAREFIED GASES

176. Temperature Jump and the Accommodation Coefficient. In analogy with the phenomenon of viscous slip it was suggested long ago by Poisson that at a wall bounding an unequally heated gas there might be a discontinuity of temperature. He wrote for this assumed discontinuity an equation equivalent to

$$T_K - T_w = g\, \frac{\partial T}{\partial n}, \tag{234}$$

where T_w is the wall temperature and T_K, as now understood, is what the temperature of the gas would be if the temperature gradient along the outward-drawn normal to the wall, $\partial T/\partial n$, continued without change right up to the wall itself. The constant g represents a length and may be called the *temperature jump distance.*

Upon Warburg's suggestion Smoluchowski[*] performed experiments in search of this effect and found it; he showed also that, as kinetic theory would lead one to expect, the jump distance g, for which he wrote γ, is inversely proportional to the pressure and so directly proportional to the mean free path L. He found $g = 2.7\,L$ for air but $g = 11\,L$ for hydrogen, in terms of modern values of L; the latter high value he ascribed to a difficulty experienced by the very light molecules of hydrogen in exchanging energy with the molecules of the wall.

In developing a theory[†] of the phenomenon Smoluchowski introduced a constant to represent the extent to which interchange of energy takes place when a molecule of the gas strikes a solid (or liquid) surface. There has come into common use, however, a slightly different constant introduced later by Knudsen.[‡] This constant, which he called the *accommodation coefficient* and denoted by a, can be defined as standing for the fractional extent to which those molecules that fall on the surface and are reflected or re-emitted from it, have their mean energy adjusted or "accommodated" toward what it would be if the

---

[*] SMOLUCHOWSKI, *Ann. Physik*, **64**, 101 (1898).

[†] SMOLUCHOWSKI, *Akad. Wiss. Wien*, **107**, 304 (1898); **108**, 5 (1899).

[‡] KNUDSEN. *Ann. Physik*, **34**, 593 (1911).

returning molecules were issuing as a stream out of a mass of gas at the temperature of the wall.   If E_i denotes the energy brought up to unit area per second by the incident stream, and E_r that carried away by these molecules as they leave the wall after reflection from it, and if E_w is the energy that this latter stream would carry away if it carried the same mean energy per molecule as does a stream issuing from a gas in equilibrium at the wall temperature T_w, then a is given by the equation

$$E_i - E_r = a(E_i - E_w). \tag{235}$$

Knudsen himself preferred to attach a temperature to each of these streams of molecules, just as in the reverse way we have just associated an energy E_w with a temperature T_w; he wrote the equivalent of the equation,

$$T_i - T_r = a(T_i - T_w).$$

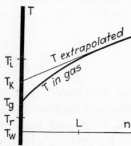

Fig. 74.—Temperature gradient near a wall.

Here T_i is not necessarily the same as T_K above, which represents the result of extrapolating the temperature gradient in the gas up to the wall; nor are T_i and T_r connected in any simple way with the mean energy or temperature T_g of the molecules that are actually present at any moment in the layer next to the wall.   For these various temperatures the theory developed below suggests some such relationship as that shown in Fig. 74.

177. Theory of the Temperature Jump.   An approximate theoretical expression for the relation between the accommodation coefficient a and the jump distance g is easily obtained from kinetic theory by completing an argument of Maxwell's in a way that is analogous to his own method of connecting f with the slip coefficient ζ.   We shall alter Maxwell's reasoning somewhat, however, by introducing Knudsen's ideas in regard to the behavior of the heat energy.

Maxwell assumes that the stream of oncoming molecules is the same right up to the wall as it is in the midst of the gas and corresponds to a temperature grading uniformly down to the value at the wall which we have called T_K.   These oncoming molecules will then bring up to unit area of the wall in each second both the heat content of a maxwellian stream issuing from a gas at temperature T_K and the excess energy which they carry as their contribution to the conduction of heat, for which we can write $\frac{1}{2} K \, \partial T / \partial n$ in terms of the thermal conductivity K of the gas.

Now the translational energy carried by a stream issuing from a gas at temperature T_K is $2RT_K$ ergs per gram, as is stated in Problem 4 at the end of Sec. 37, R being the gas constant for a gram; this is $4\!/\!3$ times as great as the mean translatory energy of a gram of gas in equilibrium at the same temperature, the difference being due to the fact that the faster molecules both issue in larger numbers and carry more energy. The total energy brought up by S g of such a stream is accordingly

$$S(2RT_K + U_{IK}),$$

where U_{IK} is the internal energy of the molecules in a gram at temperature T_K. A similar stream at temperature T_w would transport

$$S(2RT_w + U_{Iw})$$

units of energy. The difference of these two expressions can be written with sufficient accuracy

$$S(c_V + \tfrac{1}{2} R)(T_K - T_w), \tag{236}$$

where $c_V = \tfrac{3}{2} R + \dfrac{dU_I}{dT}$ and represents the specific heat at constant volume (cf. Sec. 143).

If we then add to this latter expression the excess energy carried by the incident stream as its contribution to the conduction, we have the difference between the incident energy and the energy carried away by the molecules on the assumption that they leave as a maxwellian stream at the wall temperature T_w, or

$$E_i - E_w = \frac{1}{2} K \frac{\partial T}{\partial n} + S\!\left(c_V + \frac{1}{2} R\right)(T_K - T_w),$$

where S now stands for the grams of gas brought up to unit area in a second by the incident stream. By (72b) in Sec. 37 $S = \rho(RT_K/2\pi)^{1/2} = p/(2\pi RT)^{1/2}$ nearly enough, in terms of the pressure p and the temperature T of the gas at the wall, for which we need not distinguish here between T_w, T_K, and T_g. Furthermore, by (197) in Sec. 141, $R = c_p - c_V = (\gamma - 1)c_V$ in terms of the ratio γ of the specific heats, so that

$$c_V + \tfrac{1}{2} R = \tfrac{1}{2} (\gamma + 1)c_V. \tag{237}$$

Hence we have finally

$$E_i - E_w = \frac{1}{2} K \frac{\partial T}{\partial n} + \frac{1}{2} (\gamma + 1) \frac{c_V(T_K - T_w)p}{(2\pi RT)^{1/2}}.$$

On the other hand, the net energy actually delivered to the surface can be equated to the total heat conducted across a parallel plane out in the gas. Hence

$$E_i - E_r = K \frac{\partial T}{\partial n},$$

E_r representing the energy carried away by the reflected stream. From these equations together with (235) we find

$$K \frac{\partial T}{\partial n} = a \left[\tfrac{1}{2} K \frac{\partial T}{\partial n} + \tfrac{1}{2} (\gamma + 1) \frac{c_V p (T_K - T_w)}{(2\pi R T)^{\frac{1}{2}}} \right];$$

whence, by (234),

$$g = \frac{2 - a}{a} (2\pi R T)^{\frac{1}{2}} \frac{K}{(\gamma + 1) c_V p}. \tag{238a}$$

Or, if we wish to exhibit the relation of g to the mean free path L, we can do this by introducing the viscosity $\eta = c\rho\bar{v}L$ from (126a, b) in Sec. 86; let us, however, replace ρ by p/RT and $\bar{v}$ by $2(2RT/\pi)^{\frac{1}{2}}$ from (66a) in Sec. 30, which gives

$$\eta = \frac{cp}{RT} 2 \left(\frac{2RT}{\pi} \right)^{\frac{1}{2}} L = 4 \frac{cpL}{(2\pi RT)^{\frac{1}{2}}}.$$

Then

$$g = \frac{2 - a}{a} \frac{4c}{\gamma + 1} \frac{K}{\eta c_V} L. \tag{238b}$$

Here $0.491 \leqq c \leqq 0.499$, so that $4c = 2$ very nearly.

As a special case it might happen that $a = 1$; then g should be only a little larger than L, for $1 < \gamma \leqq \tfrac{5}{3}$ or $2 < \gamma + 1 < 2.7$, and usually $1.5 < K/\eta c_V < 2.5$ (cf. Sec. 103). We should have $a = 1$ if the gas molecules were adsorbed on the surface as they struck and were then subsequently re-evaporated at the temperature of the surface, or if the surface were so irregular and cavernous that most of the molecules struck it a number of times before escaping, even though the accommodation coefficient for a single impact might be considerably less than unity. If a fraction φ of the molecules were specularly reflected, the average coefficient of accommodation for the remainder being a_1, it is easily seen that

$$a = (1 - \varphi) a_1.$$

It must be recognized that in our deduction we have tacitly assumed the accommodation coefficient to have the same value for the internal molecular energy that it has for their translatory energy. Now according to the principle of the equipartition of energy it is a fact that these two kinds of energy are distributed independently in any state of equilibrium; but there exists no general reason to suppose that in collisions they possess the same mean rates of transfer. The formulas could easily be generalized by introducing different coefficients for the two types of energy, but the accuracy so far obtained in experimental work scarcely justifies the introduction of this complication; moreover, an experiment of Knudsen's described in Sec. 181 below supports the simple assumption made above.

We have likewise assumed in all of our discussion so far that ordinary conditions occur in the gas at points a few mean free paths away from the surface. Whenever this condition is not met, the results of the present section are not applicable.

Problems. 1. Show that the heat conducted per unit area per second through a gas of conductivity K between two parallel plates separated by a relatively small distance d, per degree difference in temperature between them, is

$$\Lambda = \frac{K}{d + g_1 + g_2} \qquad (239a)$$

(except near the edges), g_1 and g_2 being the temperature jump distances at the two plates and g_1/d, g_2/d being assumed rather small.

2. Show that if the plates take the form of two coaxial cylinders of radii $r_1 < r_2$, for the inner cylinder

$$\Lambda = \frac{K}{r_1\left(\log \dfrac{r_2}{r_1} + \dfrac{g_1}{r_1} + \dfrac{g_2}{r_2}\right)}. \qquad (239b)$$

178. Free-molecule Heat Conduction between Plates. The opposite extreme of conditions, in which conduction occurs between two surfaces so close together, or at such low pressures, that collisions between molecules are rare, was likewise first treated by Smoluchowski,[*] but Knudsen's treatment[†] seems to be a little more satisfactory and will be followed here.

Consider first a layer of gas between two parallel plane surfaces or plates at temperatures T_1 and T_2. In such a layer Knudsen divides the molecules into two sets, a stream S_1 moving with a component of velocity away from the first plate and a stream S_2 moving with a component directed toward it; and he assumes the distribution of velocities to be approximately maxwellian in each stream but to correspond to temperatures T'_1 and T'_2, respectively (Fig. 75).[‡] Let E'_1,

---

[*] Smoluchowski, *Akad. Wiss. Wien*, **107**, 304 (1898); *Phil. Mag.*, **21**, 11 (1911).

[†] Knudsen, *loc. cit.*

[‡] Some support is lent to this assumption by the observations of Ornstein and van Wyk described in Sec. 182.

E_2' denote the respective actual amounts of energy carried across unit area per second by these two streams; on the other hand, let E_1, E_2 denote what these energies would be if the molecules carried the same mean energy as they do in maxwellian streams at temperatures T_1 and T_2, respectively.

Then the *first stream* is continually falling upon the *second plate* and thereby feeding its molecules into the second stream; hence, if a_1, a_2 are the accommodation coefficients for the two plates, by (235) or $E_i - E_r = a(E_i - E_w)$, we have in the present instance

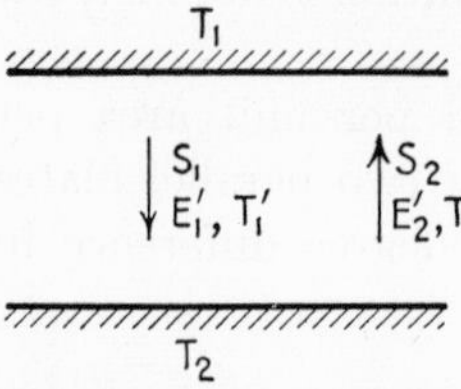

$$E_1' - E_2' = a_2(E_1' - E_2). \qquad (240a)$$

Similarly, consideration of the reverse process at the *first plate* gives

$$E_2' - E_1' = a_1(E_2' - E_1). \qquad (240b)$$

FIG. 75.—Free-molecule conduction of heat.

From these equations we find for the net amount of heat given to the second plate, or abstracted from the first one, per unit area per second

$$H = E_1' - E_2' = \frac{a_1 a_2}{a_1 + a_2 - a_1 a_2} (E_1 - E_2).$$

Now $E_1 - E_2$, being the difference in the currents of energy in two equal maxwellian streams at temperatures T_1 and T_2, must be given by (236) above with T_K and T_w replaced by T_1 and T_2, respectively, so that

$$E_1 - E_2 = S(c_V + \tfrac{1}{2} R)(T_1 - T_2).$$

Here S must represent the grams of gas carried across unit area per second by each of the actual streams in the gas under consideration, being obviously the same for both in order to prevent accumulation of gas at one plate. From (72b) in Sec. 37 we find for its magnitude

$$S = \tfrac{1}{2} \rho_1' \bar{v}_1' = \tfrac{1}{2} \rho_2' \bar{v}_2',$$

where ρ_1', ρ_2' are densities in terms of mass and $\bar{v}_1'$, $\bar{v}_2'$ mean molecular speeds in the two streams; the factor is $\frac{1}{2}$ instead of $\frac{1}{4}$ as in eq. (72b), because here ρ represents the density of molecules moving toward one side only, or just half the density in the equivalent maxwellian gas. This can also be written

$$S = \tfrac{1}{4} (\rho_1' \bar{v}_1' + \rho_2' \bar{v}_2') = \tfrac{1}{4} \rho' \bar{v}',$$

where ρ' is the total density of the gas and $\bar{v}'$ the mean speed of all of its molecules. Using $\rho' = \rho_1' + \rho_2'$, we find from these equations that

$$\frac{1}{\bar{v}'} = \frac{1}{2}\left(\frac{1}{\bar{v}'_1} + \frac{1}{\bar{v}'_2}\right).$$

It is more convenient, however, to introduce into the expression for S, in place of the mean speeds, the corresponding temperatures, T'_1, T'_2. We can convert (240a, b) into equations in terms of these temperatures merely by replacing E'_1, E'_2, E_1, E_2 by T'_1, T'_2, T_1, T_2, respectively, to which they are proportional; solution of the resulting equations then yields the values

$$T'_1 = \frac{a_1 T_1 + a_2(1 - a_1)T_2}{a_1 + a_2 - a_1 a_2}, \qquad T'_2 = \frac{a_2 T_2 + a_1(1 - a_2)T_1}{a_1 + a_2 - a_1 a_2}. \quad (241a, b)$$

Let us also write T' for the temperature of a maxwellian gas in which the mean speed is $\bar{v}'$. Then, since $\bar{v} \propto \sqrt{T}$, the last equation in $\bar{v}'$ gives

$$\frac{1}{\sqrt{T'}} = \frac{1}{2}\left(\frac{1}{\sqrt{T'_1}} + \frac{1}{\sqrt{T'_2}}\right). \quad (241c)$$

By means of these equations T' can be found in terms of the plate temperatures T_1 and T_2 and the accommodation coefficients. If T'_1 and T'_2 do not differ much, T' will lie close to their mean, and if $a_1 = a_2$ this is the same as the mean of T_1 and T_2. Of course, if $a_1 = a_2 = 1$, we have $T'_1 = T_1$, $T'_2 = T_2$.

In the equation, $S = \frac{1}{4}\rho'\bar{v}'$, let us now replace $\bar{v}'$ by $2(2RT'/\pi)^{1/2}$ according to (66a) in Sec. 30. Then substitution of the resulting value of S into the expression found above for $E_1 - E_2$, and then of this value of $E_1 - E_2$ into the expression found previously for the rate of heat transfer H gives us finally

$$H = \frac{a_1 a_2}{a_1 + a_2 - a_1 a_2}\rho'\left(\frac{RT'}{2\pi}\right)^{1/2}\left(c_V + \frac{1}{2}R\right)(T_1 - T_2).$$

For convenience let us write $H = \Lambda_{a_1 a_2}(T_1 - T_2)$, $\Lambda_{a_1 a_2}$ denoting, therefore, the conductivity per unit area of the space between the plates. Then, inserting also $\rho' = p'/RT'$ in terms of the pressure p' of the gas and using (237), we can write as our final result for free-molecule conductivity between two plates

$$\Lambda_{a_1 a_2} = \frac{a_1 a_2}{a_1 + a_2 - a_1 a_2}\Lambda_{11}, \qquad \Lambda_{11} = \frac{1}{2}(\gamma + 1)\frac{c_V p'}{(2\pi RT')^{1/2}}. \quad (242a, b)$$

Here p' is the pressure of a maxwellian gas having the same density as the gas between the plates but a temperature T'. If the surrounding gas is at a different temperature T, its pressure p should be related to p' by the equation

$$p' = \sqrt{\frac{T'}{T}}\, p,$$

for the diffusive balance between the two masses of gas is controlled by the quantity $\rho \bar{v}$ and should, accordingly, be the same as it is in thermal transpiration between gaseous masses [cf. eq. (75) in Sec. 39 above].

In the two cases $a_1 = a_2 = a$, and $a_1 = a$, $a_2 = 1$, respectively, the formula reduces to

$$\Lambda_{aa} = \frac{a}{2-a}\, A_{11} \qquad \text{or} \qquad \Lambda_{a1} = a\Lambda_{11}. \qquad (242c,\, d)$$

From these formulas we note at once that at a given temperature $\Lambda \propto p'$ and is independent of the distance between the plates. Thus under these conditions the conduction of heat, like the viscosity, follows very different laws from those obeyed under ordinary circumstances. It is, in fact, easily seen that in any free-molecule case the conduction must be proportional to the pressure of the gas, and dependent only upon the shape, but not upon the size, of the bounding surfaces.

179. Free-molecule Conduction between Coaxial Cylinders. One other case, that of coaxial cylinders, was likewise taken up by Knudsen. This case is important because cylindrical surfaces are commonly employed in experiments.

Here a new feature enters in that some molecules will strike the outer cylinder several times before striking the inner, which results in raising the effective accommodation coefficient of the outer one; in fact, if its radius is made indefinitely large, the molecules will come completely into equilibrium with it before striking the inner cylinder again, and it will therefore behave as if it had an accommodation coefficient $a = 1$.

There is, however, one curious imaginable case, pointed out by Smoluchowski, in which increasing the radius does *not* increase a: If the outer cylinder reflects a certain fraction of the molecules specularly and reflects the remainder as it would for $a = 1$, and if the inner cylinder is exactly centered, then it is easily shown that Λ is independent of the relative sizes of the cylinders, and so must have the same value in terms of unit area on the inner cylinder as it would have for parallel planes.

In general, the conduction of heat will depend a good deal upon the distribution in direction of the molecules as they return from the outer cylinder. For the case of diffuse reflection as to directions, with an accommodation coefficient a as regards energy at both surfaces, Smoluchowski deduced a formula which seems to be right and can be obtained in the following way.

In obtaining a result accurate to the first power of the temperature difference, we may assume the total density of molecular impacts to be the same on both surfaces even when these are curved; this is exactly true when the gas is in equilibrium, and since conduction depends on the impact rate itself and not on its differences, any slight departure from equality at the two surfaces can produce only a second-order effect on the conduction. Now all molecules that leave the inner cylinder strike the outer; but, if r_1, r_2 are the radii of the inner and outer cylinders, respectively, these molecules, constituting the "first" stream in the terminology employed above, form only a fraction r_1/r_2 of all of those that strike the outer one, since r_1/r_2 is the ratio of the areas of the two; the remainder of the molecules that strike the outer cylinder come from the outer one itself and so belong to the "second" stream.

Accordingly, we can apply (240a) to the process going on at the outer cylinder, provided we replace E_1' by $E_1' \frac{r_1}{r_2} + E_2'\left(1 - \frac{r_1}{r_2}\right)$. The resulting equation,

$$\frac{r_1}{r_2}(E_1' - E_2') = a_2\left[\frac{r_1}{r_2}E_1' + \left(1 - \frac{r_1}{r_2}\right)E_2' - E_2\right],$$

can be written in the form

$$\left(\frac{r_1}{r_2} - a_2\frac{r_1}{r_2} + a_2\right)(E_1' - E_2') = a_2(E_1' - E_2);$$

but this is equivalent to the original equation (240a) with a_2 replaced by

$$a_2\left(\frac{r_1}{r_2} - a_2\frac{r_1}{r_2} + a_2\right)^{-1}.$$

Equation (240b) holds unchanged. Hence in the general result obtained from those equations, which is eq. (242a), we need only replace a_2 by the same expression, and then set $a_1 = a_2 = a$, since the surfaces are here assumed to be alike. We thus find for the heat conducted per unit area per second from the inner cylinder,

$$H = \Lambda_{r_1 r_2}(T_1 - T_2),$$

where

$$\Lambda_{r_1 r_2} = \frac{a}{1 + (1 - a)(r_1/r_2)}\Lambda_{11}, \qquad (242e)$$

T' in the expression given for Λ_{11} in (242b) being obtained from (241a, b, c) by making there also the changes just described in a_2 and then in a_1 and a_2.

For $r_1 = r_2$ this formula passes into (242c), as it must. For $r_2 \to \infty$ it becomes

$$\Lambda_{r\infty} = a\Lambda_{11} \; ; \tag{242f}$$

and in this latter case $T'_2 = T_2$ while $T'_1 = aT_1 + (1 - a)T_2$ for the temperature of the stream leaving the inner cylinder.

180. Observed Variation of the Accommodation Coefficient. The most illuminating observations of the accommodation coefficient for a gas in contact with a heated surface are undoubtedly those reported recently[*] by Blodgett and Langmuir, by Roberts, and by Michels. The method employed in all these cases consisted in measuring the heat loss from a wire stretched along the axis of a cylindrical tube kept at a fixed temperature; in this method the observed resistance of the wire serves to measure its temperature, while the power spent in it measures the heat loss.   The pressure was made low enough so that the mean free path was at least six times the diameter of the wire, in order that the equivalent of our eq. (242f) taken together with (242b) might be employed in calculating the accommodation coefficient a. The last two of the investigators named simply assumed that the impinging molecules had the temperature of the tube, but Blodgett and Langmuir assumed them to have the mean temperature of the gas at a distance of one mean free path from the wire, and then calculated the temperature drop from this point to the tube by means of the ordinary theory of mass conduction, which resulted in a correction in their case of 5 to 10 per cent.

All of these investigators found that the value of the accommodation coefficient depended greatly upon the past history of the filament. This effect was studied in great detail by Blodgett and Langmuir in the case of a tungsten filament of diameter 0.00779 cm surrounded by hydrogen at a pressure of 0.2 mm; the filament, 40 cm in length, was stretched along the axis of a tube 6.4 cm in diameter immersed in liquid air.   They reached the conclusion that $a = 0.54$ when the tungsten was really clean, but that this value holds only at temperatures above 1000°C because at lower temperatures a film of adsorbed hydrogen forms on the tungsten and lowers a, even to 0.14 under

* Blodgett and Langmuir, *Phys. Rev.*, **40**, 78 (1932).   Roberts, *Proc. Roy. Soc.*, **129**, 146 (1930); **135**, 192 (1930); **142**, 518 (1933).   Michels, *Phys. Rev.*, **40**, 472 (1932).

certain conditions. Furthermore, if there was any oxygen in the tube, a film of that gas or of tungsten oxide seemed to form, and this lowered a to 0.2 or even to 0.1. Such a *lowering* of a by a gas film is not easy to understand; they suggest nothing that might explain it.

An effect presumably due to a gas film was likewise found by Roberts and by Michels in the case of the rare gases, but it was in the opposite direction. Using mostly a tungsten filament, they found that when it had just been "flashed" at an elevated temperature, a was much reduced, but as time passed it increased, at first from minute to minute, and then more slowly for many hours. The value found immediately after flashing was considered to represent the accommodation coefficient for clean tungsten. Several ways can be imagined in which a layer of adsorbed gas might assist the transfer of heat from the gas to the tungsten and so raise a; for example, heat energy might first be imparted to an adsorbed molecule and then transferred to the tungsten as this molecule vibrates under the forces which hold it on the surface, or the presence of the adsorbed molecules might cause the impinging one to strike either the adsorbed molecules themselves or the tungsten several times before escaping again. Another possibility suggested by Roberts is that the clean metal may reflect specularly or may diffract a considerable part of the incident molecules, just as Stern and others have found a great deal of reflection and diffraction to occur when molecular beams are incident on certain crystals, and it might well be that this effect is greatly diminished by the presence of adsorbed gas.

Roberts found also that for helium on tungsten a increased markedly *after prolonged heating of the tungsten;* the initial difference between the clean and the gassy states of the surface still persisted, however. This effect of prolonged heating he ascribed to a fine-grained roughening of the surface caused by the attendant evaporation. The principal values of a obtained by him are collected along with others in a table on page 323. Those described as referring to clean tungsten were obtained by making several observations in quick succession just after the filament had been flashed and then extrapolating to zero time, while those referring to gas-filmed tungsten were obtained after the filament had stood overnight. The decrease in a observed at low temperatures suggests that perhaps at absolute zero it may practically vanish; this would be reasonable, since at that temperature the molecules of a solid must be frozen into a very rigid lattice. The much higher values found for argon would naturally be ascribed to the heavier mass of its molecule, were it not that Roberts obtained about the same value for neon ($M = 20$) as for helium ($M = 4$); the true cause is, perhaps, more likely to be found somehow in the stronger attractive force-fields of the argon molecule.

181. Magnitude of the Accommodation Coefficient. Also included in the table on page 323 are some values of the accommodation coefficient a obtained in the pioneer investigations of Soddy and Berry[*] and of Knudsen[†], as recalculated with better formulas by Smoluchowski;[‡] because of imperfections in the experimental method they are of interest chiefly because of the variety of substances investigated.

It is quite otherwise, however, with Knudsen's much later investigation made in 1930,[§] in which he measured the heat loss through hydrogen and through helium from a platinum strip, first with both sides bright and then with one side blackened with platinum black. From these observations and the equivalent of eq. (242f) the accommodation coefficient for both sorts of platinum surface could be found. Furthermore, he measured also the *force* on the strip when its sides were dissimilar, and then compared this force with a calculated value obtained on the assumption that the recoil from molecules rebounding from a surface is proportional to the kinetic energy that they carry away. This comparison was assumed to give the value of the accommodation coefficient for *translatory* energy alone. The latter came out within 2 per cent the same as the coefficient for the entire energy as determined from the thermal measurements; this agreement he interpreted as lending support to the assumption made in the theoretical work as to the equality of the coefficient for all kinds of molecular energy.

The results quoted in the table from Dickins' paper[||] were obtained at much higher pressures, at which the other type of theory should be applicable (Sec. **177**). He measured the heat loss from a platinum wire of radius 0.00376 cm stretched down the center of a tube cooled by water. Various gases were employed in the tube, and the pressure, ranging mostly from 1 to 10 cm (13 to 62 in the case of H_2), was high enough to keep the mean free path under one tenth of the diameter of the wire.

Our eq. (239b) should apply to this case. In it the term g_2/r_2 can be neglected in comparison with g_1/r_1, since $r_2/r_1 = 89$, and g_1, the slip distance for the gas in contact with the wire, being inversely proportional to the pressure, can be written g_{11}/p where g_{11} is at most

---

[*] Soddy and Berry, *Roy. Soc. Proc.*, **83**, 254 (1910); **84**, 576 (1911).

[†] Knudsen, *Ann. Physik*, **34**, 593 (1911); **36**, 871 (1911).

[‡] Smoluchowski, *Phil. Mag.*, **21**, 11 (1911); *Ann. Physik*, **35**, 983 (1911).

[§] Knudsen, *Ann. Physik*, **6**, 129 (193C`

[||] Dickins, *Roy. Soc. Proc.*, **143**, 517 (1933).

a function of the temperature. With these changes (239*b*) can be written

$$\frac{1}{\Lambda} = \frac{r_1}{K} \log \frac{r_2}{r_1} + \frac{g_{11}}{pK},$$

K being the thermal conductivity of the gas. From this equation it is evident that $1/\Lambda$ plotted against $1/p$ should be a straight line, since K is independent of the pressure; from its intercept K can be calculated, and from its slope, g_{11}, and from this the accommodation coefficient. Dickins' data gave good straight lines when plotted in this way except at the highest pressures, where a drop in the curves indicated a more rapid increase in Λ, which he ascribes to incipient convection. Correction was made for the small radiation losses. The wire temperature ranged from 10 to 40°C with the tube kept at zero, so he also extrapolated the results to 0°C.

ACCOMMODATION COEFFICIENTS

On platinum:

	He	Ne	Ar	H_2	CO	O_2	N_2	N_2O	CO_2	NH_3	SO_2	CH_4	C_2H_2
(1)	0.38	0.75	0.80	0.24, 0.18	0.59	0.62	0.68	0.56	0.52				
(2)	0.50	....	0.88	0.34	0.80	0.82	0.81	0.76	0.78	0.66	0.73	0.49	0.52

(3) H_2 on glass (recalc. by Smoluchowski) 0.36

(4) He on glass, 130°C . . . . . (0.32)

(5) On bright platinum:
   H_2 . . . . 0.32
   He 0.44
  On Pt-blackened Pt:
   H_2 . . . . 0.74
   He 0.91

(6) H_2 on clean tungsten (1000°C) 0.54
  H_2 on tungsten:
   H_2 film . . . . $a \geqq 0.14$
   O_2 or oxide film . . . . . . 0.1 to 0.2

(7) He on clean fresh tungsten 0.07
  He on clean long-heated tungsten 0.18
  He on gas-filmed fresh t 0.19
  He on gas-filmed long-heated tungsten 0.55
  He on clean fresh tungsten, 22°C 0.057
   −78°C, 0.046; −194°C 0.025
  He on nickel 0.085

(8) He on clean tungsten (old?) 0.17
  He on gas-filmed tungsten (old?) 0.82
  Ar on clean tungsten (old?) 0.53
  Ar on gas-filmed t (old?) . . . 1.00

(1) Soddy and Berry, mostly as recalculated by Smoluchowski; (2) Dickins, recalculated; (3) Knudsen, 1911; (4) Ornstein and van Wyk. Especially reliable: (5) Knudsen, 1930; (6) Blodgett and Langmuir; (7) Roberts; (8) Michels.

Unfortunately, however, the formulas used by Dickins in calculating a from g are unsatisfactory; he employed an old formula suggested tentatively at one time by Smoluchowski, and combined with it

Meyer's old formula for the viscosity. The values of a that would be obtained by substituting his values of g, obtained in the manner just described, into our formula (238a) can be found by multiplying the value that he gives in his paper for the quantity $\dfrac{2-a}{a}$ by $\dfrac{15}{16}$ $(\gamma + 1)\,\dfrac{\eta c_v}{K}$; this gives the value of $\dfrac{2-a}{a}$ that corresponds to our (238a).

Values of a obtained in this way from Dickins' data are given in the table above. They are smaller than the values calculated by Dickins himself, but are at the same time considerably larger than the older values calculated from the data that were obtained at much lower pressures by Soddy and Berry. This latter discrepancy is not surprising, however, in view of the imperfection of the older work; furthermore, it must not be forgotten that our formula (238a), while probably the best available, is itself subject to some uncertainty.

It appears on the whole that our knowledge of the actual value of the accommodation coefficient is not yet very extensive.

The fact that a as calculated from the theoretical formulas never exceeds unity and is never absurdly small indicates, however, that we must be on the right track in our analysis of these phenomena.

182. Spectral Emission by an Unequally Heated Gas. The illuminating experiment reported by Ornstein and van Wyk* deserves mention because it furnishes a direct test of the assumption that we have been making in regard to the distribution of velocities among the molecules.

These investigators passed an electric discharge through a thin layer of helium at extremely low pressure between two glass tubes, of which one was heated electrically to 650°K while the other was kept at 370°, and observed the shape of a spectral line emitted by the helium in a direction perpendicular to the tubes. With this arrangement, one half of the observed line comes from molecules that last struck the hot tube and the other half from those that last struck the cold one, which had been roughened with CuO. It was found that the half line from the colder molecules, when interpreted by the usual Doppler theory (cf. Sec. 35), corresponded exactly to a maxwellian distribution of velocities at a temperature of 400°K, whereas the other half, corresponding roughly to a temperature of 480°K, was not quite maxwellian but exhibited a slight relative deficit of low-speed molecules. A departure from the maxwellian form to the extent observed in this experiment would, however, introduce no serious error into the theory.

* Ornstein and van Wyk, *Zeits. Physik*, **78**, 734 (1932).

From their data they calculate an accommodation coefficient of $(480 - 400)/(650 - 400) = 0.32$ for helium on glass. They recognize, however, that their observations really furnish information in regard to the energy of the molecules which are present at a given moment in a given volume, rather than of those which strike a surface in a given time.

183. Theoretical Calculations of the Accommodation Coefficient. Up to this point we have treated the accommodation coefficient as a constant to be determined experimentally and have dealt with its relation to the process of heat conduction. The value of the coefficient itself, however, must depend upon the properties of the molecules, and a number of attempts have been made to calculate its value on the basis of some hypothesis concerning the mode of interaction of gas molecules with solid or liquid surfaces.

In terms of classical theory Baule showed[*] that, if all molecules concerned behave like elastic spheres and have random directions of motion, and if m_1 denotes the mass of a gas molecule and v_1, v_1' its speeds, respectively, before and after striking a molecule of the surface, while m_2, v_2 denote mass and speed of the latter molecule before collision, then for the average squares

$$\overline{v_1'^2} = \frac{m_1^2 + m_2^2}{(m_1 + m_2)^2} \overline{v_1^2} + \frac{2m_2^2}{(m_1 + m_2)^2} \overline{v_2^2}.$$

The mean loss of energy by the gas molecules is thus

$$m_1\overline{v_1^2} - m_1\overline{v_1'^2} = \frac{2m_1m_2}{(m_1 + m_2)^2} (m_1\overline{v_1^2} - m_2\overline{v_2^2}),$$

in which $\frac{1}{2} m_2\overline{v_2^2}$ may also be regarded as representing the mean kinetic energy of a gas molecule at the temperature of the surface. Accordingly, comparison of this equation with the defining equation for the accommodation coefficient, eq. (235), shows us that, if only kinetic energy of translation had to be considered, and if each gas molecule struck the surface only once before returning into the gas, the coefficient would have the value

$$a = \frac{2m_1m_2}{(m_1 + m_2)^2}.$$

This expression has the maximum value $a = \frac{1}{2}$ when $m_1 = m_2$ and becomes small whenever the molecular masses are very unequal. Larger values of a than $\frac{1}{2}$ could occur for hard spheres moving as

---

[*] BAULE, *Ann. Physik*, **44**, 145 (1914).

classical mass points only if the gas molecule made several impacts with the surface before escaping, as it might well do if the surface were very rough on the molecular scale, or if the gas molecules were heavier than those composing the surface.

The correct theory must, however, be a wave-mechanical one; and an attempt to develop such has been made for helium in contact with tungsten by Jackson and Howarth.* According to modern ideas, the atoms in metallic tungsten are arranged in a tightly bound crystal lattice having, for a total number N of atoms, $3N$ degrees of freedom. To simplify their calculations, however, Jackson and Howarth replace this lattice by a continuous block of material; and they assume then that an approaching helium atom has with the surface mutual potential energy $V = Ce^{-by}$. The latter law of force agrees well in form with what we know of atomic fields at short ranges. On the other hand, it represents repulsion at all values of the distance y of the center of the approaching atom from the surface of the tungsten, whereas there is undoubtedly in reality at the larger distances an attraction of van der Waals nature; in the particular case of helium, however, the effect of the latter forces can be shown to be pretty small.

The $3N$ possible modes of vibration of the tungsten mass were then treated in the manner introduced by Debye for handling the specific heat of solids. The impact of the helium atom excites these modes in varying degrees, and the wave-mechanical treatment leads eventually to a probability formula for the energy with which a helium atom is reflected, as a function of its incident velocity; from this formula the accommodation coefficient for a maxwellian stream of atoms is then calculated. In the Debye theory the stiffness of the solid is represented by a certain characteristic temperature; for this the authors insert the value 205°K as given by Lindemann's empirical relation between this quantity and the melting point. The constant C in the potential energy was eliminated by adjusting the theoretical curve to fit the data at one temperature.

In this way the authors secured a good fit with Roberts' data for three temperatures as given in the preceding table. The constant in the potential-energy function, $V = Ce^{-by}$, was assumed to have the value $b = 4 \times 10^8$; this is not very different from the corresponding constant in Slater's formula for the mutual field of two helium atoms, which is, as stated in eq. (177a) in Sec. 121,

$$\frac{2.43}{5.29 \times 10^{-9}} = 4.6 \times 10^8.$$

* JACKSON and HOWARTH, *Roy. Soc. Proc.*, **142**, 447 (1933).

Such an agreement is encouraging, since we should expect these two constants to be at least of the same order of magnitude.

An extension of the theory to include the effect of the attraction at larger distances, so that it should apply to neon as well, has been given recently by Devonshire on the basis of work by Lennard-Jones.*

THERMAL CREEP AND THE RADIOMETER

184. Thermal Creep. One of the most striking and peculiar phenomena at low pressure is the radiometric force that acts in an unequally heated gas upon any foreign body suspended in it. A fairly satisfactory explanation of this force has been achieved in recent years, but it is rather involved, and accordingly it is conducive to clarity to consider first the fundamental process that was pointed out by Maxwell as the probable cause of the phenomenon.

In seeking an understanding of the radiometric action, Maxwell first investigated the stresses in an unequally heated stationary mass of gas and showed, for his special type of molecule repelling as the inverse fifth power of the distance, that the stresses are unaffected in the first order of a temperature gradient. The same conclusion can be drawn for any type of molecule from our own first approximation to the modified velocity distribution; we wrote for this $f_0 + f_s$, where

$$f_0 = Ae^{-\beta^2 v^2}, \qquad f_s = Cv_x(\tfrac{5}{2} - \beta^2 v^2)e^{-\beta^2 v^2}$$

as in eqs. (141b) and (148b) in Secs. 95 and 97 above, and if these functions are substituted in the expressions for the transfer of normal and tangential momentum, $\sum v_x^2 = \int v_x^2(f_0 + f_s)\,d\kappa$ and $\sum v_x v_y = \int v_x v_y(f_0 + f_s)\,d\kappa$ [cf. (124) and (125) in Sec. 85], the contribution of f_s to the integrals is found to be nil.

At an unequally heated boundary of the gas, however, Maxwell showed that a special effect was to be expected in the form of a steady creep of the gas over the surface from colder to hotter regions. The cause lies in the fact that, when the gas is hotter over one part of the wall than over an adjacent part, molecules impinging obliquely upon it strike with higher average velocity when they come from the hotter region than when they come from the colder, and so are kicked back more strongly by the wall (except in the special case of specular reflection), with the result that the gas acquires tangential momentum directed toward the hotter side. Maxwell's result for the rate of the resulting creep can easily be obtained from our approximate distribution function for a conducting gas.

* DEVONSHIRE, *Roy. Soc. Proc.*, **158**, 269 (1937).

185. The Creep Velocity. Near a bounding wall let the temperature of the gas vary so that it increases uniformly at the rate $T' = dT/ds$ in a direction inclined at an angle θ to the normal to the wall (cf. Fig. 76). Let us take the x-axis outward along the normal and place the xy-plane so that the gradient T' is parallel to it. For an approxi-

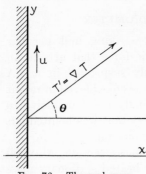

mate theory let us now make an assumption corresponding to that made in treating temperature jump, i.e., that all of the molecules which have a component of motion *toward* the wall are distributed in velocity like the same group in the midst of the gas. Their distribution function will then be $f = f_0 + f_s$, with the values of f_0 and f_s stated in the last paragraph, except that in the expression for f_s we must now replace v_x by the component of **v** in the direction of T' or $v_x \cos \theta + v_y \sin \theta$.

Fig. 76.—Thermal creep.

The total component of momentum in the y-direction of those molecules that strike unit area of the surface in a second will then be [cf. (125) in Sec. 85]

$$-nm\int_{v_x<0} v_x v_y [A + C(v_x \cos \theta + v_y \sin \theta)(\tfrac{5}{2} - \beta^2 v^2)]e^{-\beta^2 v^2}\, d\kappa,$$

$d\kappa$ standing as usual for $dv_x\, dv_y\, dv_z$, but the integral over v_x extending only over negative values. Here the A and $\cos \theta$ terms go out by symmetry as v_y ranges from $-\infty$ to $+\infty$; but the $\sin \theta$ term gives*

$$-\frac{\pi}{8}\frac{nmC}{\beta^6}\sin \theta.$$

Now under our assumptions C must have the value proper to a steady state in the conducting gas several free paths out from the wall, and accordingly our theory of conductivity gives for it the value obtained from eq. (154a) in Sec. 100 with the value of $D\Sigma v_x v^2$ inserted from (154c) in Sec. 101. In the latter equation dT/dx represents the temperature gradient, which we are now denoting by T'. We obtain in this way

$$C = \left(\frac{3}{4}\frac{\beta^8}{\pi\sqrt{2}}\frac{1}{n^2 S_{vc}}\right)\frac{5}{4}\frac{\pi^{3/2}}{\beta^7}\frac{nA}{T} T'.$$

For S_{vc} it is best to employ the value given by (156b) at the end of Sec. 101,

---

* Cf. table of integrals at end of the book.

$$\frac{1}{S_{vc}} = \frac{32\sqrt{2}}{5\pi}\frac{\eta}{m\bar{v}},$$

for the viscosity η is in most gases more simply related to the translatory molecular motion than is the thermal conductivity.

If we then also insert $A = \beta^3/\pi^{3/2}$, our expression for the stream density of y-momentum reduces to

$$-\frac{3}{4\pi}\frac{\eta}{\beta^2\bar{v}}\frac{T'}{T}\sin\theta.$$

Now suppose that in rebounding from the wall these molecules lose to it at least part of their average tangential momentum. Then the layer of gas next to the wall will experience a steady drain of momentum, and this is not counterbalanced by a net inflow from the remainder of the gas; for we have seen above that the flow of tangential momentum across any plane drawn in the midst of the gas vanishes. This layer will accordingly be set into tangential motion, and it will then set adjacent layers into motion by viscous drag upon them.

Suppose the final result is that the whole mass of gas moves at uniform velocity u toward $y = +\infty$. Then this motion will add to the flow of tangential momentum up to the wall a superposed stream of density $\frac{1}{4}\rho\bar{v}u$ units of momentum per unit area per second [cf. (72b) in Sec. 37]. To keep the gas moving steadily the two streams of y-momentum must just cancel each other. This will be the case provided

$$u = \frac{3}{\pi}\frac{\eta}{\rho\beta^2\bar{v}^2}\frac{T'}{T}\sin\theta = \frac{3}{4}\frac{\eta R}{p}\frac{\partial T}{\partial y}, \tag{243}$$

the second form following by means of (65a) or $\beta\bar{v} = 2/\sqrt{\pi}$, $p = \rho RT$ and the observation that $T'\sin\theta = \partial T/\partial y$. Here p = pressure in terms of dynes, R = gas constant for a gram of the gas, η = viscosity, and $\partial T/\partial y$ represents the gradient of the temperature along the bounding wall.

In most cases, however, the surroundings will prevent the whole mass of gas from moving uniformly. Under such circumstances velocity gradients will be set up in the gas, and these may then be accompanied by viscous slip over the surface, such as was discussed in Secs. 165 to 169 above. To the first order, however, the velocity of slip will simply be superposed at the boundary upon the *velocity of thermal creep u* as given by (243). It is to viscous stresses indirectly called into play in this manner that Maxwell ascribed the radiometric force.

It should not be forgotten that formula (243) is subject to considerable uncertainty because of the arbitrary assumption upon which it rests in regard to the form of the departure from Maxwell's law near the boundary.

To give some idea of the rapidity of the creep, we may insert in (243), for air at 15°C, $\eta = 179.5 \times 10^{-6}$ and $R = 2.871 \times 10^6$; then, at atmospheric pressure or $p = 1.013 \times 10^6$, we find

$$u = 3.8 \times 10^{-4} \frac{\partial T}{\partial y} \text{ cm/sec.}$$

This is small, but if we lower the pressure to 1 mm Hg and make the temperature gradient over the surface $\partial T/\partial y = 10°$ per centimeter, we find $u = 2.9$ cm/sec.

186. Thermal Pressure Gradients and Transpiration. Thermal creep will obviously have an effect upon the motion of gases in tubes, and in some cases this may be of practical importance. If the tube is unequally heated, there may be a resulting flow of gas along it, even in the absence of a pressure gradient; or, if the circumstances are such as to prevent such a flow, then a steady pressure gradient may be set up with the gas at rest. Measurements of gaseous pressure by means of external gauges at a different temperature may require correction for pressure differences arising in this way in the connecting tubes.

Such effects constitute in part what has been called thermal transpiration, which has already been discussed to some extent. As usual, the two limiting cases of high and low density can be handled easily but require different methods, whereas the intermediate case presents great difficulty.

Let us consider first the free-molecule case, assuming the pressure to be so extremely low that the mean free path is many times the diameter of the tube. The appropriate formula can then be found immediately by modifying the calculation given in Sec. 171 above; we have only to allow $\bar{v}$ to vary with the temperature along the tube, replacing the relation $\bar{v}n' = \bar{v}\left(n + x\frac{dn}{dx}\right)$ as there written by

$$n'\bar{v}' = n\bar{v} + x\frac{d(n\bar{v})}{dx}.$$

We then obtain for the mass passing per second, in place of the expression previously found,

$$Q_m = -\frac{1}{2\sqrt{2\pi R}}\left[\int dS \int_0^{2\pi} s\, d\varphi\right]\frac{d}{dx}\left(\frac{p}{\sqrt{T}}\right),$$

or, in a round tube of radius a, where $\int dS \int_0^{2\pi} s \, d\varphi = 16\pi a^3/3$,

$$Q_m = -\frac{4}{3}\sqrt{\frac{2\pi}{R}} \, a^3 \frac{d}{dx} \frac{p}{\sqrt{T}}.$$

As a check, we note that, when T is constant, these equations yield (233a) and (233b) again upon multiplying through by RT.

The condition for zero flow is then that $p/\sqrt{T}$ be constant along the tube. We have thus a typical case of the phenomenon called thermal transpiration, which has already been sufficiently discussed (Sec. 39).

187. Thermal Gradients at Moderate Pressures. Let us next allow the density of the gas to be high enough so that the mean free path is small as compared with the diameter of the tube, and that this diameter in turn is small as compared with its length. Then it is easy to extend Poiseuille's formula so as to allow for the presence of a temperature gradient along the tube. In our deduction of that formula as given in Sec. 166 we have only to add a thermal term in the boundary condition for the velocity at the wall of the tube, writing in place of

$$v = -\zeta \frac{dv}{dr}$$

the more general expression

$$v = -\zeta \frac{dv}{dr} + \frac{3}{4} \frac{\eta R}{p} \frac{dT}{dx},$$

in which the second term represents the velocity of thermal creep as given by (243). The velocity is then found to be

$$v = -\frac{1}{4\eta}(a^2 - r^2 + 2\zeta a)\frac{dp}{dx} + \frac{3}{4}\frac{\eta R}{p}\frac{dT}{dx};$$

and integrating as before, we find for the mass of gas transferred per second past any point of a long round tube of radius a, where the pressure p and temperature T have gradients dp/dx and dT/dx, respectively,

$$Q_m = -\frac{\pi}{8}\frac{a^4 p}{\eta R T}\left(1 + 4\frac{\zeta}{a}\right)\frac{dp}{dx} + \frac{3\pi}{4}\frac{\eta a^2}{T}\frac{dT}{dx}, \tag{244}$$

R being the gas constant for a gram of the gas, η its viscosity, and ζ its slip distance at the wall of the tube.

For the case of *steady flow* the distribution of pressure and of temperature along the tube can then be found by setting Q_m equal to a constant, and the rate of flow itself can then be calculated.

Only the static case of *no flow* will be considered further here, however. In this case the temperature gradient must be accompanied by a pressure gradient whose value, found by setting $Q_m = 0$, is

$$\frac{dp}{dx} = \frac{6\eta^2 R}{a^2 p \left(1 + \frac{4\zeta}{a}\right)} \frac{dT}{dx}. \tag{245a}$$

We have here a situation in which the gas is creeping steadily along the walls of the tube and is at the same time flowing back through the central part, as is suggested in Fig. 77; the pressure gradient is necessary in order to maintain the return flow.

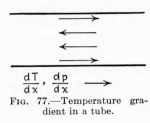

$\dfrac{dT}{dx}, \dfrac{dp}{dx} \longrightarrow$

Fig. 77.—Temperature gradient in a tube.

To integrate the last equation we need to know the mode of variation of η and ζ with x. Now ζ is nearly equal to the mean free path and so varies roughly inversely as the density, or inversely as the pressure and directly as the temperature; η also varies with temperature, but in a less simple manner. An accurate result can be obtained in any actual case by means of numerical integration. A rough estimate can, however, be obtained simply by replacing η^2 by its average value $\overline{\eta^2}$ over the actual range of temperature, and also setting $p\zeta = \zeta_1$, the value of ζ for $p = 1$ dyne/cm²; we may then give to ζ_1 its value for the average temperature, which will be denoted by $\zeta_{1\bar{T}}$. If we then also replace p by $\frac{1}{2}(p_1 + p_2)$, eq. (245a) can be integrated at once; the result can be written thus:

$$p_1 - p_2 = \frac{6\overline{\eta^2}R}{a^2 p_q}(T_1 - T_2), \qquad p_q = \frac{1}{2}(p_1 + p_2) + 4\frac{\zeta_{1\bar{T}}}{a}, \tag{245b}$$

p_1, T_1 and p_2, T_2 standing for values at the two ends of the tube.

This formula can be used in estimating the order of magnitude of possible pressure differences due to temperature gradients in vacuum apparatus, such as might, for instance, falsify measurements of the pressure. As a numerical example, for air at 15°C, $\eta = 179.5 \times 10^{-6}$, $R = 2.871 \times 10^6$, both in c.g.s. units; hence if $a = 0.5$ mm and if we use the value of η^2 at 15° for $\overline{\eta^2}$, we have $\dfrac{(p_1 - p_2)p_q}{(T_1 - T_2)} = 222$, or 1.25×10^{-4} if the pressure is expressed in millimeters Hg. If then, in particular, we make the temperature difference $T_1 - T_2 = 100$°C, omit $4 \frac{\xi_1 \bar{\imath}}{a}$, and choose for the mean pressure $\bar{p} = \frac{1}{2} (p_1 + p_2) = p_q = 0.5$ mm, which brings the mean free path to about $a/5$, (245*b*) gives for the pressure difference due to creep $p_1 - p_2 = 0.025$ mm, or 5 per cent of the mean pressure.

The relative pressure drop due to creep varies rapidly with the tube diameter and the pressure p_q, being inversely proportional to the square of both these quantities; it may thus be quite negligible under some circumstances, and very appreciable under others.

A few data for a critical test of these results are available in a paper of Knudsen's.* Without going into detail, it may be said that his observations seem to agree roughly with theoretical predictions in so far as these should apply.

188. The Radiometer and Photophoresis. It was discovered by Fresnel in 1825 that a small body suspended in a gas is sometimes set into motion when light falls upon it. The effect was exhaustively studied by Crookes (1874–1878) and has formed the subject of numerous recent investigations. Often the body in question takes the form of a wheel carrying vanes blackened on one side, which revolves continuously when illuminated; or, to measure the force, a light vane may be mounted on one end of a crossbar, with a counterpoise or another vane at the other end, and the bar may then lie suspended from a torsion fiber so that its deflection can be read with mirror and telescope. An analogous motion of microscopic particles suspended in a gas was observed in 1914 by Ehrenhaft and was called by him "photophoresis." Some particles move toward the light, others against it.

The laws governing all of these phenomena appear to be substantially the same. The force is found to be strictly proportional to the intensity of illumination, so that mechanical devices of the sort described can be used to measure a beam of radiation; for this reason they have come to be called radiometers. With increasing pressure, the force rises to a maximum at a pressure of about 1 mm Hg in the case of a disk of ordinary size, or at several hundred millimeters of Hg in the case of photophoresis, and then decreases rapidly.

It has been pretty well established that in all cases the light acts by heating the suspended body; the same effects can, in fact, be produced by establishing in the gas such a temperature gradient as will give rise to the same temperature differences at the surface of the suspended body. The general rule is that hot surfaces behave as if repelled by the gas. The movements *toward* the light which are often observed in photophoresis are ascribed to greater heating of the far side of a

* KNUDSEN, *Ann. Physik*, **31**, 205 (1910).

transparent particle; this latter effect has been successfully imitated with a radiometer carrying disks of molybdenite, one of whose surfaces was fresher than the other.

Various opinions have been expressed from time to time as to the origin of the radiometric force. A tempting hypothesis at first sight is that it is due to the reaction from gaseous molecules rebounding with higher velocities from a hot surface than from a cold one; but this is quickly seen to be untenable when we reflect that such molecules, upon reentering the gas, must drive it back and thereby thin it out until uniformity of pressure is reestablished, whereupon the force on the hot surface will become the same as on the cold one and no radiometric action can occur. The cause must, therefore, be sought in some secondary action. The effect has very commonly been regarded

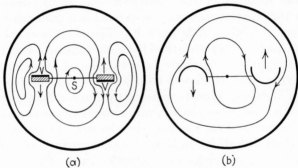

(a)   (b)

Fig. 78.—Production of the radiometer effect.

as occurring at the edge of the radiometer disk, where conditions in the gas must be far from uniform; experiments designed to show that it is simply proportional to the length of the perimeter failed, however, to yield this result. Recent theoretical and experimental studies have now made it pretty clear that most, if not all, radiometric phenomena are due, in one way or another, as Maxwell suggested in 1879, to the thermal creep of the gas over an unequally heated solid (or liquid) surface, as described in Sec. 184 above.

It can be seen easily that this creep must give rise to forces on the surface whenever the resulting flow of gas is hindered in any way. In a simple two-vane radiometer, for example, the gas will creep around the edges toward the centers of the blackened and therefore heated surfaces, and must then flow out and around somewhat as suggested in Fig. 78(a), in which the vanes *VV* are supposed to be transparent but blackened on one side; this circulatory motion is then hindered by viscosity, and consequently the gas accumulates somewhat over the blackened surfaces and exerts a slightly increased pressure on these and so pushes them back, thus tending to produce revolution about the suspension S. If, on the other hand, the vanes are alike on both sides but are given a cup-shaped form, as in Fig. 78b, or are fitted with points, the edges of the cups or the points are observed to move toward the light. Presumably these parts are more effectively cooled by the gas than are other parts, so that a circulation is set up as suggested in the figure, and those eddies which reach out to the surroundings are effective by reaction in moving the vanes. Most practical cases can readily be understood in this way.

The existence of such streams in the gas as we have here postulated was shown directly by Gerlach and Schütz.* They suspended a tiny vanelet near the radiometer and observed that it became deflected, presumably by the action of the streaming gas, in the right direction. Another interesting experiment pointing to the same conclusion is that of Czerny and Hettner,† who mounted a movable disk parallel to another disk along which a temperature gradient was maintained (Fig. 79). They observed that a tangential force acted on the movable disk in such a direction that it could be explained

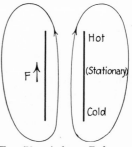

Fig. 79.—A force F due to thermal creep.

as arising from viscous drag by the gas as it creeps along the unequally heated disk.

189. The Quantitative Theory of Radiometer Action. Qualitatively the creep theory of radiometric action is completely successful. A quantitative calculation of the force, however, presents, unfortunately, a difficult problem. One has first to solve the thermal problem in order to find the distribution of temperature, which is determined, under the given conditions of illumination or of boundary temperature, by the conduction of heat through the gas and through the disk itself; allowance must also be made, if accuracy is desired, for convection of heat by the creep motion itself. Then one has to solve the hydrodynamical problem of the streaming as determined by the velocity of creep as a boundary condition; and, finally, from this the total pressure on the disk is found by integration.

The complete problem has been solved only for the ideal case of an ellipsoidal disk, circular in principal outline but of elliptical cross section, which, if thin, should present some approximation to a flat

* Gerlach and Schütz, *Zeits. Physik,* **78,** 43, 418 (1932); **79,** 700 (1932); **81,** 418 (1933).

† Czerny and Hettner, *Zeits. Physik,* **30,** 258 (1924).

disk. The best treatment is that of Epstein.* His result for the force F on the disk in terms of the temperature difference ΔT between the centers of its sides can be written, for a thin disk,

$$F = -3\pi \frac{R\eta^2}{p} \Delta T,$$

R being the gas constant for a gram of the gas, η its viscosity, and p its pressure. ΔT is here assumed to arise either from a temperature gradient, which at great distances is parallel to the axis of the disk and of uniform magnitude dT/dx, or from a uniform beam of light of intensity J ergs/cm²/sec; the values of ΔT for these two cases are

$$(1) \quad \Delta T = \frac{4}{\pi} \frac{a}{1 + \frac{2}{\pi} \frac{k_d}{k_g} \frac{a}{\delta}} \frac{dT}{dx}, \qquad (2) \quad \Delta T = \frac{2}{\pi} \frac{aJ}{k_g + \frac{2}{\pi} k_d \frac{a}{\delta}}.$$

Here a is the radius of the disk, δ its thickness, and k_d the conductivity of its material, while k_g is the conductivity of the surrounding gas.

If the disk is *nonconducting* ($k_d = 0$), the force under illumination is

$$F = -\frac{6R\eta^2 aJ}{pk_g},$$

and is thus proportional to the radius, or also to the perimeter, of the disk. This latter fact is suggestive of an edge effect, but the analysis shows that the force is in reality distributed over the surface.

At the opposite extreme of a very highly conducting or extremely thin disk ($k_d a/k_g \delta$ large), the force is

$$F = -3\pi \frac{R\eta^2 \delta J}{pk_d}$$

and so independent of the radius.

For a quantitative test of Epstein's formula, Gerlach and Schütz (*loc. cit.*) constructed an almost nonconductive disk by mounting platinum foil on both sides of a mica disk 9 mm across, the foil on the side toward the light being smoked. Their observed forces exceeded those which they calculated from Epstein's formula. Their calculations were made, however, from a formula into which Epstein had converted his result by inserting $\eta = 0.35\rho\bar{v}L$,† but in this they inserted

---

* Epstein, *Zeits. Physik*, **54,** 537 (1929).

† It seems rather better as a rule not to introduce L into the statement of any final results if that can be avoided, because so many different formulas for it have been employed.

Sexl [*Zeits. Physik*, **52,** 249 (1928)] obtains a final expression for the force that

values of L, presumably taken from a table, which were obviously calculated from the modern formula, $\eta = 0.499\rho\bar{v}L$. If the latter is employed in converting Epstein's expression, the theoretical forces in Gerlach and Schütz's experiment come out nearly twice as large; the experimental force is then only about half as large as the theoretical in air, whereas in hydrogen it exceeds the theoretical value only by 20 per cent at the higher pressures and drops below it at the lower. The pressure ranged from 0.1 to 1 mm in both cases.

In view of the many uncertainties this degree of agreement between theory and experiment must be regarded as very encouraging, particularly because, as remarked by Gerlach and Schütz, an overestimate by theory is to be expected, since in the theoretical treatment cooling by creep convection is neglected, and also L/δ was assumed to be small; the latter was not true in the actual case.

---

differs from Epstein's, when $n = 0$, only because he writes $\eta = \frac{1}{3}\rho\bar{v}L$; his result is really limited to the case $n = 0$ because of an assumption that is made in regard to the value of K or k_g.

CHAPTER IX

STATISTICAL MECHANICS

In this chapter we shall finally take up for discussion the basis of those statistical principles which we have already employed several times without proof. This forms the subject matter of what is called statistical mechanics. It is a branch of theory which is very abstract and also, because of its difficulty, incompletely worked out. We have space here only to survey briefly the main line of thought, confining our discussion for the most part to those topics which bear on the theory of gases.

190. Nature of Statistical Mechanics. In statistical work we are concerned, not with complete knowledge of the state of a dynamical system, but only with certain broad features of its behavior which happen to be physically significant. Very often these features are of the nature of an average of some sort; for example, we have already noted that quantities such as pressure or density represent averages, taken over macroscopically small spaces and times, of molecular quantities that vary rapidly. Often it is convenient to deal with probabilities, but these can likewise be identified at will with certain averages; for example, the probability that a molecule is in a certain element of volume $d\tau$ is the same as the fraction of the time during which it is there when the total interval under consideration is made indefinitely long. We may even have to average over various possible molecular motions which are macroscopically indistinguishable. For convenience we shall refer to all such averages and probabilities as *ultimate statistical* features of the system.

Statistical mechanics can accordingly be said to deal with the ultimate statistical features of the behavior of dynamical systems when subjected to specified conditions. Now, since the molecular motions are regulated by mechanical laws, we should naturally expect to be able to derive these features from those laws alone, without being compelled to introduce further postulates representing additional independent laws of nature. To be sure, probability can never be deduced from certainty; probability must somewhere be introduced if we wish to get it out again. But it will be observed that, in all of the conclusions concerning probability which are drawn from

338

statistical mechanics, the element of probability is introduced or postulated in describing the situation to which the conclusion refers, and what we deduce from mechanical laws is only the relation between two probabilities. A simple example would be the calculation from mechanical laws of the chance that a clock pendulum, viewed at a random moment, is close to the end of its swing; here we introduce the idea of probability in posing the question, when we specify that the pendulum is to be viewed at a random moment.

We shall begin with the classical treatment as worked out by Maxwell, Boltzmann, Gibbs, and others, and shall then take up the modifications that are required by wave mechanics. The classical theory, besides its theoretical interest as a limiting case, serves as a guide for the wave-mechanical treatment; and its results seem also to be correct within the range of experimental error for the translatory motion of the molecules in ordinary gases.

A. CLASSICAL STATISTICAL MECHANICS

191. System Phase Space. In the theory of mechanics it is shown that the motion of a dynamical system having s degrees of freedom can conveniently be described in terms of s generalized coordinates q_1, q_2 $\cdots$ q_s, together with s corresponding generalized momenta, p_1, p_2 $\cdots$ p_s; the latter become the ordinary components of momentum, $m\dot{x}$, $m\dot{y}$, $m\dot{z}$ when cartesian coordinates x, y, z are taken as the q's. Each phase of any motion of the system is then represented by a set of values of the s q's and the s p's; and during a particular motion these values vary as definite functions of the time. For example, in the case of a falling body we may take as q the distance the body has fallen from rest; then the momentum is $p = m\dot{q} = gt$, and $q = \frac{1}{2} gt^2$.

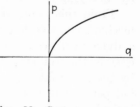

Fig. 80.—System-space trajectory for a falling body.

To many minds it is helpful to think of these variables as the coordinates of a point in a space of $2s$ dimensions, in which the q's and p's play the role of cartesian coordinates. Such a space is commonly called a *phase space;* we shall call it, more specifically, for a reason that will appear later, the *system phase space* or simply *system space.* As the system executes a particular motion its representative point traces out a certain trajectory in system space. Geometrical language such as this will be used freely in what follows. Any reader who finds it distasteful can easily replace our geometrical statements by equivalent analytical ones; for instance, a "trajectory in system space" can be interpreted as meaning merely a succession of sets of values of the q's and p's.

In the example of the falling body the system space is obviously a plane (so long as we leave all lateral motion out of account), and the trajectory of the representative point on this plane is the parabola $q = p^2/2g$, obtained by eliminating t from the equations $p = gt$, $q = \frac{1}{2} gt^2$ (cf. Fig. 80).

192. Representative Ensembles. Instead of contemplating directly the succession of phases through which a single system passes in the course of time, Boltzmann showed that it is more convenient to contemplate an equivalent distribution of phases belonging to different systems, all considered at the same moment. For this purpose we contemplate a huge collection or *ensemble* of replicas of the original system, each of which is executing the same motion but is at any given instant in a different phase of it. If these systems are properly spaced they will give us a complete picture of the behavior throughout time of the given system. In the ensemble we can also include, if we wish, other sets of systems representing in the same way all different motions that the system can execute under the given conditions. The statistical features of the behavior of a single system can then all be obtained by surveying the ensemble at a given moment.

From this point of view the fundamental problem of statistical mechanics is the determination of the correct ensemble to represent a dynamical system under given conditions. The most important case is that of statistical equilibrium. This case is characterized by the fact that the long-time behavior of the system is definite and independent of time. The ensemble that represents it must accordingly be a steady one; it must be represented in system space by a steady density of the moving points, their number in any element of the space $dG = dq_1 dq_2 \cdots dq_s dp_1 dp_2 \cdots dp_s$ being $\rho\, dG$, where ρ does not change with time, although the identity of the points that are momentarily in the element may change.

The simplest type of system for which such an ensemble can readily be set up in full detail is, perhaps, the harmonic oscillator, the study of which led Planck to the quantum theory. The system space for a simple oscillator is, like that of the falling body, a plane, on which its coordinate q and momentum p figure as variables. For the kinetic energy of the oscillator we can write $\frac{1}{2} ap^2$, and for its potential energy, $\frac{1}{2} bq^2$, a and b being constants; hence during an undisturbed oscillation we have, by the conservation of energy,

$$\tfrac{1}{2} ap^2 + \tfrac{1}{2} bq^2 = E = \text{const.}$$

This equation defines for an undisturbed oscillator the trajectory of the representative point on the system plane; the trajectory is obviously an ellipse (cf. Fig. 81).

If we now sow moving points along this ellipse, they will represent oscillators all moving with the same energy E but in different phases of the motion. We can space these points in such a way that they give us at a glance a quantitative picture of the statistical features of the motion of any one oscillator; to do this, we need only allow fresh points to start out one after the other at equal short intervals of time from some chosen location on the ellipse, continuing this process until the first point has gone round once. The points will then form a steady ensemble, for the number of points on any segment of the ellipse will be constant although their identity changes; and it can be shown (cf. Liouville's theorem, Sec. 194) that the fraction of them on any segment is the same as the fraction of the time spent by any one point on that segment.

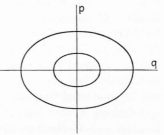

Fig. 81.—Trajectories for a simple harmonic oscillator.

It must be noted, however, that in one important respect this example is misleading. The trajectory corresponding to a definite energy is here a closed curve, but that is not generally true. Unfortunately, open trajectories confined to a finite region can occur only in systems of two or more dimensions, and for these system space is at least four-dimensional and so is difficult to picture.

193. The Ergodic Surmise. The most important case of equilibrium is that of a system that is either isolated or restrained by a fixed force-field, such as the field of the vessel holding a gas; and only this case will be considered in detail.

The point representing a system under these conditions cannot wander widely in system space but is confined to a surface defined by the condition that the energy has a certain constant value; this is called an *ergodic surface*. In the example of the oscillator described above the ergodic surfaces are obviously the elliptical trajectories there described.

In setting up an ensemble to represent the system, we are then confronted at once by the fundamental question whether all systems whose representative points lie on the same ergodic surface have the same ultimate history, and must, therefore, be included in the ensemble.

Physical intuition would answer this question in the affirmative. The ultimate behavior of an isolated mass of homogeneous gas, for instance, is not observed to depend upon its initial condition.   Much effort has been expended in the effort to establish such a conclusion rigorously, but so far, unfortunately, without success, at least in terms that are of any use in physics.   At this point, therefore, it is necessary to introduce some sort of hypothesis, or rather a *surmise*, since we are presumably dealing with a consequence that should follow rigorously from the laws of mechanics and there is, therefore, no room for any new hypothesis expressing an independent law of nature.

The situation is complicated by the fact that special cases can be cited in which the question must be answered in the negative.   As an example, a mass of gas inside a perfectly smooth spherical vessel, if undisturbed, would retain its initial angular momentum forever. Replicas of the gas, represented by points on the same ergodic surface but having different angular momenta, will, therefore, execute radically different motions; the path of the representative point for each one will be confined to a small part of the ergodic surface.   Again, in a rectangular box, hard-spherical molecules composing a rarefied gas can be so started that each moves forever back and forth at constant speed along a fixed line; in such a case there would be a permanent distribution of velocities which might be anything but maxwellian.

Such cases, however, will be dismissed at once by the physicist as very exceptional.   The slightest scratch on the surface of the spherical vessel, or the slightest deflection of one of the molecules in the box will undoubtedly result in bringing about the normal distribution. Accordingly, we shall assume that in general the affirmative answer is the correct one.   We have not space to discuss here the famous "ergodic" and "quasiergodic" "hypotheses" or surmises which have been suggested in support of this conclusion, but shall simply adopt as true the following statement, which lies close to physical intuition:

Ergodic Surmise.   The ultimate statistical features of the behavior of a dynamical system in statistical equilibrium in a fixed force-field are in general independent of its initial condition, except in so far as this condition consists of the general restrictions that determine the equilibrium.   Whether a given case is or is not a "general one" remains at present, unfortunately, a question that has to be decided in the light of physical intuition and ultimately by experiment.   As a special case, of course, the force-field may be everywhere zero, the system being then isolated.

As applied to a gas, for example, this means that whatever initial state of motion or inequality of temperature, etc., we may give to the gas in the beginning, has no influence in the end on its statistical behavior. Of course, there will be certain features of the initial state that do have such an influence; for instance, if the system is isolated, its energy is fixed by the initial state, and this determines its subsequent history. There is, however, an immense variety of different initial states corresponding to any given value of the energy, all followed, in the long run, by the same ultimate macroscopic behavior.

This principle being adopted, we are guided to a determinate choice of the proper ensemble to represent a system by the following famous theorem:

194. Liouville's Theorem. *If any portion of system phase space is sown thickly and evenly with moving points representing a dynamical system in different possible states of motion, then the laws of motion are such that the density of these points in system space remains constant.*

This theorem is most easily proved from the equations of motion in the Hamiltonian form, which are.

$$\dot{q}_i = \frac{\partial H}{\partial p_i}, \qquad \dot{p}_i = -\frac{\partial H}{\partial q_i}, \qquad (i = 1, 2 \cdots s); \qquad (H)$$

here $\dot{q}_i = dq_i/dt$, etc., and H is the Hamiltonian function of the q's and p's, which may also contain the time explicitly. For the sake of vividness we shall call H the energy, but it must be understood that the theory developed in this chapter is applicable to any case in which there is a Hamiltonian function, whether the latter represents the energy or not.

The proof of Liouville's theorem follows so closely the deduction of the Boltzmann distribution equation, (87) in Sec. 51, that we shall leave the reader to construct most of the details. ρ denoting the density of the moving points, there will be

$$\rho \, \Delta q_1 \, \Delta q_2 \, \cdots \, \Delta q_s \, \Delta p_1 \, \Delta p_2 \, \cdots \, \Delta p_s$$

of them representing systems in which q_1 lies within a range Δq_1, etc. As time goes on, points will cross each of the two faces of the element $\Delta q_1 \cdots \Delta p_s$ which are perpendicular to the q_1-axis at a rate

$$\rho \dot{q}_1 \, \Delta q_2 \, \cdots \, \Delta p_s,$$

in which $\rho \dot{q}_1$ has the value proper to that face; the net outflow across these two faces will thus be

$$\left[\frac{\partial(\rho \dot{q}_1)}{\partial q_1} \right] \Delta q_1 \, \Delta q_2 \, \cdots \, \Delta p_s.$$

Adding up expressions of this sort for all pairs of faces, equating the sum to the net loss of points from the element, and passing to the limit as all Δ's → 0, we obtain as a general differential equation for ρ

$$\frac{\partial \rho}{\partial t} + \sum_{i=1}^{s}\left[\frac{\partial(\rho \dot{q}_i)}{\partial q_i} + \frac{\partial(\rho \dot{p}_i)}{\partial p_i}\right] = 0.$$

Now suppose that at a given moment ρ is uniform throughout a certain region. Then the last equation gives in this region

$$\frac{\partial \rho}{\partial t} = -\rho \sum_{i=1}^{s}\left[\frac{\partial \dot{q}_i}{\partial q_i} + \frac{\partial \dot{p}_i}{\partial p_i}\right] = 0,$$

each term in the sum vanishing by the Hamiltonian equations of motion. Thus ρ remains uniform and constant, as the theorem asserts.*

In consequence of this theorem, a large (strictly speaking, an infinite) group of systems, strewn uniformly over any region in system space, remains uniformly distributed over a region of the same size, although the location and shape of this region may change continually. The region may, of course, include all of system space.

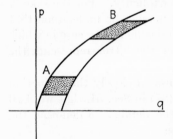

FIG. 82.—A uniform spread of system points for a falling particle.

As an example, we may take the falling particle mentioned in Sec. 191 above, whose ergodic "surfaces" are parabolic curves on the system plane to which system space reduces in such a one-dimensional case. An area such as that dotted at A in Fig. 82, strewn uniformly with moving points, represents many replicas of the falling body dropped from various initial heights and at various times. The area occupied by these points changes its shape as time goes on, as at B; but the reader should be able to verify without difficulty that it does not change in size.

195. The Ergodic Layer and the Microcanonical Ensemble. Let us now return to the consideration of a system which is either isolated or subjected to a fixed force-field, and attack the problem of finding the proper ensemble to represent its statistical behavior.

* "ρ = const. and uniform" is a solution of the differential equation, satisfying the stated initial condition; and there is only one such solution.

Under the conditions specified, H does not contain the time explicitly, and it then follows from the Hamiltonian equations that H remains constant. The representative point in system space moves, therefore, on a fixed ergodic surface defined by the equation,

$$H(p, q) = \text{const.}$$

Suppose, now, we draw two such surfaces corresponding to values $H = E$ and $H = E + \delta E$, enclosing between them a thin slice of system space which we shall call an *ergodic layer;* let us fill this layer uniformly with moving points representing the systems of an ensemble (Fig. 83). Then these points will remain permanently in the layer; and by Liouville's theorem they will remain distributed uniformly over it. The statistical properties of such a *microcanonical* ensemble, as it was called by Gibbs, are obviously the same as those of uniformly distributed *fixed* points in the layer, and so can be studied by geometrical methods.

Furthermore, for the same reason the statistical properties of such an ensemble do not vary with the time; and because of this steadiness we can show, on the basis of principles already laid down, that they are also sensibly the same as the statistical properties of any one system in the layer, in so far as these are not appreciably affected when the energy of the system is varied a little. We can, in fact, infer what we shall call the

Fig. 83.—Diagram representing an ergodic layer in system space.

Principle of Statistical Equivalence. The ultimate statistical properties of a system in statistical equilibrium, either in a fixed force-field or isolated, are the same as those of a microcanonical ensemble containing the system, and are also the same as those of the ergodic layer of fixed points containing the representative points of this ensemble. In particular, the fraction f of the time during which a system possesses some property P is equal to the fraction φ of the systems in the ensemble which possess that property at a given moment, and it is also equal to the fraction of the volume of the ergodic layer whose fixed points represent systems having the property P; and similarly the average of any quantity Q for the system is equal to the instantaneous average of Q over the systems of the ensemble, or to its average as a function of position in the ergodic layer. By volume is meant, of course, $\int dq_1 \cdots dq_s\, dp_1 \cdots dp_s$, and the average of Q over the ergodic layer is $\bar{Q} = \int Q(q_1 \cdots p_s)\, dq_1 \cdots dp_s / \int dq_1 \cdots dp_s$, all integrals extending over the layer. The principle is limited to fractions f or to averages $\bar{Q}$ which do not vary sensibly when the energy of the system is changed by a very small amount δE.

To prove this principle, suppose, first, that each system possesses some property P during a fraction f of the time. Then f will be the same for all systems, in consequence of the ergodic surmise laid down in Sec. 193 above; and the number of "system seconds" during which P is possessed by all ν systems in the ensemble during a long time t will be $\nu f t$. But this number can also be written $\varphi \nu t$, where φ is the steady fraction of the systems of the ensemble that possess P at any given moment. It follows that $f = \varphi$. In the second place, the average value of any molecular variable Q during time t for any one system is $(\bar{Q})_t = \frac{1}{t}\int Q\,dt$, and this by the ergodic surmise is the same for all systems; hence, summing over the ensemble,

$$\nu(\bar{Q})_t = \sum \frac{1}{t}\int Q\,dt = \frac{1}{t}\int \Sigma Q\,dt.$$

But $\Sigma Q = \nu(\bar{Q})_\nu$ where $(\bar{Q})_\nu$ denotes the steady average of Q over the ensemble. Hence, $\nu(\bar{Q})_t = \nu(\bar{Q})_\nu \frac{1}{t}\int dt = \nu(\bar{Q})_\nu$, and $(\bar{Q})_t = (\bar{Q})_\nu$.

As a homely example of the same argument, if at a reception all guests spend the same length of time in the refreshment room, and if at every instant half of them are there, then it must be that each individual guest spends just half his time in that room.

This principle of statistical equivalence furnishes the basis for the entire treatment of systems in equilibrium. Its great advantage lies in the fact that the determination of statistical quantities is thereby reduced to integrations over system space. We shall now consider the application of the principle to some cases that have an important bearing on the theory of gases.

196. The Point-mass Perfect Gas. As a first example, consider a set of N similar monatomic molecules, without internal motion, constituting a perfect gas in a rigid vessel. For their Hamiltonian or energy function we can write

$$H = \frac{1}{2m}\sum_{j=1}^{N}(p_{xj}^2 + p_{yj}^2 + p_{zj}^2) + U_0,$$

of which the first term represents the kinetic energy expressed in terms of the cartesian components of momentum, p_x, p_y, p_z, and U_0 is a potential-energy term expressing the restraining effect of the vessel and so has the value zero except when a molecule comes exceedingly close to the wall.   Of course, there must in reality be still a third term in H representing interaction between the molecules, in order to guarantee statistical equilibrium, but we shall suppose this term to be so small that its effect is otherwise negligible.

For such a system the volumes in system space that we need to evaluate in order to apply the principle of equivalence can easily be found directly.   To find the entire volume of an ergodic layer, it is convenient first to evaluate the volume of all of system space up to a limiting energy E, which is represented by the integral

$$\sigma(E) = \int_{H<E} dp_{x1}\, dp_{y1}\, dp_{z1}\, dp_{x2} \cdot \cdot \cdot dp_{zN}\, dx_1\, dy_1\, dz_1 \cdot \cdot \cdot dz_N,$$

integrated over all values of the momenta and of the coordinates of the N particles such that the Hamiltonian function $H < E$.   The indicated integration over the coordinates themselves can be carried out at once; for the integration pertaining to any one particle gives simply the volume $V = \iiint dx\, dy\, dz$ of the vessel.   Hence

$$\sigma = V^N \int dp_{x1} \cdot \cdot \cdot dp_{zN}, \qquad \frac{1}{2m}\sum_{j=1}^{N}(p_{xj}^2 + p_{yj}^2 + p_{zj}^2) < E$$

(the inequality specifying the range of integration).   Let us introduce here $3N$ new variables μ_1, μ_2, $\cdot \cdot \cdot \mu_{3N}$, each equal to one component of momentum divided by $\sqrt{2mE}$.   Then the integral becomes

$$\int dp_{x1} \cdot \cdot \cdot dp_{zN} = (2mE)^{\frac{3N}{2}} \int d\mu_1 \cdot \cdot \cdot d\mu_{3N}, \qquad \sum_{\tau=1}^{3N}\mu_\tau^2 < 1.$$

The new integral occurring here is independent of E; let it be denoted by C_{3N}.*   Then

$$\sigma = C_{3N}V^N(2mE)^{\frac{3N}{2}}.$$

Since in any practical case N is a huge number, we see from this result that σ varies with E at a prodigious rate.   On the other hand, writing σ' for $d\sigma/dE$, we have

$$\frac{\sigma'}{\sigma} = \frac{3N}{2E},$$

* It is the volume of a unit sphere in $3N$-dimensional space or [cf. (292)]

$$C_{3N} = \frac{\pi^{3N/2}}{\Gamma\left(\dfrac{3N}{2} + 1\right)}.$$

which, besides being of ordinary magnitude, is comparatively steady in value. It follows that E can be varied by an amount sufficient to change σ by an enormous ratio without altering σ'/σ appreciably. For such a variation in the neighborhood of some particular value E_1 we can write, therefore, as a close approximation, $\sigma'/\sigma = 3N/2E_1$, and, integrating,

$$\sigma(E) = D e^{\frac{3NE}{2E_1}},$$

D being a constant. We have then, finally, for the volume of an ergodic layer of indefinitely small thickness δE, replacing E_1 by E after differentiating,

$$\delta\sigma = \sigma'(E)\,\delta E = \frac{3N}{2E}\,\sigma(E)\,\delta E.$$

197. The Molecular Distribution. Molecular Chaos. Now, as a statistical problem to be solved for the gas under consideration, suppose we ask for the probability that, when its total energy is E, a certain molecule, which we may call 1, lies at a given moment in a small element $dK = dp_x\,dp_y\,dp_z\,dx\,dy\,dz$ of the momentum-coordinate phase space for one molecule, its energy being $\frac{1}{2}\,mv^2$ in terms of its mass m and velocity v.

By the principle of statistical equivalence, this probability will be equal to the fractional part of the volume of the ergodic layer within which this particular molecule lies within dK. To find this fraction, we note first that the volume up to E of that part of system space in which molecule 1 lies in dK is got by changing the integral for σ in such a way as to limit the variables of this molecule to dK; the energy of the remaining $N - 1$ molecules, which we shall denote as a variable quantity by H_r, must then stay below $E - \frac{1}{2}\,mv^2$. The volume in question can, therefore, be written

$$I = dK\!\int dp_{x2}\,dp_{y2}\cdots dz_N, \qquad H_r < E - \tfrac{1}{2}\,mv^2.$$

Let us use the notation

$$\sigma_1(E) = \int\limits_{H_r < E} dp_{x2}\,dp_{y2}\cdots dz_N, = a_1 e^{\frac{3(N-1)E}{2E_1}}$$

approximately, in analogy with the expression last written for $\sigma(E)$. Then

$$I = \sigma_1(E - \tfrac{1}{2}\,mv^2)\,dK = a_1 e^{\frac{3(l^r - 1)(E - \frac{1}{2}mv^2)}{2E_1}}\,dK.$$

(Cf. Fig. 84.)

We can now write for the volume of that part of the *ergodic layer* in which molecule 1 lies in dK (shaded in the figure)

$$\frac{dI}{dE}\, \delta E = \frac{3(N-1)}{2E}\, \sigma_1(E)e^{\frac{-3(N-1)mv^2}{4E}}\, dK\, \delta E,$$

E_1 being replaced again by E after differentiating. This in turn forms a fraction

$$\frac{N-1}{N}\frac{\sigma_1(E)}{\sigma(E)}\, e^{\frac{-3(N-1)mv^2}{4E}}\, dK$$

of the whole layer, whose volume $\delta\sigma$ or $\sigma'(E)\, \delta E$ was found above. Here the factors in front of the exponential are constants so long as E is fixed; and in the exponent, $E/(N-1)$ is physically indistinguishable from E/N, which equals $\frac{1}{2}\,m\overline{v^2}$ and so, by (25b) in Sec. 15, also equals $\frac{3}{2}\,kT$ in terms of the Boltzmann constant k and the absolute temperature T.

The probability that the first molecule lies in dK can, therefore, be written

$$Ce^{-\frac{mv^2}{2kT}}\, dK,$$

C being a constant dependent on E and V.

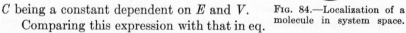

Fig. 84.—Localization of a molecule in system space.

Comparing this expression with that in eq. (57), Sec. 28, we see that we have here deduced Maxwell's law from statistical mechanics, in so far as that law expresses probabilities for a single molecule; since the space coordinates do not appear in our result, the probability is independent of position in the vessel.

By fixing several molecules in cells $dK_1, dK_2 \cdots$, respectively, one finds in the same way that the probability of such an arrangement of these molecules is proportional to

$$e^{-\frac{m_1v_1^2}{2kT}-\frac{m_2v_2^2}{2kT}} \cdots .$$

If we then consider different possible positions of just one of these molecules in its phase space, while keeping the others fixed, we obtain the same type of probability function for this one as we found above when all of the other molecules were left free. The probability for one molecule is thus the same, wherever other molecules are assumed to be located, or however they are moving. In this conclusion we have a proof from statistical mechanics of the principle of molecular chaos, which was made the basis of the deduction of Maxwell's law in Sec. 21.

Besides obtaining the probability for one molecule, or a few of them, the analysis here given can be extended so as to show that the molecules as a whole will nearly always be distributed in a manner not differing essentially from the maxwellian distribution. This is done by showing that such a distribution is, with a negligible error, characteristic of *almost all* of the points in the ergodic layer. This latter conclusion is reached a little more easily, however, as a result of the combinatorial argument in the next section.

198. The Loose Many-molecule System. The most general type of system for which a complete statistical theory has been obtained as yet is one that consists of very many subsystems interacting with each other only very slightly, or only occasionally. The only practical example of such a system is the general perfect gas whose molecules have internal as well as translational degrees of freedom; for this reason we shall for convenience call the subsystems, in general, *molecules*, and shall refer to any system of this type as a *loosely* coupled *many-molecule system*. It is, however, of theoretical interest, in connection with the canonical distribution to be discussed later, that the loosely coupled subsystems, of which the whole system is composed, need not be capable of moving around like gaseous molecules.

It is possible to treat this more general case by the phase-space method that we have just employed for the point-mass gas.* There exists, however, an older method due to Boltzmann which serves better to exhibit the true situation, and which also enjoys the advantage that it can be carried over into wave mechanics, where the phase-space method becomes inapplicable; this other method, which might be called that of *molecule space*, is usually employed and will be followed here.

To begin with, let us assume that the subsystems or molecules are all alike; and let their number be N. Then each molecule by itself can be described in terms of a certain number s of generalized coordinates together with an equal number of generalized momenta; three of these coordinates refer, of course, to its center of mass, the others to its rotation and internal condition. These $2s$ variables may be regarded as the coordinates of a point in a space of $2s$ dimensions, which we shall call the *molecular phase space*, or *molecule space*.

The instantaneous condition of the entire system, which we have been representing hitherto by the position of a single point in system space, will then be represented equally well by the position in molecule space of N points, one for each molecule (cf. Fig. 85). A representation of this sort was employed in Sec. 17 for the translational velocities. If we were to take as variables in the space there described the three

---

* Krutkow, *Zeits. Physik*, **81**, 377 (1933).

components of momentum, instead of the components of velocity, and then add three more dimensions for the coordinates themselves, we should have the six-dimensional molecule space for a monatomic gas, as already employed in the last section. In the general case, we have then to add still other dimensions corresponding to the internal motions.

From the macroscopic point of view, on the other hand, the state of such a system is determined by the character of the motions which its molecules are executing, but does not depend upon the identity of the molecule that is executing each particular motion, since the molecules are all alike. Accordingly, only the distribution of the N points in molecule space is macroscopically significant, without regard to their identity.

System space

In order to give a precise meaning to this rather vague term, *distribution*, let us adopt the customary device of dividing the whole of molecule space into small cells of equal volume, which we suppose to be numbered off in a definite order, and let us define a distribution by saying that it is specified by the numbers $N_1, N_2 \cdots$ of molecules whose representative points lie in cell 1, cell 2, and so on. Many N_i's will, of course, be zero; and obviously

Molecule space

Fig. 85.—Molecule space and system space.

$$\sum_i N_i = N, \tag{246}$$

the summation extending over all the cells.

Now, usually a given *distribution* as so defined can result from *many* different *arrangements* of the individual particles, an arrangement consisting in the assignment of each molecule to some definite cell. The number of possible arrangements for the distribution $N_1, N_2 \cdots$ will be, in fact, the number of combinations of N things taken N_1, $N_2 \cdots$ at a time or

$$M = \frac{N!}{N_1! N_2! \cdots}. \tag{247}$$

As a concrete example of the same thing, the number of ways of dividing 20 books among two shelves so as to put 12 on one shelf and 8 on another, paying no attention to the arrangement of each set on its shelf, is $20!/(12!\ 8!)$.

The *arrangements*, on the other hand, have in statistical mechanics the important property that each one corresponds to the same volume in the big system space. This becomes clear when we reflect that, as the representative points for all of the N molecules moving independently explore their cells in molecule space, the single point representing the entire system in system space traces out a region in that space whose volume G is obviously the product of the volumes of N cells in molecule space, or $G = g^N$ in terms of the volume g of a cell.* The volume G is thus obviously the same for all arrangements.

This fact leads to very important conclusions. It enables us to infer from the principle of statistical equivalence formulated in Sec. 195 above that each arrangement occurs equally often, or with equal probability, among the systems of a microcanonical ensemble (provided it can occur at all); no arrangement is favored over any other. From this we can then draw the further conclusion that the probability of a given distribution of the molecules is simply proportional to the number of arrangements that give rise to it, or to the number M whose value is given in eq. (247).

199. The Most Probable Distribution. In this conclusion we have acquired, for a loosely coupled many-molecule system, a means of comparing the probabilities of the various possible distributions of its molecules in the corresponding molecule space.

Now among these distributions there will be a *most probable* one, and it turns out that this one is of transcendent importance. Among the systems of the ensemble, appreciable departures from the most probable distribution are, in fact, rare; and for this reason Jeans called it the *normal* distribution. By the principle of equivalence, this distribution will then almost always be very close to the actual one in any single system; for the distribution that is most probable during the motion of a single system cannot change much in character with a small change δE in the energy, and so must be sensibly the same for all systems in the ensemble. Accordingly, this normal distribution can be used in place of the actual one in making statistical calculations pertaining to a single system. Therein lies its great importance.

To find the most probable distribution, we need to determine the N_i's so as to make the number M, or log M, a maximum, subject to the condition that the total number of molecules is N and that the total energy is approximately equal to E. This is not easy to do with

$$*G = \int dp_1 \cdots dp_{Ns}\, dq_1 \cdots dq_{Ns} = \left(\int dp_1 \cdots dp_s\, dq_1 \cdots dq_s \right)$$

$$\left(\int dp_{s+1} \cdots dp_{2s}\, dq_{s+1} \cdots dq_{2s} \right) \cdots \left(\int dp_{(N-1)s} \cdots dq_{Ns} \right) = g^N.$$

completeness, but if some of the N_i's are large their relative values can easily be found by using Stirling's formula for the factorial [cf. eq. (214a) in Sec. 154]:

$$\log (N_i!) = (N_i + \tfrac{1}{2}) \log N_i - N_i + \log \sqrt{2\pi}.$$

In varying these large N_i we can also treat them as continuous variables without appreciable error; and we can then keep E actually fixed, since the variation of E over the small range δE cannot shift the location of the maximum appreciably. Let the energy of a particle when in cell i be ϵ_i; then the total energy is*

$$\sum_i N_i\epsilon_i = E, \tag{248}$$

summed over all cells.

For a maximum we must have, accordingly, varying only the large N_i's in (247),

$$0 = d \log M = -\Sigma d \log (N_i!) = -\Sigma\left(\log N_i + \frac{1}{2N_i}\right) dN_i,$$

in which the dN_i are arbitrary except for the two conditions, derived from (246) and (248), that

$$\sum_i dN_i = 0, \qquad \sum_i \epsilon_i \, dN_i = 0.$$

Multiplying these last two equations by α and β, respectively, and adding to the preceding, in which we may drop the very small term $1/2N_i$, we have then

$$\sum_i (\log N_i + \alpha + \beta\epsilon_i) \, dN_i = 0;$$

and the usual argument (cf. Sec. 27) then leads to the conclusion that for any i

$$\log N_i + \alpha + \beta\epsilon_i = 0.$$

Thus, wherever its value is large,

$$N_i = Ce^{-\beta\epsilon_i}, \tag{249a}$$

C being written for $e^{-\alpha}$. Here C and β are the same for all cells, their values being fixed in terms of the total number of particles and the value of the energy by eqs. (246) and (248).

---

* Variation of the energy as the points move about in their cells is here neglected. The rigorous handling of this point is tedious but can be effected.

It will be shown in the next section that $\beta = 1/kT$, T being the absolute temperature and k the Boltzmann constant or gas constant for one molecule. For convenience of reference we may assume this result here in advance and write

$$N_i = Ce^{-\frac{\epsilon_i}{kT}} = \frac{Ne^{-\frac{\epsilon_i}{kT}}}{\sum_i e^{-\frac{\epsilon_i}{kT}}}, \tag{249b}$$

the last sum extending over all cells, and this second form of the expression resulting from substitution in the equation $\sum_i N_i = N$.

Sometimes, however, it is more convenient to employ in place of the distribution for the system as a whole a *probability function* for the individual molecule. Since all of the molecules, being similar, must spend equal times in any given cell, the probability that a given one is in cell i is obtained simply by dividing eq. (249a) or (249b) by N; since, however, the molecule is also equally likely to be in any part of the cell, it is more convenient to go over now to elements of molecule space. We can write then as the probability that a given molecule is in any given element dg or $dq_1 \cdots dq_s \, dp_1 \cdots dp_s$, where its energy is ϵ, or the fraction of its time that it spends in such an element, $P \, dg$ where

$$P = C_1 e^{-\beta\epsilon} = C_1 e^{-\frac{\epsilon}{kT}} = \frac{e^{-\frac{\epsilon}{kT}}}{\int e^{-\frac{\epsilon}{kT}} \, dg}. \tag{249c}$$

Here the integral in the last exponent extends over all of molecule space, and $C_1 = C/Ng$ or may be regarded as a new constant whose value is determined by the condition that $\int P \, dg = 1$.

It is this result that was cited above in Sec. 53 as the classical Boltzmann distribution formula, eq. (89a), and was there shown to include Maxwell's law as a special case.

200. The Most Probable as a Normal Distribution. By extending the calculation just made, it can also readily be seen that large values of N_i differing appreciably from those given by (249a) or (249b) must be rare, provided only that the total number of particles is large.

For, if the large N_i are changed by small amounts δN_i from their most probable values, which are such as to make the first-order terms in $\delta \log M$ vanish, we find from (247), upon pushing the calculation to the second order in the δN_i's, that the change in $\log M$ is approximately

$$\delta \log M = -\sum \frac{(\delta N_i)^2}{2N_i}\left(1 - \frac{1}{2N_i}\right) = -\frac{1}{2}\sum N_i\left(\frac{\delta N_i}{N_i}\right)^2;$$

M itself is then changed in the ratio $e^{\delta \log M}$ from its maximum value.

Now if we imagine N and E to be increased toward infinity at the same relative rate, a brief contemplation of eqs. (246) and (248) shows that all large N_i must increase in the same ratio (C changing but not β); hence, for given fixed values of the relative variations, $\delta N_i/N_i$, we have $\delta \log M \to -\infty$. Thus, as the molecules become numerous, any particular distribution differing from the most probable one by a given relative amount, as measured by the values of $\delta N_i/N_i$, becomes relatively rare. On the other hand, the *number* of different distributions having $\delta N_i/N_i$ in the neighborhood of given values is readily seen to change with N and E in roughly the same ratio for all values of $\delta N_i/N_i$. Hence the probability of the occurrence of any given range of values of $\delta N_i/N_i$ that does not include zero decreases indefinitely as $N \to \infty$.

Thus we reach the advantageous conclusion that in a loose many-molecule system distributions departing appreciably from the most probable one occur only very rarely; and accordingly, as was stated above, in deducing statistical behavior of such a system, we can take the actual distribution to be the same as the most probable or normal one.

201. Some Generalizations of the Loose Many-molecule System. The restriction of the preceding equations to large values of N_i may be awkward in actual cases because it may be impractical to construct cells in molecule space that are large enough to include, say, 1,000 or more molecules. This is so, for example, in considering the concentration of water vapor near a charged smoke particle of ultramicroscopic size, which we might wish to study in seeking an explanation of cloud formation due to such nuclei.

Most practical cases of this sort can be covered by remarking that what we are chiefly interested in is only the *average* expectation of molecules in a cell, which is, of course, indistinguishable from the most probable number when this is large. The distribution law already found can readily be extended to the average number in any cell, provided there are many other cells with the same value of the associated energy ϵ_i, and provided that the group of such cells as a whole contains a large number of molecules. In the example cited, for instance, we can suppose that there are many smoke particles in the vessel, each having a cell in a certain relative location near it, and all of these cells can then be grouped together.

Since any molecule moving around in a group of μ cells sweeps out μ times as much volume in system space as it does when it is confined to one cell, the probability of a distribution with N'_1 molecules in a group of μ_1 cells, N'_2 in a group of μ_2, and so on, will be proportional, not to M as given in (247), but to $(\mu_1{}^{N_1'}\mu_2{}^{N_2'} \cdots)M$ or to

$$\frac{N!}{N'_1!N'_2! \cdots} \mu_1{}^{N_1'}\mu_2{}^{N_2'} \cdots .$$

Proceeding as before, one finds then as the normal distribution, in place of (249a), for the jth group of cells

$$N'_j = \mu_j C e^{-\beta \epsilon_j}.$$

The molecules are, however, equally likely to be in any one of the various cells of a group. Hence, for the *average* number $\bar{N}_i$ of molecules in cell i, which equals N'_j/μ_j for the group containing this cell, we find

$$\bar{N}_i = C e^{-\beta \epsilon_i} = C e^{-\frac{\epsilon_i}{kT}} = \frac{N e^{-\frac{\epsilon_i}{kT}}}{\sum_i e^{-\frac{\epsilon_i}{kT}}}, \tag{249d}$$

which is of the same form as (249b) above; and for the probability function P for a given molecule in its phase space, which is $\bar{N}_i/N_g$, we obtain again eq. (249c) above.

Furthermore, considerable generalization of our results is also possible in regard to the nature of the molecules themselves. Instead of being all alike, they may be of *several different kinds*, provided there are many of each kind. In that case M is simply the product of several fractions like that in (247) above, e.g.,

$$M = \frac{N'!}{N'_1!N'_2! \cdots} \frac{N''!}{N''_1!N''_2! \cdots},$$

where primes distinguish quantities referring to the different kinds of molecules. The equations following (248) then become

$$0 = -\sum \left(\log N'_i + \frac{1}{2N'_i} \right) dN'_i - \sum \left(\log N''_i + \frac{1}{2N''_i} \right) dN''_i \cdots ,$$

$$\sum_i dN'_i = 0, \qquad \sum_i dN''_i = 0, \cdots$$

$$\sum_i \epsilon'_i \, dN'_i + \sum_i \epsilon''_i \, dN''_i \cdots = 0;$$

and when we multiply the last of these by β and the preceding ones by α', $\alpha'' \cdots$ and add to the first one, and then equate to zero the coefficient of every $dN'_i, dN''_i \cdots$, we obtain

$$\log N'_i + \alpha' + \beta\epsilon'_i = 0, \qquad \log N''_i + \alpha'' + \beta\epsilon''_i = 0, \qquad \cdots,$$

whence

$$N'_i = C'e^{-\beta\epsilon_i'}, \qquad N''_i = C''e^{-\beta\epsilon_i''} \cdots.$$

Thus there exist equations of the same form as (249a, b, c, d) for each separate kind of molecule, with different constants $C', C'' \cdots$ corresponding to the varying numbers $N', N'' \cdots$ that are present of the different kinds. The constant β, however, which again turns out to equal $1/kT$, is the same for all, owing to the fact that interchange of energy is possible between all of the molecules and there is, therefore, only a single equation expressive of the energy condition. Except for this latter feature, each kind of molecule is distributed as if the others were not present.

Finally, it does no harm if a relatively negligible part of the molecules are of miscellaneous character, perhaps even only one of a kind; for then, assuming a certain energy for these few, we can apply the preceding theory to the remainder. The quantity E in (248) is then, strictly speaking, to be interpreted as representing the variable energy of the remaining molecules alone; but no appreciable error is incurred if it is taken to represent, as before, the fixed energy of the whole system. In Sec. 205 below we shall go further and, by establishing a connection with the method employed for the gas of point masses, show that actually the same distribution law holds for such odd particles as holds for the others.

Before proceeding further, however, we must first establish for loose many-molecule systems the connection of β with the thermodynamic temperature.

202. Introduction of the Temperature. The temperature was introduced into the theory of the perfect gas in Sec. 13 by a method that is rigorous and can readily be generalized so as to apply to the general many-molecule system.

In order to identify any quantity with the thermodynamic temperature T, we must show that it possesses two essential properties: it must have the same value for any two bodies when they are in thermal equilibrium with each other; and the heat dQ absorbed by a body during any small reversible change must take the form $T\,dS$, where S is a quantity, the entropy, having a single value to correspond with every equilibrium state of the body. In mathematical language, therefore, $1/T$ must constitute an integrating factor for the reversible heat.

Such an application of thermodynamics implies a clear distinction between energy that enters a body as heat and energy that enters as work. This distinction, which is made without any trouble in elementary physics, becomes far from obvious when the system is regarded as exhibiting purely mechanical behavior. It can be reached, however, from the dynamical standpoint in the following way.

As viewed macroscopically, the effects of the surroundings upon a system are of two kinds. In part they can be represented by introducing into the Hamiltonian of the system certain parameters, $\alpha_1, \alpha_2 \cdots$, which represent physically interesting quantities averaged over molecular fluctuations, such as the volume of the vessel containing a gas; the Hamiltonian function can then be written $H(p_1, p_2 \cdots, q_1, q_2 \cdots, \alpha_1, \alpha_2 \cdots)$. Any energy lost by the system to its surroundings in consequence of changes in these parameters can then be expressed in terms of their changes and is called *work* done by the system. There may then be in addition certain irregular forces exerted by the surroundings on the system which cannot be represented by such parameters but must necessarily enter into the equations of motion as forces of external origin. All energy imparted to the system by such forces, which we shall call thermal forces, constitutes *heat* absorbed by the system.

Usually a particular molecular force has to be divided arbitrarily into two parts corresponding to this distinction. As an example, the force exerted by a molecule of the wall on the enclosed gas can be resolved into a component representing its average contribution to the pressure and another irregularly fluctuating component, and the former, which depends only upon the mean position of the wall and the positions of the gas molecules, can be taken account of by introducing into the Hamiltonian for the gas a suitable potential-energy term containing as a parameter α the mean position of the wall.

In order to identify the temperature, it will suffice now to consider a loosely coupled system in which the molecules are all alike; the subsequent extension to more general cases is so easy that no details need be given. Let us suppose that such a system is subjected to a small thermodynamic process during which the α's undergo a small change, and during which the thermal forces may or may not impart a little energy to the system. Let this process be carried out so very slowly that the system remains always very nearly in equilibrium, so that the process is reversible in the thermodynamic sense.

Then, resuming the notation of the last few sections, we can write for the energy of the system at any instant $E = \Sigma \epsilon_i \bar{N}_i$ summed over all the cells in molecule space, ϵ_i being the energy of a molecule when in cell

i and $\bar{N}_i$ the mean number of molecules in that cell. The change in E during the process just described (ignoring its fluctuations about its mean value) can, therefore, be written

$$dE = \sum_i \bar{N}_i \, d\epsilon_i + \sum_i \epsilon_i \, d\bar{N}_i. \tag{250}$$

Now suppose, first, that heating forces do not act. Then, during any element of time dt, whatever changes occur in the p's and q's of the system are governed by the Hamiltonian equations of motion and are the same as they would be if the α's were constant during that interval. Accordingly, by conservation of energy, these changes, and the resulting changes in the instantaneous values of the N_i's, do not alter the energy. The actual gain of energy during dT must, therefore, be $d'E = \sum_i N_i \, d'\epsilon_i$, where $d'\epsilon_i$ is the change in ϵ_i that arises during dt from the change in the α's. By conservation of energy, since there are no heating forces, $d'E$ is also the negative of the work done by the system. Hence, integrating $d'E$ throughout the small reversible process, during which the energy changes by $dE = \int d'E$, and assuming that the α's change at a uniform rate, so that we may write

$$\int N_i \, d'\epsilon_i = \bar{N}_i \int d'\epsilon_i = \bar{N}_i \, d\epsilon_i,$$

we have for the work during the whole process $dW = -dE$ or

$$dW = -\sum_i \bar{N}_i \, d\epsilon_i,$$

$d\epsilon_i$ standing for the whole change in ϵ_i during the process.

If we then suppose heating forces also to act during the process, the work done by the system, being determined by other forces, will not be affected to the first order; but the change in energy will now be given by the more general expression (250). Hence, an amount of reversible heat dQ is now given to the system of magnitude

$$dQ = dE + dW = \sum_i \epsilon_i \, d\bar{N}_i. \tag{251a}$$

In order to find an integrating factor for dQ, let us now multiply this equation through by β, and then insert in it the value of $\beta\epsilon_i$ proper to equilibrium, as given by the second member in (249d) above. The result is $\beta dQ = \sum_i (\log C - \log \bar{N}_i) \, d\bar{N}_i$, from which the term in C can

be dropped because $\sum_i d\bar{N}_i = 0$, leaving

$$\beta \, dQ = -\sum_i \log \bar{N}_i \, d\bar{N}_i. \tag{251b}$$

The expression on the right is now the differential of a single-valued function of the $\bar{N}_i$. This shows that β is an integrating factor for dQ.

Furthermore, as shown in Sec. 201, β, and hence also any function of β, enjoys the property of having the same value for any two loose many-molecule systems that are in equilibrium with each other; for two such systems may always be regarded as a single system containing two sorts of molecules. We can, therefore, introduce the thermodynamic temperature by the defining equation $T = 1/k\beta$, or

$$\beta = \frac{1}{kT},$$

in which k is a universal constant of proportionality.

The replacement of β by $1/kT$ in the preceding sections is thus justified. That k has its usual significance as the gas constant for one molecule follows then from the identification mentioned in Sec. 199 of our results with former expressions that included Maxwell's law as a special case.

203. Entropy. A dynamical expression for the entropy S of a loosely coupled many-molecule system can now be obtained by integrating (251b). Since $\sum_i d\bar{N}_i = 0$, this gives

$$S = \int \frac{dQ}{T} = -k\sum_i \bar{N}_i \log \bar{N}_i + S_0, \tag{252a}$$

or, after introducing $\log \bar{N}_i$ from (249d) and using $\sum_i \bar{N}_i = N$, the total

number of molecules, and $\sum_i \bar{N}_i \epsilon_i = E$, the total energy,

$$S = \frac{E}{T} - Nk \log C + S_0, \tag{252b}$$

or also, since in the last member of (249d) $\sum_i e^{-\frac{\epsilon_i}{kT}}$ can obviously be written $\frac{1}{g}\sum_i \int e^{-\frac{\epsilon i}{kT}} = \frac{1}{g}\int e^{-\frac{\epsilon}{kT}}\,dg$, the last integral extending over the whole of molecule space,

$$S = \frac{E}{T} + Nk \log \int e^{-\frac{\epsilon}{kT}}\,dg + S_0'. \tag{252c}$$

Here $S_0' = S_0 - Nk \log (gN)$ and S_0 or S_0' is an arbitrary integration constant.

The quantity $\sum_i e^{-\frac{\epsilon i}{kT}}$ is what we called in Sec. 147 the state sum;

$\int e^{-\frac{\epsilon}{kT}}\,dg$ might similarly be called the *state integral*.

In eqs. (252a, b, c) S stands for the entropy of the whole system. From the structure of the formulas it appears that, in harmony with thermodynamics, the entropy should be simply additive, provided we add the integration constants when separate systems are coupled into a larger one. A question arises, however, when subsequent interdiffusion of molecules can occur, as when two masses of gas are placed in contact with each other. If the molecules in the two part systems are different in nature, then, when equilibrium has been re-established by diffusion, the total entropy exceeds the sum of the original separate entropies; in the formulas this results from a decrease in $\bar{N}_i$, or from an increase in the state sums due to enlargement of the accessible region in molecule space. If, on the other hand, the molecules in the two part systems are exactly similar, their interdiffusion has no physical significance; it cannot be made to do macroscopic work, for instance; and no such increase in the total entropy occurs. Since, however, the same changes in $\bar{N}_i$ or in the state sums occur as in the other case, we can prevent an increase in S only by readjusting the integration constant whenever systems of similar molecules are combined into a larger one with resulting possibilities of interdiffusion. We shall find that this inconvenience disappears in the wave-mechanical theory. It is often avoided by using the formula only for the entropy of unit mass, i.e., for specific entropy.

204. Entropy of the Monatomic Gas. It will be instructive to verify the agreement of the expressions just obtained with the usual ones in the simple case of a perfect gas composed of molecules that can be treated as point masses. Let us consider a gram of gas containing N such molecules.

In the phase space for such a molecule we can take as variables the three cartesian coordinates of its center of mass and its three components of ordinary momentum, p_x, p_y, p_z, the total momentum being p. Then ϵ is the ordinary translatory kinetic energy and has the value, $\epsilon = p^2/2m$. Hence, taking spherical shells about the origin as elements in momentum space in place of $dp_x\, dp_y\, dp_z$, we have

$$\int e^{-\frac{\epsilon}{kT}}\, dg = \iiint dx\, dy\, dz \iiint e^{-\frac{\epsilon}{kT}}\, dp_x\, dp_y\, dp_z = 4\pi V \int_0^\infty e^{-\frac{p^2}{2mkT}} p^2\, dp$$
$$= (2\pi mkT)^{3/2} V,$$

since $\int_0^\infty e^{-x^2}\, dx = \frac{1}{2}\sqrt{\pi}$ and $\iiint dx\, dy\, dz = V$, the volume of the vessel. Furthermore, the classical energy of such a gas is $E = \frac{3}{2} NkT$ (cf. Sec. 143). Hence (252c) becomes

$$S = Nk \log (VT^{3/2}) + S_0'', \tag{252d}$$

where $S_0'' = S_0' + Nk\{\frac{3}{2} + \log (2\pi mk)^{3/2}\}$.

This agrees with the usual thermodynamic result as expressed by eq. (200a) in Sec. 141, in which $R = Nk$ and $c_V = 3R/2$ for a monatomic gas.

205. The General Boltzmann Distribution Law. The combinatorial method that we have been employing stands in strong contrast to the more direct phase-space method that was employed previously in dealing with the special case of a perfect gas. We shall now show that the latter method must be applicable to the more general case as well, although it may run into serious mathematical difficulties. By its use we shall endeavor to remove some of the limitations that have hitherto been laid upon the system under consideration.

Let us select any molecule A out of a system and seek to obtain a distribution law for it by the phase-space method. To do this, we first confine the molecule A to an element δg_A in its own $2s_A$-dimensional molecular phase space. Then, in analogy with the procedure followed in Sec. 196, we can write for the volume of that part of *system* space, in which the total energy H of the entire system is less than a fixed value E,

$$\sigma(E) = \iint_{H<E} dp\, dq,$$

and for that part in which A is also confined to δg_A with energy ϵ,

$$\delta\sigma = \sigma_r(E - \epsilon)\, \delta g_A, \qquad \sigma_r(E - \epsilon) = \iint_{H_r < E - \epsilon} dp'\, dq',$$

where $dp'\, dq'$ stands for the product of the differentials of all other variables than those pertaining to A, and $H_r\, (p',\, q')$ for the part of the Hamiltonian that contains just those other variables.

Now consider that part of the ergodic layer in which A lies in δg_A. The volume of this part is

$$\left[\frac{d}{dE} \delta\sigma \right] dE = \sigma'_r(E - \epsilon)\, dE\, \delta g_A.$$

This volume divided by the volume of the entire ergodic layer is the probability that in an actual system A lies in δg_A, in consequence of the principle of statistical equivalence (Sec. 195). Accordingly, we may conclude that, in an actual system having energy E, the probability at a given moment that molecule A is in any chosen element δg_A of molecule space is simply proportional to

$$\sigma'_r(E - \epsilon).$$

Now suppose that our system is of the generalized type contemplated in Sec. 201 above, most of the molecules, but not all, forming one or more large homogeneous groups. Then, if molecule A happens to belong to one of these large groups, and if, furthermore, δg_A lies in a cell containing many of these particles, another expression for the probability that A lies in δg_A is furnished by the theory of Sec. 201; according to (249c), this probability is proportional to

$$e^{-\beta\epsilon}\, \delta g_A = e^{-\frac{\epsilon}{kT}}\, \delta g_A.$$

It must be true then, under the circumstances stated, that

$$\sigma'_r(E - \epsilon) = C_1 e^{-\beta\epsilon}$$

where C_1 is a factor that is independent of the location of A and depends only on E.

This result has been obtained only for a restricted choice of the molecule A and of the element δg_A. We can safely assert, however, that the *form* of the function, $\sigma'_r(E - \epsilon)$, cannot depend appreciably upon the particular choice of A out of many millions of molecules in the system. Hence, $\sigma'_r(E - \epsilon)$ must have the same simple exponential form when any molecule of the system is chosen. A little more generally, it follows that $\sigma'(E)$ and, by integration, $\sigma(E)$ itself must be of exponential form near any value $E = E_1$, say,

$$\sigma(E) = C_2 e^{-\beta E},$$

as we found it to be for a monatomic gas (Sec. 196); for, an odd molecule with energy ϵ could be added to it, whereupon $\sigma(E)$ would function as σ_r in the analysis just given, E here being represented by $E - \epsilon$ there.

If the statement just made about σ_r be granted, then it follows, by reversing the argument, that the distribution law has the form written above or in (249c) for *any* molecule of the system, and wherever the phase-space element may be located.

One is then tempted to suspect that these results may hold likewise for much more general types of system. It is, as a matter of fact, believed that according to classical theory $\sigma(E)$ has the exponential form $Ce^{-\beta E}$, in the neighborhood of any particular value of E, for any system composed of an enormous number of molecules, whether these are loosely coupled or not. The same statement is believed to hold if a few of the generalized coordinates of the system are held fixed and only the remainder are included in the integration for σ. If these propositions are granted, then it is easy to deduce from them, by the method indicated above, the following very general form of the Boltzmann distribution law, the temperature being introduced by a special argument for which we have no space:

Suppose a few variables, either coordinates or momenta, occur only in a separate term ϵ in the Hamiltonian function H; let these variables be denoted by $\xi_1, \xi_2 \cdots \xi_s$. If any other variables occur in ϵ, let us consider only states of the system in which these variables lie in given small ranges. Then the probability that the ξ's lie in ranges $dg = d\xi_1 d\xi_2 \cdots d\xi_s$ is

$$P\,dg, \qquad P = Ce^{-\beta\epsilon} = Ce^{-\frac{\epsilon}{kT}}, \qquad (253)$$

C being a constant such that $\int P\,dg = 1$. This result constitutes merely an extension of the distribution law represented by (249c) above and includes the latter as a special case.

As a corollary, we can draw the important conclusion that, in a physical body, classical theory requires Maxwell's law to hold for the velocities of the molecular centers of mass, regardless of all other circumstances; this is true for each separate configuration or set of positions of the molecules, and no matter how strong or complicated their mutual potential energy may be. It must be remarked, however, that in wave mechanics this statement has to be modified considerably when the density is high, as in a liquid or solid.

206. The Equipartition of Energy. The distribution laws that have been obtained lead to a conclusion of considerable importance relative to the *distribution of the energy* in a system in equilibrium.

Suppose the expression for the energy (or, more generally, the Hamiltonian function) contains a term in which one variable occurs only in the form of a square. Let us write for this term $\epsilon = \frac{1}{2}\,\varphi\xi^2$, where the coefficient φ may contain some of the remaining variables; if it does, let these for the moment have fixed values.

Then eq. (253) in the last section, or (249c) in Sec. 201, if it happens to apply, gives as the probability law for ξ, $P = C_1 e^{-\frac{\varphi \xi^2}{2kT}}$, where C_1 is given by the equation $\int_0^\infty P \, d\xi = 1$. We find then for the mean value

$$\bar{\epsilon} = \frac{1}{2} \varphi \frac{C_1 \int_0^\infty \xi^2 e^{-\frac{\varphi \xi^2}{2kT}} \, d\xi}{C_1 \int_0^\infty e^{-\frac{\varphi \xi^2}{2kT}} \, d\xi} = \frac{1}{2} kT.$$

Since this result is independent of any other variables that may occur in φ, it will hold quite generally. Hence, whether other variables are kept fixed or not, the mean value of such a term is just $\frac{1}{2} kT$. This is the famous principle of the *equipartition of energy*.

The simplest example is, of course, the translatory kinetic energy of a particle, which can be written $\dfrac{p_x^2}{2m} + \dfrac{p_y^2}{2m} + \dfrac{p_z^2}{2m}$ in terms of the cartesian momenta, p_x, p_y, p_z. Each of the three terms in this expression must average $\frac{1}{2} kT$; the whole kinetic energy, therefore, averages $\frac{3}{2} kT$. This latter result was obtained for perfect gases in Sec. 15; here we have it for particles in a system of any type. According to classical mechanics it should hold even for the molecules in a liquid or solid.

Similarly, if the system is capable of *small oscillations* in the generalized sense, the potential energy associated with each normal generalized coordinate q_i can be got into the form $\frac{1}{2} \varphi_1 q_i^2$, and the associated kinetic energy can be written similarly $\frac{1}{2} \varphi_2 p_i^2$ in terms of the corresponding generalized momentum.* Each of these terms will then average $\frac{1}{2} kT$; and the whole contribution of each mode of oscillation to the energy will average kT. This is true for any simple harmonic mode of vibration.

Finally, similar results can be obtained for the rotational energy of any rigid molecule forming part of a system in equilibrium. The rotational kinetic energy of such a molecule can be written

$$K = \frac{1}{2} A \omega_A^2 + \frac{1}{2} B \omega_B^2 + \frac{1}{2} C \omega_C^2$$

in terms of the components of the angular velocity, ω_A, ω_B, ω_C, in the directions of the principal axes and the moments of inertia A, B, C about those axes. In order to express this in terms of generalized

---

* H. LAMB, "Higher Mechanics," 1929, Sec. 92.

coordinates, let us introduce the three Eulerian angles θ, ψ, φ; in terms of these

$$\omega_A = \dot\theta \sin \varphi - \dot\psi \sin \theta \cos \varphi, \qquad \omega_B = \dot\theta \cos \varphi + \dot\psi \sin \theta \sin \varphi,$$
$$\omega_C = \dot\varphi + \dot\psi \cos \theta.$$

(Cf. H. Lamb, "Higher Mechanics," Sec. 33, where p, q, r are to be identified with ω_A, ω_B, ω_C.) Then the corresponding momenta are

$$p_\theta = \frac{\partial K}{\partial \dot\theta} = A\omega_A \frac{\partial \omega_A}{\partial \dot\theta} + B\omega_B \frac{\partial \omega_B}{\partial \dot\theta} + C\omega_C \frac{\partial \omega_C}{\partial \dot\theta}, \text{ etc.,}$$

or

$$p_\theta = A\omega_A \sin \varphi + B\omega_B \cos \varphi, \qquad p_\varphi = C\omega_C,$$
$$p_\psi = -A\omega_A \sin \theta \cos \varphi + B\omega_B \sin \theta \sin \varphi + C\omega_C \cos \theta.$$

Now let us compare the molecular distribution in ω_A, ω_B, ω_C space, which we shall call ω space for short, with that in p space, in which our statistical laws hold. To a volume $d\tau$ in the latter there corresponds a volume $d\tau/J$ in ω space where J is the Jacobian

$$J = \begin{vmatrix} \dfrac{\partial p_\theta}{\partial \omega_A} & \dfrac{\partial p_\theta}{\partial \omega_B} & \cdots \\ \dfrac{\partial p_\psi}{\partial \omega_A} & \dfrac{\partial p_\psi}{\partial \omega_B} & \cdots \\ \cdots & \cdots & \cdots \end{vmatrix} = \begin{vmatrix} A \sin \varphi & B \cos \varphi & 0 \\ -A \sin \theta \cos \varphi & B \sin \theta \sin \varphi & C \cos \theta \\ 0 & 0 & C \end{vmatrix}$$
$$= ABC \sin \theta.$$

(Cf. Sec. 24.) Thus for given values of θ, ψ, φ volumes in ω space are proportional to the corresponding volumes in momentum space. Accordingly, the molecules will be distributed in the same manner in both spaces.

It is easily seen that, in consequence, the principle of equipartition will apply also to the three terms in K. Each of these terms, which can be regarded as the kinetic energy associated with one rotational degree of freedom of the molecule, will again average $\frac{1}{2} kT$; and the whole rotational energy will average $\frac{3}{2} kT$.

207. The Canonical Distribution and Ensemble. Instead of supposing the system under consideration to be isolated, we might suppose it to be connected with another system. Then its energy will undergo Brownian fluctuations. Suppose that the connection is loose and the other system is a very much larger one. Then the latter serves to control the temperature of the original system; it has been called by Fowler a temperature bath. The original system can now be treated as a "molecule" forming part of the entire combined system; and eq.

(253) then indicates that it will spend a fraction $P \, dg$ of its time in each element dg of its own phase space or system space, where

$$P = Ce^{-\frac{E}{kT}}, \tag{254}$$

E being the energy of the system when in dg.

A statistical distribution in phase according to the law expressed by (254) was called by Gibbs a *canonical* one, and an ensemble of systems so distributed, a *canonical ensemble*. Such a distribution or ensemble might be thought to represent better an actual physical body immersed in its surroundings than does a microcanonical ensemble. The macroscopic statistical properties of the two cannot differ much, however, when they correspond to the same temperature; for a canonical ensemble really consists of many microcanonical ones of different energies, and the effective relative range of these energies can be shown to be very small when the system itself contains many molecules.

The canonical ensemble, or the canonical distribution in phase, furnishes a basis for the treatment of systems whose energy cannot be written as the sum of many similar terms.

208. Entropy under a Canonical Distribution. An expression for the entropy S, defined as $\int \frac{dQ}{T}$, is easily obtained for a system that is assumed to exhibit in time a canonical distribution in phase. The argument runs so very closely parallel to that in Secs. 202 and 203, in fact, that we can at once write down as the result, in analogy with (252a) and (252c),

$$S = -k \int P \log P \, d\sigma = \frac{E}{T} + k \log \int e^{-\frac{E}{kT}} \, d\sigma. \tag{255}$$

Here the integrals extend over the whole of system space and the second one may be called the state integral for the entire system; the arbitrary constant of integration has been set equal to zero.

Different as this expression for S seems to be from the one obtained previously, as stated in eq. (252a) or (252c), it can differ from the latter only by a constant amount, since the entropy, being defined as $\int \frac{dQ}{T}$, represents a definite physical quantity. In the corresponding wave-mechanical case it will be worth while to ascertain the actual magnitude of this constant difference.

209. The Second Law of Thermodynamics. Our demonstration that a loose many-molecule system in equilibrium possesses a quality having the properties of the thermodynamic temperature constitutes a deduction of the second law of thermodynamics from the laws of mechanics, in so far as that law refers to equilibrium phenomena. Thus the thermodynamics of reversible processes is converted, at least for such systems, into a subdivision of mechanics.

It is to be noted, however, that we have consistently dealt with the normal or average state of the system, ignoring the phenomenon of fluctuations. Even the most unusual states should, however, sometimes occur, just as in shaking a mixture of black and white balls it will happen once in a great while that all of the black ones come on top. This means that occasionally the requirements of the second law will not be met. Such unusual occurrences are indeed easily observed in the Brownian motion, where a particle is seen to acquire every now and then velocities much above or below the average.

The second law of thermodynamics must, accordingly, be regarded as statistical in nature, having reference to the *normal* or *average* behavior of matter and to the *macroscopic* rather than to the molecular view of phenomena. So conceived, however, it appears to admit of no exception. It could perhaps be imagined that fluctuation phenomena, such as the Brownian motion, might some day be harnessed by means of an ingenious mechanism and utilized to effect the continuous conversion of heat into work. It seems highly probable, however, that all such schemes are doomed to defeat in consequence of the inevitable fluctuations to which the mechanism itself must be subject.

On the other hand, the second law of thermodynamics as usually stated implies the further assertion that, in an *irreversible* passage of an isolated system from one equilibrium state to another, the entropy *can never decrease*, the fact being, of course, that it usually increases. This statement, likewise, must be understood in a statistical sense as having reference to average experience. Not much has been accomplished toward the theoretical treatment of irreversible processes; hardly anything has been added to Boltzmann's *H* theorem for a point-mass gas. This question is very closely related to the proof that one would like to obtain of some principle equivalent to our "ergodic surmise."

210. Entropy and Probability. From the molecular standpoint the tendency of a system to move toward equilibrium, with an accompanying gain in entropy, is interpreted as resulting from a tendency to move from an improbable toward a more probable state. It was shown by Boltzmann in connection with his *H* theorem that, in some cases at least, a quantitative connection can be traced between the increases in entropy and in probability.

In an isolated many-molecule system, for example, the probability of any distribution, as was shown in Sec. 198, is, from (247),

$$P_D = DM = \frac{DN!}{N_1!N_2! \cdots},$$

D being a constant of proportionality. On the other hand, from (252a) in Sec. 203 the entropy of the system, when in a state of equilibrium, is

$$S = -k\sum_i' \bar{N}_i \log \bar{N}_i + S_0.$$

Let us take P_D to refer to the normal distribution, so that $N_i = \bar{N}_i$, and let us suppose that the N_i's are large enough so that we can keep only the principal term in Stirling's formula and write $\log (N_i!) = N_i \log N_i$. Then

$$\log P_D = -\sum_i' \bar{N}_i \log \bar{N}_i + \text{const.},$$

and we see that

$$S = k \log P_D + \text{const.} \tag{256}$$

This famous relation, first pointed out by Boltzmann, is often regarded as holding universally. It may be illustrated concretely by the following example. Suppose a capsule containing N molecules of perfect gas in equilibrium is introduced into an evacuated vessel r times as large in volume as the capsule, and that a hole is then made in the wall of the capsule. The gas thereupon escapes, and presently comes to thermal equilibrium in the larger vessel at its original temperature but with its volume increased in the ratio r; its entropy is at the same time increased by the amount [cf. (252d) in Sec. 204]

$$Nk \log r.$$

Now, just after the capsule has been ruptured, but before any molecule has had time to escape, the gas is in a state which, under the new conditions created by the rupture, is a highly improbable one; as the gas then issues and spreads throughout the vessel, it passes into more and more probable states. Let us find the magnitude of the total resulting increase in $\log P_D$. When the gas has again reached equilibrium, its molecules are distributed in the molecular phase space over r times as many cells as there were at the start, but with only $1/r$ times as many molecules per cell; hence the new value of the term $-\Sigma \bar{N}_i \log \bar{N}_i$ in $\log P_D$, written in terms of the original $\bar{N}_i$'s, is

$$-r \sum \frac{\bar{N}_i}{r} \log \frac{\bar{N}_i}{r} = -\sum \bar{N}_i(\log \bar{N}_i - \log r).$$

This term has thus increased during the expansion by the amount

$$\Sigma \bar{N}_i \log r = (\log r) \Sigma \bar{N}_i = N \log r.$$

Comparing this with the increase in entropy, we see that eq. (256) holds for a comparison of the initial and final states.

If, however, we direct our attention to the act of rupturing the capsule, we encounter difficulties. The act of rupture converts the existing state of the gas from a fairly probable to a highly improbable one, but without any corresponding decrease in the entropy (to lower the entropy of a body without abstracting heat from it is thermo-dynamically impossible). The difficulty persists in another form if, instead of rupturing the capsule, we allow the gas to expand adia-batically against a piston; for then it is impossible to compare the probabilities (in the ordinary sense) of the two states of the gas with the piston in different positions, each state being an impossible one, owing to the difference in energy, when the piston is in the other position. Apparently the only way to save the Boltzmann principle in the face of external interventions such as these is to lay down a suitable artificial rule specifying how the size of the cells in phase space is to be altered when such actions occur. If this is done, how-ever, an arbitrary element is introduced into the "probability" which obscures the significance of the formula.

Planck and others have endeavored to avoid these difficulties by pointing out that the quantity, $-\Sigma \bar{N}_i \log \bar{N}_i$, in the expression for S is simply the variable part of $\log M$, where M is the number of ways of arranging the molecules in their most probable distribution, as given by (247) in Sec. 198, so that we can write, dropping a constant term,

$$S = k \log M.$$

The quantity M, to which under certain conditions the true prob-ability is proportional, is then called the "thermodynamic prob-ability." This, however, is merely giving to M a new name, and it is not clear what has been gained by this procedure.

The principal field for the Boltzmann formula appears to be the irreversible behavior of systems when left to themselves. It is often employed to assign a value to the entropy under such conditions that the ordinary thermodynamic definition of entropy cannot be applied. An alternative, however, which has much to recommend it, is to regard the entropy as a strictly macroscopic quantity, devoid of significance on the molecular scale, and possessing meaning only when the thermodynamic definition *can* be applied, at least to the parts of the system taken separately.

211. Relations with Boltzmann's H.   In the case of a point-mass gas there is also a close connection between the entropy S, the probability P, and Boltzmann's H.   For in this case we can write

$$\bar{N}_i = N(\delta\tau/V)f\delta\kappa = Ngf/V;$$

here N is the total number of molecules in the volume V, f is the ordinary distribution function for velocity as defined in Sec. 17, and g is the volume of a cell in molecule space, whose extension in velocity space is $\delta\kappa$ and in ordinary space $\delta\tau$, so that $g = \delta\tau\delta\kappa$.   Then

$$\sum_i \bar{N}_i \log \bar{N}_i = (N/V)\sum f \log f \, \delta\tau \, \delta\kappa + \sum \bar{N}_i \log (Ng/V) =$$

$$N\int f \log f \, d\kappa + N \log (Ng/V),$$

and the expressions found above for $\log P_D$ and for S can be written

$$\log P_D = -NH + N \log V + \text{const.,} \qquad (257a)$$
$$S = -NkH + Nk \log V + \text{const.} \qquad (257b)$$

in terms of H, as defined by eq. (70a), or $H = \int f \log f \, d\kappa$.   Thus the proof given in Sec. 32 that H decreases carries with it a proof that, if molecular chaos holds, the probability P_D will increase toward a maximum, and likewise the entropy S in so far as (257b) is assumed to hold.

These conclusions are again only statistical in nature, however. The condition of molecular chaos is itself subject to departures in the form of fluctuations, so that the proof refers merely to the *expectation* of a change in H.   If the gas is far from equilibrium, a probability approaching certainty exists that H will decrease and that P_D and S will increase; but as equilibrium is approached, the fluctuations become relatively more important, and finally in the state of equilibrium H oscillates in Brownian fashion about a minimum value, and P_D and S about a maximum.

212. Entropy as a Measure of Range in Phase.   If we wish to find some means of lending greater concreteness to the notion of entropy, we might perhaps secure it by regarding the entropy as a measure of the *range in phase* of the system.　Greater entropy goes with a greater ranging of the molecules over molecule space, as measured by an increase in $\Sigma \bar{N}_i \log (1/\bar{N}_i)$, or in the average value of $\log (1/\bar{N}_i)$; or, if we are using the canonical distribution, there is a similar increase in phase range as measured by the increase in the average of $\log (1/P)$ [cf. (255)].　A non-equilibrium state is then one in which full use is not being made by the system of the phase-space ranges that are open to it under the conditions to which it is subject, so that its behavior exhibits less phase range than in the state of equilibrium.

213. Relativity and Statistical Theory.　Up to this point we have worked exclusively with nonrelativistic or Newtonian mechanics. This is adequate for all of the practical purposes of kinetic theory; but it is of theoretical interest to look for a moment at the modifications that are required by relativity.

For particles in a *fixed force-field* the only change required is that we must write for the mass of a particle moving at speed v

$$m' = \frac{m}{\sqrt{1 - v^2/c^2}},$$

where c is the speed of light in vacuo and m the constant mass of the particle at zero speed.　Now, even for hydrogen at a temperature of a hundred million degrees the root-mean-square speed v_s is only 1.1×10^8 cm/sec or $0.004\,c$, so that $m' = 1.000007\,m$.　Clearly, therefore, the relativistic variation of mass is quite negligible for ordinary atoms under almost every conceivable circumstance.　The same statement holds good for free electrons moving as molecules on the earth, but at a temperature of 10^8 degrees, for them $v_s = 6.7 \times 10^9$, so that $v_s/c = 0.22$ and the corresponding mass is $m' = 1.025\,m$. Thus, if the temperature should go so high as that in the interior of a star, the increase of mass of free electrons would begin to become appreciable.

Accordingly, we shall add only the following remarks concerning the relativistic theory.　If as p's we take the components of the momentum $m'\mathbf{v}$, the Hamiltonian equations of motion still hold; everything that we have done or might have done in terms of momenta still holds good, therefore, including the phase-space theory.　Maxwell's law holds, provided it is stated in terms of momentum instead of velocity.　The scattering coefficient is slightly altered, both because of the variation of mass and because of the effects of retardation of the forces, which are propagated only with the speed of light; but this effect is no more appreciable than is the mass variation.

B. STATISTICAL WAVE MECHANICS

We must now consider how the statistical investigation is to be conducted when wave mechanics is substituted for classical theory. It turns out that a decidedly different method of attack is required.

214. The Wave-mechanical Description. The fundamental physical ideas of wave mechanics have been described in Secs. 75 and 76 and will be assumed to be familiar. As a basis for our statistical work we shall now add a concise statement of the general mathematical principles, in so far as these will be needed for our purpose. This statement will be made essentially complete; but it must be admitted that any discussion of wave-mechanical theory can hardly be appreciated properly unless the reader is already somewhat familiar with the mathematics of the theory of a particle.

A system of N fundamental particles (electrons, protons, etc.), which could be represented in classical theory by its $3N$ cartesian coordinates $q_1 \cdots q_{3N}$ and its $3N$ momenta $p_1 \cdots p_{3N}$, regarded as functions of the time, is represented in nonrelativistic wave mechanics by a *wave-function*,

$$\Psi(q_1 \cdots q_{3N}, s_1 \cdots s_N, t),$$

which contains as variables, besides the time t, the coordinates and the spin symbols $s_1 \cdots s_N$ of all the particles, but not their momenta. $\sum_s |\Psi|^2 \, dq_1 dq_2 \cdots dq_{3N}$, summed over all types of spin for all of the particles, is considered to represent the probability that an accurate determination of the values of the coordinates would yield a value of the first one lying in the range dq_1, of the second in dq_2, etc.; for this reason Ψ is often called a *probability amplitude*. It follows that Ψ must be normalized so that $\sum_s \int |\Psi|^2 \, dq_1 \cdots dq_{3N} = 1$, the integral extending over all values of the q's.

As the analogue of the ordinary equations of motion, we have then, as a basic postulate of the theory, the *wave equation*

$$\frac{h}{2\pi i} \frac{\partial \Psi}{\partial t} + H\left(\frac{h}{2\pi i} \frac{\partial}{\partial q_1}, \cdots \frac{h}{2\pi i} \frac{\partial}{\partial q_{3N}}; \, \sigma_1, \cdots \sigma_N; q_1 \cdots q_{3N}; t\right)\Psi = 0;$$

$$(258)$$

here h is Planck's constant and H is the Hamiltonian operator, which contains in general the spin vectors $\sigma_1 \cdots \sigma_N$ of the particles (if we employ Pauli's approximate theory of spin).

There are many problems in which the operator H does not contain the time explicitly; this is true, in fact, for any isolated dynamical system. In such cases a step toward the solution of the wave equation can at once be taken by the usual method of separating the variables. As a result of the mathematical analysis it turns out that the general solution of (258) can then be written down in the form,

$$\Psi = \sum_n a_n e^{-\frac{2\pi i E_n t}{h}} \psi_n(q_1 \cdots q_{3N}, s_1 \cdots s_N), \qquad (259)$$

where the a_n's are arbitrary constants and the ψ_n's are the various solutions of the *amplitude equation*

$$H\psi_n = E_n\psi_n; \qquad (260)$$

the constant E_n must be limited to such values that any Ψ formed out of the ψ_n's, as in (259), can be normalized to unity. This condition will be assumed here to limit E to a discrete set or "spectrum" of values; only when this is true can the system exist in a state of equilibrium. It is in this way, of course, that spectroscopic energy levels are calculated.

The functions ψ_n and the corresponding allowed values of E_n are the *characteristic* or *proper* functions (or eigenfunctions) and values (or eigenvalues) for the operator H. This operator usually represents the energy, and for greater concreteness we shall henceforth assume that it does. States of the system in which Ψ contains only one ψ_n, e.g., one represented by

$$\Psi = e^{-\frac{2\pi i E_j t}{h}} \psi_j$$

are often called *quantum* (or eigen) states. We shall assume the ψ_n's themselves to be normalized by a proper choice of the arbitrary factor that enters into any solution of (260) in such a way that

$$\int |\psi_n|^2 \, dq_1 \cdots dq_{3N} = 1.$$

When this is done, the constants in (259) can be shown to have the significance that $|a_n|^2$ represents the probability that observation would reveal the system in quantum state n, with energy exactly equal to E_n.

The formulation just described is adequate for the general treatment of an isolated system. If, on the other hand, we wish to include also the influence upon it of its surroundings, we can often do this by writing

$$H = H_0 + H_1, \qquad (261)$$

where H_0 represents the Hamiltonian for the system by itself and does not contain the time, while H_1 represents the influence of the surroundings. Then we can still write Ψ for the system in the form of a series as in (259) if we wish, the ψ_n's being solutions of

$$H_0\psi_n = E_n\psi_n,$$

but the a_n's will now be functions of the time; their changes with time, which are determined by H_1, can be interpreted as representing, in a certain sense, transitions of the system from one of its own quantum states to another. This is the method by which, for example, the absorption of light is treated.

215. The Exclusion Principle. There is one other peculiar feature for which allowance must often be made, viz., *exchange degeneracy.* The Hamiltonian operator is always symmetric in the coordinates and spins of any two similar particles; and for this reason, if in any solution ψ_n of the amplitude equation the coordinates of any two particles are interchanged, the result is again a solution of the equation, and one corresponding to the same energy. Thus, in the case of an N-dimensional system, there may be for any particular value of E_n as many as $N!$ independent ψ_n's.

Nature is not really so prodigal as this mathematical fact suggests, however. There is always one of these solutions which is *antisymmetric* in the particles, i.e., which changes sign whenever the coordinates of any two particles are interchanged; and for some unknown reason only solutions of this type alone can represent physically possible cases. Ψ itself must, accordingly, always be antisymmetric in the coordinates of similar particles. This requirement is commonly called the *exclusion principle;* it represents an extension in wavemechanical terms, made by Fermi and by Dirac, of a more limited principle proposed in the old quantum theory by Pauli.

216. The State of Equilibrium. From what has been said it is obvious that in statistical wave mechanics no immediate significance can be attached to the old phase space, in which half the variables were momenta. We must work primarily, not with p's and q's, but with the quantum states.

The analogue of a classical system moving on an ergodic surface with energy E seems, at first sight, to be obviously a system in a single one of its quantum states [e.g., in (259) $a_m = 1$, say, all other a_n's = 0]. At this point, however, we encounter a strong contrast with ordinary atomic theory. Whereas an atom or molecule may often be regarded as existing in a definite quantum state, it appears from the general principles of wave mechanics that the large bodies dealt with in statistical mechanics must always be regarded as being in a state in which many a_n's are different from 0, so that the system is, as it were, smeared over a large number of quantum states. The energy is then fixed only within a certain range ΔE, which may, perhaps, be macroscopically inappreciable, but which is yet very large relative to the spacing of the energies of the quantum states.

Regarding a system in equilibrium in this light, we are at once confronted by the question as to the relative values that must be assigned to the various a_n's. This problem appears to be the analogue in the new theory of the old ergodic question. Unlike the classical problem, however, this one does not seem to be answerable even in principle on the basis of the equations of motion alone; for the values of the a_n's represent the initial conditions with which the system was started, and so appear to be arbitrary.

To throw light on the question, let us consider how we would treat in wave mechanics a system that is started in some special physical condition different from equilibrium, like a gas with gradients of temperature and pressure in it. Initially the system, assumed isolated, can be represented by

$$\Psi_{t=0} = \sum_n a_n \psi_n$$

with suitable values of the constants $a_1, a_2 \cdots$. Thereafter it will be represented, as in (259), by

$$\Psi = \sum_n c_n \psi_n, \qquad c_n = a_n e^{-\frac{2\pi i E_n t}{h}}; \qquad (262)$$

the correctness of these values of the c_n's can be verified by substituting this value of Ψ in (258) and using (260). We note that as time goes on, the coefficients c_n do not change in absolute magnitude, since $|c_n| = |a_n|$ and so is constant; this fact corresponds to the classical circumstance that the systems of an ensemble remain on their respective ergodic surfaces. The c_n's do change, however, in *phase* (i.e., in the angle of c_n as a complex number).* It is, in fact, obvious that if any two E_n's are unequal, the relative phase of the corresponding c_n's will traverse at a uniform rate all possible values; if the E_n's are also incommensurable, the phases will finally come to be distributed chaotically.

---

* We can write $c_n = |c_n| e^{i\zeta}$, ζ being a real number; then ζ is the phase angle or phase of c_n. The "relative" phase of two c_n's is, of course, the difference of their ζ's.

Now, from the macroscopic standpoint, what happens in the long run is that a system generally passes into a state of equilibrium. This observation suggests the hypothesis that chaotic relative phases of the c_n's constitute the essential characteristic, from the wave-mechanical viewpoint, of the equilibrium state.

Accordingly, we shall forthwith assume that a system in thermal equilibrium can be represented by a Ψ, as in (262), in which an enormous number of c_n's occur with values differing appreciably from zero, but that the relative phases of these c_n's are distributed chaotically.

In the light of this hypothesis, our remark that in the case of incommensurable E_n's the phases must eventually become chaotic constitutes an actual proof, based on the wave equation, that equilibrium will, in general, come into existence automatically. In this simple remark we appear to have the physical equivalent, extended now to systems in general, of Boltzmann's H-theorem for point-mass gases in classical theory.

217. A Priori Probabilities. From the principle just laid down it can be shown that the statistical properties of a system in equilibrium can be found simply by averaging the properties of the various quantum states, each one weighted in proportion to $|c_n|^2$ or $|a_n|^2$. For example, the average result of measuring any quantity represented by an operator Q is, according to a rule of wave mechanics,

$$\bar{Q} = \int \Psi^* Q \Psi \, dq = \sum_n |c_n|^2 \int \psi_n^* Q \psi_n \, dq + \sum_n \sum_m c_n^* c_m \int \psi_n^* Q \psi_m \, dq.$$

Here Ψ^* denotes the complex conjugate of Ψ. The integrals

$$\int \psi_n^* Q \psi_m \, dq$$

may be expected to have similar values for many different pairs of quantum states, but they will eventually decrease as the two states of a pair become very dissimilar; and at the same time the chaotic phases of the c_n's will cause $c_n^* c_m$ to take on the negative of any given value as often as it does the value itself. Hence the double series on the right will be negligible compared to the single one, and we can write, for the equilibrium state,

$$\bar{Q} = \sum_n |c_n|^2 \int \psi_n^* Q \psi_n \, dq.$$

Here the integral $\int \psi_n^* Q \psi_n \, dq$ represents the average of Q for the system when it is in its nth quantum state, and, since $\sum_n |c_n|^2 = 1$, the whole expression represents the weighted average of Q over all quantum states.

The problem of the equilibrium state thus reduces to the question as to the proper values to be assigned to the a_n's. To fix these values some new principle is necessary; and in wave mechanics, in contrast with the situation in classical theory, it appears that this principle must take the form of an *additional fundamental postulate* which is coordinate in status with the wave equation itself, or at least with the rules for the physical interpretation of Ψ. Apparently the correct assumption is to require all of the a_n's in the range ΔE to be given the same value. This is equivalent to representing a given system by an ensemble containing one system in each of these quantum states; and accordingly we can formulate the new principle in the following way:

Principle of A Priori Probability. The statistical properties of an isolated system with macroscopically definite energy E are, in general, those of an ensemble having one system in each quantum state whose energy is contained in a range ΔE about E, this range being macroscopically small but covering a large number of quantum states. Or, quantum states belonging to such a range ΔE are to be treated, in general, as equally probable independent cases, the statistical features of the given system being obtained by averaging over these states.

The quantum states contemplated here and in all of the preceding discussion are the fundamental states of unit multiplicity. If, however, some of these states have the same energy, we can, if we prefer, group them into a multiple state, and such multiple states can then be employed as the statistical unit provided we assign weights to them equal to their respective multiplicities or numbers of component states. If then, as a special case, all of these multiple states have the same multiplicity, as frequently happens when the multiplicity arises from nuclear causes, their weights can be ignored after all and they can be treated as if they were simple.

In the historical development this principle was arrived at originally by noting that, in a certain sense, each quantum state of an s-dimensional system corresponds to a region of volume h^s in the classical phase space, in which equal regions represented equal probabilities. Some support can be lent to it from the wave equation by showing that the effect of an external disturbance upon the c_n's is such that a system initially in a state n is caused to pass into another state j at the same rate as one initially in j is caused to pass into n, so that no state appears to be favored over any other; but it remains essentially a new postulate.

Just as in the classical theory, the principle is subject to exceptions in special cases, for example, in the case of a gas in a smooth sphere as described above in Sec. 193. We shall assume, however, that it holds in general; and henceforth we shall confine our attention to those cases in which it does hold.

218. The Many-molecule System without Interaction. Following the line suggested by the classical argument, let us now consider a system that is composed of a large number N of exactly similar and only slightly interacting subsystems, all of which are confined in the same way to the same region of space. An ordinary gas is an obvious example of such a system; but the subsystems may also be bare fundamental particles such as electrons, or they may have any degree of complexity. The restriction that the same region must be accessible to all subsystems, in order to make them exactly similar, is a modification of the classical idea that is required by wave mechanics; this restriction makes it even more appropriate here to call the subsystems "molecules."

Let us suppose, first, that there is no interaction at all between the molecules. The problem is then so simple that we can actually construct the characteristic functions for the system as a whole by building them up out of one-molecule functions, in the following way.

Each molecule now moves independently in the containing vessel, and there will exist for each of them a series of one-molecule quantum states; let the corresponding antisymmetric characteristic functions and energies for one molecule be u_j and ϵ_j, the amplitude equation for u_j being

$$H'u_j = \epsilon_j u_j. \tag{263}$$

The amplitude equation for the entire system is then

$$\sum_{\kappa=1}^{N} H_\kappa' \psi_n = E_n \psi_n,$$

where H_κ' means H' written in terms of the κth set of molecular coordinates and $\Sigma H_\kappa'$ takes the place of H in (260). A solution of this equation is obviously the product function*

$$u_{j_1}(1)u_{j_2}(2) \cdots u_{j_N}(N),$$

each number in parenthesis meaning that the coordinates in the function are to be those of the molecule bearing that number; the

* For

$$H_\kappa'u_{j_1}(1) \cdots u_{j_N}(N) = u_{j_1}(1) \cdots u_{j_{(\kappa-1)}}(\kappa - 1)[H_\kappa'u_{j_\kappa}(\kappa)]u_{j_{(\kappa+1)}} \cdots u_{j_N}(N).$$

corresponding energy is

$$E_n = \epsilon_{j_1} + \epsilon_{j_2} + \cdots + \epsilon_{j_N}. \tag{264}$$

To obtain an antisymmetric function for the whole system corresponding to energy E_n as given by (264), we have then only to form the usual normalized combination of such product functions:

$$\psi_n = (\nu)^{-\frac{1}{2}} \Sigma \pm P u_{j_1}(1) u_{j_2}(2) \cdots u_{j_N}(N), \tag{265}$$

where the symbol P is to be understood as producing in the expression following it some permutation of the order of the sets of coordinates of the fundamental particles, these sets of coordinates being supposed written in a definite order in the original product function, and the particles of each kind being permuted only with each other; the sign is to be taken plus or minus according as the permutation leaves an even or an odd number of pairs of the sets in inverted order, and the sum is to be extended over all such permutations, whose number is denoted by ν. It is readily seen that a ψ_n so formed changes sign whenever the coordinates of any two similar particles are interchanged.

As a very simple example, suppose there are just two molecules, each containing one electron and one proton; let the coordinates of the electrons be denoted collectively by x_1 and x_2 and those of the protons by y_1 and y_2, respectively. Then the initial product function is

$$u_{j_1}(x_1, y_1) u_{j_2}(x_2, y_2);$$

and the antisymmetric combination, according to (265), is

$$\psi_n = (4)^{-\frac{1}{2}}[u_{j_1}(x_1, y_1) u_{j_2}(x_2, y_2) - u_{j_1}(x_2, y_1) u_{j_2}(x_1, y_2) - $$
$$u_{j_1}(x_1, y_2) u_{j_2}(x_2, y_1) + u_{j_1}(x_2, y_2) u_{j_2}(x_1, y_1)].$$

The order of the u_j's in any product function is immaterial; each combination of u_j's yields just one independent ψ_n. In the simple example just described, for instance, $u_{j_1}(x_1, y_1) u_{j_2}(x_2, y_2)$ and

$$u_{j_2}(x_1, y_1) u_{j_1}(x_2, y_2)$$

lead to the same ψ_n. This reduction in the number of independent ψ_n's for a system of similar particles is a direct consequence of the exclusion principle.

219. Fermi-Dirac and Bose-Einstein Sets of Similar Molecules. There is another aspect of the reduction just mentioned which depends upon the *number of particles in the molecule*, and which serves to divide sets of *similar* molecules into two classes.

Suppose that two u_j's happen to be the same; i.e., the same one-molecule function is repeated two or more times in the product func-

tion.   Then, when we form an antisymmetric ψ_n by combining product
functions as in (265), a permutation which consists only in interchanging the coordinates of similar particles between the two identical
u_j's does not really alter the product function.

Suppose, now, that each molecule contains an *odd* number of
particles; such a system is said to be of Fermi-Dirac type, which we
shall abbreviate to F-D.   Then any interchange between two molecules reverses the order of an odd number of particles; for example,
if in the sequence $ABCDE$ molecules A and E are interchanged, an
odd number of particles in A paired with those in E are reversed
in order, also the pairs formed by particles in A and E with those
in the intervening molecules BCD, but the latter pairs are necessarily
even in total number, and hence on the whole an odd number of pairs
of particles undergo reversal.   Accordingly, the new term formed
by the interchange of two molecules is opposite in sign to the original.
It follows that all the terms in the sum cancel each other in pairs;
and hence this particular ψ_n is identically zero and must be discarded.

If, on the other hand, the number of particles in a molecule is
even, no such loss of a ψ_n occurs when two or more u_j's are the same.
Such a system is said to be of Bose-Einstein (or B-E) type.

Each ψ_n formed as just described may obviously be regarded as
specifying a distribution of the N molecules among the one-molecule
quantum states, N_1 being assigned to the first state if the corresponding one-molecule function u_1 occurs N_1 times in each term of ψ_n, N_2
similarly to the second state if u_2 occurs N_2 times, and so on.   It is
not specified, however, which molecule is in each occupied state;
the molecules, like the fundamental particles, are not completely
individualized in wave mechanics.   In the B-E case there is no restriction upon the values of the N_j's; in the F-D case, on the other hand,
each $N_j = 1$ or 0, or "no two molecules can occupy the same quantum
state."

Up to this point we have assumed the molecules to be all alike.
The extension to a system containing several different kinds of molecules, each very numerous and moving perhaps in a force-field of its
own, is so easy that no equations need be written down.   In the
absence of interaction, the Hamiltonian operator H in eq. (260) is
simply the sum of several terms, one for each kind of molecule; and
the solutions of the equation are simply the products of the ψ_n's for
the separate kinds.

The final wave-function must then be antisymmetric even for
interchanges of similar fundamental particles between molecules of
different kinds.   When we secure this condition, however, by building

up ψ_n out of product functions, as in eq. (265), it is now impossible for two u_j's to be identical in form, and hence there can never be such a loss of ψ_n's as we found to occur with similar molecules. Each ψ_n for one kind of molecule, combined with each ψ_n' for every other kind, yields one independent zero-order function for the whole system. The process of antisymmetrizing between molecules of different kinds can, accordingly, be ignored.

The theory of similar molecules is thus to be applied separately to each homogeneous set of molecules that may be present in the system. In a mixed gas, for example, some molecules may be of F-D type while others are of B-E type; those of each type will then form a gas exhibiting the behavior characteristic of that type, just as if the others were not present.

220. The Loosely Coupled Many-molecule System. Having constructed in this manner characteristic functions for the system with the molecules moving independently, let us reintroduce the slight interaction that was originally postulated to exist between them (Sec. 218), so that in (260) we must write

$$H = \sum_{\kappa=1}^{N} H_\kappa' + H'',$$

H'' representing the interaction.

Then we can infer from the usual perturbation theory that the characteristic functions for the whole system will differ a little from ψ_n and E_n as given by (265) and (264) (with the usual proviso in case of degeneracy); but for a zero-order approximate treatment, which is all that will be contemplated here, this difference may be neglected. Hence we may continue to work with the zero-order ψ_n's that we have already constructed just as if these were the accurate characteristic functions for the actual system. As a matter of fact, they could also be used, although in a somewhat different way, even when the interaction is large; for each characteristic function can always be expanded as a series in terms of our zero-order ψ_n's, e.g., we can write for them $\psi_l' = \sum_n b_{ln}\psi_n$. When this is done, it can be shown that, if N_{jn} is the number of molecules represented by ψ_n as being in state j, ψ_l' represents $\sum_n |b_{ln}|^2 N_{jn}$ molecules as being in this state.

221. Statistics of the Loose Many-molecule System. From what has been said it follows that the principle of a priori probability (Sec. 217) can be applied to the zero-order quantum states represented by our ψ_n's as given by (265) above. Accordingly, when a system ccm-posed of similar molecules is in equilibrium, with energy confined to a small range ΔE, we may regard as equally probable each *distribution* of its *molecules* among their zero-order quantum states, i.e., among the u_j's. Let N_j denote the number of molecules in the jth state; then each set of values of the N_j's represents an equally probable case.

As a statistical feature let us seek the mean number or expectation of molecules in each of these quantum states when the system is in equilibrium at a given temperature. As before, suppose first that the molecules are all alike; let their number be N.

All distributions being now equally probable, it is hopeless to look for a most probable or "normal" one as we did in the classical case. The customary and simplest way of overcoming this difficulty is to redefine the term "distribution" in such a way that all distributions will *not* have equal probabilities. In order to be able to do this, we must further restrict the type of system under consideration by supposing the one-molecule states to lie so extremely

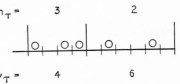

Fig. 86.—A Fermi-Dirac distribution.

close together that, after dividing them into groups of ν_r states each, we can suppose the ν_r's to be large and yet can neglect the variation of the energy within any given group of states. Let us denote the number of molecules in the τth group by n_r.

We can then ask for the probability of any particular set of values of the n_r's, regarding each such set as representing a macroscopic distribution. According to what was said above, this probability will be proportional to the number of ways in which the molecules can be parceled out among the molecular states with n_1 falling into the first group of states, n_2 into the second, etc., with no attention paid to the individuality of the molecules that fall into a given group.

In the F-D case, in which only one molecule is allowed per state (cf. Fig. 86), this number is simply the number of ways of selecting n_1 out of the first group of ν_1 states to hold n_1 molecules, n_2 out of the second group of ν_2, and so on, or

$$M = \frac{\nu_1!}{n_1!(\nu_1 - n_1)!} \frac{\nu_2!}{n_2!(\nu_2 - n_2)!} \cdots ,$$

with the convention that $0! = 1$.

To find the corresponding number in the B-E case (Fig. 87a), imagine the n_r molecules that are to fall into the τth group laid out in a row and $\nu_r - 1$ partitions inserted to divide them among the

ν_r cells, several partitions being allowed perhaps to fall together (Fig. 87b). The number of ways of arranging the $n_r + \nu_r - 1$ molecules and partitions in order in the row is $(n_r + \nu_r - 1)!$; but we must divide this by $n_r!$, the number of ways of permuting the molecules among themselves, and by $(\nu_r - 1)!$, the number of ways of permuting the partitions among themselves, since any such permu-

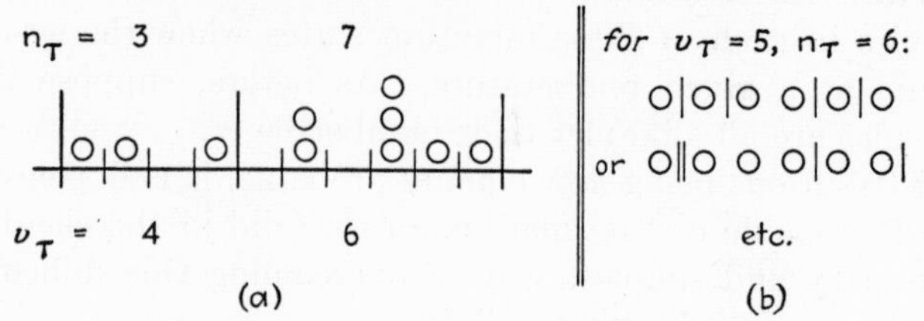

FIG. 87.—The Bose-Einstein distribution.

tation does not change the distribution of the molecules among the states. Hence in the B-E case

$$M = \frac{(\nu_1 + n_1 - 1)!}{n_1!(\nu_1 - 1)!} \frac{(\nu_2 + n_2 - 1)!}{n_2!(\nu_2 - 1)!} \cdots$$

Now let us suppose that many of the n_r's are large, and let us apply to them Stirling's formula, eq. (214b) in Sec. 154, or

$$\log n = (n + \tfrac{1}{2}) \log n - n + \log \sqrt{2\pi};$$

here we will at once suppress $\frac{1}{2}$ in comparison with n, and also lump together terms which are independent of the n_r's either because $\sum_r n_r = N$ or otherwise. Then we can write, with accuracy so far as the large n_r's are concerned, in the two cases:

F-D: $\log M = -\sum_r n_r \log n_r - \sum_r (\nu_r - n_r) \log (\nu_r - n_r) + \text{const.}$,

B-E: $\log M = -\sum_r n_r \log n_r + \sum_r (\nu_r + n_r - 1) \log (\nu_r + n_r - 1)$

$$+ \text{const.}$$

Proceeding then exactly as in Sec. 199, we seek those values of n_r which make M or $\log M$ a maximum, subject to the two conditions that

$$\sum_r n_r = N, \qquad \sum_r \epsilon_r n_r = E,$$

ϵ_τ being the energy of a state in the τth group and E the total energy. For these values of n_τ, if large, we find:

F-D: $- \log n_\tau + \log (\nu_\tau - n_\tau) - \alpha - \beta \epsilon_\tau = 0,$ $\quad \dfrac{\nu_\tau}{n_\tau} - 1 = e^{\beta \epsilon_\tau + \alpha},$

B-E: $- \log n_\tau + \log (\nu_\tau + n_\tau - 1) - \alpha - \beta \epsilon_\tau = 0,$ $\quad \dfrac{\nu_\tau}{n_\tau} + 1 = e^{\beta \epsilon_\tau + \alpha},$

after dropping $1/n_\tau$ for the sake of consistency with previous approximations.

Let us now write $\bar{N}_j$ for the mean number of molecules per state in the neighborhood of state j, whose energy is ϵ_j; we can identify $\bar{N}_i$ with n_τ / ν_τ for the group containing this state, and its energy ϵ_j with the value of ϵ_τ for the group. Then the last equations give, respectively:

$$\bar{N}_j = \frac{1}{e^{\beta \epsilon_j + \alpha} + 1}, \qquad \bar{N}_j = \frac{1}{e^{\beta \epsilon_j + \alpha} - 1}. \qquad (266a, b)$$

When the molecules are of several kinds, there being many of each kind, one finds easily that a formula must hold for each kind which is like (266a) or (266b) according as the number of particles is odd or even in that kind of molecule; α may vary from one kind to another, but β, as in the classical case, must be the same for all.

222. Introduction of the Temperature. The constant β can now be connected with the temperature by an argument which parallels so closely the classical one given in Sec. 202 that we need mention only the differences.

The ϵ_j's and u_j's are here functions of the parameters which were there called α's, for the latter will occur in H' in the one-molecule amplitude equation, (263). During the small thermodynamic process contemplated in Sec. 202, any system can be represented by a Ψ of the form given in eq. (262) above, but the a_n's themselves will now be functions of the time. The number of molecules in state j at any instant is then $N_j = \sum\limits_{n} |a_n|^2 N_{jn}$ where N_{jn} denotes the number that are in that state when the system is in its quantum state n and $|a_n|^2$ or $|c_n|^2$ represents the probability for the occurrence of this quantum state. If the α's mentioned above are changed extremely slowly, it follows from a theorem of wave mechanics (the "adiabatic" theorem) that this change does not appreciably alter the a_n's; changes in the a_n's and the N_j's arise here, therefore, only from the action of heating forces.

Accordingly, if there are no heating forces, the change in the energy, which latter can be written $E = \sum\limits_{j} \bar{N}_j \epsilon_j$, is $\sum\limits_{j} \bar{N}_j \, d\epsilon_j$; and this is the negative of the work done by the system. If, then, heating forces do act, the work is unaffected by their presence to the first order. Hence we can write for the work done during the infinitesimal process under consideration

$$dW = -\sum_j \bar{N}_j \, d\epsilon_j. \tag{267}$$

The reversible heat absorbed during the process is then, in analogy with (251a), $dQ = dE + dW = d\sum_j \bar{N}_j\epsilon_j + dW$, or

$$dQ = \sum_j \epsilon_j \, d\bar{N}_j. \tag{268}$$

Now, during this process we assume the system to remain close to equilibrium, so that $\bar{N}_j$ is given by (266a) or (266b). Both of these equations, like the classical one, are special cases of the more general form,

$$\bar{N}_j = F_j(\beta\epsilon_j + \alpha),$$

the F_j's being certain functions. Whenever $\bar{N}_j$ has such a form, eq. (268) multiplied through by β, can be written, since $\sum_j d\bar{N}_j = 0$,

$$\beta \, dQ = \sum_j (\beta\epsilon_j + \alpha) \, d\bar{N}_j = \sum_j (\beta\epsilon_j + \alpha) \, dF_j(\beta\epsilon_j + \alpha). \tag{269}$$

Here the last member is obviously the differential of a quantity which has a definite value corresponding to each state of the whole system. Hence we can, as before, write $\beta = 1/kT$ in terms of Boltzmann's constant k and the thermodynamic temperature T.

The final distribution formulas (266a, b) for a loose many-molecule system composed of similar molecules can, accordingly, be written

$$\bar{N}_j = \frac{1}{Be^{\frac{\epsilon_j}{kT}} + 1}, \qquad \bar{N}_j = \frac{1}{Be^{\frac{\epsilon_j}{kT}} - 1}, \tag{270a, b}$$

the first of these equations referring to the Fermi-Dirac or odd-particle case and the second to the Bose-Einstein or even-particle case. Here B takes the place of e^α above and B and T are determined by the two conditions that

$$\sum_j \bar{N}_j = N, \qquad \sum_j \epsilon_j \bar{N}_j = E;$$

N is the total number of molecules in the system and E its total energy (the slight molecular interaction being ignored), and the sums extend over all of the molecular quantum states.

As in the classical case, the distribution represented by these formulas is to be regarded, not only as the most probable one, but also as normal in the sense that appreciable departures from it are rare. Strictly speaking, the formulas are limited to cells which lie within a group containing a large number n_r of molecules, but this limitation is of no practical importance.

223. Case of Large Energies: Classical Theory as a Limit Form. The exact significance in any particular case of the formulas that have just been obtained will obviously depend upon the law according to which ϵ_j varies from one molecular state to the next; and this in turn will depend upon the nature of the external force-field to which all of the molecules are subjected. The special case of the ideal gas will be taken up in the next chapter.

There is one general case, however, that of large energy, in which both formulas approximate to a simpler form that is very important. In order to make the total energy E large, the molecules must obviously move out for the most part to states of high energy. According to (270a, b), however, $\bar{N}_j$ is such a function of ϵ_j that it can never be smaller for any state of lower energy; hence E can be large only if the molecules spread so widely that the N_j's all become small, and this means that for all values of ϵ_j

$$Be^{\frac{\epsilon_j}{kT}} \gg 1.$$

We can, therefore, write approximately for either a F-D or a B-E system, when E is large enough,

$$\bar{N}_j = Ce^{-\frac{\epsilon_j}{kT}}, \tag{270c}$$

where $C = 1/B$. If all $\epsilon_j > 0$, $C \ll 1$.

This very useful formula is just like the Boltzmann formula of classical theory, eq. (249d) in Sec. 201, except that here reference to a particular quantum state replaces the mention of a cell in phase space; historically, this formula was inferred many years ago as the appropriate quantum modification. We note, however, that it represents only an approximation valid for energies sufficiently high to justify neglect of the characteristic peculiarities of the more exact wave-mechanical formula as given in (270a) or (270b).

224. Entropy of a Loose Many-molecule System. The entropy can be found by putting $\beta = \dfrac{1}{kT}$ in (269) and evaluating $\int \dfrac{dQ}{T}$. After an integration by parts, we thus find for it the general expression,

$$S = k \sum_j x_j F_j(x_j) - k \sum_j \int F_j(x_j)\, dx_j$$

where

$$x_j = \frac{\epsilon_j}{kT} + \alpha.$$

In the actual cases before us we have, writing $B = e^\alpha$ again in (270a, b),

$$\bar{N}_j = F_j(x_j) = \frac{1}{e^{x_j} \pm 1},$$

the upper sign referring to the F-D case and the lower to the B-E. Hence here

$$\int F_j(x_j)\, dx_j = \int \frac{dx_j}{e^{x_j} \pm 1} = \mp \log(1 \pm e^{-x_j}) + \text{const.},$$

$$= \mp \log(1 \pm B^{-1} e^{-\frac{\epsilon_j}{kT}}) + \text{const.}$$

since $e^\alpha = B$. Noting that $\sum_j \epsilon_j F_j = E$, the total energy, and $\sum_j F_j = N$, whereas $\alpha = \log B$, we have, therefore, if we omit the constant of integration,

$$S = \frac{E}{T} + Nk \log B \pm k \sum_j \log(1 \pm B^{-1} e^{-\frac{\epsilon_j}{kT}}). \qquad (271a)$$

An equivalent expression in terms of the mean densities can also be found by substituting, in the original expression for S,

$$x_j = \log\left(\frac{1}{\bar{N}_j} \mp 1\right),$$

and in the expression found for $\int F_j(x_j)\, dx_j$,

$$(1 \pm e^{-x_j}) = 1 \pm \left(\frac{1}{\bar{N}_j} \mp 1\right)^{-1} = 1 \pm \frac{\bar{N}_j}{1 \mp \bar{N}_j} = \frac{1}{1 \mp \bar{N}_j}.$$

We thus obtain

$$S = k \sum_j \bar{N}_j \log\left(\frac{1}{\bar{N}_j} \mp 1\right) \mp k \sum_j \log(1 \mp \bar{N}_j). \qquad (271b)$$

or

$$S = -k\sum_j \bar{N}_j \log \bar{N}_j \mp k\sum_j (1 \mp \bar{N}_j) \log (1 \mp \bar{N}_j). \quad (271b')$$

In the classical limit discussed in the last section, where $\bar{N}_j$ is given with sufficient accuracy by (270c), and all $\bar{N}_j$'s are small, these expressions become approximately

$$S = \frac{E}{T} + Nk \log B + Nk = -k\sum_j \bar{N}_j \log \bar{N}_j + Nk, \quad (271c)$$

as may be verified by expanding the logarithms in (271a) and (271b')

and keeping only first powers of $\bar{N}_j$ or $B^{-1}e^{-\frac{\epsilon_j}{kT}}$. These expressions agree with the classical ones as given in (252a, b) in Sec. 203, except that here S_0 is given the special value Nk; physically, the latter difference is of no significance because it concerns only an arbitrary constant.

It may be remarked again that, contrary to our previous usage in dealing with gases, S stands here for the whole entropy of the system, not for the entropy of a unit mass.

225. Statistics of Mixed Systems. The results that have been obtained for homogeneous systems are easily extended to loosely coupled systems in which there are several different kinds of molecules, many of each kind being present. In Sec. 219 we have seen that in the zero-order approximation, in which the slight interaction is ignored, each kind of molecule can be treated as if the others were not present; interchange of coordinates between molecules of different kinds need not be considered and the quantum states for the whole system can be formed simply by taking all possible combinations of the quantum states for the separate groups. Accordingly, when we employ the method of one-molecule states, we have to consider all distributions of the separate kinds taken independently.

The mode of generalizing the calculations of Sec. 221 follows so closely the lines of the parallel process in classical theory, as described in Sec. 201, that few details need be given. The number of arrangements M is simply the product of expressions like that written in Sec. 221, one for each kind of molecule, and its logarithm is the sum of corresponding terms. There is a separate equation of the type, $\sum_\tau n_\tau = N$, for each kind, but a single equation expressing conservation of the total energy E. The result is then a distribution law of type (266a) or (266b), or (270a) or (270b), for each kind of molecule, according as it is of F-D or B-E type; the constant α or B varies from one kind to another, but β or $1/kT$ does not.

In brief, each kind of molecule is distributed as if it alone were present, except that the common temperature of all is determined by their total energy. The entropy, likewise, is easily seen to be simply the sum of the separate entropies.

226. The Canonical Distribution in Wave Mechanics. In classical statistical mechanics we dealt not only with distribution laws for the separate molecules but also with a probability distribution in phase, called canonical, of the entire system. It is natural to seek for something similar in terms of wave mechanics.

Now the lack of complete individuality of similar systems which results from the exclusion principle puts great difficulties in the way of an exact imitation of the classical argument which led us above to the canonical distribution, so that we seem here to be thrown back upon a more indirect procedure. We shall find in the next chapter (Sec. 232) that a perfect gas of point-mass molecules, behaving as nearly classically as desired, can be realized at any temperature by making the density low enough. If such a gas containing a huge number N of molecules is used as a temperature bath in slight contact with any given system, the statistical distribution of the latter among its quantum states can readily be found. Since the macroscopic behavior of the system can scarcely depend upon whether it is coupled to a gas or not, it seems plausible to assume that we may adopt its distribution when so coupled as the canonical one.

Let the energies of the quantum states of the system be E_i, and of the gas, E'_κ. Then the zero-order quantum states of the combined system formed by the given system and the gas will consist of each quantum state of the one combined with each state of the other, the total energy being $E_i + E'_\kappa$. Each of these states whose energy lies in a small range δE can then be treated as equally probable (Sec. 217).

The relative probability of each state of the original system with energy E_i will accordingly be proportional to the number $\delta\nu'_q$ of states of the gas with which that state of the system can combine in such a way as to make a total energy lying within δE; for such states the energy of the gas alone lies in a range of width δE about the value $E' = E - E_i$. Now, according to eq. (293) in Sec. 233 of the next chapter, the gas has $\nu_q = X E^{\frac{3N}{2}}$ states below energy E, X being a coefficient independent of E; hence it has

$$\nu'_q = X(E - E_i)^{\frac{3N}{2}}$$

states below $E - E_i$. Accordingly, to δE there correspond

$$\delta \nu_q' = \frac{3N}{2} X(E - E_i)^{\frac{3N}{2}-1} \delta E$$

states; and the ratio of the probabilities of two states of the original system with energies E_1 and E_2 is, therefore,

$$\frac{P_1}{P_2} = \frac{(\delta \nu_q')_1}{(\delta \nu_q')_2} = \left(\frac{E - E_1}{E - E_2}\right)^{\frac{3N}{2}-1} = \left(\frac{1 - \dfrac{E_1}{E}}{1 - \dfrac{E_2}{E}}\right)^{\frac{3N}{2}-1}.$$

Here E consists mostly of the energy E' of the gas and so is vastly larger than E_i; hence we can write with sufficient accuracy

$$E = E' = \tfrac{3}{2} NkT$$

in terms of the Boltzmann constant k and the absolute temperature T. Then, writing $\log (1 - x) = -x + \cdots$, we have

$$\log \frac{P_1}{P_2} = \left(\frac{3N}{2} - 1\right)\frac{E_2 - E_1}{E} = \frac{E_2 - E_1}{kT}$$

after dropping the factor $(\tfrac{3}{2} N - 1)/(\tfrac{3}{2} N)$, which is indistinguishable from unity. Thus the probability of any state of energy E_i for the first system is proportional to $e^{-\frac{E_i}{kT}}$ and can be written

$$P_i = Ce^{-\frac{E_i}{kT}} = \frac{e^{-\frac{E_i}{kT}}}{\sum_i e^{-\frac{E_i}{kT}}}, \tag{272}$$

the value of C being fixed by the condition that $\sum_i P_i = 1$.

This is obviously the exact analogue of the canonical distribution in classical theory as expressed by eq. (254) in Sec. 207 above. Presumably it can be taken as a basis in quantum theory for obtaining the statistical properties of any system in equilibrium.

227. The Entropy. From (272) one obtains readily, by the method we have several times used, as the wave-mechanical analogue of (255) in Sec. 208, for the entropy of any system at temperature T:

$$S = -k\sum_i P_i \log P_i = \frac{E}{T} + k \log \sum_i e^{-\frac{E_i}{kT}}, \tag{273}$$

E representing the mean energy, $\sum_i E_i P_i$, and the additive constant being set equal to zero. The last sum here is Planck's state sum.

The first expression for S given in (273) reduces at $T = 0$ to

$$S = k \log w_0,$$

where w_0 is the degree of degeneracy of the state of lowest energy, or the number of fundamental quantum states having that energy; for at absolute zero $P_i = 1/w_0$ for each of these states and $P_i = 0$ for all others. Thus, according to (273), the entropy of any system is finite at $T = 0$, as it has been widely inferred to be from the Nernst heat theorem. For any given system it could be made actually zero, if not zero already, by means of a different and rather unnatural choice of the arbitrary additive constant in S.

At this point we are in contact with the question, so important in chemistry, whether all changes of entropy during chemical transformations vanish at absolute zero. This question lies entirely outside the subject of gases, however, and will not be discussed here (but cf. Sec. 235).

The system under consideration may, of course, be itself a loose many-molecule one, perhaps a gas. In that case statistical mechanics gives us in (273) here and in (271a, b, c) in Sec. 223 two different expressions for the entropy which seem even to arise physically in different ways. If both forms are correct, they can differ in reality only by a constant. In the next chapter we shall investigate the difference in the special case of a point-mass gas (Sec. 234); in that case it turns out that, in so far as the earlier formulas (271a, b, c) are valid at all, they happen to agree completely with the new one, (273), just as written.

Thus the same duplicity of method and of results that are found in classical statistical mechanics persist in the wave-mechanical formulation. The only important difference is that in wave mechanics similar particles are not completely independent of each other, and consequently the canonical distribution of the system can be made to yield the distribution law directly only for dissimilar molecules, not for a group of similar ones.

CHAPTER X

WAVE MECHANICS OF GASES

The most important applications of wave mechanics to the theory of gases have already been discussed in Chap. III (Secs. 54, 55, 75, 76, 77). In that discussion, however, the gas was conceived of as a collection of molecules moving about in space like classical particles, and wave mechanics was applied only to their collisions with each other or to their internal heat energy, and only in an approximate form. This method is adequate for the treatment of most problems. For the sake of completeness, however, the theory should somewhere be formulated from the beginning entirely in terms of wave mechanics. This will be done in the present chapter; and we shall at the same time consider the conditions under which deviations may be looked for from the properties predicted by classical theory.

228. The Perfect Gas in Wave Mechanics. The perfect gas constitutes the principal example of the loose many-molecule type of system whose theory has already been developed in Secs. 218 to 221 of the last chapter. To avoid repetition we shall build directly upon the results there obtained. It is necessary to add only a special assumption constituting the mathematical definition of a perfect gas; we shall find that it is then possible to work out the theory completely.

External force-fields will be assumed to be entirely absent except for the restraining influence of the walls of the vessel. The effect of the walls can be represented by a potential-energy term in the Hamiltonian function, and we shall assume that this can be expressed with sufficient accuracy in terms of the centers of mass of the molecules alone. Then, when the interaction between the molecules can be ignored, the functions for the whole gas can be built up out of functions each of which represents one molecule alone in the vessel; and the wave equation for one molecule can be written, as a special case of (263) in Sec. 218,

$$(H'_m + H'_I + U_W)u_j = \epsilon_j u_j,$$

in which H'_m is that part of the Hamiltonian which contains the coordinates of the center of mass, H'_I is a term containing the internal coordinates of the molecule (representing rotation, vibration, etc.), and U_W is the potential energy between the molecule and the wall.

We can suppose U_W to be zero everywhere except that it rises with extreme rapidity toward infinity when the molecule comes extremely close to the wall. The effect of any such term in the Hamiltonian can be shown to consist in forcing ψ to vanish as $U_W \to \infty$. Accordingly, we can also drop U_W entirely and write as the wave equation for one molecule simply

$$(H'_m + H'_I)u_j = \epsilon_j u_j, \tag{274}$$

provided we add the boundary condition that $u_j = 0$ at the walls of the vessel.

The limitation of the translatory motion only by a wall of this sort, together with the absence of interaction between the molecules themselves, may be regarded as the wave-mechanical definition of a perfect gas. As in classical theory, the idealization is excessive, since with no interaction whatever there would be nothing to bring the gas into a state of equilibrium. To represent an actual gas we must suppose that a slight molecular interaction does in fact exist; such a gas might be called, in contrast with the absolutely perfect type considered here, a *physically* perfect gas. The interaction will enter into the equations as a small perturbation and, in harmony with the explanation in Sec. 220, will affect the quantum states of the gas only to a negligible extent. The theory of the absolutely perfect gas, as we shall develop it, may accordingly be regarded as a good zero-order approximation to the theory of a physically perfect gas.

In eq. (274) the variables can now be separated. Substituting in it

$$u_j = \varphi_\mu\,(x,\ y,\ z)\chi_\nu,$$

where φ_μ is a function of the cartesian coordinates of the center of mass of the molecule while χ_ν is a function of its internal coordinates alone, we find that u_j so defined is a solution of (274), provided

$$H'_m\varphi_\mu = \zeta_\mu\varphi_\mu, \qquad H'_I\chi_\nu = \eta_\nu\chi_\nu, \qquad \epsilon_j = \zeta_\mu + \eta_\nu. \tag{275a, b, c}$$

Here ζ_μ and η_ν are arbitrary new constants which can be regarded as representing, respectively, special values of the translatory kinetic and internal energies.

The χ_ν's represent a set of internal quantum states of the molecule, including its various nuclear states, and will not be considered in further detail here; the determination of these functions and of the allowed values of η_ν is taken up as the most important problem in treatises on wave mechanics. The φ_μ's, however, present a problem that belongs to kinetic theory.

229. The Point-mass Perfect Gas.   It is simplest to develop first the theory of a gas in which all the molecules are in the same internal state; for convenience in the applications, however, we shall allow this state to have a multiplicity w, due perhaps to electron spin or to nuclear causes.   As a special case, of course, it may happen that $w = 1$.   The function χ_ν and its associated energy η_ν can then be ignored and the theory becomes the same as that for a set of point masses.   For the present we shall also suppose the molecules to be all alike.

Equation (275a) can be written explicitly in the familiar form

$$\left(\frac{\partial^2}{\partial x^2} + \frac{\partial^2}{\partial y^2} + \frac{\partial^2}{\partial z^2}\right)\varphi_\mu + \frac{8\pi^2 m}{h^2}\,\zeta_\mu\varphi_\mu = 0, \tag{276}$$

where m is the mass of a molecule, h is Planck's constant, and the first term multiplied by $(-h^2/8\pi^2 m)$ represents $H'_m\varphi_\mu$.   It can be shown that nothing of physical interest is changed if we give to the vessel a special shape in order to simplify the mathematical form of the φ_μ's; accordingly, we shall assume it to have the shape of a parallelepiped of edges l_1, l_2, l_3, and we shall take axes along three of these edges. Then the boundary condition stated above requires that $\varphi_\mu = 0$ whenever the molecule comes up to the wall of the vessel, i.e., whenever $x = 0$ or l_1, or $y = 0$ or l_2, or $z = 0$ or l_3.

The only type of function that satisfies all of these conditions is

$$\varphi_\mu = C \sin \mu_1\pi \frac{x}{l_1} \sin \mu_2\pi \frac{y}{l_2} \sin \mu_3\pi \frac{z}{l_3}, \tag{277}$$

in which C is a normalization constant, while μ_1, μ_2, μ_3 may be any three positive integers.   The corresponding kinetic energy is

$$\zeta_\mu = \zeta = \frac{h^2}{8m}\left(\frac{\mu_1^2}{l_1^2} + \frac{\mu_2^2}{l_2^2} + \frac{\mu_3^2}{l_3^2}\right). \tag{278}$$

It is easily verified by substitution that any φ_μ so defined is a solution of (276).

In its mathematical form this solution recalls the classical standing oscillations of a solid rectangular block, and like the latter it can be regarded as formed by the superposition of eight trains of running waves, each of which is continually being converted into one of the other seven by reflection from the walls.   These eight trains can be expressed in the form

$$\varphi = \pm\frac{C}{8i}\, e^{\frac{2\pi i(p_x x + p_y y + p_z z)}{h}},$$

where*

$$p_x = \pm \mu_1 \frac{h}{2l_1}, \qquad p_y = \pm \mu_2 \frac{h}{2l_2}, \qquad p_z = \pm \mu_3 \frac{h}{2l_3}, \qquad (279)$$

and hence $p^2 = p_x^2 + p_y^2 + p_z^2 = 2m\zeta$. According to the theory of a single particle, an infinite train of waves of this character represents the molecule as moving in a certain direction with momentum p and kinetic energy ζ. Hence we can say, speaking roughly, that any φ_μ of the form of (277) represents a molecule as moving with kinetic energy ζ_μ and with an equal chance of being found going in any one of the eight directions whose cosines are proportional to $\pm \mu_1/l_1$, $\pm \mu_2/l_2$, $\pm \mu_3/l_3$.

As to position, however, a molecule in a state represented by a single φ_μ is equally likely to be found in any part of the vessel, aside from the characteristic quantum phenomenon represented by the rapid fluctuation of $\varphi_\mu{}^2$ over distances of the order of the molecular wave length, $\lambda = h/p$.

An antisymmetric wave-function ψ_n for the whole gas can now be built up out of the one-molecule functions φ_μ as a special case of (265) in Sec. 218, viz.,

$$\psi_n = (\nu)^{-\frac{1}{2}} \Sigma \pm P \varphi_{\mu_1}(1) \varphi_{\mu_2}(2) \cdots \varphi_{\mu_N}(N),$$

N being the total number of molecules; the corresponding kinetic energy is then

$$E_n = \zeta_{\mu_1} + \zeta_{\mu_2} + \cdots \zeta_{\mu_N}.$$

Such a function may be regarded as representing a state of the gas in which, if N_j is the number of times that any particular φ_μ occurs repeated in each of the product functions out of which ψ_n is constructed, then there are N_j molecules moving with kinetic energy ζ_μ and momentum $p = (2m\zeta_\mu)^{\frac{1}{2}}$; and there is no harm in imagining that one eighth of them are moving in each of the eight directions that we have associated with each φ_μ. We cannot say which molecules are so moving, however; they are not individually distinguishable. Then if the gas is in a more general state, represented, as in eq. (262) in Sec. 216, by a wave-function

$$\psi = \sum_n c_n \psi_n,$$

---

* The $\pm$'s in p_x, p_y, p_z are independent and the $\pm$ written in front is the product of all three of them.

we can say that $\sum_n |c_n|^2 N_{\mu n}$ molecules are moving with energy ζ_μ, $N_{\mu n}$ denoting the number so moving when the gas is in state ψ_n and $|c_n|^2$ representing the probability of this state.

In the particular case of a gas in equilibrium we can go farther and assert that these molecules are moving equally in all directions; for, this statement holds for each quantum state represented by a single n, and, for systems in equilibrium, according to the principle of a priori probability laid down in Sec. 217, whatever is true for all quantum states must likewise be true for the gas in its actual state. When the gas is not in equilibrium, on the other hand, the phases of the c_n's cannot be assumed to be chaotic, and interference between the φ_μ's belonging to different ψ_n's may then result in nonisotropic distribution of the molecular velocities.

230. The Two Types of Point-mass Gas. In accord with the general principle explained in Sec. 219 homogeneous perfect gases with point-mass molecules will now fall into two distinct classes, the Fermi-Dirac (or F-D) type with molecules composed of an odd number of fundamental particles, and the Bose-Einstein (or B-E) type, in which this number is even. In the F-D type no two molecules can be in the same quantum state; this means here that, if w is the multiplicity of the internal molecular state, at most w molecules can have the same kinetic energy ζ_μ and the same associated eight directions of motion, one being in each of the w fundamental internal states. In the B-E type there is no such restriction.

It must not be concluded, however, that in a F-D gas a molecule in one corner of the vessel cannot move in a certain manner if another molecule somewhere else is doing it, or that after a multiple collision two molecules cannot move off with sensibly the same vector velocities and energies. For statements of this sort to have a meaning, ψ must consist of a series, $\psi = \sum_n c_n \psi_n$, in which the c_n's for many quantum states differ from zero and also do not have chaotic phases; and then it can be shown that the indetermination principle described in Sec. 76 results in a sufficient degree of indefiniteness in the molecular velocities to prevent us from telling with the requisite precision whether two molecules really do have identical velocities or not.

231. The Homogeneous Point-mass Gas in Equilibrium. The molecular distribution law for either type of gas can be obtained from (270a, b) in Sec. 222 by substituting the kinetic energy ζ_μ for ϵ_j, changing $\bar{N}_j$ to $\bar{N}_\mu$, and multiplying by the multiplicity w of the internal state. We thus obtain, as the mean total number of molecules in the μth state, under equilibrium conditions,

$$\bar{N}_\mu = \frac{w}{Be^{\frac{\zeta_\mu}{kT}} + 1}, \qquad \bar{N}_\mu = \frac{w}{Be^{\frac{\zeta_\mu}{kT}} - 1}, \qquad (280a, b)$$

the two formulas referring to the Fermi-Dirac and to the Bose-Einstein types, respectively (k = the Boltzmann constant, T = absolute temperature).

Usually the molecules are widely distributed among their translational quantum states, and then it is convenient to treat the energy as a continuous variable. The number of one-molecule quantum states having energies in a range $d\zeta$ will be equal to the number of positive integral sets of μ_1, μ_2, μ_3 for which ζ as given by (278) lies in $d\zeta$. To find this number, let us take as new variables the components of momenta

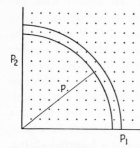

P_2

P_1

FIG. 88.—Molecular states plotted in p space.

$$p_1 = \frac{\mu_1 h}{2l_1}, \qquad p_2 = \frac{\mu_2 h}{2l_2}, \qquad p_3 = \frac{\mu_3 h}{2l_3},$$

in terms of which $\zeta = (p_1^2 + p_2^2 + p_3^2)/2m = p^2/2m$. Then in all practical cases it turns out that l_1, l_2, l_3 are extremely large relative to h/p_1, h/p_2, h/p_3 (the quantity h/p representing the molecular wave length), at least in all states that are of statistical importance; and accordingly p_1, p_2, p_3 can be treated as if they varied continuously. Now the number of integrally spaced values of μ_1 within a unit of p_1 is obviously $2l_1/h$; hence, by extension of this result to three dimensions, the number of quantum states per unit cube of p_1, p_2, p_3 space is $(2l_1/h)(2l_2/h)(2l_3/h)$ or $8V/h^3$ in terms of the volume of the vessel, $V = l_1 l_2 l_3$. The number of translational states included in the triply positive octant of p space up to a given numerical value of p is, therefore (cf. the two-dimensional Fig. 88),

$$\nu_\zeta = \frac{1}{8}\frac{4}{3}\pi p^3 \frac{8V}{h^3} = \frac{4}{3}\frac{\pi V}{\lambda^3} = \frac{4}{3}\pi(2m)^{3/2}\frac{V\zeta^{3/2}}{h^3} \qquad (281)$$

where $\lambda = h/p$, the limiting wave length [cf. eq. (115)], and $\zeta = p^2/2m$. The number of states included in the range $d\zeta$ is thus

$$d\nu_\zeta = 2\pi h^{-3}(2m)^{3/2}V\zeta^{1/2}\,d\zeta, \qquad (281a)$$

and any sum over a range of values of μ can be converted into an integral with respect to ζ in accordance with the general formula

$$\sum_{\mu} f(\zeta_{\mu}) = 2\pi h^{-3}(2m)^{3/2} V \int \zeta^{1/2} f(\zeta) \, d\zeta. \tag{281b}$$

To express the *distribution law* in terms of ζ, let us now multiply the expression found for $d\nu_\zeta$ by $\bar{N}_\mu$, as given in (280a, b), and write for the result $Vn_\zeta \, d\zeta$, n_ζ thus denoting the number of molecules in unit volume per unit of the energy ζ. We thus obtain

$$n_\zeta = \frac{2}{\sqrt{\pi}k^{3/2}} \frac{Q\zeta^{1/2}}{Be^{\zeta/kT} \pm 1}, \qquad Q = w\frac{(2\pi mk)^{3/2}}{h^3}, \tag{282a, b}$$

the upper sign referring to the F-D type and the lower to the B-E.

The condition fixing the constant B is that $\int_0^\infty n_\zeta \, d\zeta = n$, the total molecular density, or, after setting $\zeta = kTx$,

$$\frac{2}{\sqrt{\pi}} \frac{Q}{n} T^{3/2} \int_0^\infty \frac{x^{1/2} \, dx}{Be^x \pm 1} = 1. \tag{283}$$

The *total energy* E is similarly given by $V\int_0^\infty n_\zeta \zeta \, d\zeta = E$ or, since $V = N/n$,

$$\frac{2}{\sqrt{\pi}} Nk \frac{Q}{n} T^{5/2} \int_0^\infty \frac{x^{3/2} \, dx}{Be^x \pm 1} = E. \tag{284}$$

The two integrals in these equations define unfamiliar functions of B and in general can be evaluated only by indirect methods.

The detailed discussion of these formulas can best be done for each type of gas separately. This will be postponed, however, until several other matters have been discussed which are common to both types.

The *entropy* can be found from the expression given in (271a) in Sec. 224 for any loose many-molecule system:

$$S = \frac{E}{T} + Nk \log B \pm k \sum_{j} \log \left(1 \pm B^{-1}e^{-\frac{\epsilon_j}{kT}}\right).$$

In the case of the point-mass gas the sum over j becomes w times a sum over μ, and this in turn can be converted, by following (281a), into an integral over ζ or over $x = \zeta/kT$. In this way, after introducing Q from (282b) and $V = N/n$, and setting $\epsilon_j = \zeta$, we obtain

$$S = \frac{E}{T} + Nk \log B \pm \frac{2}{\sqrt{\pi}} \frac{NkQT^{3/2}}{n} \int_0^\infty x^{1/2} \log [1 \pm B^{-1}e^{-x}] \, dx.$$

In the present instance, however, the last term can be expressed in terms of the energy, for an integration by parts* converts it into $2/3T$

* At ∞, $x^{3/2} \log [1 \pm B^{-1}e^{-x}] \rightarrow \pm x^{3/2}B^{-1}e^{-x} \rightarrow 0$.

times the expression given in (284) for E.   Hence we can also write, for either type of point-mass gas,

$$S = Nk \log B + \frac{5}{3}\frac{E}{T}. \tag{285}$$

The *pressure* p can be found from S, but it is simplest and most illuminating to find it directly by inserting in its defining equation, $dW = p\,dV$, the value of dW given in eq. (267) in Sec. 222, which here takes the form,

$$dW = -\sum_i \bar{N}_i \epsilon_i = -\sum_\mu \bar{N}_\mu\,d\zeta_\mu.$$

The determination of the latter sum can be simplified by giving to the vessel the special form of a cube with edge l.   Then (278) above can be written

$$\zeta_\mu = \frac{h^2}{8ml^2}\,(\mu_1^2 + \mu_2^2 + \mu_3^2) = \frac{h^2}{8mV^{2/3}}\,(\mu_1^2 + \mu_2^2 + \mu_3^2). \tag{286}$$

Hence as V is altered with no change in μ_1, μ_2, μ_3,

$$\frac{d\zeta_\mu}{\zeta_\mu} = -\frac{2}{3}\frac{dV}{V},$$

and, substituting for $d\zeta_\mu$ in the expression just written for dW,

$$dW = \frac{2}{3}\frac{dV}{V}\sum_\mu \bar{N}_\mu \zeta_\mu = \frac{2}{3}\frac{E}{V}\,dV.$$

Thus

$$p = \frac{2}{3}\frac{E}{V}, \tag{287}$$

or, the pressure is two thirds of the kinetic energy per unit volume just as it is for a classical gas [cf. eq. (5) in Sec. 5].

From (283) it is evident that, for a given kind of gas, the value of B depends only upon the temperature and the density but not, as might perhaps have been anticipated, directly upon the size of the vessel, although the latter determines the molecular quantum states.   The relative distribution of the molecules in energy, as represented by n_ζ, the mean energy per molecule, E/N, and the entropy per molecule, S/N, are likewise functions of the temperature T and density n alone. In these respects the conditions are as in classical theory.

S stands in the above formulas for the total entropy of any mass of gas containing N molecules.   It can then easily be taken to refer to a gram, or to a gram molecule, by assigning the appropriate meaning to E and N.

232. The Approach to Classical Behavior. In Sec. 223 it was shown that the distribution law approximates to the classical form whenever for all quantum states $Be^{\frac{\epsilon_i}{kT}} \gg 1$. Here, since $\epsilon_i = \zeta \geqq 0$, this is equivalent to the condition that

$$B \gg 1.$$

When this is so, the term ± 1 can be dropped in all denominators. The distribution laws then take on the Boltzmann form,

$$\bar{N}_\mu = wCe^{-\frac{\zeta_\mu}{kT}}, \qquad n_\zeta = \frac{2}{\sqrt{\pi}k^{\frac{3}{2}}} QC\zeta^{\frac{1}{2}}e^{-\frac{\zeta}{kT}},$$

where $C = 1/B$. Both integrals in (283) and (284) thus become special cases of the following more general form which can easily be connected with $\int_0^\infty e^{-y^2}\, dy = \frac{1}{2}\sqrt{\pi}$ by the substitution $x = y$ (cf. table of integrals at end of book):

$$\int_0^\infty x^{\frac{1}{2}}e^{-sx}\, dx = \frac{\sqrt{\pi}}{2s^{\frac{3}{2}}}, \qquad \int_0^\infty x^{\frac{3}{2}}e^{-sx}\, dx = \frac{3\sqrt{\pi}}{4s^{\frac{5}{2}}}. \qquad (288a, b)$$

Using the first of these with $s = 1$, we find from eq. (283)

$$\frac{2}{\sqrt{\pi}}\frac{Q}{n}T^{\frac{3}{2}}\frac{1}{B}\frac{\sqrt{\pi}}{2} = 1,$$

whence

$$B = \frac{QT^{\frac{3}{2}}}{n}, \qquad (289)$$

approximately. Since there is no upper limit to the values of B, it follows that large values of B and of $QT^{\frac{3}{2}}/n$ occur together, and the condition for the validity of classical theory can be stated also in terms of the latter quantity.

An interesting alternative expression can be obtained by noting that $\frac{3}{2}kT$ represents the mean kinetic energy of a molecule at temperature T and hence can be written $p_s^2/2m$ in terms of the root-mean-square momentum p_s; with the latter let us associate the root-mean-square molecular wave length, $\lambda_s = h/p_s$ [cf. eq. (115) in Sec. 75]. Then $kT = h^2/3m\lambda_s^2$, and from (282b)

$$QT^{\frac{3}{2}} = w\frac{(2\pi mkT)^{\frac{3}{2}}}{h^3} = \left(\frac{2\pi}{3}\right)^{\frac{3}{2}}\frac{w}{\lambda_s^3}.$$

Let us also introduce $\bar{\delta} = (n/w)^{-\frac{1}{3}}$ to represent the mean linear spacing of the molecules in each internal state.

Then we can write as the condition for the approximate validity of classical theory:

$$\frac{QT^{\frac{3}{2}}}{n} = w\frac{(2\pi mkT)^{\frac{3}{2}}}{nh^3} = \left(\frac{2\pi}{3}\right)^{\frac{3}{2}}\left(\frac{\bar{\delta}}{\lambda_{\cdot s}}\right)^3 \gg 1. \tag{290}$$

This condition can be expressed by saying that the mean spacing of the molecules must greatly exceed their wave length; for, in the last expression, $(2\pi/3)^{\frac{3}{2}}$ is only of the order of 3.

The condition can always be met at any given temperature by making the density low enough, so that even at low temperatures it is possible to have a gas behaving classically; or, at any given density it can be met by raising the temperature sufficiently. At a given density and temperature the approach to classical behavior is better for heavy molecules than for light ones, and it also improves with an increase in the internal multiplicity.

It may be noted that if the integral in (284) is evaluated for a large value of B by means of (288b) with $s = 1$, and if $QT^{\frac{3}{2}}/n$ is then substituted for B, eq. (284) gives $E = \frac{3}{2}NkT$ or the classical value for a gas of point masses.

233. The Number of States. At this point it may be interesting to interrupt the discussion in order to consider one or two special points.

In Sec. 231 we obtained in eq. (281) an expression for the number ν_ζ of one-molecule states whose energy is less than a given value ζ. By an extension of the argument there given we can find also the total number of translational quantum states for an entire gas containing N point-mass molecules.

Each of these states is represented by a complete set of the μ's for all of the molecules; and if we think of the corresponding p's, defined as they are below eq. (280a, b) in Sec. 231, as coordinates p_1, $p_2 \cdots p_{3N}$ in a space of $3N$ dimensions, there will be

$$(2l_1/h)^N(2l_2/h)^N(2l_3/h)^N$$

or $(8V/h^3)^N$ sets of μ's whose p's lie in a unit cube in this space. The total energy is $\sum \zeta = \sum_{\rho=1}^{3N}\frac{p_\rho^2}{2m}$. Accordingly, extending the range of integration for each p_ρ to $-\infty$ as well as $+\infty$, and then dividing by 2^{3N} to correct for this extension, we seem to find for the number of quantum states of the gas corresponding to energy less than E

$$\frac{1}{2^{3N}} \left(\frac{8V}{h^3}\right)^N \int_{\Sigma p_\rho^2/2m < E} dp_1 \, dp_2 \cdots dp_{3N} =$$
$$\left(\frac{V}{h^3}\right)^N (2mE)^{\frac{3N}{2}} \int_{\Sigma y_\rho^2 < 1} dy_1 \cdots dy_{3N} \quad (291)$$

after substituting $p_\rho = (2mE)^{1/2} y_\rho$. The last integral here represents the volume of a unit sphere in $3N$ dimensions and can be written in iterated form as

$$2^{3N} \int_0^1 dy_{3N} \cdots \int_0^{(1-y_3^2-\cdots-y_{3N})^{1/2}} dy_2 \int_0^{(1-y_2^2-y_3^2-\cdots y_{3N}^2)^{1/2}} dy_1;$$

evaluating the integrals in succession, we then find ultimately

$$\int_{\substack{\Sigma y_\rho^2 < 1 \\ \rho}} dy_1 \cdots dy_{3N} = \frac{\pi^{\frac{3N}{2}}}{\Gamma\left(\frac{3N}{2} + 1\right)}, \quad (292)$$

where $\Gamma(n) = \int_0^\infty x^{n-1} e^{-x} \, dx$.*

An error has been made, however, in allowing all μ's to vary independently. In reality, all points that can be transformed into each other by permutations of the N molecular sets of μ's as wholes represent the same wave-function; for in forming an antisymmetric combination of one-molecule functions as in Sec. 229 it is immaterial in what order we first write down the φ_μ's. Since there are $N!$ such permutations, we must, therefore, divide the result just obtained by $N!$ Strictly speaking, this is still wrong as regards points for which two sets of μ's are identical; in dealing with a gas of F-D type these particular points ought actually to be omitted entirely. When E is large, however, so that the μ's are mostly large numbers, it can be shown that the points at which two or more sets are identical form a negligible fraction of the whole, just as points regularly spaced near the line $x = y = z$ are negligible among all points so spaced inside a large sphere.

Hence, inserting the value given in (292) for the integral into (291) and dividing by $N!$, we have for the number of translational states of the gas whose energy is less than E, with vanishing relative error as $E \to \infty$,

$$\nu_a = \frac{V^N \left(2\pi m \dfrac{E}{h^2}\right)^{\frac{3N}{2}}}{N! \, \Gamma\left(\dfrac{3N}{2} + 1\right)}. \quad (293)$$

* Cf. B. O. Peirce, "Table of Integrals," p. 62; the result can be worked out by means of formulas on that page. An equivalent form is given as a Dirichlet integral in B. Williamson's "Integral Calculus," p. 320.

As an illustration, let us see what the order of magnitude of ν_q and ν_ζ are in a practical case. Consider a cube 0.0001 cm on a side containing 26 molecules of hydrogen at 15°C and a pressure of 10^{-6} atm. Then $m = 3.35 \times 10^{-24}$ g, $h = 6.62 \times 10^{-27}$, and if we let ζ become equal to the mean kinetic energy of a molecule at 15°C, so that $\zeta = \frac{3}{2}kT = \frac{3}{2} \times 1.38 \times 10^{-16} \times 288 = 5.97 \times 10^{-14}$ erg, we find from (281) in Sec. 231

$$\nu_\zeta = 2.5 \times 10^{32}\, \zeta^{3/2} = 3.6 \times 10^{12}.$$

Again, if we take $\zeta = E/N$, we can write from (293)

$$\nu_q = \frac{N^{\frac{3N}{2}}}{N!\, \Gamma\!\left(\dfrac{3N}{2} + 1\right)} \left(3\frac{\sqrt{\pi}}{4}\nu_\zeta\right)^N$$

in terms of ν_ζ from (281). Let us take $N! = (N/e)^N$ by Stirling's formula and $\Gamma\!\left(\dfrac{3N}{2} + 1\right) = \left(\dfrac{3N}{2}\right)! = \left(\dfrac{3N}{2e}\right)^{\frac{3N}{2}}$ nearly enough (since $\Gamma(n+1) = n!$ for integral n). Then, inserting $N = 26$ and the value just found for ν_ζ, we find

$$\nu_q = \left(\frac{2}{3}\right)^{\frac{3N}{2}} \frac{e^{\frac{5N}{2}}}{N^N} \left(\frac{3\sqrt{\pi}}{4}\,\nu_\zeta\right)^N = 10^{315}$$

roughly. This is a tremendous number and shows how very far below the reach of macroscopic observation are the quantum states with which the theory operates.

A much quicker method of making such estimates is to make a calculation in terms of wave lengths. If we drop the factor $4\pi/3$ from the middle expression in (281), we have $\nu_\zeta = V/\lambda^3$ or the number of cubic wave lengths in the volume V. Since $V = 10^{-12}$ cc, and at 15°C the wave length λ of a hydrogen molecule moving at mean speed is 1.14×10^{-8} cm, we find $\nu_\zeta = 10^{-12}/10^{-24} = 10^{12}$, roughly, which is almost correct. The number of states for 26 molecules should then be $\nu_q = \nu_\zeta{}^{26} = 10^{312}$, which is again very close.

It is worth noting that (291), the value obtained for ν_q before making the reduction required by the exclusion principle, is equal to σ/h^{3N}, where σ is the classical value of the phase space up to energy E, as given in Sec. 196 above. The same thing is likewise true for just one molecule, of course, for nothing prevents us from setting $N = 1$; and in that case there is no reduction to be made, eq. (291) being correct. This is one way of establishing the old result that for a point mass without internal multiplicity each quantum state corresponds to a volume h^3 in classical phase space.   For a large group of N *similar* point masses, however, the added factor $1/N!$ in (293), which is required by the exclusion principle, reduces the volume corresponding to a quantum state of the group from h^{3N} to $h^{3N}/N!$ (approximately).

234. The Zero-point Entropy.   It is interesting to compare the expression furnished by quantum theory for the entropy of a gas, under conditions such that classical theory should hold, with the expression furnished by the classical theory itself.

According to eq. (285) in Sec. 231 the entropy of a perfect gas composed of N point-mass molecules, with or without internal multiplicity, can be written

$$S = Nk \log B + \frac{5}{3}\frac{E}{T}.$$

In the classical limit this differs from the classical expression itself as given in (252b) in Sec. 203 or

$$S = \frac{E}{T} - Nk \log C,$$

in which for a point-mass gas $C = 1/B$, only in the integration constant; for in the limit $E = \frac{3}{2} NkT$ and the two expressions thus differ merely by Nk.

If we insert in the first of these expressions both $E = \frac{3}{2} NkT$ and a suitable value of B, using (289) and (290), we obtain for the classical limit the alternative form, given long ago by Planck (for $w = 1$),

$$S = Nk \log \left[w \frac{(2\pi mkT)^{3/2}e^{5/2}}{nh^3} \right]. \qquad (294a)$$

Here m = molecular mass, k = Boltzmann's constant, T = absolute temperature, n = density in molecules per unit volume, h = Planck's constant, w = multiplicity of the internal molecular state.   For a gram (or a gram molecule) of gas in volume V_1, containing N_1 or nV_1 molecules, we can write the last formula in the two forms

$$S = N_1k \log (V_1 T^{3/2}) + S_0 = N_1k \log \frac{T^{5/2}}{p} + S_0'; \qquad (294b, c)$$

these differ from the usual phenomenological formulas [cf. (252d) in Sec. 204] only in that here the integration constants are assigned the definite values

$$S_0 = N_1 k \log \left[w \frac{(2\pi m k)^{3/2} e^{5/2}}{N_1 h^3} \right], \tag{294d}$$

$$S_0' = N_1 k \log \left[w \frac{(2\pi m)^{3/2}(ke)^{5/2}}{h^3} \right] = S_0 + R \log R, \tag{294e}$$

where $R = N_1 k$.

The integration constant is, or was, of particular interest in connection with the Nernst heat theorem and its applications to chemistry. This theorem is concerned with temperatures near absolute zero. Now at such low temperatures the formulas that we have hitherto obtained become open to doubt because the discrete spacing of the quantum states then assumes importance; the whole basis of our calculation for the point-mass gas, in fact, disappears. There is another method, however, that of the *canonical ensemble* or *distribution* as described in Sec. 226, which is open to no such restriction.

This latter method furnishes in eq. (273) of Sec. 227 the following expression:

$$S = \frac{E}{T} + k \log \sum_i e^{-\frac{E_i}{kT}}, \tag{295}$$

where E_i is the energy of the whole gas in its ith quantum state and the sum extends over all states. This formula has the advantage that it should hold all the way down to absolute zero, the lower quantum states being those of the liquid or solid phase. Let us see what form it assumes in the classical limit.

Paralleling the procedure used for one molecule in Sec. 231, we can replace the sum in (295) by $w^N \int (d\nu_q/dE)\, dE$, where ν_q is the number of quantum states having energy below E, as given in eq. (293) above; the factor w^N arises from the fact that each of the w^N ways of arranging the N molecules in their w internal states, combined with each translational state, yields a separate quantum state of the gas. We thus obtain

$$\sum_i e^{-\frac{E_i}{kT}} = \frac{3}{2} w^N N V^N \left[\frac{\left(\frac{2\pi m}{h^2}\right)^{\frac{3N}{2}}}{N!\,\Gamma\left(\frac{3N}{2}+1\right)} \right] \int_0^\infty E^{\frac{3}{2}N-1} e^{-\frac{E}{kT}}\, dE.$$

The integral by itself can be written

$$(kT)^{\frac{3N}{2}} \int_0^\infty x^{\frac{3}{2}N-1} e^{-x}\, dx = (kT)^{\frac{3N}{2}} \Gamma\left(\frac{3}{2}N\right) = (kT)^{\frac{3N}{2}} \frac{\Gamma\left(\frac{3}{2}N+1\right)}{3N/2}$$

(cf. Peirce, "Table of Integrals," p. 62). Let us also suppose N to be so huge that $N!$ can be replaced again by the ultimately important factor in Stirling's formula, $(N/e)^N$. Then the value of the state sum becomes

$$\sum_i e^{-\frac{E_i}{kT}} = w^N \left(\frac{2\pi m k T}{h^2}\right)^{\frac{3N}{2}} \frac{e^N}{n^N},$$

where n stands for N/V; and for the entropy we have, after inserting as usual $E = \frac{3}{2} NkT$,

$$S = \frac{3}{2} Nk + Nk \log \left[w \frac{(2\pi m k T)^{\frac{3}{2}} e}{nh^3} \right].$$

It is interesting that this expression agrees exactly with that in (294a) above. Since the original formula as given in eq. (285) can differ from that given in eq. (295) only by a constant, it follows that these two formulas must give the same value for S, not only in the classical limit, but whenever validity can be claimed for both.

Thus the choice of the integration constant that was made in obtaining our general formulas for the entropy of a loose many-molecule system had the advantage that the resulting formulas, at least when applied to a perfect gas, agree throughout their range of validity with another formula that holds down through the liquid and solid states to the absolute zero of temperature. The values of the constants as given in (294d, e) are, consequently, consistent with the assumption that the entropy at $T = 0$ is $k \log w_0$, where w_0 is the multiplicity of the state of the substance at that temperature, and is zero if this state is simple (cf. Sec. 227).

235. Chemical Constant and Vapor Pressure. The entropy of gases is of great importance in chemistry because of its bearing on gaseous reactions. It follows from thermodynamics that at constant temperature any system tends to settle into its state of lowest free energy. Now in the expression for the free energy, $F = U - TS$, the change in the energy U involved in a reaction is simply the heat of reaction and so can be measured or calculated from other data; if, therefore, the change in entropy that is involved in a reaction can be ascertained, it is possible to calculate the temperature or other conditions under which the reaction will take place. A direct experimental determination of the change in entropy may be impracticable, however, because to effect it the reaction must be carried out reversibly.

Now Nernst's heat theorem asserts that, at absolute zero, not only is the entropy always finite (provided the volume is kept finite), but

also the change in entropy during any chemical reaction vanishes.*
If this principle is true, we have only to find expressions for the
entropies of the substances concerned in a reaction, with the integration constants so chosen that all of them vanish at $T = 0$, and then
the difference between these expressions at any other temperature will
give the change in entropy at that temperature. For a gas such a value
of the entropy can be obtained by evaluating $\int \dfrac{dQ}{T}$ with the help of
specific-heat data and the heat of sublimation or vaporization at one
temperature.

In studying such a determination theoretically we are led to a relationship between the entropy constant and the vapor pressure. The
change in entropy during vaporization is L/T, where L is the heat of
vaporization; as $T \to 0$, L approaches a limiting value L_0, hence the
gain in entropy becomes infinite and relatively equal to L_0/T. Now the
vapor can certainly be treated as a classical perfect gas, for the vapor
pressure falls so very fast with decreasing T that the density diminishes
rapidly and Q actually increases without limit; the molecules can be
treated also as point masses, for they will all be in their lowest internal
state, simple or multiple. Hence, writing S_s for the entropy of the
solid phase at $T = 0$ and using (294c) above, we have for the entropy of
the saturated vapor near absolute zero

$$S = \frac{L_0}{T} + S_s = R \log \frac{T^{5/2}}{p} + S_0',$$

approximately, from which

$$\log p = -\frac{L_0}{RT} + \frac{5}{2} \log T + i, \qquad i = \frac{1}{R} (S_0' - S_s).$$

If for any reason $S_s = 0$, $i = S_0'/R$. Because of this connection with
S_0' the constant i has commonly been called the "chemical constant."

The expression thus obtained for the vapor pressure p has an interest of its own. A possible value of the integration constant S_0' is
given in (294e) above. A value of S_s that is consistent with this
choice of S_0' is given in Sec. 227, as we found in the last section; it is,
at $T = 0$, $S_s = k \log w_0$, where we can write $w_0 = w_{s1}^N$ in terms of
the internal multiplicity w_s of each of the N_1 molecules composing
the solid. Inserting these values of S_0' and S_s, and $R = N_1 k$, in the
expression for i, we find

* For a good and readable discussion of Nernst's heat theorem see "Ergebnisse
der exakten Naturwissenschaften," vol. 9, section by Simon (1930); cf. also R. H.
Fowler, "Statistical Mechanics," 2d ed., 1936, Sec. 7.5.

$$p = \frac{w}{w_s} \frac{(2\pi m)^{3/2}}{h^3} (keT)^{5/2} e^{-\frac{L_0}{RT}}.$$

Here and in the last two equations R and L_0 may refer to either a gram or a mole. If $w_s = 1$, there is nothing in this equation referring to the internal structure of the solid phase at all; in that case the solid appears to become, so to speak, a physical point without internal features.

On the chemical side, however, the practical significance of these relationships promises to be less than was formerly expected. It is probable that, even if Nernst's heat theorem is universally true, its practical usefulness will sometimes be limited by changes in entropy which occur at temperatures extremely close to absolute zero, as the solid sinks into its final simple state, and which are thus beyond the reach of experiment.*

On the other hand, wave mechanics holds out the prospect of obtaining from molecular theory a consistent set of theoretical values of the constant S_0' for various substances, which will give the chemist what he needs. A simple example of the method is furnished by the case of dissociation that is treated in a later section.

236. The Fermi-Dirac Gas of Point Masses. The two types of point-mass gas will now be taken up for a more detailed discussion, beginning with the Fermi-Dirac type.†

The distribution law for a F-D gas of N point-mass molecules is, according to (282a, b) in Sec. 231,

$$n_\zeta = \frac{2}{\sqrt{\pi} k^{3/2}} \frac{Q\zeta^{1/2}}{Be^{\frac{\zeta}{kT}} + 1}, \qquad Q = w\frac{(2\pi mk)^{3/2}}{h^3}, \qquad (296a, b)$$

ζ being the kinetic energy of a molecule and $n_\zeta\, d\zeta$, the number in unit volume having energy in the range $d\zeta$. B and the total energy E are determined by the equations

$$\frac{2}{\sqrt{\pi}} \frac{Q}{n} T^{3/2} \int_0^\infty \frac{x^{1/2}\, dx}{Be^x + 1} = 1, \qquad \frac{2}{\sqrt{\pi}} \frac{Q}{n} NkT^{5/2} \int_0^\infty \frac{x^{3/2}\, dx}{Be^x + 1} = E,$$

$$(297a, b)$$

in which x represents ζ/kT and n is the total number of molecules per unit volume.

For $B > 1$, the integrals in these equations are readily integrated in terms of series; for then we can write

$$(Be^x + 1)^{-1} = B^{-1}e^{-x}(1 - B^{-1}e^{-x} + B^{-2}e^{-2x} \cdots).$$

---

* Cf. R. H. FOWLER, *loc. cit.*

† E. FERMI, *Zeits. Physik*, **36**, 902 (1926).

Substituting this series in (297a) and then carrying out the integration term by term with the help of formulas (288a, b) in Sec. 232, we obtain

$$\frac{QT^{3/2}}{nB}\left(1 - \frac{1}{2^{3/2}B} + \frac{1}{3^{3/2}B^2} - \cdots\right) = 1,$$

whence

$$B = \frac{QT^{3/2}}{n}\left(1 - \frac{n}{2^{3/2}QT^{3/2}} + \cdots\right).$$

With this value of B the distribution formula becomes, after using the series again with ζ/kT substituted for x,

$$n_\zeta = \frac{2n}{\sqrt{\pi}(kT)^{3/2}}\left(1 + \frac{n}{2^{3/2}QT^{3/2}} \cdots\right)\zeta^{1/2}e^{-\frac{\zeta}{kT}}\left(1 - \frac{n}{QT^{3/2}}e^{-\frac{\zeta}{kT}} \cdots\right).$$

Comparison of this equation with (61b) in Sec. 28 shows that here the two series represent the departure from classical behavior as the temperature sinks or the density rises. We note a relative increase in the number of fast molecules.

The energy can be found by integrating eq. (297b) in a similar way, which gives

$$\frac{3}{2}\frac{Q}{n}NkT^{5/2}\frac{1}{B}\left(1 - \frac{1}{2^{5/2}B} + \frac{1}{3^{5/2}B} - \cdots\right) = E,$$

or, after substituting the value found for B,

$$E = \frac{3}{2}NkT\left(1 + \frac{n}{2^{5/2}QT^{3/2}} \cdots\right).$$

The series represents the increase in energy over the classical value due to the increase in fast molecules.

The pressure p is increased in the same ratio, since according to (287) in Sec. 231 it is $(2/3)(E/V)$ as in classical theory; since $N/V = n$, we have

$$p = nkT\left(1 + \frac{n}{2^{5/2}QT^{3/2}} \cdots\right).$$

The specific heats, on the other hand, are decreased. At constant volume

$$c_V = \left(\frac{\partial}{\partial T}\frac{E}{Nm}\right)_V = \frac{3}{2}N_1k\left(1 - \frac{n}{2^{7/2}QT^{3/2}} \cdots\right),$$

N_1 being the number of molecules in a gram and N_1k representing the classical value. At constant pressure, E/V is constant, hence $dE/E = dV/V$ and

$$dQ = dE + p\,dV = dE + \frac{2}{3}\frac{E}{V}\,dV = \frac{5}{3}\,dE.$$

From the preceding equations

$$dE = \frac{3}{2}Nk\left(1 - \frac{n}{2^{7/2}QT^{3/2}} \cdots \right)dT + \frac{3}{2}Nk\frac{dn}{2^{5/2}QT^{1/2}}$$

and

$$dp = nk\,dT + kT\,dn$$

to zero order in n, which is sufficient for our purpose, so that if $dp = 0$, $dn = -n\,dT/T$, and

$$dE = \frac{3}{2}Nk\left(1 - \frac{3n}{2^{7/2}QT^{3/2}} \cdots \right)dT.$$

Hence

$$c_p = \frac{1}{Nm}\left(\frac{dQ}{dT}\right)_p = \frac{5}{2}N_1k\left(1 - \frac{3n}{2^{7/2}QT^{3/2}} \cdots \right),$$

$$\gamma = \frac{c_p}{c_V} = \frac{5}{3}\left(1 - \frac{n}{2^{5/2}QT^{3/2}} \cdots \right).$$

For completeness we may add also the series for the entropy, as found similarly from (285) in Sec. 231 with the help of

$$\log(1 + y) = y - \tfrac{1}{2}y^2 + \cdots :$$

$$S = Nk\left[\log\frac{QT^{3/2}}{n} + \frac{5}{2} + \frac{n}{2^{7/2}QT^{3/2}} + \cdots \right]$$

$$= Nk\left\{\log\left[w\frac{(2\pi mkT)^{3/2}e^{5/2}}{nh^3}\right] + \frac{n}{2^{7/2}QT^{3/2}} \cdots \right\}.$$

These equations exhibit at a glance the manner in which the various magnitudes pertaining to the gas begin to depart from their classical values as $QT^{3/2}/n$ decreases from infinity. In a later section we shall consider whether there is any hope of detecting such effects experimentally, but it is more convenient first to complete the theoretical discussion of other cases.

The complete series all converge down to $QT^{3/2}/n = 1.38$, at which $B = 1$. Below this point, however, we must resort to other methods such as numerical integration. The theoretical treatment becomes simple again only when $QT^{3/2}/n$ is actually small; then the gas exhibits a maximum degree of departure from classical behavior and is said to be "degenerate." To this case we shall now turn.

237. The Degenerate Fermi-Dirac Gas. Suppose that

$$Q\frac{T^{3/2}}{n} = w\frac{(2\pi mk)^{3/2}}{h^3}\frac{T^{3/2}}{n} \ll 1; \qquad (298)$$

this means that the molecular wave length is large relative to the linear spacing of the molecules in any one of the w internal states [cf. eq. (290)]. Then the integral in eq. (297a) must be large in order to make that equation true, and this can happen only if B is small; as $QT^{3/2}/n \to 0$, it is necessary that $B \to 0$.

n_{ζ} as given by (296a) must now vary as $\zeta^{1/2}$ for small ζ, but ultimately for large ζ as $e^{-\frac{\zeta}{kT}}$. Between these two extremes lies a transition region containing that value ζ_1 that makes $Be^{\frac{\zeta_1}{kT}} = 1$. This value ζ_1 constitutes a sort of turning point; we can write

$$B = e^{-\frac{\zeta_1}{kT}},$$
$$n_{\zeta} = \frac{2Q}{\sqrt{\pi}k^{3/2}}\frac{\zeta^{1/2}}{e^y + 1}, \qquad y = \frac{\zeta - \zeta_1}{kT}. \qquad (299)$$

From this formula it is evident that if kT/ζ_1 is small, the departure of

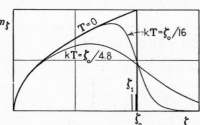

FIG. 89.—Fermi-Dirac distribution near $T = 0$. ζ = kinetic energy.

n_{ζ} from proportionality with $\zeta^{1/2}$ will occur relatively abruptly, the curve leaving the neighborhood of the $\zeta^{1/2}$ curve and dropping rapidly almost to zero as ζ varies over a range that is small as compared to ζ_1 itself. At $T = 0$ the curve must actually be cut off vertically at $\zeta = \zeta_1$; but for $T > 0$, there is a tail of maxwellian form, since for large y or $(\zeta - \zeta_1)/kT$, approximately,

$$n_{\zeta} = \frac{2Q}{\sqrt{\pi}k^{3/2}}\zeta^{1/2}e^{-(\zeta-\zeta_1)/kT}.$$

The situation is illustrated graphically in Fig. 89.

The *ideal case of $T = 0$* is especially interesting and is important in connection with the electron theory of metals. Writing ζ_0 for the value of ζ_1 belonging to $T = 0$, we have at this temperature

$$n_\zeta = \frac{2Q}{\sqrt{\pi} k^{3/2}} \zeta^{1/2}$$

for $0 < \zeta < \zeta_0$ and $n_\zeta = 0$ for $\zeta > \zeta_0$, as shown in Fig. 89.

To find ζ_0, we can first keep T finite but very small and then in the integral in eq. (297a) drop Be^x in the denominator and change the upper limit to

$$x_0 = \frac{\zeta_0}{kT},$$

in order to harmonize with the discontinuous n_ζ curve. The equation then becomes

$$\frac{2}{\sqrt{\pi}} \frac{Q}{n} T^{3/2} \frac{2}{3} \left(\frac{\zeta_0}{kT}\right)^{3/2} = 1,$$

whence

$$\zeta_0 = k\left(\frac{3\sqrt{\pi}}{4} \frac{n}{Q}\right)^{2/3} = \frac{h^2}{2m}\left(\frac{3n}{4\pi w}\right)^{2/3}.$$

This means that the limiting molecule has a wave length

$$\lambda_0 = \left(\frac{4\pi}{3}\right)^{1/3}\left(\frac{w}{n}\right)^{1/3}$$

or only $(4\pi/3)^{1/3}$ times the linear spacing of the molecules in a particular internal state, $\delta = (w/n)^{1/3}$; for the corresponding momentum is $p_0 = h/\lambda_0$ [cf. (115) in Sec. 75] and the value of λ_0 as stated makes the kinetic energy, $p_0^2/2m$, equal to ζ_0.

Division of (297b) by (297a) and the evaluation of both integrals, similarly treated, then gives for the total energy

$$E_0 = NkT \times \frac{3}{5} x_0 = \frac{3}{5} N\zeta_0 = \frac{3}{10} \frac{Nh^2}{m}\left(\frac{3n}{4\pi w}\right)^{2/3}.$$

Thus at $T = 0$ the energy of the gas is by no means zero, as it would be according to classical theory; this is called the zero-point energy and is a very characteristic feature of quantum theory. The mean energy of a molecule amounts to $\frac{3}{5}$ of the maximum, ζ_0. There will also be a zero-point pressure, equal to two thirds of the energy per unit volume (cf. Sec. 231) or of magnitude (since $N/V = n$)

$$p_0 = \frac{2}{3} \frac{E_0}{V} = \frac{2}{5} n\zeta_0 = \frac{h^2}{5m}\left(\frac{3}{4\pi w}\right)^{2/3} n^{5/3},$$

varying, therefore, as the $\frac{5}{3}$ power of the density.

This pressure is an immediately observable quantity, but the significance of the zero-point energy is less certain, since in ordinary physical observations only changes in energy are detected. Of course, if energy and mass are universally proportional, as is required by relativity, then the zero-point energy would be evidenced by a slight increase in mass.

The *initial departure* from complete degeneracy as T rises from 0 can be found by a calculation that is a bit intricate but straightforward. The equation $\int_0^\infty n_\zeta \, d\zeta = n$, the number of molecules per unit volume, can be written, in terms of

$$x_1 = \frac{\zeta_1}{kT}$$

and n_ζ, as given in (299), since $\zeta = kTy + \zeta_1 = kT(y + x_1)$, thus:

$$\frac{2Q}{\sqrt{\pi}} T^{3/2} \int_{-x_1}^\infty \frac{(y + x_1)^{1/2}}{e^y + 1} \, dy = n.$$

Now

$$\int_{-x_1}^0 \frac{(y + x_1)^{1/2}}{e^y + 1} \, dy = \int_0^{x_1} \frac{(x_1 - y)^{1/2}}{e^{-y} + 1} \, dy = \int_0^{x_1} (x_1 - y)^{1/2} \left[1 - \frac{1}{e^y + 1} \right] dy.$$

$$\therefore \quad \int_{-x_1}^\infty \frac{(y + x_1)^{1/2}}{e^y + 1} \, dy = \int_0^{x_1} (x_1 - y)^{1/2} \, dy$$

$$+ \int_0^{x_1} [(x_1 + y)^{1/2} - (x_1 - y)^{1/2}] \frac{dy}{e^y + 1} + \int_{x_1}^\infty \frac{(x_1 + y)^{1/2}}{e^y + 1} \, dy.$$

Here the last integral is negligible when $kT/\zeta_1 \ll 1$ or $x_1 \gg 1$, because of the large size of $e^y + 1$; and for the same reason, after expanding the radicals in the next to the last integral, we can extend its upper limit to infinity and write for it

$$x_1^{-1/2} \int_0^\infty \frac{y \, dy}{e^y + 1} + x_1^{-5/2} (\cdots) \cdots .$$

Now by the substitution* $y_1 = -\log z$

$$\int_0^\infty \frac{y \, dy}{e^y + 1} = -\int_0^1 \frac{\log z}{1 + z} \, dz = \frac{\pi^2}{12}.$$

Hence the original equation can be written

$$\frac{2Q}{\sqrt{\pi}} T^{3/2} \left(\frac{2}{3} x_1^{3/2} + \frac{\pi^2}{12} x_1^{-1/2} \cdots \right) = n,$$

* Cf. Peirce, "Short Table of Integrals," no. 510.

from which

$$x_1 = \left(\frac{3\sqrt{\pi}n}{4QT^{3/2}} - \frac{\pi^2}{8} x_1^{-1/2}\right)^{2/3} = \left[\left(\frac{\zeta_0}{kT}\right)^{3/2} - \frac{\pi^2}{8} x_1^{-1/2} \cdots\right]^{2/3},$$

and, after expanding and inserting $x_1 = \zeta_0/kT$ to zero order,

$$\zeta_1 = kTx_1 = \zeta_0\left[1 - \frac{\pi^2}{12}\left(\frac{kT}{\zeta_0}\right)^2 \cdots\right].$$

In a similar way one finds for the energy $E = V\int_0^\infty n_\zeta \zeta\, d\zeta$ or, since $V = N/n$ in terms of the total number of molecules N,

$$E = \frac{N}{n}\frac{2Q}{\sqrt{\pi}} kT^{5/2}\left(\frac{2}{5} x_1^{5/2} + \frac{\pi^2}{4} x_1^{1/2} \cdots\right),$$

or, introducing the expression just found for n,

$$E = NkTx_1 \frac{\dfrac{2}{5} x_1^{3/2} + \dfrac{\pi^2}{4} x_1^{-1/2}}{\dfrac{2}{3} x_1^{3/2} + \dfrac{\pi^2}{12} x_1^{-1/2}} = \frac{3}{5} N\zeta_1\left(1 + \frac{\pi^2}{2} x_1^{-2} \cdots\right)$$

or

$$E = \frac{3}{5} N\zeta_0\left[1 + \frac{5}{12}\pi^2\left(\frac{kT}{\zeta_0}\right)^2 \cdots\right]$$

by means of the value found above for ζ_1.

The pressure is then $2E/3V$ as usual or

$$p = \frac{2}{5} n\zeta_0\left[1 + \frac{5}{12}\pi^2\left(\frac{kT}{\zeta_0}\right)^2 \cdots\right].$$

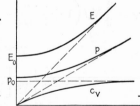

FIG. 90.—The Fermi-Dirac gas. E = energy, p = pressure, c_V = specific heat.

We note that the first departure from complete degeneracy, as represented by the increase in the energy and pressure and the decrease in the critical energy ζ_1, is only of order T^2. The specific heat, on the other hand, starts out linearly, for

$$c_V = \left(\frac{\partial}{\partial T}\frac{E}{Nm}\right)_V = \frac{\pi^2 k^2}{2m\zeta_0} T \cdots.$$

Putting all of these results together, we can now construct the qualitative picture of the behavior of a Fermi-Dirac gas at fixed density that is suggested in Fig. 90.

238. The Bose-Einstein Gas of Point Masses. For a gas of B-E type, according to (282a, b) in Sec. 231, the distribution law is

$$n_\zeta = \frac{2}{\sqrt{\pi} k^{3/2}} \frac{Q \zeta^{1/2}}{B e^{\frac{\zeta}{kT}} - 1}, \qquad Q = w \frac{(2\pi mk)^{3/2}}{h^3}.$$

In this case B must remain greater than unity, else $\int_0^\infty n_\zeta \, d\zeta \to \infty$. For such values of B the expression for n_ζ is of such form that it can be got from the corresponding expression for the F-D gas merely by changing the signs of both B and Q; hence by making these changes in the equations for $B > 1$ in Sec. 236, which are actually valid mathematically for $|B| > 1$, we obtain at once the corresponding equations for the B-E gas, as follows:

$$\frac{QT^{3/2}}{nB}\left(1 + \frac{1}{2^{3/2}B} + \frac{1}{3^{3/2}B} + \cdots \right) = 1, \tag{300}$$

$$B = \frac{QT^{3/2}}{n}\left(1 + \frac{n}{2^{3/2}QT^{3/2}} + \cdots \right);$$

$$n_\zeta = \frac{2n}{\sqrt{\pi}(kT)^{3/2}}\left(1 - \frac{n}{2^{3/2}QT^{3/2}} \cdots \right)\zeta^{1/2} e^{-\frac{\zeta}{kT}}\left(1 + \frac{n}{QT^{3/2}} e^{-\frac{\zeta}{kT}} \cdots \right);$$

$$E = \frac{3}{2} NkT\left(1 - \frac{n}{2^{5/2}QT^{3/2}} \cdots \right),$$

$$p = nkT\left(1 - \frac{n}{2^{5/2}QT^{3/2}} \cdots \right);$$

$$c_V = \frac{3}{2} N_1 k\left(1 + \frac{n}{2^{7/2}QT^{3/2}} \cdots \right), \qquad c_p = \frac{5}{2} N_1 k\left(1 + \frac{3n}{2^{7/2}QT^{3/2}} \cdots \right),$$

$$\gamma = \frac{5}{3}\left(1 + \frac{n}{2^{7/2}QT^{3/2}} \cdots \right);$$

$$S = Nk\left\{\log\left[w\frac{(2\pi mkT)^{3/2}e^{5/2}}{nh^3}\right] - \frac{n}{2^{7/2}QT^{3/2}} \cdots \right\}.$$

We note that in an almost classical B-E gas the quantum effect is to decrease energy and pressure below their classical values, slower molecules being relatively more common than they would be according to Maxwell's law. The specific heats and γ, on the other hand, are increased. The numerical magnitude of the first-order effect is in all cases the same as in the F-D type.

The complete series of which we have written only the first terms converge for all allowed values of B, and the formulas are, therefore, mathematically accurate. As B approaches unity, however, we seem to be led to an astonishing conclusion; for the series in eq. (300)

rises only to the value 2.61 when $B = 1$. The equation implies, therefore, that $QT^{3/2}/n$ cannot be decreased below $1/2.61$!

The explanation lies in a general failure of all of the formulas when $QT^{3/2}/n$ approaches or sinks below the value $1/2.61$. When B is very close to unity, the formula for n_ζ indicates a great crowding of the molecules into the few quantum states of lowest energy, and when this occurs we are no longer justified in grouping the one-molecule states as we did in arriving at the molecular distribution, nor can we treat ζ as a continuous variable.

At the limit, $T = 0$, the molecules are all in their lowest one-molecule state, whose energy is given by (286) in Sec. 231 with

$$\mu_1 = \mu_2 = \mu_3 = 1.$$

The total energy E_0 and the pressure p_0 are, therefore,

$$E_0 = \frac{3Nh^2}{8mV^{2/3}} = \frac{3N^{1/3}h^2}{8m} n^{2/3}, \qquad p_0 = \frac{2}{3}\frac{E_0}{V} = \frac{h^2}{4mN^{2/3}} n^{5/3}.$$

These are roughly $1/N^{2/3}$ times as great as in a F-D gas and are too minute to be of interest. Furthermore, in a gas of finite density but infinite extent (i.e., $V \to \infty$) both the pressure and the energy *per molecule* (E_0/N) are zero. In this latter sense a B-E gas can be said to possess no zero-point energy or pressure at all.

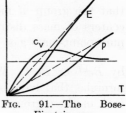

Since as T increases the energy is at first *less* than the classical value, we see that the specific heat must start out small (actually it is

Fig. 91.—The Bose-Einstein gas.

0 at $T = 0$) and then rise to values above the classical value, as found above. We are thus led to the qualitative picture sketched in Fig. 91 for a B-E gas. (But cf. F. London, *Phys. Rev.*, **54**, 947 (1938).)

239. Complex Gases. The discussion of the last few sections has been limited to a very simple type of gas in which the molecules not only are all alike, but also behave as mere point masses. The extension to cover the presence of several different kinds of molecules is easily made, however; for it was shown in the last chapter (Sec. 219) that, so long as interaction can be neglected, each kind of molecule behaves as if the other kinds were not there, except, of course, that there is a common temperature. The energy and the entropy are simply additive. When, on the other hand, the internal state of the molecules can vary, the theory requires a slight further development. It will be sufficient to describe this only for the case of a homogeneous gas,

In the general distribution formula for a loose many-molecule system, as represented by eq. (270a, b) in Sec. 222, ϵ_j must be interpreted, in general, as the total energy of a molecule, which can be written, as in Sec. 228, as the sum of the kinetic energy ζ_μ and the internal energy η_ν. For the number of molecules in the μth translatory and νth fundamental internal state we can write, therefore,

$$N_{\mu\nu} = \frac{1}{Be^{\frac{\zeta_\mu + \eta_\nu}{kT}} \pm 1},$$

the upper sign referring to the F-D and the lower to the B-E case. If the internal states are degenerate, forming multiple states of energy η_τ and multiplicity w_τ, the number of molecules in the μth translatory and τth multiple internal state is

$$N_{\mu\tau} = \frac{w_\tau}{Be^{\frac{\zeta_\mu + \eta_\tau}{kT}} \pm 1}.$$

Comparison of these formulas with (280a, b) in Sec. 230 shows that the group of molecules in any given internal state have their centers of mass distributed just as if they formed by themselves a pure point-mass gas, the constant B in (280a, b) being replaced here by $Be^{\frac{\eta_\nu}{kT}}$ or $Be^{\frac{\eta_\tau}{kT}}$. With this change in B, accordingly, all of the formulas that have been developed for a pure gas can be applied to each of these groups separately. Since the groups will usually vary in density, their translatory properties will vary; the molecules in a populous internal state, such as the lowest one, might, for instance, exhibit strong degeneracy while those in less populous states of higher energy might at the same time behave almost classically.

In any case, ζ_μ can usually be replaced by a continuous variable ζ, just as in Sec. 231; $N_{\mu\tau}$ is then replaced by

$$n_{\zeta\tau} = \frac{2}{\sqrt{\pi}k^{3/2}} \frac{w_\tau Q_0 \zeta^{1/2}}{Be^{\frac{\zeta + \eta_\tau}{kT}} \pm 1}, \qquad Q_0 = \frac{(2\pi mk)^{3/2}}{h^3}, \qquad (301a, b)$$

as a generalization of (282a, b), $n_{\zeta\tau}\, d\zeta$ being the number of molecules in unit volume with kinetic energy between ζ and $\zeta + d\zeta$ and internal energy η_τ. B and the temperature T will then be determined by the total number of molecules and the energy.

The resultant distribution in kinetic energy can be obtained by summing over all internal states, thus:

$$n_\zeta = \frac{2Q_0}{\sqrt{\pi}k^{3/2}} \zeta^{1/2} \sum_\tau \frac{w_\tau}{Be^{\frac{\zeta+\eta_\tau}{kT}} \pm 1}.$$

Or, as an alternative, we may integrate over the kinetic energy and obtain as the total number of molecules per unit volume in internal state no. τ

$$n_\tau = \frac{2w_\tau Q_0}{\sqrt{\pi}k^{3/2}} \int_0^\infty \frac{\zeta^{1/2}\, d\zeta}{Be^{\frac{\zeta+\eta_\tau}{kT}} \pm 1}. \tag{302}$$

These formulas can be discussed along the lines followed in preceding sections. It is clear, however, that the general situation is rather complicated.

240. Free Electrons in Metals. By far the most important application of the theory lies in a direction where it might be least expected, viz., in the electron theory of solids. Following Riecke (1898) and Drude (1900), it had become common in classical theory to regard the free electrons that carry the electric current in metals as behaving like a perfect gas interspersed among the solid atoms. Wild as this conception seems, in view of the relatively enormous repulsion between electrons so close together, it led to some success in accounting for the electrical and thermal properties of metals. A serious stumbling-block, however, was presented by the failure of the electrons to contribute to the heat energy; for the latter could be completely accounted for upon the supposition that the metallic atoms, vibrating under forces proportional to their displacements, had on the average as much potential as kinetic energy, and hence a specific heat $c_V = 3R$ (cf. Sec. 144).

Soon after the new statistics of gases had been proposed, it was pointed out by Sommerfeld[*] that, if the electrons could be treated as a gas at all, they ought to constitute one of Fermi-Dirac type in a high state of degeneracy. This view has been developed into a valuable first step toward a complete theory.[†] The necessary fundamental theory has already been developed in Secs. 236 and 237, with a fullness of detail that was aimed at the present application. It is only necessary to add an allowance for spin; the latter is equivalent to an internal degree of freedom for the electron and doubles the number of its quantum states. For an electron gas, therefore, $w = 2$, and the characteristic quantity Q defined by eq. (282b) in Sec. 231 or (296b) in Sec. 236 is

---

[*] SOMMERFELD, *Zeits. Physik*, **47**, 1 (1928).

[†] Cf. the thorough discussion in "Handbuch der Physik," 2d ed., vol. 24/2, pp. 333–620.

$$Q = \frac{2(2\pi mk)^{3/2}}{h^3} = 4.85 \times 10^{15},$$

m being the electronic mass or $0.9119 \times 10^{-27} g$, k the Boltzmann constant, 1.3812×10^{-16}, and h, Planck's constant, 6.62×10^{-27}.

The density that should be assumed for the free electrons in a metal is not definitely known but should presumably be that of the valence electrons. In silver, for example, with one valence electron per atom, there should be $n = 10.5 \times 6.02 \times 10^{23}/107.88 = 5.86 \times 10^{22}$ free electrons per cubic centimeter. Thus at 0°C or $T = 273$ the critical quantity

$$\frac{QT^{3/2}}{n} = 3.7 \times 10^{-4} \ll 1.$$

From this example it is clear that the electron gas in pure metals, at temperatures that occur on the earth, must be highly degenerate.

In silver the values given, when substituted into the equations in Sec. 237, give for the maximum electronic energy at absolute zero

$$\zeta_0 = k\left(\frac{3\sqrt{\pi}}{4} \frac{n}{Q}\right)^{2/3} = 8.8 \times 10^{-12} \text{ erg.}$$

The mean energy per electron is then $\frac{3}{5} \zeta_0$; if we divide this latter by $\frac{3}{2} k$, we find 25,500°K as the temperature at which the electrons in a *rarefied* electron gas would possess the same mean kinetic energy that they do in silver. According to the theory they should exert a pressure

$$p_0 = \frac{2}{5} n\zeta_0 = 2.06 \times 10^{11} \text{ dynes/cm}^2 = 2.03 \times 10^5 \text{ atm.}$$

That the electrons stay in the metal in spite of this enormous pressure is due, of course, to the powerful attraction of the positively charged atoms for any electron that starts to leave, which is usually viewed as an attraction of the electron by its electrostatic image in the conductor.

These results become slightly modified when the temperature is raised above absolute zero. The electrons even contribute a little then to the specific heat; according to the value given for c_V at the end of Sec. 237, they would contribute in a gram of silver of density $\rho = 10.5$, at 0°C, the amount

$$\frac{nm}{\rho} c_V = \frac{n}{\rho} \frac{\pi^2 k^2}{2\zeta_0} T = 1.63 \times 10^4 \text{ ergs/deg.} = 0.00039 \text{ cal/deg.}$$

This is, however, only a negligible part of the total observed specific heat of 0.056 cal/deg.

The velocity distribution function also develops a slight maxwellian tail when $T \neq 0$; the number of electrons with kinetic energy in a range $d\zeta$ many times kT above ζ_0 is $n_\zeta \, d_\zeta$, where

$$n_\zeta = \frac{2Q}{\sqrt{\pi} k^{3/2}} \zeta^{1/2} e^{-\frac{\zeta - \zeta_0}{kT}}$$

The occurrence of thermionic emission is attributed to these few electrons of exceptionally high energy. It is noteworthy that their density, like the chemical constant, depends only upon universal constants; the special internal properties of a particular substance seem, so to speak, to exhaust themselves in determining ζ_0. As a consequence, the theory furnishes a universal formula for the thermionic current.

We have not space here, however, to take up the theory of thermionic emission and of the other electrical properties of metals, which involves the continual use of the wave-mechanical theory of solids.

241. Degeneracy in Actual Gases. When the numerical values pertaining to actual gases are inserted in the formulas, it turns out, unfortunately, that there is almost no hope of detecting any of the quantum effects that we have been discussing, at least under present experimental conditions. The temperature has to be made so low, or the density so high, that the effect of molecular interaction becomes strong enough effectively to mask the minute quantum effects.

The most favorable gas for a test is helium. Its molecules are light and, being monatomic, possess no momentum due to nuclear rotation; and the nucleus appears to be in a simple state. The normal state of the electron shell is also simple, being of spectroscopic S type; and the first excited state has energy so much higher that at ordinary temperatures it rarely occurs. Helium has the further advantage that it can be worked with at very low temperatures. The number of particles in the atom being even, viz., two protons and two neutrons in the nucleus and two electrons outside it, the atom should be of Bose-Einstein type; this is confirmed by experiments on the deflection of alpha-rays by helium atoms.* Thus at ordinary temperatures helium should behave like a pure Bose-Einstein gas of point masses.

The degree of degeneracy is determined, according to (290) in Sec. 232, by the value of

$$\frac{QT^{3/2}}{n} = w \frac{(2\pi mkT)^{3/2}}{nh^3}.$$

* Cf. "Handbuch der Physik," 2d ed., vol. 24, part 1, p. 794.

If we insert here $w = 1$, $m = 6.65 \times 10^{-24}$ g, $k = 1.381 \times 10^{-16}$, $h = 6.62 \times 10^{-27}$, and also $T = 273.1$ and $n = n_0 = 2.686 \times 10^{19}$, so as to have standard conditions, we find $QT^{3/2}/n = 2.54 \times 10^5$, which is enormous. If we lower T to $20°K$ and keep the pressure at one atmosphere, $QT^{3/2}/n$ becomes 368. If, however, we lower T to the boiling point, $4°K$, and still keep the pressure at 1 atmosphere, $QT^{3/2}/n$ becomes only 6.6. Under these conditions the second terms in the series in Sec. 238 take on easily detectable values. On the other hand, the density is now so high that the effect of molecular fields is considerable. Since the latter cannot be distinguished experimentally from the quantum effect, the only hope of testing the theory lies in making theoretical calculations of the field effect and then correcting for it. This is not easy to do, however, and conclusive results have not yet been obtained.

Among other gases, only hydrogen is at all favorable to a test. At ordinary temperatures its molecules are divided, not only among several rotational states, but also, as explained in Sec. 150, into the para and ortho types, with internal multiplicities $w = 1$ and $w = 3$, respectively. As the temperature sinks, however, all molecules settle into their lowest rotational state; if at the same time the transformation from ortho to parahydrogen is catalyzed, the gas becomes almost pure para by the time its boiling point is reached at $20°K$, and it should then behave, like helium, as a simple Bose-Einstein gas of point masses with $w = 1$. Inserting $m = 3.35 \times 10^{-24}$ g and $n = (273/20)n_0$, we find, then, at one atmosphere pressure, $QT^{3/2}/n = 131$. This is discouragingly large, especially when we remember that allowance has somehow to be made for the effects of molecular fields.

242. Dissociation. In our treatment of mixed gases we have hitherto assumed that the total number of molecules of each kind is a fixed quantity. Sometimes this is not so. Chemical reactions may occur by which molecules are changed from one type to another; such cases are of great importance in chemistry. It may also happen at extremely high temperatures that, not only are compound molecules dissociated into their constituent atoms, but ionization also occurs, so that some of what we are here calling molecules are free electrons; processes of this sort appear to occur freely in stellar atmospheres and so play an important role in astrophysics.

Since such phenomena are of little importance in present-day physics, however, we shall take space here only to treat a simple case of dissociation into two constituents.*

---

* An excellent discussion of the general formulas and their applications is contained in the "Handbuch für Astrophysik," vol. III, 1 part 3, p. 259.

Suppose a molecule of type KL can dissociate into two molecules of types K and L.   An example is the dissociation of PCl_5 into PCl_3 and Cl_2.   Then in a gas composed of such molecules processes will continually be going on in which KL molecules undergo dissociation, or in which a K unites with an L to reform a KL; and when equilibrium exists the two processes will be going on at equal rates.   These dynamical processes need not be investigated here, however; our general principles furnish us with a short cut to the statistical result.

The wave-mechanical description of such a situation is the following.   The gas is built up out of fixed numbers of fundamental particles (electrons, protons, neutrons); and it possesses a set of quantum states determined by the interactions between these particles and by the vessel in which they are confined.   The peculiarity of the case before us is that these quantum states fall into distinct groups or series; the wave-functions for the states of each series have such a form that they can be interpreted as representing approximately a grouping of the fundamental particles into a certain definite number of molecules of each of the three types KL, K, and L.

Each of these wave-functions, if the gas is not too dense, can then be written approximately as an antisymmetric combination of products of three functions, one function representing each of the three groups of molecules, treated as a separate constituent gas.   The KL, K, and L gases may be independently either of Fermi-Dirac or of Bose-Einstein type, according to the number of fundamental particles in each type of molecule; and the wave-function for each can be built up in its turn, in the zero-order approximation, out of one-molecule functions, just as we did this for a simple gas.

Each of the quantum states of the whole gas can then be treated as equally probable.   From this point on the argument is a simple generalization of that contained in Secs. 221 and 222 in the last chapter.   We divide the molecular states for the respective KL, K, and L types into groups of $\nu_{\tau'}$, $\nu_{\tau''}$, and $\nu_{\tau'''}$ states each; let $N_{\tau'}^{K}$, $N_{\tau''}^{L}$, $N_{\tau'''}^{LK}$ denote the number of molecules in each group corresponding to a particular distribution.   The number of equally probable states corresponding to a specified distribution, which we shall denote by M', is then the product of three M's like those written down in Sec. 221, one for each type.   We can write, therefore, for its logarithm,

$$\log M' = \sum_{\tau'} \log \varphi_{\tau'}{}^{K} + \sum_{\tau''} \log \varphi_{\tau''}{}^{L} + \sum_{\tau'''} \log \varphi_{\tau'''}{}^{KL},$$

where $\varphi_\tau = \nu_\tau!/N_\tau!(\nu_\tau - N_\tau)!$ for molecules of F-D type but

$$\varphi_\tau = \frac{(\nu_\tau + N_\tau - 1)!}{N_\tau!(\nu_\tau - 1)!}$$

for the B-E type, and the superscripts have obvious meanings.

M' being now proportional to the probability of the distribution, we maximalize it by varying $N_{\tau'}{}^{K}$, $N_{\tau'}{}^{L}$ and $N_{\tau''}{}^{KL}$. In the present instance the total number of molecules of each type is not fixed, however. The proper conditions can conveniently be stated in terms of the total numbers N_0^K and N_0^L of K and L molecules that would be present if dissociation were complete; it is readily seen then that in general

$$\sum_{\tau'} N_{\tau'}{}^{K} + \sum_{\tau'''} N_{\tau'''}{}^{KL} = N_0^K, \qquad \sum_{\tau''} N_{\tau''}{}^{L} + \sum_{\tau'''} N_{\tau'''}{}^{KL} = N_0^L. \quad (303a, b)$$

The energy condition can be written

$$\sum_{\tau'} \epsilon_{\tau'}{}^{K} N_{\tau'}{}^{K} + \sum_{\tau''} \epsilon_{\tau''}{}^{L} N_{\tau''}{}^{L} + \sum_{\tau'''} \epsilon_{\tau'''}{}^{KL} N_{\tau'''}{}^{KL} = E.$$

The result of maximalizing M' is then easily seen to be, $(\varphi_\tau)'$ being written for $d\varphi_\tau/dN_\tau$,

$$\frac{(\varphi_{\tau'}{}^{K})'}{\varphi_{\tau'}{}^{K}} - \alpha_K - \beta\epsilon_{\tau'}{}^{K} = 0, \qquad \frac{(\varphi_{\tau''}{}^{L})'}{\varphi_{\tau''}{}^{L}} - \alpha_L - \beta\epsilon_{\tau''}{}^{L} = 0,$$

$$\frac{(\varphi_{\tau'''}{}^{KL})'}{\varphi_{\tau'''}{}^{KL}} - \alpha_K - \alpha_L - \beta\epsilon_{\tau'''}{}^{KL} = 0,$$

α_K, α_L, and β being constants. These equations give, after working out φ'/φ as in Sec. 221 and introducing the temperature T as in Sec. 222, as generalizations of $(270a, b)$:

$$N_{j'}{}^{K} = \left(B_K e^{\frac{\epsilon_{j'}{}^{K}}{kT}} \pm 1\right)^{-1}, \qquad N_{j''}{}^{L} = \left(B_L e^{\frac{\epsilon_{j''}{}^{L}}{kT}} \pm 1\right)^{-1},$$

$$N_{j'''}{}^{KL} = \left(B_{KL} e^{\frac{\epsilon_{j'''}{}^{KL}}{kT}} \pm 1\right)^{-1};$$

here ϵ_j is the energy of a molecule in its jth fundamental quantum state and $B_K = e^{\alpha_K}$, $B_L = e^{\alpha_L}$, $B_{KL} = e^{\alpha_K + \alpha_L}$, so that

$$B_{KL} = B_K B_L.$$

These results show that each type of molecule is distributed in energy just as if the others were not present; each type exhibits, therefore, its own degree of degeneracy as determined by its density. The presence of molecules of other types has an influence only upon the total number of each type that is present.

Obviously the general situation promises to be complicated. Accordingly we shall pass at once to the classical limit, which is adequate for most of the applications.

243. Dissociation in the Classical Limit. Under such conditions that classical theory holds, as described in Sec. 232, we can reduce our result to the approximate form

$$N_{j'}{}^{K} = D_{K}\, e^{-\frac{\epsilon_{j'}{}^{K}}{kT}}, \qquad N_{j''}{}^{L} = D_{L}\, e^{-\frac{\epsilon_{j''}{}^{L}}{kT}}, \qquad N_{j'''}{}^{KL} = D_{KL}\, e^{-\frac{\epsilon_{j'''}{}^{KL}}{kT}}$$

where $D_{K} = 1/B_{K}$, etc. and $D_{KL} = D_{K}D_{L}$. We can now separate the molecular energy ϵ_j into kinetic energy ζ_μ and internal energy η_ν, as in Sec. 228.

The only result of special interest is obtained by summing over all kinetic energies; this can be done by means of (281b) in Sec. 231, according to which

$$\sum_\mu e^{-\frac{\zeta_\mu}{kT}} = 2\pi h^{-3}(2m)^{3/2} V \int_0^\infty \zeta^{1/2}\, e^{-\frac{\zeta}{kT}}\, d\zeta = (2\pi m k T)^{3/2}\frac{V}{h^3}$$

by (288a). Let us also provide for a grouping of the fundamental states into multiple ones; the formulas can then be applied at any time to the fundamental states themselves merely by setting all multiplicities equal to unity. Then, dividing also by V, we find for the number per unit volume of molecules of each of the three types in their internal states of energy $\eta_{\tau'}{}^{K}$, $\eta_{\tau''}{}^{L}$, $\eta_{\tau'''}{}^{KL}$ and multiplicity $w_{\tau'}{}^{K}$, $w_{\tau''}{}^{L}$, $w_{\tau'''}{}^{KL}$, respectively,

$$n_{\tau'}{}^{K} = w_{\tau'}{}^{K} C_{K}\, e^{-\frac{\eta_{\tau'}{}^{K}}{kT}}, \qquad n_{\tau''}{}^{L} = w_{\tau''}{}^{L} C_{L}\, e^{-\frac{\eta_{\tau''}{}^{L}}{kT}}, \qquad (304a, b)$$

$$n_{\tau'''}{}^{KL} = w_{\tau'''}{}^{KL} C_{KL}\, e^{-\frac{\eta_{\tau'''}{}^{KL}}{kT}}, \qquad (304c)$$

where C takes the place of $(2\pi m k T)^{3/2}\dfrac{D}{h^3}$ and hence

$$C_{KL} = \left(\frac{m_{KL}h^2}{2\pi m_K m_L k T}\right)^{3/2} C_K C_L, \qquad (305)$$

m_K, m_L and m_{KL} or $m_K + m_L$ being the masses of the three types of molecules. The total number of molecules per unit volume of each type is then

$$n^{K} = C_{K}\sum_{\tau'} w_{\tau'}{}^{K} e^{-\frac{\eta_{\tau'}{}^{K}}{kT}}, \qquad n^{L} = C_{L}\sum_{\tau''} w_{\tau''}{}^{L} e^{-\frac{\eta_{\tau''}{}^{L}}{kT}}, \qquad (306a, b)$$

$$n^{KL} = C_{KL}\sum_{\tau'''} w_{\tau'''}{}^{KL} e^{-\frac{\eta_{\tau'''}{}^{KL}}{kT}}. \qquad (306c)$$

The n's are subject to the conditions, derivable from (303a, b), that

$$n^K + n^{KL} = n_0^K, \qquad n^L + n^{KL} = n_0^L,$$

n_0^K and n_0^L being the densities of the K and L types when dissociation is complete; and these equations together with (305) fix the C's.

The equation representing the *law of mass action*, which plays such an important role in physical chemistry, can now be written down for our gas in the following form:

$$\frac{n_K n_L}{n_{KL}} = \left(\frac{2\pi m_K m_L k}{m_{KL} h^2} \right)^{3/2} T^{3/2} \frac{\sum_{\tau'} w_{\tau'}{}^K e^{-\frac{\eta_{\tau'}{}^K}{kT}} \sum_{\tau''} w_{\tau''}{}^L e^{-\frac{\eta_{\tau'}{}^{,L}}{kT}}}{\sum_{\tau'''} w_{\tau'''}{}^{KL} e^{-\frac{\eta_{\tau'''}{}^{KL}}{kT}}}. \qquad (307a)$$

According to this result the "constant" on the right of the equation varies, in general, in a very complicated manner with temperature. In special cases, however, the variation may become simple. For example, suppose it is possible to ignore all internal states except those of lowest energy, and let these have respective multiplicities w_0^K, w_0^L, w_0^{KL}. Then

$$\frac{n_K n_L}{n_{KL}} = \frac{w_0^K w_0^L}{w_0^{KL}} \left(\frac{2\pi m_K m_L k}{m_{KL} h^2} \right)^{3/2} T^{3/2} e^{-\frac{u}{kT}}, \qquad (307b)$$

where $u = \eta_0^K + \eta_0^L - \eta_0^{KL}$ and represents the energy of dissociation. In a particular case one or all of the w_0's may be 1; but they must include nuclear as well as electronic multiplicities. The equation may take on a similar form even when molecular rotation occurs.

Equation (307b) ought to hold very commonly whenever all of the molecules concerned are monatomic. This restriction really limits it to the dissociation of an atom into an electron and an ion; but just this case is of great interest in connection with vacuum tubes, and it also finds an important application in stellar theory.

For the process of simple ionization the formula is usually written in a somewhat different form. Taking the ions as the molecules of type K and the electrons as those of type L, the un-ionized atoms being the KL type, let us write x for the fraction of all atoms that are ionized; then $x = n_K/(n_L + n_{KL})$ and $n_K = n_L = n_{KL} x/(1 - x)$, whereas the pressure is $p = nkT = (2n_K + n_{KL})kT = n_{KL}kT \dfrac{1 + x}{1 - x}$.

Let us write w_a and w_i for the multiplicities of the normal states of atom and ion, respectively, and $w_0^L = 2$ for the electron, because of its spin, also m for the electronic mass. We can put $m_K = m_{KL}$ nearly enough. Then (307b) multiplied by kT becomes:

$$\frac{p}{1+x}\frac{x^2}{1-x} = \frac{2w_i}{w_a}\left(\frac{2\pi mk}{h^2}\right)^{3/2} kT^{5/2} e^{-\frac{u}{kT}}, \qquad (307c)$$

u being now the energy of ionization. Except for the w's, this is equivalent to the equation first applied in astrophysics by Eggert (1919) and Saha (1921).

The last equation is based, however, upon the assumption that electrons and ions are equally numerous, the gas being electrically neutral as a whole. If this is not the case, we can write, from (307b),

$$\frac{n_i n_e}{n_a} = \frac{2w_i}{w_a}\left(\frac{2\pi mk}{h^2}\right)^{3/2} T^{3/2} e^{-\frac{u}{kT}}, \qquad (307d)$$

n_i, n_e, and n_a being the densities of ions, electrons and nonionized atoms, respectively.

A very interesting application of the latter equation was made by Langmuir and Kingdon in connection with the ionization of cesium atoms by impact upon heated surfaces.* In a heated enclosure containing a minute amount of cesium vapor the electron density is controlled by the walls. If the latter are of tungsten at 1200°K, the electron density is only 9.25 electrons per cubic centimeter. If this value is inserted for n_e in (307d), together with the known ionization energy u of cesium and $w_i = 1$ for the cesium ion and $w_a = 2$ for the neutral cesium atom, we find $n_i/n_a = 577$, so that the cesium is almost completely ionized. Calculation shows that the density of the cesium vapor may easily be high enough so that the Saha equation predicts only a very small degree of ionization [e.g., $x < 0.001$ in (307c)]; in the present instance the electrons are drained off by the tungsten and the ionization is thereby greatly increased. If, however, the walls are covered with thorium, $n_e = 6 \times 10^7$, and then $n_i/n_a = 8.9 \times 10^{-5}$, so that ionization is practically absent. These facts harmonize beautifully with the observation that neutral cesium atoms are reflected from tungsten at 1200° almost entirely as positive ions, whereas ionization is negligible if they fall upon a thoriated filament.

244. A Gas Not in Equilibrium. In developing the properties of a gas in equilibrium we were able to draw conclusions by summing over the separate quantum states because the phases of these could be assumed to be chaotically distributed. When equilibrium does

---

* LANGMUIR and KINGDON, *Roy. Soc. Proc.*, **107**, 61 (1925).

not exist, as when a gas is conducting heat or carrying sound waves, this is no longer possible. In dealing with such cases we are compelled to recognize that one part of the gas differs from another in its physical state. We shall now show how a distribution of the molecules both in velocity and in space can be specified on the wave-mechanical basis; to facilitate grasping the essential idea, this will be done first in a one-dimensional case.

Suppose a particle of mass m can move along a line between two termini A and B separated by a distance L, being reflected elastically when it strikes either terminus. Its wave equation can then be written

$$\frac{h}{2\pi i}\frac{\partial \Psi}{\partial t} - \frac{h^2}{8\pi^2 m}\frac{\partial^2 \Psi}{\partial x^2} = 0,$$

with the boundary condition that $\Psi = 0$ at A and B. This equation has stationary solutions of the form $\Psi = e^{-2\pi i \zeta_n t}\psi_n$ where ψ_n stands for $C_n \sin \pi n x/L$, in analogy with φ_μ in eq. (277); but we shall not use these.

In order to localize the particle on a particular part of the stretch L, let us now divide the whole range into a number of equal segments of length l; and let us fix our attention upon the values that Ψ has at points on one of these segments S at the instant $t = t_1$. A new solution Ψ_1 of the wave equation can readily be constructed that reduces, at $t = t_1$, to zero everywhere outside of the segment S and to the actual values of Ψ within S. This function Ψ_1 constitutes a wave packet representing the particle as initially localized in S with a certain probability. Treating all of the segments in the same way we have the whole probability for the particle broken up into such wave packets, each localized at $t = t_1$ in a single segment.

Let us consider, now, what state of motion of the particle is represented by the single wave packet Ψ_1. For this purpose we may resolve it at $t = t_1$ into a complex Fourier sum, thus:

$$\Psi_1 = \sum_\mu \alpha_\mu e^{2\pi i \left(\frac{\mu x}{l} - \frac{\zeta t_1}{h}\right)},$$

μ ranging over all integral values from $-\infty$ to $+\infty$ and ζ standing for $\mu^2 h^2 / 2ml^2$. Any one term of this sum represents a piece of length l cut out of an infinite train of homogeneous plane waves, e.g.,

$$\alpha_\mu e^{2\pi i \left(\frac{\mu x}{l} - \frac{\zeta t}{h}\right)},$$

where x is now unrestricted in range. Such a train represents in turn a particle moving with definite momentum $p = \mu h/l$ or a velocity

$v = \mu h/ml$ and kinetic energy ζ. The infinite train travels on forever without change of shape. A finite piece of it will not do this; but it can be shown that, if the initial length l of the piece is large relative to the wave length λ, where $\lambda = l/\mu$, then the piece will spread only slowly at the ends and will travel many times its own length before becoming greatly altered.

Accordingly, each of the terms in the series for Ψ_1 may be regarded as representing the particle as localized in the segment S and moving more or less definitely with a velocity v, energy ζ, and wave length λ given by

$$v = \frac{\mu h}{ml}, \qquad \zeta = \frac{\mu^2 h^2}{2ml^2}, \qquad \lambda = \frac{l}{\mu},$$

the velocity and the energy being more nearly definite as μ, or the number of wave lengths contained in l, increases. We have here a typical compromise between definiteness of position and definiteness of momentum such as is required by the indetermination principle. The amount of the probability belonging to this term is

$$\int_{x_0}^{x_0+l} \left| \alpha_\mu e^{2\pi i \left(\frac{\mu x}{l} - \frac{\zeta t_1}{h} \right)} \right|^2 dx = l |\alpha_\mu|^2,$$

x_0 being x at the left end of S. The total probability of finding the particle in S is then $l \sum_\mu |\alpha_\mu|^2$, which also equals $\int |\Psi_1|^2 \, dx$.

The procedure thus outlined is easily generalized now so as to apply to three-dimensional motion, and then to a gas composed of a large number N of molecules. For this purpose we cut space up into macroscopically small cubes with edges of length l parallel to the axes, and then contemplate a particular one of these cubes; let its innermost corner be at x_0, y_0, z_0. Then we expand Ψ inside the cube into a three-dimensional Fourier series in terms of the coordinates of molecule τ, thus:

$$\Psi = l^{-3/2} \sum_{\mu_1} \sum_{\mu_2} \sum_{\mu_3} \gamma_{\mu_1\mu_2\mu_3}(\tau) e^{2\pi i \left[\frac{\mu_1 x_\tau + \mu_2 y_\tau + \mu_3 z_\tau}{l} - \frac{\zeta t}{h} \right]},$$

μ_1, μ_2, and μ_3 standing for any integer, positive or negative. $\gamma_{\mu_1\mu_2\mu_3}(\tau)$ will be a function of all the remaining molecular coordinates, of course, and also of the time. A single term of this series then represents, with such definiteness as is allowed by the ratio l/λ in accord with the indetermination principle, molecule τ moving inside the cube with components of velocity v_x, v_y, v_z, energy ζ, and wave length λ given by:

$$v_x = \mu_1 \frac{h}{ml}, \qquad v_y = \mu_2 \frac{h}{ml}, \qquad v_z = \mu_3 \frac{h}{ml}; \qquad \zeta = \frac{h^2}{2ml^2}(\mu_1^2 + \mu_2^2 + \mu_3^2);$$

$$\lambda = \frac{h}{mv} = \frac{l}{(\mu_1^2 + \mu_2^2 + \mu_3^2)^{1/2}}.$$

The probability of finding the molecule in the cube and moving in this way is

$$\int_{z_0}^{z_0+l} dz_\tau \int_{y_0}^{y_0+l} dy_\tau \int_{x_0}^{x_0+l} dx_\tau \int \left| l^{-3/2}\gamma_{\mu_1\mu_2\mu_3}{}^{(\tau)} e^{2\pi i \left[\frac{\mu_1 x_\tau + \mu_2 y_\tau + \mu_3 z_\tau}{l} - \frac{\zeta t}{h}\right]}\right|^2 dx^{(\tau)}$$

$$= \int |\gamma_{\mu_1\mu_2\mu_3}{}^{(\tau)}|^2 \, dx^{(\tau)},$$

where $dx^{(\tau)}$ includes all other coordinates but x_τ, y_τ, z_τ.

We obtain then the total number of such molecules per unit volume by summing this last expression for all molecules and dividing by the volume l^3 of the cube; denoting this number by $n_{\mu_1\mu_2\mu_3}$, we have

$$n_{\mu_1\mu_2\mu_3} = \frac{1}{l^3}\sum_{\tau=1}^{N} \int |\gamma_{\mu_1\mu_2\mu_3}{}^{(\tau)}|^2 \, dx^{(\tau)}.$$

The quantity $n_{\mu_1\mu_2\mu_3}$ thus obtained may be regarded as corresponding to the general distribution function nf of classical theory (Sec. 50). For large μ's, however, it is more convenient to go over again to a continuous approximation. The number of sets of μ's belonging to the range $dv_x \, dv_y \, dv_z = d\kappa$ in velocity space is $(m^3l^3/h^3) \, d\kappa$. Hence, if we write as usual n for the total number of molecules per unit volume and $f(\mathbf{v}) \, d\kappa$ for the fraction of them having velocities in the range $d\kappa$, we have $nf(\mathbf{v}) \, d\kappa = (m^3l^3/h^3)n_{\mu_1\mu_2\mu_3} \, d\kappa$ and

$$nf(\mathbf{v}) = \frac{m^3}{h^3}\sum_{\tau=1}^{N} \int |\gamma_{\mu_1\mu_2\mu_3}{}^{(\tau)}|^2 \, dx^{(\tau)},$$

μ_1, μ_2, μ_3 standing here for a set of integers having as nearly as possible the correct relation with v_x, v_y, v_z.

This result furnishes us with a distribution function nf in terms of the wave scalar Ψ. We can then proceed to deduce for it, by means of the wave equation, a differential equation such as classical theory gave us in eq. (87) in Sec. 51. It is found, as a matter of fact, that nothing at all needs to be changed in the latter equation as written; it retains its validity in wave mechanics.

The only thing needed is a change in the relation between the term that occurs on the right in (87), expressing the effect of molecular interaction, and the scattering coefficient. In the new theory the number of molecules deflected from one direction into another is found to depend not only upon the number moving in the first direction, as in classical theory, but also upon those that are already moving in the new direction; it can be said that molecules already moving in a given direction tend to hinder others from being scattered in that direction in a Fermi-Dirac gas, but to attract them into it in a Bose-Einstein gas. This does not mean, however, that molecules which can be said to approach along definite paths and to undergo a real collision are influenced in the way they rebound by the motion of other molecules elsewhere; we are dealing here with the interaction between molecules that are localized in space only to the degree that they are all contained within a certain small region.

Such a departure from classical behavior is required in order to harmonize with the statistical properties that we have found to be required by quantum theory. It appears to possess at present little practical interest, however;* so we shall not pursue the subject further.

* UEHLING and UHLENBECK, *Phys. Rev.,* **43,** 552 (1933).

CHAPTER XI

ELECTRIC AND MAGNETIC PROPERTIES OF GASES

As a closing topic we shall take up in this chapter the electric and magnetic properties of gases. Two of these properties, the dielectric constant and the magnetic permeability or susceptibility, while not of first-rate importance in themselves, are characteristic of gases in equilibrium, and some consideration of them falls naturally within the scope of any text on kinetic theory. These topics will be discussed first. We shall confine our attention for the most part to the kinetic-theory aspect of the phenomena; the reader who desires to pursue the subject further can do so in Debye's readable little book* or in Van Vleck's thoroughgoing treatise.†

The motion of ions and the flow of current through gases, on the other hand, represent by their very nature departures from equilibrium; and they constitute an extremely intricate set of phenomena for which no completely adequate theory exists even to this day. For the latter reason these topics are best handled as separate subjects, and several books devoted to their study are in existence. We shall devote to them only a short closing section.

THE DIELECTRIC CONSTANT

245. Polarization and the Dielectric Constant. The presence of a material insulator or dielectric in an electrostatic field is observed to modify the electrical phenomena. For example, the capacity of a condenser is increased when a material dielectric is substituted for vacuum between the plates; the ratio of the increase in such a case is a measure of the dielectric constant of the insulating material, and is sometimes cited as the fundamental definition of this quantity. According to views that have been current in one form or another since Faraday's time, this effect is due to a polarization of the dielectric; each molecule of it has, in the presence of a field, a certain average electric moment, equivalent to that of an electric dipole of a certain strength, and the electrical effect of the dielectric arises from the fields of these dipoles.‡

---

* P. Debye, "Polar Molecules," 1929.
† J. H. Van Vleck, "Theory of Electric and Magnetic Susceptibilities," 1932.
‡ Cf. Page and Adams, "Principles of Electricity," Chap. II.

In a gas, as in any isotropic body, the average vector electrical moment of the molecules has the direction of the field; let us denote its magnitude by $\bar{g}$. This represents both the average component, taken in the direction of the field, of the moment of a single molecule during a macroscopically short time, and also the instantaneous average value of this component for all molecules in a macroscopically small volume. The total electrical moment per unit volume, which is taken as a measure of the polarization, is then

$$P = n\bar{g},$$

n being as usual the number of molecules per unit volume; and electrostatic theory leads to the familiar relations with the dielectric constant ϵ, the electric induction D, and the electric intensity or field strength E:

$$\epsilon = \frac{D}{E}, \qquad \mathbf{D} = \mathbf{E} + 4\pi\mathbf{P},$$

$$\epsilon = 1 + \frac{4\pi n\bar{g}}{E}. \tag{308}$$

Thus from measurements of ϵ we can calculate experimental values of $\bar{g}$; and the theory of the dielectric constant resolves itself into the theoretical determination of this mean moment. Its magnitude must depend, among other things, upon the strength of the field. Since, however, the macroscopic electric field is of the nature of an average and is itself determined in part by the dielectric, it is quite possible that the field which acts on an individual molecule and tends to give it a mean moment in one direction may not be the same as the macroscopic field; for the contributions of neighboring molecules to the average field may be different from their action upon a particular molecule. This point must first be investigated.

246. The Local Electric Field. The electrostatic potential due to a polarized dielectric can be written

$$V_P = \int \frac{P \cos (P, r)}{r^2} \, d\tau,$$

r being the length of a line drawn from the field point at which V_P is the potential to an element $d\tau$ of the dielectric, and (P, r) standing for the angle between this line and the direction of the polarization $\mathbf{P}$ in $d\tau$. The integral converges even at a point in the midst of the dielectric, and its gradient defines the macroscopic field strength there, $\mathbf{E} = -\nabla V_P$. If, however, we attempt to find from this integral the partial field that acts upon a small portion of the dielectric due to the polarization of the remainder, we encounter a serious difficulty; for it turns out that this field depends greatly upon the shape of the selected portion. If in thought we isolate a small slender filament parallel to **P,** the field due to the remainder and to electric charges elsewhere is the ordinary macroscopic field E; but if the isolated portion has the form of a thin plate, the field due to the remainder has a component normal to the faces of the plate that is equal to the component in that direction of **D** or **E** + 4π**P.** For other shapes intermediate results hold.

The macroscopic method thus fails to elucidate the action of the dielectric upon itself, and we are compelled to adopt a frankly molecular approach. The accepted procedure is to single out a macroscopically small sphere S with a given molecule at its center, and then divide the electric field into two parts; let us write E_2 for the mean field due to matter within the sphere itself (exclusive of the given molecule), and E_1 for the field due to all other causes.

Then E_1 is the same as the field in a spherical cavity cut in uniformly polarized dielectric. We can obtain this by subtracting from the ordinary field E the part contributed by the omitted sphere, which is

$$-\tfrac{4}{3}\pi P$$

in terms of the polarization P of the sphere,* which can be assumed to be uniform. Thus

$$E_1 = E + \tfrac{4}{3}\pi P.$$

The magnitude of E_2 will obviously depend upon the distribution of the molecules inside the local sphere S. It was shown by Lorentz that if they are arranged in cubical array E_2 is actually zero.† It is easy to show that the same thing is true on the average in a gas composed of elastic-sphere molecules with dipoles at their centers. For in such a case the principle of molecular chaos tells us that the mean density of molecular centers is the same in the neighborhood of any given molecule as its general average elsewhere; hence the average effect is the same as if the medium extended in continuous

---

* Cf. Page and Adams, "Principles of Electricity," 1931, p. 96, where the field due to the sphere itself is obtainable as $E_0 - (E_x)_i$, the polarization being

$$P = \frac{(K - 1)(E_x)_i}{4\pi},$$

or p. 144, where the exact analogue is given in eq. (44-2) for the magnetic case.

† H. A. Lorentz, "Theory of Electrons," 1908, p. 308.

form right down to the surface of the sphere of influence of the given molecule, inside which the centers of neighboring molecules cannot get. Accordingly, by the argument of the last paragraph, the total mean field acting on the given molecule is just $E + \frac{4}{3}\pi P$. It must be, therefore, that in this case $E_2 = 0$.

For a more general type of molecule, E_2 may not quite vanish. In any case, however, we should expect it to have the direction of the polarization, because of the isotropy of the gas. Let us write, therefore, in general, $E_2 = cP$. In sufficiently weak fields we should expect c to be practically a constant.

Then we have for the local field in general

$$E' = E_1 + E_2 = E + (\tfrac{4}{3}\pi + c)P, \tag{309a}$$

and for an elastic-sphere gas with dipoles at the molecular centers,

$$E' = E + \frac{4}{3}\pi P = \frac{\epsilon + 2}{3} E. \tag{309b}$$

247. The Mean Molecular Moment ḡ. Ideas concerning the nature of the electrical moment of the molecules have undergone a slow development as the knowledge of molecular structure has accumulated. A hundred years ago the molecules were commonly compared with small conductors, perhaps spherical, which would acquire moments when brought into a field because of the charges induced upon them. With the rise of the electronic theory of atoms, the assumption became current that the electrons become displaced a little under the influence of the field, and their electric field then ceases to cancel completely that of the nuclei at a distance from the molecule and combines with the latter to form a dipole field. Modern wave mechanics indicates that a closely analogous distortion of the molecule should occur, and such an effect is believed to contribute largely to the polarization in all dielectrics.

If such a displacement occurs in a symmetrical molecule, it ought to be independent of the motion of thermal agitation; if this were the sole cause of polarization, the dielectric constant ought, therefore, to be independent of the temperature. This is actually true in many cases, but it has long been known that in other cases the dielectric constant decreases with rise of temperature. The suggestion was put forward by Debye in 1912* that some molecules may possess permanent moments; he assumed that in the absence of an electric field these moments are oriented impartially in all directions and so have no resultant macroscopic effect, but that under the influence of a field

---

* P. DEBYE, *Phys. Zeits.*, **13**, 97 (1912); "Polar Molecules," 1929.

their orientation is slightly altered so that they have a mean component in the direction of the field. Thermal agitation will then be tending continually to restore the random orientation, and the existing condition will be one of statistical equilibrium; as the temperature rises and thermal agitation becomes more vigorous, the distribution will become more nearly a random one and the mean moment and the dielectric constant will, therefore, decrease.

248. The Molecular Polarizability α. Whatever its origin, the mean moment of a molecule in a weak field should be proportional to the field that acts upon it. It is convenient, therefore, to write, for a molecule acted on by a field E,

$$\bar{g} = \alpha E,$$

where α, representing the ratio of mean moment to field strength, is called the polarizability of the molecule and should be independent of the field so long as the latter is not too strong; it may, however, vary with the temperature.

Then in the dielectric we shall have, by (309a),

$$\bar{g} = \alpha E' = \alpha[E + (\tfrac{4}{3}\pi + c)P]$$

or, since $P = n\bar{g}$,

$$\bar{g} = \frac{P}{n} = \frac{\alpha E}{1 - (\tfrac{4}{3}\pi + c)n\alpha}. \tag{310}$$

Hence, by (308),

$$\epsilon = \frac{1 + (\tfrac{8}{3}\pi - c)n\alpha}{1 - (\tfrac{4}{3}\pi + c)n\alpha}, \tag{311}$$

or, if $c = 0$, as it should be in a gas,

$$\epsilon = \frac{1 + 2n\tau}{1 - n\tau}, \qquad \tau = \frac{4}{3}\pi\alpha. \tag{312a, b}$$

In a gas where $n\tau$ is very small we can also write, approximately,

$$\epsilon = 1 + 3n\tau = 1 + 4\pi n\alpha. \tag{312c}$$

From these equations α can be calculated in terms of observed values of ϵ.

The quantity τ has obviously the dimensions of a volume; it is, in fact, the volume of a conducting sphere that would have the same polarizability as has one of the actual molecules, for such a sphere of radius a acquires by induction an electric moment $a^3 E$, so that for it $\alpha = a^3$. The quantity $n\tau$ occurring in the expression for ϵ is then the total volume of such equivalent spheres for all molecules in unit volume. It is of some interest to compare values of $2a$ calculated in this manner from α with molecular diameters obtained in other ways. Such a comparison is shown for a few gases in the following table, σ_η denoting values of the equivalent diameter for viscosity (cf. Sec. 86):

	H_2	He	N_2	CO_2	NH_3	C_2H_4
$2a$ ($\times 10^{-8}$ cm)	1.83	1.21	2.4	2.8	5.6	3.2
σ_η($\times 10^{-8}$ cm)	2.74	2.18	3.75	4.59	4.43	4.9

It is satisfactory that $2a$ generally comes out smaller than σ_η, for a conducting sphere is, of all electrical structures, the most easily polarized in proportion to its size, and for this reason the equivalent sphere should be smaller than the actual molecule. For NH_3, however, and some other strongly polar molecules, $2a$ exceeds σ_η, but not by a large factor.

All of the molecules have hitherto been tacitly assumed to be alike. It is readily seen, however, that if several kinds of molecules are present and if we distinguish quantities pertaining to them by a subscript, then, if also $c = 0$, the relation $P = n\bar{g}$ and eqs. (308), (310), and (312a, b) are replaced by

$$P = \sum_\sigma' n_\sigma \bar{g}_\sigma, \qquad \epsilon = 1 + \frac{4\pi}{E} \sum_\sigma' n_\sigma \bar{g}_\sigma$$

$$\bar{g}_\sigma = \alpha_\sigma \left[E + \frac{4}{3} \pi \sum_\sigma' n_\sigma \bar{g}_\sigma \right], \qquad P = \frac{\displaystyle\sum_\sigma' n_\sigma \alpha_\sigma}{1 - \frac{4}{3} \pi \displaystyle\sum_\sigma' n_\sigma \alpha_\sigma} E,$$

$$\epsilon = \frac{1 + 2\displaystyle\sum_\sigma' n_\sigma \tau_\sigma}{1 - \displaystyle\sum_\sigma' n_\sigma \tau_\sigma}, \qquad \tau_\sigma = \frac{4}{3} \pi \alpha_\sigma,$$

all sums extending over the various kinds of molecules that are present. The polarization volumes τ_σ are thus simply additive.

249. The Clausius-Mossotti Law. From eqs. (312a, b) is easily obtained, when $c = 0$,

$$\frac{\epsilon - 1}{\epsilon + 2} \frac{1}{n} = \tau = \frac{4}{3} \pi \alpha. \tag{313a}$$

The left-hand member of this equation should, therefore, be a constant as the density of the gas is varied, so long as the temperature is not changed. This conclusion is known as the Clausius-Mossotti law; it was derived long ago by Clausius and independently by Mossotti from tentative theories of dielectric action. The equation is sometimes written

$$\frac{\epsilon - 1}{\epsilon + 2}\, \frac{M}{\rho} = \frac{4}{3}\, \pi N_0 \alpha, \tag{313b}$$

M being the molecular weight, N_0 the Avogadro number, and ρ the density in grams per cubic centimeter; or, the right-hand member may be written as an undefined function of the temperature, which Debye called the "molar polarization" and denoted by P.

At ordinary densities, however, ϵ differs so slightly from unity for a gas that $\epsilon + 2$ can be replaced by 3 and we can write simply

$$\epsilon - 1 = 4\pi n \alpha = 3n\tau, \tag{313c}$$

so that $\epsilon - 1$ should be proportional to the density.

Careful experiment has shown that the Clausius-Mossotti law holds very accurately for gases even up to pressures of many atmospheres. (Cf. "Handbuch der Physik," vol. XII, 1927, p. 517.) Values of α can, accordingly, be calculated with considerable confidence from observed values of ϵ for gases by means of this equation.

250. Polarization Due to a Permanent Moment. The theory of dielectric constants thus reduces to the determination of molecular polarizabilities. In so far as these are due to a distortion of the molecule they will be constants whose values depend upon the molecular structure. If, however, the molecules possess permanent electric moments, we have a statistical problem to solve. Debye handled this problem on the basis of classical mechanics by translating into electrical language the analysis that had already been given by Langevin* in 1905 for the analogous magnetic problem. It is more convenient to proceed here in the reverse direction and to develop the theory for the electrical case first.

Let us assume that the molecules can be treated as rigid bodies possessing a permanent electric moment g. Then in the absence of a field they will have the axes of their moments oriented in all directions at random; the fraction of the axes making an angle between θ and $\theta + d\theta$ with any given direction will be, therefore, $\frac{1}{2} \sin \theta\, d\theta$.

Suppose now that a uniform electric field E' is applied, and let θ be measured from its direction. Then in this field each molecule will

---

* Langevin, *Jour. physique*, **4**, 678 (1905); *Ann. Chim. Phys.*, **5**, 70 (1905).

have potential energy $\omega = -gE' \cos \theta$.* According to the statistical principle of classical theory that is represented by eq. (89a) in Sec. 53, the probability of each position of the molecule under conditions of thermal equilibrium is now proportional to the Boltzmann factor

$$e^{-\frac{\omega}{kT}} = e^{\frac{gE' \cos \theta}{kT}}$$

independently of the molecular velocities of translation or of rotation. Such a position could be specified as regards orientation by means of three coordinates such as the three Eulerian angles,† of which θ might be one; the general relation holding between these coordinates and the spatial orientation would then be unaltered by the introduction of the field.   Hence we can write for the fraction of the molecules that now have their axes in a range $d\theta$, or the fraction of the time during which a particular molecule has its axis in that range, the product of the value of this fraction when $E' = 0$ and the Boltzmann factor or

$$dP = Ce^{\frac{gE' \cos \theta}{kT}} \sin \theta \, d\theta.$$

The constant C must have such a value that $\int dP = 1$; hence

$$C \int_0^\pi e^{\frac{gE' \cos \theta}{kT}} \sin \theta \, d\theta = -C \frac{kT}{gE'} e^{\frac{gE' \cos \theta}{kT}} \Big|_0^\pi = 1$$

and, in terms of $\sinh x = \frac{1}{2} (e^x - e^{-x})$,

$$C = \frac{gE'}{2kT} \left[\sinh \left(\frac{gE'}{kT} \right) \right]^{-1}.$$

The mean component of electric moment in the direction of the field (perpendicular components averaging out) is then the average value of $g \cos \theta$ or

$$\bar{g}_g = \int g \cos \theta \, dP = Cg \int_0^\pi e^{\frac{gE' \cos \theta}{kT}} \cos \theta \sin \theta \, d\theta =$$

$$Cg \left[-\frac{kT}{gE'} e^{\frac{gE' \cos \theta}{kT}} \cos \theta \Big|_0^\pi - \frac{kT}{gE'} \int_0^\pi e^{\frac{gE' \cos \theta}{kT}} \sin \theta \, d\theta \right].$$

Here in the brackets the new integral is just $1/C$, whereas the integrated term equals $(2kT/gE') \cosh (gE'/kT)$ in terms of

$$\cosh x = \frac{1}{2} (e^x + e^{-x}).$$

---

*Cf. Page and Adams, "Principles of Electricity," 1931, p. 130, where the mathematically identical formula for a magnetic dipole in a given field is established.

† Cf. H. Lamb, "Higher Mechanics," 1929, p. 83.

Hence we can write, after introducing the value just found for C,

$$\bar{g}_g = g\left(\coth x - \frac{1}{x}\right) = g\,L(x), \qquad x = \frac{gE'}{kT}, \qquad (314a, b)$$

where

$$\coth x = \frac{\cosh x}{\sinh x} = \frac{e^x + e^{-x}}{e^x - e^{-x}}.$$

The contribution of the permanent moments to the polarizability α will then be $\bar{g}_g/E'$. To this a constant term α_0 can be added to represent the effect of molecular distortion; to the first order in E' the effects of distortion and of the permanent moment will simply be superposed. For the total molecular polarizability we have then

$$\alpha = \alpha_0 + \frac{\bar{g}_g}{E'}. \qquad (315)$$

Here in a dielectric E' must be understood to represent the local field described in Sec. 246 or

$$E' = \frac{\epsilon + 2}{3}\,E, \qquad (316)$$

in terms of the macroscopic field intensity E. The dielectric constant ϵ itself is then given by (312a, b) in terms of α and n, the number of molecules per cubic centimeter, viz., for a homogeneous gas in which $c = 0$,

$$\epsilon = \frac{1 + 2n\tau}{1 - n\tau}, \qquad \tau = \frac{4}{3}\pi\alpha.$$

These equations give us α and ϵ as functions of E, but only implicitly.

In the special case of *weak fields*, however, the formulas become much simpler. If

$$x = \frac{gE'}{kT} \ll 1$$

we can keep only the largest term in each of the series,

$$\sinh x = x + \frac{x^3}{6}\cdots, \qquad \cosh x = 1 + \frac{x^2}{2}\cdots,$$

whence $\coth x = \dfrac{\cosh x}{\sinh x} = \dfrac{1}{x} + \dfrac{x}{3}\cdots$; then to the first order $L(x) = \dfrac{x}{3}$ and $\bar{g}_g = g^2\dfrac{E'}{3kT}$, so that

$$\alpha = \alpha_0 + \frac{g^2}{3kT}. \tag{317}$$

Thus in a weak field there is a constant polarizability, and hence a corresponding dielectric constant independent of field strength. These might be called *initial* values of α and ϵ.

251. Behavior in Intense Fields.   The function $L(x) = \coth x - \dfrac{1}{x}$ is plotted in Fig. 92.   The initial slope of the curve represents the contribution of permanent moments to the initial polarizability, giving rise to the second term in α as given by eq. (317) above.   As $x \to \infty$, on the other hand, $L(x) \to 1; 1 - L(x) = 1/x$ nearly.   Thus $\bar{g}_g \to g$ and the polarization approaches the value, $P = ng$, while α decreases toward α_0 as a limit, and the dielectric constant also decreases.

Thus in sufficiently strong fields polarization due to permanent moments should exhibit saturation analogous to that of the magnetism of iron in a strong magnetic field.   In practice, however, it is very difficult to get above the linear part of the $L(x)$ curve.   The moment g appears always to be of the order of 10^{-18} electrostatic units, and at 15°C

$$kT = 3.98 \times 10^{-14} \text{ erg};$$

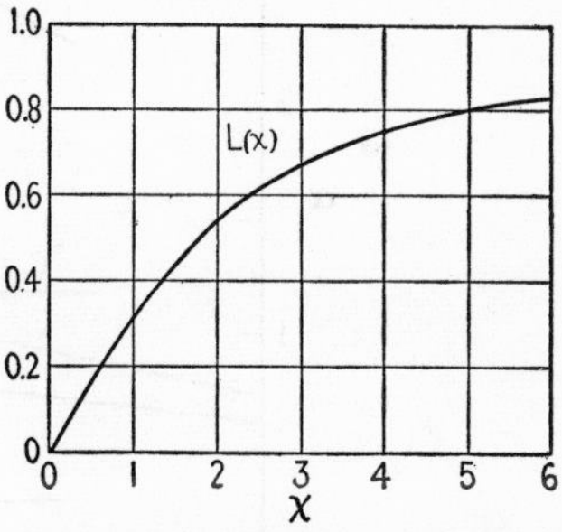

Fig. 92.—Dielectric saturation.

thus even to make $x = 0.1$ we should have to have E' of the order of 4,000 electrostatic units or 1,000,000 volts per centimeter.   Such field strengths can be realized only in gases and at such low pressures that measurement of the dielectric constant becomes very difficult.   A slight variation of this constant in an intense field has, however, been observed in certain liquids.

252. The Variation with Temperature.   According to eq. (317), the initial polarizability α should plot against $1/T$ as a straight line; the intercept of this line at $1/T = 0$ or $T = \infty$ should be α_0, and the slope, $g^2/3k$, should at once give us the permanent moment g.

In Fig. 93 values of α for a number of gases, calculated from observed values of ϵ by means of the approximate eq. (313c), are plotted against $1/T$.   The linear relation predicted by theory clearly holds very satisfactorily.

A good many electric moments have been determined in this way.   In a qualitative way they are in agreement with what would be expected in the light of modern knowledge of chemical combination;

and they are frequently employed, in turn, as evidence in doubtful cases in regard to the arrangement of the atoms in the molecule. Thus compounds such as CH_4 and CCl_4 are of the type often called, on chemical grounds, nonpolar, and a zero moment would be expected for them because of the tetrahedral symmetry of the carbon atom and the symmetrical loading of all four of its bonds. In such a molecule as CH_2Cl_2, however, the dissymmetry of the loading results in an electric moment. HCl and HBr likewise exhibit distinct electric moments; and they have long been regarded by the chemist as polar, the molecule being composed, perhaps, of a positively charged hydrogen atom and a negatively charged one of chlorine or bromine.

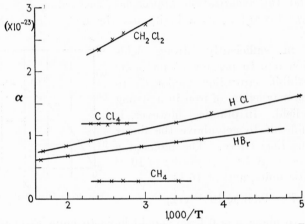

Fig. 93.—Polarizability α as function of absolute temperature T.

Water (H_2O) might, perhaps, have been expected to be nonpolar, but in reality it has a rather large moment ($g = 1.82 \times 10^{-18}$); this is taken to mean that the two hydrogen atoms must lie on the same side of the oxygen atom. H_2, N_2, O_2, and Ar all have zero moments.

Further discussion of this subject, and also of the influence of the polarizability upon refractive indices, which is a complicated affair involving no fresh use of kinetic theory, will be found in Debye's and Van Vleck's books cited above.

253. Quantum Theory of Polarization. Classical theory is thus able to account satisfactorily for the observed facts in regard to the dielectric constant. We cannot safely leave the subject, however, until we have ascertained whether our results are also in harmony with wave mechanics; for we have seen in other connections that an adequate treatment of the internal properties of molecules required the use of quantum theory. Now the old quantum theory, when applied to the polarization problem, merely made trouble because of its insistence that only certain classical orientations could occur in the presence of a field. These difficulties have been completely removed, however, by the substitution of the less classical conceptions of wave mechanics.

According to the new theory each molecule of a gas may be supposed to be at each instant in one of a discrete series of fundamental internal states, which we shall suppose to be numbered off in the order of increasing energy; these quantum states take the place of the whole collection of possible internal motions in classical theory (cf. Secs. 54, 147). In each quantum state the condition of the molecule can be described by means of a probability amplitude or wavefunction, which we shall denote for state n by ψ_n. Then $|\psi_n|^2$ serves as a probability function for the various configurations in which the particles composing the molecule might be found. This interpretation of ψ suggests that the mean electrical effect of the molecule might be calculated by averaging over all configurations, each one weighted in proportion to $|\psi|^2$; inferences of this sort are dangerous in wave mechanics, but in the present instance the conclusion can be rigorously justified so far as concerns effects at a considerable distance from the molecule.

The contribution of a molecule to the dielectric constant will be measured, then, by its electrical moment averaged in the manner described over all configurations. Now the moment of a dipole composed of two charges $\pm q$ placed a short distance l apart is ql, its x-component being ql_x, where l_x is the x-component of the vector **l** drawn from the negative charge to the positive; if x_+, x_- denote the x-coordinates of the two charges, the x-component of the moment is $q(x_+ - x_-)$. Any concentrated group of charges containing equal amounts of positive and negative electricity can be viewed as built up out of dipoles by introducing at any convenient point within the group fictitious charges equal and opposite to the actual ones, and then pairing off all charges to form dipoles; the total amount of fictitious charge thus introduced at the point is nil. Let x_0 be the common x-coordinate of the fictitious charges and x_τ the coordinate of any actual charge q_τ. Then the total x-component of dipole moment is $\sum_\tau q_\tau(x_\tau - x_0) = \sum_\tau q_\tau x_\tau - x_0\sum_\tau q_\tau$ or, since $\sum_\tau q_\tau = 0$, simply $\sum_\tau q_\tau x_\tau$.

The mean x-component of the moment when the molecule is in quantum state n is, therefore,

$$g_n = \int \sum_\tau q_\tau x_\tau |\psi_n|^2 \, dq$$

integrated over the entire ranges of all coordinates, q_τ being the (algebraic) charge and x_τ the x-coordinate of the τth charged particle, and the summation including the nuclei.

The effect of applying an electric field is now a twofold one. It will alter each ψ_n, and may thereby alter g_n; and it will also affect the statistical frequency with which the different quantum states occur. Let ψ'_n denote the nth wave function in the presence of the field E, and ϵ'_n the corresponding molecular energy; let ϵ_n be the energy in the absence of the field (including energy of rotation, internal vibration and electronic motions in the atoms). Then the Boltzmann equation, (93*b*) in Sec. 55, gives for the probability of the occurrence of fundamental state n (for which $w = 1$)

$$ P_n = \frac{e^{-\frac{\epsilon_n'}{kT}}}{\sum_n e^{-\frac{\epsilon_n'}{kT}}}. $$

Taking the x-axis in the direction of the field we have, therefore, for the mean component of the moment in the direction of the field

$$ \bar{g} = \frac{\sum_n g'_n e^{-\frac{\epsilon_n'}{kT}}}{\sum_n e^{-\frac{\epsilon_n'}{kT}}}, \tag{318} $$

where the sums extend over all quantum states and

$$ g'_n = \int \sum_\tau q_\tau x_r |\psi'_n|^2 \, dq. \tag{319} $$

This value of $\bar{g}$ divided by E then gives us the polarizability of the molecule in the field E, $\alpha = \bar{g}/E$.

To calculate $\bar{g}$ and α theoretically we need, therefore, to find both ϵ'_n and ψ'_n. If ϵ_j and ψ_j, the corresponding energies and wave-functions for $E = 0$, are known for all quantum states, their values for small E are readily found by the standard methods of perturbation theory; only this case of small E will be treated further here.

254. Initial Polarizability by Perturbation Theory.* After separating off the translational motion of a molecule, the wave-functions ψ_n for its internal condition (without the time factor) in the absence

---

* For the perturbation method cf. E. U. Condon and Morse, "Quantum Mechanics," 1929, p. 116.

of a field are solutions of a wave equation that can be written

$$H_0\psi_n = \epsilon_n\psi_n, \tag{320}$$

H_0 being the unperturbed Hamiltonian operator; the latter contains as variables the coordinates of the nucleus or nuclei as well as those of the electrons and their spins. Let the ψ_n's be normalized so as to form an orthonormal set of functions with the property that (when the variables are suitably chosen)

$$\int \psi_n{}^*\psi_n\, dq = \int |\psi_n|^2\, dq = 1, \qquad \int \psi_n{}^*\psi_k\, dq = 0 \qquad (n \neq k), \tag{321a, b}$$

ψ^* denoting the complex conjugate of ψ and the integrals extending over the entire range for all variables. A field E in the x-direction then adds to H_0 the potential-energy term, $-E\sum_{\tau}q_{\tau}x_{\tau}$, as is easily seen from the fact that this expression represents the work done in displacing all of the particles of (algebraic) charge q_{τ}, both electrons and nuclei, from the origin to their actual positions x_{τ}; the location of the origin itself affects only the arbitrary additive constant in the energy, which is immaterial. Accordingly, the new wave-functions ψ'_n and characteristic energies ϵ'_n are determined by the equation

$$(H_0 + ES)\psi'_n = \epsilon'_n\psi'_n, \qquad S = -\sum_{\tau}q_{\tau}x_{\tau}. \tag{322a, b}$$

The perturbation method now consists in writing ϵ'_n and ψ'_n as power series in terms of the perturbation parameter, thus:

$$\epsilon'_n = \epsilon_n + E\omega_{n1} + E^2\omega_{n2} + \cdots,$$
$$\psi'_n = C(\psi_n + E\varphi_{n1} + E\varphi_{n2} + \cdots).$$

The φ_{nk}'s are functions to be found, and if ϵ_n is degenerate, ψ_n must stand for a suitable linear combination of the various wave-functions corresponding to the same ϵ_n; the arbitrary factor C is added to facilitate normalizing so that $\int \psi'_n{}^2\, dq = 1$.

When we substitute these series into (322a), each power of E in the resulting equation must balance by itself; hence we can replace that equation by a sequence of equations, in which the first repeats (320) while the next two are (C and E or E^2 canceling out)

$$(H_0 - \epsilon_n)\varphi_{n1} = (\omega_{n1} - S)\psi_n, \tag{323a}$$
$$(H_0 - \epsilon_n)\varphi_{n2} = (\omega_{n1} - S)\varphi_{n1} + \omega_{n2}\psi_n. \tag{323b}$$

Solved in turn, these equations give us φ_{n1} and φ_{n2}. The solutions are not unique, however; for we can add to any φ_{n1} or φ_{n2} so found

ψ_n multiplied by any constant, this addition canceling out on the left in the equations. For simplicity let us adjust this constant in each case so that

$$\int \psi_n^* \varphi_{n1}\, dq = 0, \qquad \int \psi_n^* \varphi_{n2}\, dq = 0. \qquad (324a, b)$$

The equations give us also the values of ω_{n1} and ω_{n2}. Let us multiply the first one by $\psi_n^* dq$ and then integrate; the operator H_0 being such that (hence called Hermitean) $\int F^* H_0 G\, dq = \int G H_0^* F^*\, dq$, we have

$$\int \psi_n^* H_0 \varphi_{nk}\, dq = \int (H_0^* \psi_n^*) \varphi_{nk}\, dq = \epsilon_n \int \psi_n^* \varphi_{nk}\, dq = 0$$

by (320) and (324a, b), and hence, from (323a),

$$\omega_{n1} = -g_{n0}, \qquad g_{n0} = -\int \psi_n^* S \psi_n\, dq = \int \sum_\tau q_\tau x_\tau |\psi_n|^2\, dq. \qquad (325a, b)$$

In a similar way, from (323b) we obtain

$$\omega_{n2} = -\alpha_{n1}, \qquad \alpha_{n1} = -\int \psi_n^* S \varphi_{n1}\, dq = \int \sum_\tau q_\tau x_\tau \psi_n^* \varphi_{n1}\, dq. \qquad (326a, b)$$

It can be shown that all α_{nk}'s are real.

For the electric moment of the molecule when in state n we have then, as far as the first power of E,

$$g_n' = \int \sum_\tau q_\tau x_\tau \psi_n'^* \psi_n'\, dq = |C|^2 \left\{ \int \sum_\tau q_\tau x_\tau |\psi_n|^2\, dq \right.$$
$$\left. + E \int \sum_\tau q_\tau x_\tau (\psi_n^* \varphi_{n1} + \psi_n \varphi_{n1}^*)\, dq \right\},$$

since $|\psi_n'|^2 = \psi_n'^* \psi_n'$. Now C is fixed by the condition that

$$1 = \int \psi_n'^* \psi_n'\, dq = |C|^2 \left[\int |\psi_n|^2\, dq + E \left(\int \psi_n^* \varphi_{n1}\, dq + \int \psi_n \varphi_{n1}^*\, dq \right) \right.$$
$$\left. + E^2(\,\cdots\,) + \cdots \right] = |C|^2 [1 + E^2(\,\cdots\,) + \cdots]$$

because of (321a) and (324a). Thus to the first order in E, $|C|^2 = 1$, and for our purpose we can set $C = 1$. Then, α_{n1} being real, to the first order in E

$$g_n' = g_{n0} + 2\alpha_{n1} E. \qquad (327)$$

The value of g_{n0} is given by eq. (325b) in terms of the unperturbed function ψ_n. We can obtain α_{n1} in similar terms by taking a further step that is common in perturbation work. Let us expand φ_{n1}, thus:

$$\varphi_{n1} = \sum_{k \neq n} a_k \psi_k,$$

ψ_n being omitted because φ_{n1} is to be orthogonal to it.   Substituting this series for φ_{n1} in (323a) and noting that by (320) $H_0\psi_k = \epsilon_k\psi_k$, we have

$$\sum_{k \neq n} (\epsilon_k - \epsilon_n)a_k\psi_k = (\omega_{n1} - S)\psi_n.$$

Now multiply this equation through by $\psi_r{}^* \, dq$ $(r \neq n)$, and integrate; then, because of the normalization and orthogonality of the ψ_k's, most of the terms on the left cancel and we obtain

$$(\epsilon_r - \epsilon_n)a_r = -\int \psi_r{}^* S\psi_n \, dq.$$

Hence we can write, changing r back to k, if $\epsilon_k \neq \epsilon_n$,

$$a_k = -\frac{S_{kn}}{\epsilon_k - \epsilon_n},$$

$$S_{kn} = \int \psi_k{}^* S\psi_n \, dq = -\int \psi_k{}^* \sum_{\tau} q_\tau x_\tau \psi_n \, dq; \qquad (328)$$

if $\epsilon_k = \epsilon_n$ but $k \neq n$, then it must be that $S_{kn} = 0$, which is secured by means of a suitable choice of the ψ_n's.   Then (326b) reduces to

$$\alpha_{n1} = \sum_{k \neq n} a_k \int \sum_{\tau} q_\tau x_\tau \psi_n{}^* \psi_k \, dq = -\sum_{k \neq n} a_k S_{kn}{}^* = \sum_{k \neq n} \frac{S_{kn}S_{kn}{}^*}{\epsilon_k - \epsilon_n}$$

or

$$\alpha_{n1} = \sum_{k \neq n} \frac{|S_{kn}|^2}{\epsilon_k - \epsilon_n}. \qquad (329)$$

The *mean moment* of such molecules in a gas in equilibrium can now be obtained by substituting the values that we have found for g_n' and ϵ_n' into (318) above; this gives for it

$$\bar{g} = \sum_{n} (g_{n0} + 2E\alpha_{n1})e^{-\frac{\epsilon_n'}{kT}} / \sum_{n} e^{-\frac{\epsilon_n'}{kT}}.$$

Here we can expand the exponential thus:

$$e^{-\frac{\epsilon_n'}{kT}} = e^{-\frac{(\epsilon_n - g_{n0}E \cdots)}{kT}} = e^{-\frac{\epsilon_n}{kT}}\left(1 + \frac{g_{n0}E}{kT} + \cdots\right).$$

The expression for $\bar{g}$ then contains a term that has $\sum_{n} g_{n0}e^{-\frac{\epsilon_n}{kT}}$ in the numerator; but this sum must somehow vanish in a gas because of its isotropy, else $\bar{g}$ would not vanish when $E = 0$. The other two terms in the numerator both contain E, hence to obtain a result correct to the first power of E we can write ϵ_n for ϵ_n' in the denominator under those two terms. We thus find for the polarizability

$$\alpha = \frac{\bar{g}}{E} = \sum_n \left(\frac{g_{n0}^2}{kT} + 2\alpha_{n1}\right)e^{-\frac{\epsilon_n}{kT}} / \sum_n e^{-\frac{\epsilon_n}{kT}}. \tag{330}$$

According to this formula each quantum state can contribute to α in two different ways. The molecule may have a natural moment g_{n0} in the direction of the field when in state n. This must not be confused with the permanent moment that forms the basis of Debye's theory; a structural moment of the latter sort is represented in wave mechanics by a term of special form in the Hamiltonian operator. A single quantum state corresponds in a blurry fashion to a whole group of possible classical motions or configurations, and g_{n0} is thus the analogue of a mean moment in one direction such as might be characteristic of a molecule while executing a certain type of motion.

On the other hand, α_{n1} represents, so to speak, the effect of a distortion of the state under the influence of the field, in consequence of which the molecule acquires a mean moment.

It may be remarked that the same constant α_{n1}, occurring as $-\omega_{n2}$ in the second-order term in the energy ϵ_n' above, is responsible for the second-order Stark effect in spectroscopic emission. A first-order Stark effect can arise only from the constant g_{n0} or ω_{n1}, representing a moment already existent when the molecule is in one of the quantum states that are involved in the emission of the line.

Actual polarizabilities arise mostly from α_{n1} rather than from g_{n0}. It is not at all obvious, however, how such terms in (330) can give rise to a Debye term inversely proportional to T. Accordingly, we shall postpone discussion of the general formulas and take up next the wave-mechanical treatment of the model that was actually employed by Debye in his original theory.

255. Wave Mechanics of the Dumbbell Molecule. A rigid structure with an electric moment, not analyzed further into elementary parts, does not harmonize well with the modern theory of the atom. It can be shown, however, that the wave-function for the internal state at ordinary temperatures usually can be made to approximate closely to the product of two factors, of which one represents a rotation of the molecule as a rigid body; there may be three principal moments of inertia, or, in special cases, as always when there are only two nuclei, there may be an axis of symmetry and a single moment of inertia about any perpendicular axis.* The energy is then very nearly the sum of two corresponding terms, of which that associated with the rotational factor may be regarded as kinetic energy of rotation (cf. Secs. 146 and 147). In such cases it may happen that the molecule behaves as if it possessed an electric moment fixed in position in it, the direction of this moment being along the axis of symmetry when there is one.

Only the simple symmetrical case will be treated here. In this case the position of the axis, drawn positively in the direction of the structural moment g_0, can be fixed by assigning the angle θ that it makes with some fixed line of reference and the angle φ between a plane containing this line and the axis and a second fixed plane through the line of reference. Let us take the line of reference in the direction of the electric field E.

Then the amplitude equation for the rotational motion can be written†

$$-\frac{h^2}{8\pi^2 I}\left[\frac{1}{\sin\theta}\frac{\partial}{\partial\theta}\left(\sin\theta\frac{\partial\psi'}{\partial\theta}\right) + \frac{1}{\sin^2\theta}\frac{\partial^2\psi'}{\partial\varphi^2}\right] - (g_0 E\cos\theta)\psi'$$
$$= \epsilon'\psi', \quad (331a)$$

I being the moment of inertia about an axis perpendicular to that of symmetry and $-g_0 E\cos\theta$ representing the classical potential energy of the dipole moment in the field. When E is zero the equation reduces to

$$H_0\psi = -\frac{h^2}{8\pi^2 I}\left[\frac{1}{\sin\theta}\frac{\partial}{\partial\theta}\left(\sin\theta\frac{\partial\psi}{\partial\theta}\right) + \frac{1}{\sin^2\theta}\frac{\partial^2\psi}{\partial\varphi^2}\right] = \epsilon\psi; \quad (331b)$$

thus in the notation of the last section the perturbing term is ES,

$$S = -g_0\cos\theta.$$

The characteristic solutions of (331b), familiar from the theory of the hydrogen atom, can be written‡

$$\psi_{jm} = C_{jm}e^{im\varphi}P_j^m(\cos\theta)$$

where P_j^m is an "associated function of Legendre," which in Darwin's form can be defined thus:

---

* For the quantum theory of molecules cf. Pauling and Wilson, "Introduction to Wave Mechanics," 1935, Chap. X.

† Cf. Debye, "Polar Molecules," 1929, Chap. IX.

‡ Cf. W. E. Byerly, "Fourier's Series and Spherical, Cylindrical and Ellipsoidal Harmonics," or L. Pauling and Wilson, *loc. cit.* in Sec. 26. There m is restricted to positive values and the functions are used twice over, but this restriction is unnecessary.

$$P_j^m(x) = \frac{1}{2^j j!} (1 - x^2)^{\frac{m}{2}} \frac{d^{j+m}}{dx^{j+m}} (x^2 - 1)^j;$$

here j and m are any integers such that $0 \leq |m| \leq j$. (The older procedure was to employ $P_j^{|m|}$ in place of P_j^m for negative m, with an altered value of C_{jm}.)

The different ψ_{jm}'s are orthogonal, but in integrating in terms of our variables it is necessary to replace dq by $\sin \theta \, d\theta \, d\varphi$; as the equivalent of eqs. (321a, b) we have, therefore, since $(e^{im\varphi})^* = e^{-im\varphi}$,

$$\int \psi_{jm}^* \psi_{jm} \, dq = C_{jm}^2 \int_0^{2\pi} d\varphi \int_0^\pi [P_j^m(\cos \theta)]^2 \sin \theta \, d\theta = 1, \quad (332a)$$

$$\int \psi_{j'm'}^* \psi_{jm} \, dq = C_{j'm'} C_{jm} \int_0^{2\pi} e^{i(m-m')\varphi} \, d\varphi \int_0^\pi P_{j'}^{m'} P_j^m \sin \theta \, d\theta = 0 \quad (332b)$$

unless $j' = j$ and $m' = m$; for $m' \neq m$ this latter result follows from

$$\int_0^{2\pi} e^{i(m-m')\varphi} \, d\varphi = \frac{e^{i(m-m')\varphi}}{i(m - m')} \bigg|_0^{2\pi} = 0, \quad (333)$$

but if $m' = m$, it rests on the fact that*

$$\int_0^\pi P_{j'}^m P_j^m \sin \theta \, d\theta = 0 \qquad \text{if } j' \neq j. \quad (334)$$

The value of C_{jm} necessary to make (332a) true is

$$C_{jm} = \left(\frac{2j + 1}{4\pi} \frac{(j - m)!}{(j + m)!} \right)^{\frac{1}{2}} \quad (335)$$

(with the understanding that $0! = 1$).

The corresponding energies, independent of m, are

$$\epsilon_{jm} = \epsilon_j = j(j + 1) \frac{h^2}{8\pi^2 I}, \quad (336)$$

h being Planck's constant.

256. Polarizability of a Dumbbell Molecule with a Structural Moment. In terms of the functions just found eq. (325b) obtained from perturbation theory for the natural state-moment g_{n0} becomes

$$g_{jm,0} = -\int \int S \psi_{jm}^* \psi_{jm} \sin \theta \, d\theta \, d\varphi$$

$$= g_0 C_{jm}^2 \int_0^{2\pi} d\varphi \int_0^\pi \cos \theta [P_j^m(\cos \theta)]^2 \sin \theta \, d\theta.$$

(To each value of n in the previous notation corresponds now a pair of values of j and m.) The last integral here vanishes by symmetry,

* Cf. W. E. Byerly, "Fourier's Series," etc., p. 202.

however, each P_j^m being of either even or odd degree in $\cos \theta$. Hence $g_{jm,0} = 0$ for all quantum states. This is reasonable in spite of the existence of a permanent structural moment g_0 because for any one quantum state we are averaging over many configurations.

On the other hand, (328) becomes here

$$S_{j'm',jm} = -g_0 C_{j'm'} C_{jm} \int_0^{2\pi} e^{i(m-m')\varphi}\, d\varphi \int_0^\pi P_{j'}^m P_j^m \sin \theta \cos \theta\, d\theta.$$

This vanishes by (333) if $m \neq m'$. It is for this reason that the ψ_{jm}'s as written can be used as zero-order functions in applying the perturbation method; it is not necessary to make linear combinations of those with the same j but different m's, which correspond to the same energy. If $m = m'$, we may use the formula*

$$(2j' + 1)P_{j'}^m \cos \theta = (j' + m)P_{j'-1}^m + (j' - m + 1)P_{j'+1}^m;$$

by this means we can replace $P_{j'}^m \cos \theta$ in our last integral by a combination of $P_{j'-1}^m$ and $P_{j'+1}^m$. But then the orthogonality relation (334) makes everything vanish unless either $j' = j - 1$ and $|m| < j$, or $j' = j + 1$. In either of the latter cases the final result can readily be found with the help of (332a) and (335); it is:

$$S_{j-1,m;j,m} = -g_0 \left[\frac{(j + m)(j - m)}{(2j + 1)(2j - 1)} \right]^{1/2}, \qquad (|m| < j),$$

$$S_{j+1,m;j,m} = -g_0 \left[\frac{(j + m + 1)(j - m + 1)}{(2j + 1)(2j + 3)} \right]^{1/2}, \qquad (|m| \leqq j).$$

Hence, when $S_{j'm',jm}$ is substituted for S_{kn} in (329), the sum over k, i.e., over j' and m', reduces to not more than two terms; inserting values of ϵ_n or ϵ_{jm} from (336) and noting that $(j - 1)j - j(j + 1) = -2j$, $(j + 1)(j + 2) - j(j + 1) = 2(j + 1)$, we find

$$\alpha_{n1} = \alpha_{jm,1}$$

$$= \frac{4\pi^2 g_0^2 I}{h^2} \left[\frac{(j + m + 1)(j - m + 1)}{(j + 1)(2j + 1)(2j + 3)} - \frac{(j + m)(j - m)}{j(2j + 1)(2j - 1)} \right],$$

except that if $j = 0$, $\alpha_{jm,1}$ has the value (the sum then containing only one term, in which $m = 0$)

$$\alpha_{00,1} = \frac{4\pi^2 g_0^2 I}{3h^2}.$$

For any other state $\alpha_{jm,1}$ reduces to

$$\alpha_{jm,1} = \frac{4\pi^2 g_0^2 I}{h^2} \frac{3m^2 - j(j + 1)}{j(j + 1)(2j - 1)(2j + 3)}.$$

---

* Pauling and Wilson, *loc. cit.*, eq. (40–21). Or, for the evaluation of the integral cf. A. Sommerfeld, "Wave-mechanics," 1929, p. 56.

To find the polarizability α we have now to substitute these values of $\alpha_{jm,1}$ for α_{n1} in (330), in which $g_{n0} = 0$ for all n in the present case. Since, according to (336), the energy is independent of m, we can ignore the Boltzmann factor as we sum over m. For a given $j > 0$, m ranges from $-j$ through 0 to j. But

$$3\sum_{-j}^{j} m^2 = j(j + 1)(2j + 1),$$

as is easily verified for $j = 0$ or 1 and then extended by induction. Hence the sum over all values of m for given $j > 0$ vanishes; and so states with $j > 0$ contribute nothing on the whole to the mean moment.

This conclusion, at first sight surprising, becomes reasonable when we reflect upon the contribution of different molecules to the mean moment in the classical case. A molecule with close to the minimum of energy must be almost exactly lined up with the field, oscillating slightly from side to side, and so must contribute heavily to the mean moment. As the energy rises, however, the amplitude of oscillation increases, until finally, as a special case, the molecule may be revolving in a plane parallel to the field. Now it is clear that in such a motion its velocity will be greatest at the instant when it is lined up, and least when it has the opposite direction, and hence it spends more time with a component of moment opposed to the field than with a component in the other direction. The mean moment of such a molecule is, therefore, actually negative. On the other hand, a molecule can revolve lying almost in a plane but with a slight steady inclination in the direction of the field, and it will then make a positive contribution to the mean moment. These two extreme cases suggest that the *rapidly moving molecules may contribute nothing on the whole to the mean moment* even in the classical case; and it can be shown that such is actually the fact.*

The polarization arises, therefore, solely from the molecules having the least energy of rotation, that is, with $j = m = 0$. The first sum in (330) reduces to one term, in which $\alpha_{n1} = \alpha_{00,1}$ and $\epsilon_n = \epsilon_{00} = 0$. In the denominator each group of $2j + 1$ terms with the same energy ϵ_n can be grouped together. Hence, introducing the value of ϵ_n from (336), we find

$$\alpha = \frac{8\pi^2 g_0^2 I}{3h^2} \left[\sum_{j=0}^{\infty} (2j + 1) e^{-\frac{j(j+1)h^2}{8\pi^2 I k T}} \right]^{-1} \tag{337a}$$

* Cf. Debye, "Polar Molecules," p. 151.

The sum that appears here cannot be evaluated in terms of ordinary functions. At common temperatures, however, the quantity $a = h^2/8\pi^2 IkT$ is rather small; if we write $I = I_1 \times 10^{-40}$ g-cm^2, $a = 40/(I_1 T)$, and for light polar molecules I_1 is at least greater than 2 (hydrogen, with $I_1 = 1$, is not polar), so that at $0°C$ $a < \frac{1}{13}$. Hence at least at ordinary temperatures a good approximation should be obtained if we replace the sum by an integral, thus:

$$\sum_{j=0}^{\infty} (2j + 1)e^{-j(j+1)a} = \int_0^{\infty} (2x + 1)e^{-ax(x+1)}\, dx = \frac{1}{a} = \frac{8\pi^2 IkT}{h^2}.$$

Then

$$\alpha = \frac{1}{3} \frac{g_0^2}{kT}. \tag{337b}$$

The factor T in the denominator of (337b) arises here from the state sum. Accordingly, we can say that in wave mechanics the effect of a permanent moment decreases with rise of temperature because the state of lowest energy of the molecule becomes rarer.

According to (337b) the contribution of a permanent moment to the polarization is exactly the same as in classical theory, where it was represented by the last term in eq. (317).

If the temperature could be made low enough, the difference between the sum in (337a) and the integral that we substituted for it would become appreciable, and a departure from the classical formula should then be detectable. Unfortunately, however, it turns out to be very difficult to attain the necessary experimental accuracy when the gas is rarefied sufficiently to remain a gas in spite of the low temperature and also to be free from excessive effects due to molecular interaction. A more detailed discussion of this point, and also of the general conditions under which a variation of α as $1/T$ may be expected, is to be found in Van Vleck's book.*

A few other models besides the rotating dipole have been worked out by wave mechanics; but more interest attaches to attempts to calculate the polarizability from the fundamental theory of atoms and molecules. In regard to these attempts, which are few as yet, we shall only remark that in the case of helium fair success has been attained; Slater and Kirkwood† find for the dielectric constant $\epsilon = 1.0000715$ as against the observed value of 1.0000653 at $0°C$ and 1 atmosphere.

---

* VAN VLECK, *loc. cit.* near Sec. 245, Chap. VII.

† SLATER and KIRKWOOD, *Phys. Rev.*, **37**, 682 (1931).

MAGNETIC SUSCEPTIBILITY

257. Magnetism and Molecular Magnetizability. The theory of magnetism is in most respects so similar to that of dielectric polarization that we have only to make suitable changes of symbols in the equations already derived in order to obtain formulas pertaining to magnetism. It will suffice, accordingly, to emphasize in the discussion only the few differences between the two cases.

The effects of magnetism in a gas arise from the fact that each molecule behaves as if it possessed a certain *mean magnetic moment*, which we shall denote by $\bar{\mu}$. The vector sum of these moments in unit volume, or the total magnetic moment per unit volume, is the vector magnetization, I; if for simplicity we write simply $\bar{\mu}$ for the mean component of moment of a molecule in the direction of I, assumed to be the same for all molecules, we have

$$I = n\bar{\mu}$$

where n is the number of molecules in unit volume.

Ordinary magnetic theory is developed in terms of the magnetic induction, $B = H + 4\pi I$, and of the permeability, B/H, which is analogous to the dielectric constant; but in molecular theory it is customary to work with the susceptibility,

$$\kappa = \frac{I}{H} = \frac{n\bar{\mu}}{H}.$$

Furthermore, in dealing with bodies whose density ρ varies considerably the susceptibility per gram, κ/ρ, is often employed, or, still better, the molar susceptibility, $M\kappa/\rho$, where M = molecular weight, which refers to a fixed number of molecules, and either of these quantities is often denoted by χ.

The theory of the local field in a magnetic medium runs as in the electric case, but this field differs so little from the ordinary field strength in a gas, even at rather high densities, that we may ignore the difference. Accordingly, we shall write simply

$$\bar{\mu} = \gamma H,$$

where γ is a coefficient called the molecular *magnetizability;* then

$$\kappa = n\gamma,$$

or for a mixed gas

$$\kappa = \sum_{\sigma} n_\sigma \gamma_\sigma.$$

258. Langevin's Theory of Paramagnetism. From the time of Ampere (1821) magnetism has commonly been ascribed to electrical currents of some sort circulating in the molecule. Weber ascribed diamagnetism to the induction of such currents in a molecule that was originally free from them; according to Lenz's law these induced currents would circulate in such a direction as to prevent changes in the magnetic flux through their circuits, and so would give rise to molecular moments and magnetization opposed to the applied field and thus to a negative value of κ. The molecular circuits were assumed, of course, to be free from resistance.

Paramagnetism and ferromagnetism were ascribed to the orientation of pre-existing currents under the influence of the field; but the first exact theory of such an effect was that given in terms of classical conceptions by Langevin in 1905.[*] As this theory applies particularly to gases we shall give it; for this purpose we need only translate back Debye's modification of it as given for dielectrics in Sec. 250.

Let us assume that each molecule is a rigid structure having a permanent magnetic moment μ. Then the forces exerted by a magnetic field H on the molecule will be exactly the same as they would be if it merely possessed a potential energy $-\mu H \cos \theta$, θ being the angle between the axis of the moment and the field. Hence the same statistical law will apply here as holds for permanent electric dipoles, and in the results of Secs. 250 to 252 above we need only replace g, E, and α by μ, H, and γ.

The resulting mean magnetic moment in the direction of the field is, therefore, in analogy with (314a, b),

$$\bar{\mu}_\mu = \mu\left(\coth x - \frac{1}{x}\right), \qquad x = \frac{\mu H}{kT}. \tag{338a, b}$$

For generality let us suppose there is also a certain amount of magnetization due to some other cause than the permanent moment; let it be $\gamma_0 H$, where γ_0 is a constant. Probably all substances exhibit a relatively weak diamagnetism superposed on whatever paramagnetism they may possess; this will be included in γ_0. Then the total mean moment in the direction of the field is $\bar{\mu} = \gamma_0 H + \bar{\mu}_\mu$, and the magetizability is

$$\gamma = \frac{\bar{\mu}}{H} = \gamma_0 + \frac{\bar{\mu}_\mu}{H}. \tag{339a}$$

In the case of a gas, as in any sufficiently weak field, we can then expand the Langevin function in the formula for $\bar{\mu}_\mu$ as in the electrical

[*] LANGEVIN, *Ann. Chim. Phys.*, **5**, 70 (1905).

case, thereby obtaining for the initial magnetizability

$$\gamma = \gamma_0 + \frac{\mu^2}{3kT}. \tag{339b}$$

If we set $\gamma_0 = 0$, $\gamma = \mu^2/3kT$; then for the molar susceptibility, $\chi = N_0\gamma$, where N_0 is the Avogadro number,

$$\chi T = \text{const.}$$

In this latter form we have Curie's law, which was discovered as an empirical law before the publication of Langevin's theory. The law holds more or less accurately for most gases and for many solids. For oxygen, which is rather strongly paramagnetic, it holds quite accurately right down to the boiling point. Departures from the law can frequently be ascribed to a relatively small superposed diamagnetism.

In contrast with the effect of a permanent moment, diamagnetic susceptibility ought to be independent of temperature, for there is no reason to expect the magnitude of induced molecular currents to be affected by the rapidity of the thermal motion. At least in gases such is always the case, or very nearly so.

Classical theory was thus broadly successful in interpreting the phenomena cf dia- and paramagnetism. Considerable success even attended efforts to apply the Langevin theory to the elucidation of ferromagnetism, and in that case the saturation effect, which was mentioned in dealing with dielectrics but is of no interest in the case of gases, becomes important; but here a serious difficulty was encountered in the mysterious inner self-magnetizing field that Weiss found himself compelled to postulate. In recent years the latter has been pretty well identified as a peculiar quantum effect due to "exchange."

We must now see how wave mechanics handles molecular magnetism.

259. Quantum Theory and Magnetizability. The broad outline of wave-mechanical theory which we developed in Secs. 253 and 254 for the electrical case requires only a few changes in order to adapt it to the treatment of magnetism.

Consider a molecule immersed in a uniform magnetic field H. If μ'_n denotes its mean component of magnetic moment in the direction of H when it is in quantum state n, its mean moment in that direction under conditions of equilibrium will be

$$\bar{\mu} = \frac{\sum_n \mu'_n e^{-\frac{\epsilon_n'}{kT}}}{\sum_n e^{-\frac{\epsilon_n'}{kT}}} \tag{340}$$

in analogy with (318); and its magnetizability is then

$$\gamma = \frac{\bar{\mu}}{H}. \tag{341}$$

The next step, as in the electrical case, is the determination of the moments μ'_n characterizing the various quantum states. This is again a problem that really lies outside of kinetic theory, and it involves a good deal of technical wave-mechanical work. Accordingly we can give only a description of the theoretical argument and its results; but it seems worth while to do this in order to round out the picture.

260. Sources of Molecular Magnetism. With the rise of the electronic theory of the atom it became customary to ascribe all magnetism to electrons revolving within the atom or molecule. In classical electromagnetism an electron revolving, for example, in a circle of radius a and making ν revolutions per second is equivalent on the average to a current flowing around the circle of magnitude $e\nu/c$. (The algebraic charge e on the electron is measured in electrostatic, the current in electromagnetic units, c being the speed of light.) The average resulting magnetic field at a distance is that of a dipole of moment

$$\mu = \pi a^2 \frac{e\nu}{c}.$$

Now such an electron also possesses angular momentum due to its motion, of average amount

$$\Gamma = mav = 2\pi m a^2 \nu,$$

m being its mass. Hence we can write

$$\mu = \frac{e}{2mc}\,\Gamma. \tag{342a}$$

This relation can be shown to hold for any statistically steady motion confined to a small region of space. By its means a classical theory of diamagnetism is readily constructed for the Rutherford atom. For the induced electric field associated with the setting up of a magnetic field is such that it generates in the electrons a certain amount of angular momentum about a line drawn through the nucleus in the direction of the field; this momentum then persists, being due in fact to the Larmor precessional motion, and is accompanied by a definite magnetic moment, whose direction is easily seen to be such as to lead to a diamagnetic effect.

When experiments on this subject were performed by Einstein and de Haas and by others, however, it was found that in iron and some other materials the actual relationship is

$$\mu = \frac{e}{mc}\, \Gamma. \tag{342b}$$

It was pointed out by the author that this would be the correct relation if magnetism were due to electrons of the Lorentz type (spheres uniformly charged on the surface), rotating about their own axes instead of moving bodily. As wave mechanics developed, however, it was discovered by Dirac that the simplest modification of the theory that was in harmony with relativity automatically required a point electron to behave as if it always possessed a certain internal angular momentum, and an associated magnetic moment in harmony with eq. (342b); these effects are commonly said to be due to "spin," but there is in the new theory no suggestion of a spatial structure of the electron.

Molecular magnetism thus arises from two distinct sources, the wave-mechanical equivalent of electronic translatory motion, and electron spin.   There also may be similar but much smaller contributions from the nuclei.

261. Wave Mechanics in a Magnetic Field.   The wave-mechanical treatment of magnetism is best understood if we first write down the classical Hamiltonian function.   For a charged particle moving in a fixed magnetic field under the influence of any potential function V this function is

$$F = \frac{1}{2m}\left(\mathbf{p} - \frac{e}{c}\mathbf{A}\right)^2 + V = \frac{p^2}{2m} - \frac{e}{cm}\mathbf{A}\cdot\mathbf{p} + \frac{e^2}{2c^2m}A^2 + V,$$

where $\mathbf{A}$ is the vector potential for the magnetic field $\mathbf{H}$ (i.e., $\mathbf{H} = \text{curl } \mathbf{A}$), $c = $ speed of light, $e = $ charge on the particle and $m = $ its mass, and $\mathbf{p}$ is the vector generalized momentum for the particle; that is, the components p_x, p_y, p_z of $\mathbf{p}$ form with x, y, z as coordinates a set of variables obeying the Hamiltonian equations (Sec. 194), which can then be shown to lead to the usual equations of motion for the particle.   The scalar product $\mathbf{A}\cdot\mathbf{p}$ can be written out in either of the two forms

$$\mathbf{A}\cdot\mathbf{p} = Ap\cos\,(\mathbf{A},\mathbf{p}) = A_x p_x + A_y p_y + A_z p_z,$$

$(\mathbf{A},\mathbf{p})$ denoting the angle between the directions of $\mathbf{A}$ and $\mathbf{p}$; and, of course,

$$p^2 = p_x^2 + p_y^2 + p_z^2.$$

$\mathbf{p}$ is not the ordinary momentum, however, for the components of the velocity $\mathbf{v}$ are given by three of the Hamiltonian equations of which a typical one is

$$v_x = \frac{dx}{dt} = \frac{\partial F}{\partial p_x} = \frac{p_x}{m} - \frac{e}{cm} A_x.$$

Thus

$$\mathbf{p} = m\mathbf{v} + \frac{e}{cm} \mathbf{A}, \tag{343}$$

where $m\mathbf{v}$ is the ordinary momentum of the particle.

When the magnetic field is uniform, as it will be assumed to be hereafter, $\mathbf{A}$, which is in part arbitrary, can be supposed to take the following form: it is everywhere perpendicular to $\mathbf{H}$, at any point it is also perpendicular to a line joining that point to some reference line which itself is parallel to $\mathbf{H}$, and, if R is the distance of the point from this line, $A = HR/2$ (cf. Fig. 94). Thus $A = \frac{1}{2} \mathbf{H} \times \mathbf{R}$. In dealing with an atom or molecule the reference line or axis will be drawn through the center of mass. With this choice of $\mathbf{A}$,

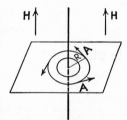

FIG. 94.—Vector potential $\mathbf{A}$ for a uniform magnetic field $\mathbf{H}$.

$$\mathbf{A} \cdot \mathbf{p} = \tfrac{1}{2} H\, Rp \cos (\mathbf{A}, \mathbf{p});$$

and since $p \cos (\mathbf{A}, \mathbf{p})$ is the component of $\mathbf{p}$ in the direction of $\mathbf{A}$, which is perpendicular to $\mathbf{R}$, we recognize

$$G_H = Rp \cos (\mathbf{A}, \mathbf{p})$$

as representing what the angular momentum of the particle about the axis would be if $\mathbf{p}$ were its momentum. G_H, in turn, is the component in the direction of $\mathbf{H}$ of a vector $\mathbf{G} = \mathbf{r} \times \mathbf{p}$, $\mathbf{r}$ being distance from the molecular center of mass; $\mathbf{G}$ is called the orbital angular momentum. The Hamiltonian function can now be written in terms of H itself:

$$F = \frac{p^2}{2m} + V - \frac{e}{2cm} HG_H + \frac{e^2}{8c^2m} H^2R^2.$$

The actual angular momentum of the particle about the axis is then, from (343) and $A = HR/2$,

$$\Gamma_H = Rmv \cos (\mathbf{A}, \mathbf{v}) = G_H - \frac{eH}{2cm} R^2.$$

Furthermore, averaging this expression over a macroscopically small time, we have from (342a) for the mean magnetic moment in the direction of $\mathbf{H}$

$$\bar{\mu} = \frac{e}{2mc} \bar{\Gamma}_H = \frac{e}{2mc} \bar{G}_H - \frac{e^2 \overline{R^2}}{4c^2 m^2} H. \tag{344}$$

Now in wave mechanics the correct Hamiltonian operator for such a particle is believed to be obtained by substituting in the classical Hamiltonian function $(h/2\pi i)\nabla$ for **p**. The same substitution in **G** gives the orbital-momentum operator; and henceforth the symbol **G** will be understood to stand for this operator. A term must be added, however, to represent the effect of spin; for this purpose we may use the approximate form of theory given by Pauli. In this way we obtain as the amplitude equation for a stationary state

$$\left[F_{01} - \frac{e}{2cm} H(G_H + 2\sigma_H) + \frac{e^2}{8c^2 m} H^2 R^2 \right] \psi_1' = \epsilon_1' \psi_1',$$

in which

$$F_{01} = -\frac{h^2}{8\pi^2 m} \nabla^2 + V$$

and σ_H is the component in the direction of **H** of the angular momentum of spin. The factor 2 on σ_H represents the difference between (342b) and (342a) above. For a complete atom or molecule the magnetic terms are simply the sum of such terms for the separate electrons, if we neglect the minute effects of the nuclei; hence for a molecule we can write

$$\left[F_0 - \frac{e}{2cm} H \sum (G_H + 2\sigma_H) + \frac{e^2}{8c^2 m} H^2 \sum R^2 \right] \psi' = \epsilon' \psi', \tag{345}$$

F_0 being the Hamiltonian function in the absence of a magnetic field.

The magnetic moment of the molecule in the direction of H, when it is in state n with wave-function ψ_n', can then be shown to be

$$\mu_n' = \frac{e}{2cm} \sum (\bar{G}_H + 2\bar{\sigma}_H) - \frac{e^2 H}{4c^2 m^2} \sum \overline{R^2}, \tag{346}$$

$$\sum (\bar{G}_H + 2\bar{\sigma}_H) = \int \psi_n'^* \Sigma (G_H + 2\sigma_H) \psi_n' \, dq, \qquad \Sigma \overline{R^2} = \int \Sigma R^2 \, \psi_n'^* \psi_n' \, dq,$$

ΣR^2 being the sum of the squares of the distances of the electrons from the axis and $\Sigma \overline{R^2}$ representing an average of this sum.

262. Magnetizability by Perturbation Theory. The effect of a weak field can now be found by the perturbation method, as in the electrical case. Dropping the quadratic term in H^2, we can write the wave equation (345) in the form

$$(F_0 + HQ)\psi' = \epsilon'\psi', \qquad Q = -\frac{e}{2cm}\sum_\tau(G_H + 2\sigma_H).$$

The theory of Sec. 254 will then at once apply, provided we change E to H and S to Q, H_0 there being the same as F_0 here.   We must also add the diamagnetic or R^2 term in the moment μ_n', which has no analogue in the electrical case.

We thus obtain from (346), in analogy with (327), (325b), (326b), (328) and (329) in the electrical case,

$$\mu_n' = \mu_{n0} + (2\gamma_{n1} - \gamma_{nD})H, \tag{347}$$

$$\mu_{n0} = \frac{e}{2cm}\int\psi_n^*\sum_\tau(G_{H\tau} + 2\sigma_{H\tau})\psi_n\,dq,$$

$$\gamma_{n1} = \frac{e}{2cm}\int\psi_n^*\sum_\tau(G_{H\tau} + 2\sigma_{H\tau})\varphi_{n1}\,dq = \sum_{k\neq n}\frac{|Q_{kn}|^2}{\epsilon_k - \epsilon_n}, \tag{348}$$

$$Q_{kn} = -\frac{e}{2cm}\int\psi_k^*\sum_\tau(G_{H\tau} + 2\sigma_{H\tau})\psi_n\,dq,$$

$$\gamma_{nD} = \frac{e^2}{4c^2m^2}\sum_\tau\overline{R_\tau^2}, \qquad \overline{R_\tau^2} = \int R_\tau^2\psi_n^*\psi_n\,dq, \tag{349a, b}$$

the sums in terms of τ extending over all electrons in the molecule. Then, in analogy with eqs. (318) and (330), for the mean moment $\bar{\mu}$ per molecule under conditions of equilibrium and for the mean magnetizability, $\gamma = \bar{\mu}/H$, of a molecule in an isotropic body, for which $\sum_n\mu_{n0}e^{-\frac{\epsilon_n}{kT}} = 0$, we have

$$\bar{\mu} = \frac{\sum_n\mu_n'e^{-\frac{\epsilon_n'}{kT}}}{\sum_n e^{-\frac{\epsilon_n'}{kT}}} = \gamma H, \tag{350}$$

$$\gamma = \frac{\sum_n\left(\frac{\mu_{n0}^2}{kT} + 2\gamma_{n1} - \gamma_{nD}\right)e^{-\frac{\epsilon_n}{kT}}}{\sum_n e^{-\frac{\epsilon_n}{kT}}}, \tag{351}$$

to the first power in H. Here ϵ_n and ψ_n refer to states for zero field, which must be chosen in case of degeneracy so as to pass continuously into states with field.

This formula seems to indicate a complicated variation of γ with temperature. In practice, however, the Boltzmann factors very commonly disappear as effective influences. In large part this arises from those features of the quantum states that were described in Sec. 147. A molecule not subject to an external field may be supposed to have a definite angular momentum, associated with a certain value of a quantum number J, and also a definite component of this momentum about any chosen axis equal to $Mh/2\pi$, M being a quantum number that ranges in integral steps from $-J$ to $+J$. The composite normal state of the atom or molecule then includes fundamental states corresponding to a single J, or to a limited number of J's (a multiplet); and it may happen that any other state has, at ordinary temperatures, an energy exceeding that of the normal state by many times kT. In such a case, in evaluating the sums in eq. (351) these other or "excited" states can all be ignored because of the relative minuteness of their Boltzmann factors. Further simplification then often results from the fact that fundamental states differing only in M have the same energy ϵ_n and hence also the same Boltzmann factors.

Suppose, for instance, that all of the normally occurring states have the same ϵ_n, at least within a fraction of kT; this may result from the occurrence of just one J, or from the extremely close spacing of a multiplet state. Then the denominator in (351) reduces to the number of occurring states multiplied by $e^{-\frac{\epsilon_n}{kT}}$, and, the latter factor canceling out,

$$\gamma = \frac{\overline{\mu_{n0}^2}}{kT} + 2\,\overline{\gamma_{n1}} - \overline{\gamma_{nD}}, \qquad (352a)$$

where a bar denotes the average for these states. Or, regardless of the ϵ_n's, it may happen that μ_{n0}, γ_{n1}, and γ_{nD} are the same (perhaps zero) for all of these states. In that case the sum over the Boltzmann factors cancels and

$$\gamma = \frac{\mu_{n0}^2}{kT} + 2\gamma_{n1} - \gamma_{nD}. \qquad (352b)$$

263. Diamagnetism. When for all of the normally occurring states $\mu_{n0} = 0$ and $\gamma_{n1} = 0$ we have pure diamagnetism. Then (352a) or (352b) becomes

$$\gamma = -\,\overline{\gamma_{nD}} \qquad \text{or} \qquad -\gamma_{nD},$$

the latter if γ_{nD} is the same for all of these states, and we have a diamagnetic magnetizability independent of temperature, in agreement with observation.

The formula for γ_{nD} is usually written

$$\gamma_{nD} = \frac{e^2}{6c^2m^2}\sideset{}{'}\sum_\tau \overline{r_\tau^2}$$

in terms of $\overline{r^2}$, the average square of the distance of an electron from the center of mass of the molecule, since in a spherically symmetrical atom, or in any case upon averaging over all states forming the composite normal one, it must turn out that

$$\sideset{}{'}\sum_\tau \overline{R_\tau^2} = \sum_\tau (\overline{x_\tau^2} + \overline{y_\tau^2}) = \tfrac{2}{3}\sum_\tau (\overline{x_\tau^2} + \overline{y_\tau^2} + \overline{z_\tau^2}) = \tfrac{2}{3}\sideset{}{'}\sum_\tau \overline{r_\tau^2}.$$

For helium (where $J = 0$) it has been possible to calculate $\Sigma \overline{r^2}$ from wave-mechanical theory with fair accuracy;* the result for the molar susceptibility is $\chi = N_0\gamma = -N_0\gamma_{nD} = -1.85 \times 10^{-6}$, as against Hector and Wills' experimental value of -1.88×10^{-6}. This agreement is very gratifying. Rougher estimates for some other atoms also agree well.

In the absence of such calculations, of course, one can reverse the process and calculate $\overline{r^2}$ from observed diamagnetic susceptibilities, e.g., we could calculate a sort of root-mean-square average distance r_s by the formula

$$r_s = \left(-\frac{\chi}{N_0}\frac{6c^2m^2}{\nu e^2}\right)^{\frac{1}{2}},$$

ν being the number of electrons in the atom or molecule. Values of r_s calculated in this way are always well within the radius as estimated in other ways.

264. Paramagnetism. In general the term $\overline{\gamma_{nD}}$ in eq. (352a) is much smaller than the other terms whenever these are not exactly zero, and $\overline{\gamma_{n1}}$, if not zero, is positive. Then we have paramagnetism. If also $\overline{\gamma_{n1}} = 0$, and if $\overline{\gamma_{nD}}$ can be neglected,

$$\gamma = \frac{\overline{\mu_{n0}^2}}{kT}$$

and Curie's law is obeyed.

The occurrence of a natural state moment μ_{n0} would be expected to be common, because of the close relationship of magnetic moment and angular momentum. In atomic theory it is customary to write

---

* SLATER, *Phys. Rev.*, **32**, 349 (1928).

$$\mu_{n0} = \frac{eh}{4\pi cm} gM,$$

where g is a factor called the Landé factor and $eh/4\pi cm = 9.26 \times 10^{-21}$ represents a natural unit of magnetic moment called the Bohr magneton. For a single electron with one unit, $h/2\pi$, of orbital angular momentum (spin being neglected) $M = 1$ and $g = 1$, so that $\mu_{n0} = 1$ Bohr magneton; if the moment is due to the spin of one electron alone, $M = +\frac{1}{2}$ or $-\frac{1}{2}$ and $g = 2$, so that again $|\mu_{n0}| = 1$ magneton. Often g has fractional and sometimes even negative values.

An interesting example is furnished by potassium vapor, whose susceptibility was measured by Gerlach.* The potassium atom is normally in a spectroscopic ^2S state, with $J = \frac{1}{2}$ and $M = \pm\frac{1}{2}$; the next state lies too high to occur with appreciable frequency even at a temperature between 600 and 800°C. For this state all $Q_{nk} = 0$, hence $\gamma_{n1} = 0$ and Curie's law should hold. The Landé g factor is 2 (magnetism due entirely to spin), hence $\mu_{n0} = eh/4\pi cm$ or one magneton for both values of M, and the molar susceptibility should be $\chi = N_0\gamma = N_0\mu_{n0}^2/kT = 0.374/T$. Gerlach found $\chi = 0.38/T$, which agrees within his rather large experimental errors; and he also found that Curie's law is obeyed.

For oxygen, theory indicates in a somewhat similar way that $\chi = 0.993/T$, as against the best experimental value of $1.011/T$. Oxygen obeys Curie's law down to very low temperatures.

MOTION OF ELECTRICITY IN GASES

The phenomena attending electrical currents in gases are among the most varied and the most interesting in all of physics. The theory of these phenomena involves a continual use of some of the methods of kinetic theory, but on the other hand it forms a very large and intricate subject and has been exhaustively discussed in a number of special treatises.† Accordingly we shall discuss here only one or two fundamental phases in which a straightforward application of kinetic theory can be made and which thus serve as a good illustration of the use of that theory in such cases. No experimental arrangements will be described at all, the reader being left to seek the experimental basis for the facts that we shall cite in the special treatises just named or in the original papers there cited.

265. The Motion of Ions in Gases. Electricity is conveyed through gases by means of ions of some sort. Under suitable condi-

---

* Cf. Van Vleck, *loc. cit.* near Sec. 245, p. 239.

† Cf. K. K. Darrow, "Electrical Phenomena in Gases," 1932; J. J. and G. P. Thompson, "Conduction of Electricity through Gases," 3d ed. in 2 vols., 1928.

tions, especially in very dry gas at low pressures, these ions are in large part free electrons; under other conditions they are known to be heavier bodies, but whether these are charged atoms or molecules, or clusters each composed of several molecules, has not definitely been made out to this day. There is a great variety of ways of bringing about the existence of ions in the gas, but this subject will not be discussed here; nor will we concern ourselves with the destruction of ions by recombination or otherwise.

Our discussion will, in fact, be limited to cases in which the density of the ions is low enough, or the space over which they move small enough, so that recombination can be neglected entirely. Furthermore, we shall assume that the electric field is not strong enough to produce fresh ions by collision. These two restrictions mark off a very small portion of the whole subject, but it is a part that is of fundamental importance, and it is also a part in which there exist simple general laws.

If we now add the further restriction that the electric field is weak enough to allow the ions to remain in approximate thermal equilibrium, their motion becomes a case of the simple forced diffusion that we have already discussed in Sec. 115; the analysis there developed should be applicable here. Upon the rapid and irregular motion of thermal agitation which the ions must share with the surrounding molecules, the forces due to the field superpose a small steady drift at some speed u. This speed is proportional to the electrical intensity E; hence in practice it is more convenient to work with the ratio $U = u/E$, which is called the *mobility* of the ion.

The mobility is obviously connected with the electrical conductivity of the gas. For if n is the number of a given kind of ion in unit volume, nu is the rate at which they cross unit area drawn normal to the field, and, if q is the numerical charge on an ion, nuq is the rate at which they carry charge across; but the latter is also the resulting current density, and this by definition is CE in terms of the conductivity C. Thus $nuq = CE$, and when only one kind of ion is present, we have, in terms of the mobility $U = u/E$,

$$C = nqU.$$

If several kinds of ions are present each kind makes its own independent contribution to the current and

$$C = \sum_j n_j q_j U_j$$

summed over the various kinds.

On the other hand, we showed in Sec. 115 that a steady motion of drift under the influence of a force is equivalent to diffusion caused by a certain equivalent concentration gradient. The force on an ion being $F = qE$, eq. (170c) of that section gives at once

$$U = \frac{u}{E} = \frac{qD}{kT} \qquad (353a)$$

in terms of the coefficient of diffusion D of the ions through the gas, the numerical charge q on the ion, the Boltzmann constant k, and the absolute temperature T. We assume their relative concentration to be small enough so that (170c) can be used instead of (170a).

This formula, which is often written

$$\frac{D}{U} = \frac{kT}{q}, \qquad (353b)$$

is of great interest because everything in it can be found experimentally; both U and D can be measured for the ions, sometimes even in the same apparatus, and we possess independent means of estimating T and q. For heavy ions, indeed, T should be indistinguishable from the temperature of the surrounding gas; in the case of free electrons, however, it is often higher, as explained in greater detail below, and in that case the equation is, in fact, more frequently employed for a calculation of T. A common method of measuring U is to measure the conductivity C and then apply a strong field and sweep all of the ions quickly upon a conductor connected to an electrometer; from the total charge thus collected the density N of the ions can be calculated if the charge q is known, and U can then be calculated. A good method of measuring D is to blow the gas at a known rate through narrow metal tubes and note the rate at which the ions disappear by diffusion to the walls of the tubes.

Instead of discussing experiments further, however, we shall merely state that eq. (353a) is "singularly well confirmed" (Darrow) by the results of experiment.

266. The Mobility. By inserting one of our theoretical values of D into eq. (353a) we can obtain a theoretical value of the mobility U in terms of molecular constants. According to eq. (166a) in Sec. 109. the coefficient of diffusion for ions of mass m moving among gas molecules of mass M should be very nearly

$$D = \frac{3}{8} \sqrt{\frac{\pi}{2}} \frac{1}{nS_D} \left(\frac{m + M}{mM} kT \right)^{\frac{1}{2}}, \qquad (354)$$

the correction term λ_{12} in (168a) being very small (probably not over 2 per cent under ordinary conditions). With this value of D eq. (353a) gives for the mobility

$$U = \frac{3}{8} \sqrt{\frac{\pi}{2}} \frac{q}{nS_D} \left(\frac{m+M}{mM} \frac{1}{kT} \right)^{\frac{1}{2}}. \tag{355}$$

Here k is the Boltzmann constant, T the absolute temperature, n the total number of molecules (including ions) per unit volume, q the numerical charge on an ion, and S_D the "equivalent cross section for diffusion." If both ions and gas molecules have a maxwellian distribution at the same temperature, S_D is given by (165b) in Sec. 109 or

$$S_D = 2\pi \int_0^\infty \left[\int_0^\pi G\left(x\sqrt{\frac{m+M}{mM} 2kT},\ \theta \right)(1 - \cos\theta)\sin\theta\, d\theta \right] x^5 e^{-x^2}\, dx. \tag{356a}$$

Here $G(v, \theta)$ stands for the scattering coefficient for an ion impinging at speed v upon a gas molecule (Sec. 68), or $NG(v, \theta)\, d\omega$ is the fractional part of the ions incident on unit area in a uniform beam of such ions that are deflected by N scattering molecules into a solid angle $d\omega$ at an angle θ with their direction of approach; the molecules are supposed to be initially at rest but free to move. If both ions and molecules are elastic spheres with mean diameter σ_{av}, $G = \sigma_{av}^2/4$ and

$$S_D = \pi\sigma_{av}^2 \tag{356b}$$

[cf. Sec. 109 and (110c) and (110d) in Sec. 70]. With this value of S_D eq. (354) agrees with that found by Langevin in 1905[*], and the equation is often cited as Langevin's formula.

The determination of G and S_D is a problem that lies outside of kinetic theory, but if this problem can be solved by means of molecular theory, or if S_D can be calculated by means of (356a) from observed values of the scattering coefficient $G(v, \theta)$, then (354) and (355) should give D and U, respectively. Very little has been accomplished as yet toward the theoretical calculation of mobilities in this manner.

In discussing the formulas further it is convenient to separate the two cases of free electrons and of heavy ions. We begin with the latter.

267. Mobility of Heavy Ions. If an ion consists of a molecule that has lost or gained an electron or two, the equations obtained ought

---

[*] Langevin, *Ann. Chim. Phys.* **5**, 245 (1905).

certainly to hold. In such cases it is more usual to replace S_D by the mean free path; the most satisfactory definition of the latter seems to be

$$L = \frac{1}{\sqrt{2}\,nS_D}$$

as in eq. (106b) in Sec. 64, n being the total number of molecules per unit volume. This would actually be the mean free path of the ions if both they and the neutral molecules were hard spheres of mutual cross section $S_D = \pi\sigma_{av}^2$, free from mutual force-action except during collision. With this substitution (354) and (355) become, for the mobility U and the diffusion coefficient D,

$$D = \frac{3}{8}\sqrt{\pi}\,L\left(\frac{m+M}{mM}\,kT\right)^{\frac{1}{2}}, \qquad U = \frac{3}{8}\sqrt{\pi}\,qL\left(\frac{m+M}{mM}\,\frac{1}{kT}\right)^{\frac{1}{2}}.$$

$$(357a, b)$$

A great many measurements on heavy ions have been made. The mobility of the negatively charged ones is nearly always found to be greater than that of the positives, the difference often being considerable. The mobility of both kinds is observed to be inversely proportional to the density at constant temperature, as according to (357b) it should be, except that at low pressures the apparent mobility of all negative ions rises, at first moderately and then prodigiously. This rise is interpreted as meaning that as the pressure falls the negative ions come to consist largely, and in the end wholly, of free electrons. The transition occurs in ordinary gases at a few per cent of an atmosphere of pressure, but it occurs at much higher pressures if all water vapor and other impurities are carefully removed.

So far as the influence of density is concerned, the theory is thus in harmony with experiment. Most of the other observed properties of heavy ions have, however, proved to be very difficult of explanation. The mobility does not appear to vary with temperature in the way that theory indicates. In a mixed gas there seems to be only a single mobility, with a very considerable spread of values about a maximum, instead of several distinct mobilities corresponding to the different kinds of ions that we should naturally suppose to be present.

Finally, mean free paths calculated from observed mobilities by means of (357b), on the assumption that the ions are single gaseous molecules, are several times smaller than those obtained from the mechanical properties of the gas; for example, positive ions in nitrogen have a mobility $U = 1.27$ cm/sec in a field of 1 volt per centimeter, or 381 cm/sec in a field of 1 electrostatic unit, from which we find

with $m = M = 46.54 \times 10^{-24}$ g, $T = 288$, and $q = 4.805 \times 10^{-10}$,
$L = 1.1 \times 10^{-6}$ cm, as against 6.28×10^{-6} as found from the viscosity (Sec. 86).   Of course, a value of L calculated from S_D is not strictly comparable to one calculated from the viscosity, which depends upon the rather different quantity S_{vc} [cf. eq. (156b) at the end of Sec. 101].   On the other hand, from some observations on the diffusion of ions in air, which does depend upon S_D , Townsend found $D = 0.028$, whereas for ordinary oxygen and nitrogen diffusing through each other $D = 0.18$, and these values of D stand in as strong contrast to each other as do the values of L .

These facts, taken together with the fact that the ratio D/U does seem for all ions to have its kinetic-theory value, kT/q , point to the conclusion that our general viewpoint must be correct, only there is something very peculiar about the nature of positive ions. Now it is obvious that their motion must be greatly influenced by an attraction between them and the neutral molecules.   Since, however, this attraction, being due to a polarization of the molecule by the electric field of the ion, must fall off as the inverse fifth power of the distance, calculation shows that large effects upon G and S_D cannot occur unless the attraction becomes so strong that molecules actually adhere to the ion, forming a cluster.*

This latter conclusion brings us to a view that is, in fact, very commonly held, viz., that gaseous ions, when they are not free electrons, usually consist of a cluster of molecules with a charged particle of some sort at the center.   Such a theory fits the facts pretty well. We are still, however, far from possessing a complete quantitative understanding of these complicated phenomena.

268. The Mobility of Free Electrons.   Because of its relatively minute mass a free electron may be expected to behave rather differently from a molecular ion.   In Langevin's formula we can neglect the electronic mass, for which we shall write m , when it is added to the mass of a molecule.   Equation (355) for the mobility then becomes

$$U_e = \frac{3}{8} \sqrt{\frac{\pi}{2}} \frac{e}{nS_e} \frac{1}{(mkT)^{\frac{1}{2}}}, \tag{358}$$

e being the numerical electronic charge, n the number of molecules per unit volume, and S_e the value of S_D or the equivalent cross section for diffusion of electrons among the gas molecules. S_e is given in terms of the scattering coefficient for electrons from the molecules, $G_e(v, \theta)$, by eq. (356a), with $m + M$ replaced by M :

* J. J. THOMSON, *Phil. Mag.*, **47**, 337 (1924).

$$S_e = 2\pi \int_0^\infty \left[\int_0^\pi G\left(x\sqrt{\frac{2kT}{m}},\ \theta\right)(1 - \cos \theta) \sin \theta \, d\theta \right] x^5 e^{-x^2} \, dx. \quad (359)$$

If we prefer to introduce the mean free path L_e of the electrons among the gas molecules, the appropriate formula is (99b) or

$$L_e = \frac{1}{nS_e}$$

rather than $L = 1/\sqrt{2}nS_e$; for the molecules may be considered as standing practically still in comparison with the hundredfold more rapidly moving electrons. Then in terms of L_e

$$U_e = \frac{3}{8} \sqrt{\frac{\pi}{2}} \frac{eL_e}{(mkT)^{1/2}}. \quad (360)$$

The favorite model for a gas molecule in this connection has been a solid sphere from which point electrons are assumed to bounce off elastically, and hence equally in all directions. According to this assumption, the mean diameter of electron and molecule, or the radius of the sphere of influence, is half of the diameter σ of the molecule, so that in (356b) $\sigma_{av} = \sigma/2$ and

$$S_e = \tfrac{1}{4}\,\pi\sigma^2.$$

In this case it is also appropriate to introduce the Chapman correction factor, $(1 + \lambda_{12})$ in eq. (168a) of Sec. 111; for we can now give to λ_{12} the special and very appreciable value which it takes on for elastic spheres of extremely unequal mass, viz., $1 + \lambda_{12} = 32/9\pi = 1.132$. Thus on this assumption we obtain the somewhat modified formulas

$$U_e = \frac{8}{3} \sqrt{\frac{2}{\pi}} \frac{e}{n\pi\sigma^2} \frac{1}{(mkT)^{1/2}} = \frac{2}{3} \sqrt{\frac{2}{\pi}} \frac{eL_e}{(mkT)^{1/2}}. \quad (361)$$

The electronic mean free path L_e is related to that of the gas molecules themselves by the formula

$$L_e = 4\sqrt{2}L, \quad (362)$$

which can be used to calculate values of L_e from a table for L.

It must be remembered, however, that all of these formulas for the mobility of a free electron rest upon the assumption that their velocities are distributed in the maxwellian manner proper to absolute temperature T. As we shall see later, under many experimental conditions there is good reason to doubt this assumption.

269. Elementary Theory of Electronic Mobility. When the electrons are assumed to move among small stationary spheres distributed at random, from which they rebound equally in all directions, an accurate formula for the mobility is easily obtained by elementary methods.   Although no new results are obtained thereby, it will be instructive to see how this can be done, especially since the first step in the reasoning is often taken in elementary discussions of the subject.

In 1900 Drude published a very simple theory which was intended to apply to electrons in a metal but is also applicable without change to a gas.   It was based upon the idea that in a uniform electric field an electron must undergo a displacement due to the field of magnitude $s = \frac{1}{2} eE\tau^2/m$ during its time of flight τ between successive collisions (eE/m being its acceleration), and so should start each free path a distance s farther along in the direction of the field.   If we suppose it to move with average speed v and to have a mean free path L_e, then we can write, at least approximately, $\tau = L_e/v$, whence

$$s = \frac{1}{2} \frac{eEL_e^2}{mv^2};$$

then in the course of all free paths executed in a second, v/L_e in number, it undergoes a total displacement $vs/L_e = \frac{1}{2} eEL_e/mv$, and this divided by E is the mobility U_e.   Hence

$$U_e = \frac{1}{2} \frac{eL_e}{mv}.$$

There are, however, several errors in this calculation.   For one thing, if we contemplate an electron that is moving directly with or against the field, it is at once obvious that the displacement s has no effect whatever upon the starting point of its next free path but merely causes it to start the next one at an earlier or later time than it otherwise would.   It is, in fact, in all cases only the *component* of s transverse to the original velocity **v** that is effective, and also only the component of this component in the direction of E.   The average value of the latter is easily found; a fraction $\frac{1}{2} \sin\theta \, d\theta$ of the electrons start out in a direction with θ in the range $d\theta$, hence the average of $\sin^2\theta$ is

$$\frac{1}{2}\int_0^\pi \sin^2\theta \sin\theta \, d\theta = \frac{2}{3}.$$

Making this correction, we have for the factor in the expression for U_e the value $\frac{1}{3}$ instead of $\frac{1}{2}$.

A second point at which objection can be raised is the replacing of τ^2 in s by the square of L_e/v.   In many cases rough averaging of this sort is fully justified, especially if we wish only to find the order of magnitude of an effect, but in the present instance it may lead to a

numerical error of considerable size.   In Drude's original application
of the theory to the free electrons in a metal the error due to this cause
is rather uncertain because the distribution as to lengths of free paths
among the closely packed molecules of a solid is open to question,
so that in Drude's theory the omission could be justified.

In a rarefied gas, however, where the molecules are small in comparison to the intermolecular spacing and are distributed at random,
the free paths must certainly be distributed exponentially, as shown
in Sec. 59; the magnitude of the correction in question is then scarcely
open to doubt.   According to eq. (98b) in Sec. 59, the fraction of the
free paths that have lengths in a range dl is

$$\psi(l) \, dl = \frac{1}{L_e} e^{-\frac{l}{L_e}} dl = \frac{v}{L_e} e^{-\frac{v\tau}{L_e}} d\tau$$

in terms of the time of flight, $\tau = l/v$; hence the average of τ^2 is

$$\overline{\tau^2} = \frac{v}{L_e} \int_0^\infty \tau^2 e^{-\frac{v\tau}{L_e}} d\tau = 2 \frac{L_e^2}{v^2}.$$

We must, therefore, replace τ^2 in s by $2L_e^2/v^2$ instead of L_e^2/v^2; this
multiplies the result by 2.

Combining the two corrections, we thus obtain for the mobility
of the electrons when moving at uniform speed v

$$U_e = \frac{2}{3} \frac{eL_e}{mv}.$$

A final correction is then to be made for the distribution of speeds.
This is easy to do in the present instance because L_e cannot vary with
v.   The magnitude of the correction will depend, however, upon the
distribution of the molecular velocities; let us suppose that this is a
maxwellian one, corresponding to some temperature which we shall
denote by T_e.   Then, by (61a) in Sec. 28, the fraction $4\pi Av^2 e^{-\beta^2 v^2} dv$ of
the electrons are moving with speed in the range dv.   The mean displacement in the field would obviously be the same if the electrons
composing this fraction were always the same individuals, moving con-
stantly at speed v and drifting in unit field with the average drift
velocity U_e as just found.   The average rate of drift in a unit field,
or the ordinary mobility, will be, therefore,

$$U_e = \int_0^\infty \frac{2}{3} \frac{eL_e}{m} 4\pi Ave^{-\beta^2 v^2} dv = \frac{4\pi}{3} \frac{eL_e}{m} \frac{A}{\beta^2},$$

or, after inserting $A = \beta^3/\pi^{3/2}$ from (60) and either $\beta = 2/(\sqrt{\pi}\bar{v})$ in
terms of the mean speed $\bar{v}$ from (65a) in Sec. 30 or $\beta^2 = m/2kT_e$ from
(56) in Sec. 28,

$$U_e = \frac{8}{3\pi} \frac{eL_e}{m\bar{v}} = \frac{2}{3} \sqrt{\frac{2}{\pi}} \, eL_e \left(\frac{1}{mkT_e}\right)^{\frac{1}{2}}.$$ (363)

Thus in the present instance the correction for Maxwell's law, besides replacing v by $\bar{v}$, raises the numerical factor from $\frac{2}{3} = 0.667$ to $8/3\pi = 0.849$, or by the rather large amount of 27 per cent. We can readily see why the effect should be so much larger here than in the case of viscosity, where it was only 5 per cent (Sec. 83); here the slow-moving electrons enjoy relatively long times of flight and drift a long way, whereas a slow-moving gas molecule is apt to have its free path cut short through being struck by another molecule.

This formula for U_e was first obtained by Lorentz by the method of correcting the velocity distribution.* It agrees exactly with eq. (361) quoted above as Chapman's result; but the truth is that Chapman inferred his limiting value of λ_{12} for spheres of very unequal mass from Lorentz's result. Equation (361) or (363) must be regarded as the correct formula for the mobility of electrons moving with maxwellian velocities at a temperature T or T_e among relatively fixed molecules which scatter them equally in all directions, the molecules being spaced at random and far apart.

270. Actual Electron Mobilities. Because of the roughly four times smaller cross section, and still more because of the ten to a hundred thousand times smaller mass, our formulas predict electron mobilities many hundreds of times greater than those of heavy ions. This expectation is amply confirmed by experiment.

The usual mode of comparing observation and theory is to calculate from the data by means of the theoretical formula values of the mean free path L_e or, better, the collision cross section S_e or the equivalent elastic-sphere diameter $\sigma_e = \sqrt{4S_e/\pi}$; the latter can then be compared with diameters obtained from other sources. If this is done on the assumption that the electrons have a maxwellian distribution at the temperature of the gas itself, values of σ_e are obtained that are *much larger* than the molecular diameters calculated from the viscosity.

It was early suspected, especially by Townsend and K. T. Compton, that this discrepancy arose from the fact that the experiments are usually performed at such high field strengths that the electrons acquire energy from their descent in potential at too rapid a rate for effective equalization with the gas molecules to occur. The amount of energy that an electron can lose to a molecule in an elastic impact is, in fact, very small. An approximate expression for it is easily found if we suppose the molecule to be a sphere, initially stationary.

---

* Cf. H. A. Lorentz, "Theory of Electrons," 1909, p. 274.

Let the electron approach at speed v and leave at speed v' in a direction making an angle θ with that of v; let the molecule, initially at rest and having mass M, acquire a speed V with components $V_\perp$, $V_\parallel$, respectively perpendicular and parallel to **v**. Then by conservation of momentum $mv' \sin \theta = MV_\perp$, $m(v - v' \cos \theta) = MV_\parallel$, whence, since $V_\perp{}^2 + V_\parallel{}^2 = V^2$,

$$M^2V^2 = m^2(v^2 + v'^2 - 2vv' \cos \theta).$$

Now certainly $v' < v$ and $|\cos \theta| < 1$; hence $M^2V^2 < 4m^2v^2$ and

$$\frac{1}{2} MV^2 < \frac{4m}{M} \left(\frac{1}{2} mv^2 \right).$$

Since $M/m > 3{,}500$ at least, this shows that the loss of energy by the electron, which equals $\frac{1}{2} MV^2$, must be minute. Hence we can set $v = v'$ in the preceding equation, and we can also assume $\cos \theta$ to be equally often positive and negative, as it would be if the molecule were fixed (cf. Sec. 70, Problem 1). For the average kinetic energy acquired by the molecule we thus obtain

$$\frac{1}{2} M\overline{V^2} = \frac{2m}{M} \left(\frac{1}{2} mv^2 \right),$$

so that the electron loses on the average only the fraction $2m/M$ of its energy in a single impact.

If the electron continues to drift indefinitely it will, therefore, accumulate energy until this relatively slow loss balances the rate at which it acquires energy from the field. Now it acquires energy at a rate $eEu = eE^2U_e$, e being here the numerical electronic charge and u its rate of drift or U_e its mobility in the field of intensity E. Hence if we write for the terminal value of its energy $\frac{3}{2} kT_e$, in terms of the Boltzmann constant k and an equivalent temperature T_e, we have as the condition of energy balance

$$\frac{\bar{v}}{L_e} \frac{2m}{M} \frac{3}{2} kT_e = eE^2U_e,$$

$\bar{v}/L_e$ representing the number of collisions made in a second; hence

$$T_e = \frac{1}{3} \frac{MeL_eU_e}{m\bar{v}k} E^2,$$

or, if the distribution is maxwellian and the mean speed, therefore, $\bar{v} = 2(2kT_e/\pi m)^{1/2}$,

$$T_e = \frac{1}{2k} \left(\frac{M}{3} \sqrt{\frac{\pi}{m}} \, eL_eU_eE^2 \right)^{2/3}.$$

This formula might be used to calculate equivalent temperatures for the electron, but more commonly its equivalent is employed to eliminate T_e from the formula for the mobility.   If we do this in (363), we obtain for the terminal mobility

$$U_e = \left(\frac{8eL_e}{3\pi\sqrt{mM}} \frac{1}{E} \right)^{\frac{1}{2}}.$$

Formulas equivalent to this but with somewhat different constants in place of $8/3\pi$ occur in the literature; the differences arise from the omission of one or more of the corrections that we have introduced or from approximations of some kind.   Values of L_e calculated from observed data by means of such formulas yield values of the mean free path for gas molecules, $L = L_e/4\sqrt{2}$, agreeing much better with values obtained in other ways.   Very slow electrons often show anomalies, however; for example, as their energy sinks below 10 electron volts, their mean free path in the heavier noble gases becomes considerably less than $4\sqrt{2}$ times the value of L, but as the energy sinks below 1 volt it becomes several times greater (the Ramsauer effect).   Sometimes several such oscillations can be observed.   Such phenomena must find their explanation in the wave mechanics of collisions between electrons and atoms, and some progress has been made toward their elucidation.

The gradual acquisition of energy by electrons in a field can be followed experimentally up to the point at which they acquire enough energy to ionize the gas.   For these experiments, however, we shall refer to the original papers.*

At this point, in fact, we must take leave of this fascinating subject. The theory of the motion of electricity through gases involves a continual use of the methods of kinetic theory; but to survey all the attempts that have been made to develop it would require another whole volume.

* Cf. K. T. Compton, *Phys. Rev.*, **22**, 333 (1923); Hertz, *Deutsche phys. Ges. Verh.*, **19**, 268 (1917).

This formula might be used to estimate equivalent frequencies for the electron, but more commonly its equivalent is employed to eliminate T from the formula for resistivity. . . . If we do this in (XX), we obtain for the terminal mobility

$$K = \frac{N e^2 \lambda}{\sqrt{3 m}} \left(\frac{8 m \bar{c}}{\pi \gamma e E \lambda} \right)^{\frac{1}{2}}$$

formulas equivalent to this but with somewhat different constants in place of 0.75, occur in the literature; the differences arise from the omission of one or more of the corrections that we have introduced, or from approximations of some kind. Values of λ, calculated from observed data by means of such formulas yield values of the mean free path for ions or molecules $L = 4/\sqrt{2} \cdot \pi \sqrt{2}$, agreeing much better with values obtained in other ways. Very slow electrons often show anomalies, however; for example, as their energy sinks below 10 electron-volts, their mean free path in the heavier noble gases becomes surprisingly large, then $4/\sqrt{2}$, since the value of λ, and so the energy sinks below 1 volt it becomes several times greater (the Ramsauer effect). Sometimes several such oscillations can be observed. . . . In the wave mechanics of collisions between electrons and atoms, and some progress has been made toward their elucidation. . . .

The gradual acquisition of energy by electrons in a field can be followed experimentally up to the point at which they acquire enough energy to ionize the gas. For these experiments, however, we shall refer to the original paper.

At this point, in fact, we must take leave of this fascinating subject.

The theory of the conduction of electricity through gases involves a combined use of the methods of kinetic theory; but to survey all the attempts that have been made to develop it, would require another whole volume.

¹ G. S. T. Townsend, Proc. Roy. Soc. 79, 555 (1937); Electr. in Gases, pp. ...
1 G. 18, 205 (1937).

SOME INTEGRALS

(n is a positive integer or zero)

1. $\int_0^\infty e^{-\beta^2 v^2}\, dv = \dfrac{1}{2\beta}\sqrt{\pi}.$

2. $\int_0^\infty v^{2n+1} e^{-\beta^2 v^2}\, dv = \dfrac{n!}{2\,\beta^{2n+2}}.\quad (0! = 1.)$

3. $\int_0^\infty v^{2n} e^{-\beta^2 v^2}\, dv = \dfrac{(2n-1)(2n-3)\,\cdots\,1}{2^{n+1}\beta^{2n+1}}\sqrt{\pi}.$

With $r^2 = x^2 + y^2 + z^2$ and all integrals ranging over

$$-\infty < x < \infty, \qquad -\infty < y < \infty, \; -\infty < z < \infty:$$

4. $\iiint r^{2n+1} e^{-\beta^2 r^2}\, dx\, dy\, dz = \dfrac{(n+1)!}{\beta^{2n+4}}\, 2\pi.$

5. $\iiint r^{2n} e^{-\beta^2 r^2}\, dx\, dy\, dz = \dfrac{(2n+1)(2n-1)\,\cdots\,1}{2^n \beta^{2n+3}}\, \pi^{3/2}.$

6. $\iiint x^2 r^{2n+1} e^{-\beta^2 r^2}\, dx\, dy\, dz = \dfrac{2}{3}\dfrac{(n+2)!}{\beta^{2n+6}}\, \pi.$

7. $\iiint x^2 r^{2n} e^{-\beta^2 r^2}\, dx\, dy\, dz = \dfrac{(2n+3)(2n+1)\,\cdots\,1}{3\cdot 2^{n+1}\beta^{2n+5}}\, \pi^{3/2}.$

8. $\iiint x^4 e^{-\beta^2 r^2}\, dx\, dy\, dz = \dfrac{3}{4}\dfrac{\pi^{3/2}}{\beta^7}.$

9. $\iiint x^4 r e^{-\beta^2 r^2}\, dx\, dy\, dz = \dfrac{12}{5}\dfrac{\pi}{\beta^8}.$

10. $\iiint x^2 y^2 e^{-\beta^2 r^2}\, dx\, dy\, dz = \dfrac{\pi^{3/2}}{4\beta^7}.$

11. $\iiint x^2 y^2 r e^{-\beta^2 r^2}\, dx\, dy\, dz = \dfrac{4}{5}\dfrac{\pi}{\beta^8}.$

IMPORTANT CONSTANTS

Speed of light, $c = 2.99796 \times 10^{10}$ cm/sec.

Planck's constant, $h = 6.62 \times 10^{-27}$ c.g.s.

Electronic charge, $e = 4.805 \times 10^{-10}$ electrostatic unit.

Specific charge on electron, $e/m = 1.7576 \times 10^7$ electromagnetic units per gram.

Mass of electron, $m = 0.9119 \times 10^{-27}$ g.

Mass of atom of unit atomic weight ($M = 1$), $m_1 = 1.661 \times 10^{-24}$ g.

Boltzmann constant, $k = 1.381 \times 10^{-16}$ c.g.s.

Gas constant per gram molecule, $R_M = 83.15 \times 10^6$ c.g.s.

$\qquad\qquad\qquad\qquad\qquad\quad = 82.06$ atm cc/deg.

Molecules in a gram molecule, $N_M = 6.021 \times 10^{23}$.

Density of a gas under standard conditions, $n_0 = 2.686 \times 10^{19}$ molecules per cc.

Absolute temperature of ice-point, $T_0 = 273.14°$.

Bohr radius, $a_0 = \dfrac{h^2}{4\pi^2 m e^2} = 5.29 \times 10^{-9}$ cm.

Bohr magneton, $\dfrac{eh}{4\pi c m} = 9.26 \times 10^{-21}$ electromagnetic units.

INDEX

A

A priori probability, 377
Absorption of a beam, 101
Accommodation coefficient, 311
  calculations of, 325
  observations of, 320
Antisymmetric, 375
Arrangements, 351
Atmosphere, planetary, 81
  terrestrial, 79
Averages, calculation of, 48
Avogadro's law, 18
Avogadro's number, 24

B

Baule, 325
Beattie and Bridgman, 220
Blodgett, 320
Boltzmann (velocities) 32, 52, 85; (viscosity) 145, 146; (statistical mechanics) 340, 350, 369
Boltzmann constant k, 25
Boltzmann distribution law, 90–97, 352–357, 362, 387
Bose-Einstein system, 381
  distribution, 385–386
  gas, 397, 416
Boyle temperature, 223
Boyle's law, 17
Brönsted and Hevesy, 70
Brownian motion, 280–290
  and mobility, 267

C

Canonical distribution, 92, 93, 366, 390
  ensemble, 366
Chaos, molecular, 33, 349
Chapman (viscosity) 146–147, 161; (conduction) 165, 171, 179, 195; (diffusion) 195–197, 204–205, 473

Chemical constant, 407
Classical theory as limit, 387, 401
Clausing, 307
Clausius (free paths) 105, 107; (conduction) 165; (equation of state) 208; (virial) 236; (dielectrics) 438
Clausius-Mossotti law, 437
Collision cross section, 103, 113
  experiments on, 124
  in terms of scattering, 116, 176, 194
Collisions, molecular, effect of, 36
  inverse, 37
  rate of, 98–101, 104–113
  in real gas, 113
  wave-mechanical, 131
Compton, 473, 475
Conductivity, electrical, 465
Conductivity, thermal, 162–184
  by complex molecules, 181
  final formula, 178, 179
  free-molecule, 315
  properties, 182
  values, 180
Creep, thermal, 327
Critical point, 209
Curie's law, 456
Czerny and Hettner, 335

D

Dalton's law, 9
Debye, 432, 435, 438
Degeneracy, 412, 421
Dennison, 262
Detailed balancing, 55
Devonshire, 327
Diamagnetism, 455, 456, 462
Dickins, 322
Dielectric constant, 432–453
Dieterici, 220
Diffusion, 184–205, 468
  discussion and formulas, 193–201
  forced, 201

479

Diffusion, of ions, 468
  as random walk, 286
  thermal, 204
Dipole molecule, classical, 438
  wave-mechanical, 450
Dispersion of molecules, 272
Dissociation, 422
Distribution function, 28, 85
  Boltzmann, 90–97, 352–357, 387
  canonical, 92, 93, 366, 390
  gases, by wave mechanics, 399, 418, 427
    (*See also* Velocity, molecular)
  loose many-molecule system, 353–357, 385–389
Distributions, 351, 383
Dootson, 205
Drude, 471
Dushman, 307

E

Effusion, 64
Effusive molecular flow, 60, 71
Einstein, 281, 286
Electric field, local, 433
Energy, differential equation of, 240
  molecular, classical, 248, 254, 256
  translatory, 25
  wave-mechanical, 393–395, 413
  of quantized gas, 409, 410, 415
Ensembles, 340
Enskog, 146, 169, 180, 182, 195
Entropy, differential equations and formulas for, 242–244
  gases, classical, 246, 248, 361
  wave-mechanical, 399, 405, 411, 416
  and probability, 368
  and range in phase, 371
  in statistical mechanics, 360, 367, 388, 391
  zero-point, 405, 408
Epstein, 310, 336
Equation of state, 206–237
  series for, 221
  special forms, 217–218
Equilibrium state, 375
Equipartition of energy, 51, 364

Ergodic surface, layer, 344, 348
  surmise, 341
Eucken, 181, 183
Evaporation, 68
Exclusion principle, 375
Expansion, free, 14
  reversible, 11

F

Farkas, 263
Fermi-Dirac system, 381
  distribution, 385–386,
  gas, 397, 409–415
Fisher, 268
Fluctuations, 267–290
  about an average, 275
  of dispersion, 268
Force-fields, 74
Fowler, 230
Free paths, 98
  distribution, 101
    (*See also* Mean free path)
Free-molecule (defined), 291
Fry, 267
Fürth, 267, 285

G

Gaede, 299, 308
Gas constant R, 23; (table) 26
Gerlach and Schütz, 335
Gibbs, 339, 345, 367
Gram molecule, volume of, 19
Gyroscopic force, 89

H

H-theorem, 52, 371, 377
Heat, 239, 358
Helium, field for, 212
History of kinetic theory, 1–3
Hund, 262
Hydrogen, 260

I

Ideal gas, 4
Indetermination principle, 130
Initial polarizability, etc., 441–453
Ionization, 427

J

Jackson and Howarth, 326
Jeans, 352
Jones, 158, 230, 327
Joule, 14, 26
Joule-Thomson effect, 14

K

Kammerlingh Onnes, 221
Kirkwood, 212, 232, 234, 453
Knauer, 125
Knudsen (effusion) 65; (manometer) 67; (evaporation) 70. (low-density phenomena) 299, 305, 308, 311–318, 322; (creep) 333
Ko, 72
Krutkow, 350
Kundt and Warburg, 292

L

Langevin, 193, 438, 455, 467
Langevin's formula, 467
Langmuir, 71, 302. 320
Langmuir and Kingdon, 427
Line breadth, 58
Line shape, 324
Liouville's theorem, 38, 343
Lorentz, 274, 434, 473
Loose many-molecule system, 350–361, 379–390
Loschmidt's number, 24

M

Macroscopically small, 5
Magneton, Bohr, 464
Magnetizability, 454
Manometer, absolute, 67
Mass motion, 9
Massey and Mohr, 132, 159
Maxwell (velocities) 32, 52; (viscosity) 140, 146, 150; (heat) 172, 177, 179, 182; (diffusion) 191, 195, 204; (low-density phenomena) 295, 312, 327, 334, 339
Maxwellian stream, 61

Maxwell's law, 45, 349, 364
        (*See also* Velocity, molecular)
    correction for, 113, 473
Mean free path, 98–114
    across a plane, 141
    maxwellian, 110
    observations, 125
    values, 149
    variation, 100
Metals, free electrons in, 419
Meyer, 164, 168, 189
Michels, 320
Microcanonical ensemble, 344
Millikan, 295, 299, 310
Mixed systems, statistics of, 389
Mobility, dynamic, 203, 288
    ionic, 465–475
Molecule space, 350
Molecules, 3
    density, 24
    diameters, 104, 114; (table) 149, 201
    force-field of, 212, 228, 231
    mass and relative weights, 25–26
    small field, 98
Moment, molecular, electric, 435, 438, 443–453
    magnetic, 454–464
Multiple states, 93

N

Nernst's heat theorem, 407
Normal distribution, 352, 354

O

Ornstein and Van Wyk, 324
Oscillator, harmonic, 258, 340

P

Paramagnetism, 456, 463
Partition function, 256
Perfect gas, 4, 18, 22, 247
    Bose-Einstein, 397, 416
    Fermi-Dirac, 397, 409–415
    by statistical mechanics, 346
    by wave mechanics, 393–419
Perrin, 284
Phase space, 339, 350

Photophoresis, 333
Point-mass gas, wave mechanics of, 395
Poiseuille's formula with slip, 293
Poisson's formula, 277
Polarizability, of a dipole, 438, 450
    electric molecular, 436–453
    by wave mechanics, 442
Pressure, 6–7, 400, 410, 413, 415, 416
    dynamic, cohesive, repulsive, 212–213
    in a non-perfect gas, 211, 214
Probability integral, 50

Q

Quantum number, 398, 402
Quantum states, 93, 374

R

Radiometer, 333–337
Random walk, 268
Range in phase, 371
Relativity, effects of, 372
Relaxation rate, 178
Reversibility, 55
Reynolds, 66
Riegger, 68
Roberts, 320
Rotating axes, 89
Rotating gas, 90

S

Scattering, 104, 115–127, 132
    by elastic spheres, 118, 124
    by free molecules, 122
    observations of, 125
    relative, 120
    by small deflections, 119
    wave-mechanical theory of, 132
Scattering of light, molecular, 273
Schrödinger, 288
Second law, 367
Similitude, and diffusion, 198
    and viscosity, 152
Slater, 212, 453, 463
Slip, 292–298
Small-field molecules, 98
Smoluchowski, 305–306, 311, 315–319, 322

Soddy and Berry, 322
Sommerfeld, 419
Specific heats, 243–266
    classical theory of, 249
    data on, 252
    of hydrogen, 264
    of mixed gases, 265
    quantum theory of, 255
Sphere of influence, 103
State sum, 256, 392
    integral, 361, 367
Statistical equivalence, principle of, 345
Statistical mechanics, classical, 339–372
    wave-mechanical, 373–392
Statistical nature of kinetic theory, 5
Steady state, 29
Stefan, 191
Stern, 72
Stirling's formula, 269
Stokes' law, 309
Stresses in a fluid, 137
Sutherland, 154, 199
System space, 339

T

Temperature, 16, 19–22, 357, 385
Temperature jump, 311
Thermal agitation, velocity of, 10
Thermodynamics, conclusions from, 239–249
Thomson, 469
Transfer by molecules, 146
Transpiration, 64, 66, 330
Transport phenomena, 135
Trautz et al., 157, 161
Tubes, equilibrium in, 331
    flow through, 293, 302–309, 330–331

U

Ultimate statistical features, 338
Ursell, 228

V

Van der Waals, 207, 214
Van der Waals' equation, 206–211, 223, 248

Van Dyke, 298
Van Vleck, 432
Vapor, temperature of, 79
Vapor pressure near $T = 0$, 407
Velocity, molecular, distribution law, 28, 45–55
  experimental test of, 72, 324
  in force-field, 76, 90
  proof of, 32–45, 349
  rate of change of, 40
  uniqueness of, 52
  wave-mechanical, 399, 401, 412, 416, 418
  mean (table) 26, 49–50
  most probable, 48
  root-mean-square, 18, 25; (table) 26, 49–50
Velocity space, 29
Virial coefficients, 221–235

Virial theorem, 235
Viscosity, 136–162, 178
  free-molecule, 300
  of mixed gases, 160
  of two-dimensional gas, 140
  variation of, 148
Volmer and Estermann, 70

W

Wave lengths, molecular, 130, 132
  table of, 149
Wave mechanics, 373
  of collisions, 131
  of gases, 393–431
    of complex gases, 417
    of a particle, 127
Weber, 183
Work, 239, 358

DATE DUE

AUG 18 '89			
NOV 2 '30			
MAY 8 '88			
JUN 14 '89			
DEC 3 '91			
JAN 11 '92			
NOV 16 '94			
GAYLORD			PRINTED IN U.S.A.

KINETIC THEORY OF GASES, WITH AN INTRODU
QC 175 K45 c. 2

A17900 636260